MATHEMATICS
IN THE
MODERN
WORLD

MATHEMATICS IN THE MODERN WORLD

READINGS FROM
SCIENTIFIC AMERICAN

WITH INTRODUCTIONS BY
MORRIS KLINE
NEW YORK UNIVERSITY

W. H. Freeman and Company
SAN FRANCISCO AND LONDON

Library of Congress Catalog Card Number: 68-17151

PREFACE

Mathematics is the simplest systematic discipline that human beings have created. It is, for example, far simpler than physics, history, or economics. It is simple because it concentrates on very limited aspects of reality. Ten people are ten complicated physiological and psychological organisms, whose structure and functioning are only partially understood. In comparison, the quantitative fact of 10 is trivial to recognize and retain. A triangle made of wood is an untold multiplicity of complicated molecules held together by complex forces. Neither the structure of the molecules nor the forces that bind them are fully comprehended even by the greatest physicists. But the mathematician studies only the triangular shape and ignores completely the molecular structure and forces. The simplicity of the concepts with which mathematics is concerned almost guarantees that the facts it establishes about the concepts must also be elemental. Despite this simplicity most people complain about the difficulty in mastering the subject, and despite the interest which its astonishing effectiveness in almost every walk of life should arouse, these people shun mathematics.

The paradox that a basically simple subject should appear difficult to learn is in large part readily explained. Some of the difficulties are superficial. One is the vocabulary. To denote the concepts which it abstracts from real objects and real events, mathematicians use words which, to many people, are strange. Thus "quadrilateral" and "parallelogram" have specific and precise meanings which one does not encounter in many other areas and must therefore learn in the study of mathematics. However no one would contend that the acquisition of some new words is a major obstacle. It may not be an inspiring pastime, but this is another issue. The difficulty is certainly no greater than that of learning the vocabulary of French.

Another apparent but equally superficial difficulty is the use of symbols. We wish to solve a problem which calls for determining an unknown on the basis of some given information. Let us suppose that the unknown quantity is the number of feet in a particular length. Certainly it is advantageous to let x stand for the number of feet in that length and to use x thereafter in place of the long phrase. The use of symbols, however, does not present any conceptual difficulty.

A third supposed obstacle is that mathematics deals with abstractions. But because the elementary abstractions or concepts are drawn directly from common experiences, their meanings are readily kept in mind. In fact, mathematicians constantly refer to physical objects and pictures to remind themselves of the meanings of their abstractions. The early Greek mathematicians used pebbles to represent distinct objects and learned basic facts about the whole numbers by working with pebbles. Incidentally, the word "calculus," which in its general sense means any arithmetic or algebraic process, comes from the Latin word for pebble. Even the higher abstractions of mathematics, such as the concepts of derivative and integral, which one learns in the differential and integral calculus, are at worst only a step removed from the elementary concepts, and even the concepts of the calculus have pictorial and physical meaning. To learn these abstractions demands no greater feat of intellect than that required for the elementary concepts.

That mathematicians think in pictures is to an extent substantiated by a story well known in mathematical circles. A professor was presenting a proof of a theorem to his class and got stuck in the middle. He went off to the side of the blackboard, drew some pictures, thought for a second, erased the pictures, and then resumed the proof. This story also reveals some aspects of pedagogy that need not be stated explicitly.

There are other hurdles to the learning of mathematics that are perhaps more substantial. Elementary, high school, and college education are intended to prepare us for life and there is much to be learned in the course of an adequate preparation for the complex civilization into which all of us in this century are projected. The order in which the subjects and the topics within subjects are presented and the pace of the education are designed to insure this preparation. However, efficient training for life may require the sacrifice of comprehension, at least in mathematics.

In its final form mathematics is a series of concepts, processes such as methods of solving various types of equations, and facts such as theorems. Of course the processes and facts are justified by means of proofs. The inculcation of these elements of mathematics seems to be most readily achieved by presenting to the student the final or definitive form of the concepts, processes, theorems, and proofs. However, mathematics is an old subject; significant achievements in it date back to 3000 B.C. Throughout the past 5000 years, the mathematicians not only extended the subject vastly but, as they made successive extensions, as they recognized new entities and new phenomena, and as their own understanding improved, they recast their concepts, processes, and proofs to incorporate their gains. Many of these revised versions are no longer readily perspicuous.

Moreover, as the volume of mathematical knowledge increased, it became desirable to organize it so that the theorems of any one subject would be logically ordered. At the base of any subject are the axioms and these are followed by a succession of theorems, each of which is proven by using the axioms and previously established theorems. The need to fit the results into such a logically ordered system has often obliged mathematicians to seek out new and not necessarily natural or manifest proofs. As a consequence many proofs have been shorn of their intuitive, transparent, and readily comprehensible structures and have been replaced by quite artificial demonstrations. These logical presentations remind one of an incident in the life of the great literary figure, Samuel Johnson. He had expounded some subject to a man who, not satisfied, persisted in asking for more explanation. Johnson, somewhat irritated, replied tartly, "I have given you an argument but I am not obliged to give you an explanation."

Efficiency of presentation seems to dictate the omission of another feature of mathematics that is vital to its comprehension. Mathematics proper is a skeleton. The flesh and blood and the life of mathematics consist in what one does with it. Significant mathematics (the other kind also exists) serves ends that, in the words of Descartes, make men the masters and possessors of nature. The meaning of mathematics lies outside of mathematics proper just as the meaning of good literature lies beyond the collections of words on paper. To understand mathematics one must know why one wants a particular result, what bearing it has on other results, and what one can do with it.

Whether or not the schools, in view of their multitudinous goals and obligations, can offer a more enlightening presentation of mathematics, the interested student must range more widely in the search for full knowledge. To acquire a sound understanding and appreciation of mathematics, one should penetrate to the underlying ideas stripped of sophisticated and pettifogging details; one should learn its objectives and uses, the motivations of the men who created it, and the genesis of its present concepts and structure.

The articles in this volume contribute substantially to the understanding of mathematics. Their purpose is not to present bread-and-butter information or the technical details that one must master in one course to be ready for the next one, but to give insight. They transcend blocks and logical cement to portray large temples; they complement the close examination of minute details with broad vistas; and to the day-by-day struggles with symbols and processes they impart the excitement of noble schemes.

A series of articles by different authors on many different subjects is not the substitute for systematic study and technical mastery, but rather a kaleidoscope, whose varicolored bright flashes of light may illuminate, excite, and inspire—and this is the primary objective of all education.

August, 1968

MORRIS KLINE

CONTENTS

IV · THE FOUNDATIONS OF MATHEMATICS

V · THE IMPORT OF MATHEMATICS

Note on cross-references: Cross-references within the articles are of three kinds. A reference to an article included in this book is noted by the title of the article and the page on which it begins; a reference to an article that is available as an offprint but is not included here is noted by the article's title and offprint number; a reference to a SCIENTIFIC AMERICAN article that is not available as an offprint is noted by the title of the article and the month and year of its publication.

I

THE
NATURE
OF
MATHEMATICS

THE NATURE OF MATHEMATICS

INTRODUCTION

Euclid's *Elements*, the first of the extant classics of mathematics and the work which inspired one hundred generations of mathematical effort, was an intellectual triumph and a pedagogical misfortune. The world did derive from this book the notion of mathematical proof, the logical organization of a body of mathematical knowledge, and, of course, invaluable information. But far too many intellectuals, including mathematicians, mistook the import of Euclid's work and formed a concept of mathematics that is too narrow. Mathematics, they concluded, was a purely logical development. It starts with axioms and definitions, which are explicitly stated at the outset, and proves deductively results about the mathematical concepts delineated in the definitions.

Euclid did not include, nor did he seek to include in this work (of about 300 B.C.), an account of what mathematicians had done during the preceding three hundred years. Before mathematicians can obtain a body of knowledge that warrants the deductive organization which Euclid gave to geometry they must spend decades and even centuries in creating the material. And unlike the logical organization the creative work does not proceed step by step from one argument to another, each supported by some axiom or previously established conclusion. What the creative process does involve is groping, blundering, conjecturing, and hypothesizing. Imagination, intuition, divination, insight, experimentation, chance association, luck, hard work, and immense patience are applied to grasp a key concept, to formulate a conjecture, and to find a proof.

Some rational thinking may indeed enter into the decisions to discard a conjecture or line of attack or to pursue what appears to be a promising path, but on the whole mathematical creation, to use the words of the noted physicist P. W. Bridgman, consists in "doing one's damnedest with one's mind, no holds barred." No logic or infallible guide tells the mind how to think. The very fact that many great mathematicians have tackled a problem and failed and that another has come along and solved it shows how much the workings of the individual mind, rather than the systematic, ordered arguments which one reads in the final proofs, enter into creation.

The creative activity, the re-creative activity in the case of a student, is the heart of mathematics. It is in this work that the mathematician makes the supreme contribution, overcomes the greatest difficulties, and advances the subject most significantly. The creative process is essential not only in solving existing problems. Without the creation of new viewpoints, new directions of research, and new goals, mathematics would soon exhaust itself in rearranging or rigorizing old proofs and lose its life. The reshuffling of steps and the weaving of theorems into a sequence in order to make a deductive organization of knowledge already attained often require ingenuity but on the whole this work is much more like rearranging books, whereas the original creative activity may be compared to the writing of the books. Even the satisfactions which mathematics affords—the excitement of the hunt, the thrill of discovery, the sense of achievement, and the elation of success—are more numerous and more intensive in the creative work than in the final rewriting of the argument in a deductive pattern.

Though established mathematics must be formulated deductively, partly to achieve a coherent organization and partly to check the steps of the proof, the value of the logical pattern is far less than is usually believed. Throughout the many centuries from 3000 B.C. to 1900 A.D. the mathematicians gradually acquired the types of numbers and the operations with these numbers that are now comprised in the complex number system. (This development is reviewed in Davis' article in Section III.) By the time that each class of numbers and the operations with these numbers were finally received into mathematics, the mathematicians knew precisely what these numbers were and what their properties must be. In the last few decades of the nineteenth century, for reasons which are irrelevant here, the mathematicians decided to build a logical development of the complex number system. Thereupon they sought axioms from which one could deduce for the various classes of numbers the very properties which they already knew to be valid. For the purposes of gaining new knowledge about numbers or guaranteeing the properties of numbers, the logical framework was superfluous.

The logical organization of mathematics is overrated for other reasons also. Long ago mathematicians knew that intuitive conviction surpasses logic as the brilliance of the sun surpasses the pale light of the moon. In one way or another great mathematicians saw this truth. Plato was sure that mathematical truths existed in a world independent of man and that the mind recognized these truths through contemplation. Descartes affirmed that "logic is of use only in communicating what we already know." The mathematician Henri Lebesgue remarked, "Logic makes us reject certain arguments but it cannot make us believe any argument." To this Jacques Hadamard added that logic merely sanctioned the conquests of the intuition. Aiming at the same truth is the somewhat facetious remark of A. S. Besicovitch that a great mathematician is known by the number of false proofs he has published. Besicovitch did not need to add that the theorems which these men conjectured to be true were nevertheless correct and ultimately were logically established. Great mathematicians know before a logical proof is ever composed that a theorem must be true and they may be content with no more than an indication of a proof, although Fermat in his vast and classic work on the theory of numbers and Newton in his work on curves of third degree gave not even indications. Mathematics is furthered most by men who are distinguished by the power of intuition rather than by the capacity to make rigorous proofs.

In recent times we have become more aware of the limitations of logic. We shall see in Section IV that the implication of one of the deepest results of modern mathematics, Gödel's theorem, is that mathematics cannot be enchained in logic. This is why Herman Weyl remarked in his obituary on David Hilbert, "Mathematizing may well be a creative activity of man, like language or music, of primary originality, whose historical decisions defy complete objective rationalizations."

Many people, induced to grant that the creative activity may indeed be the more significant part of mathematics, nevertheless remain convinced against their will because they do not have enough experience in the act of creation. In fact they often ask, "What can one create? What problems are still open?" In his article, Halmos gives many examples not only of individual creations but of classes of investigations that offer a wide scope of possibilities.

Because the creative process is so vital and because it is intriguing, many men have sought to understand its workings. But it proves far easier to evaluate what creativity in mathematics produces than to penetrate into the operations of the human mind and determine how it creates. Nevertheless some insights have been obtained and one of these is provided in the article by Henri Poincaré, who shares only with David Hilbert the distinction of being the greatest mathematician of recent times.

The logical presentation of a body of mathematics, which is all that Euclid's *Elements* offers, omits another vital component of mathematics, namely, the purpose of the work. It is, of course, considered heresy by some mathematicians even to raise such an issue. Mathematics, they contend, is so obviously an art that to ask about its purposes or ends is to profane art. This attitude is especially common today when so much new mathematics answers questions raised only by the individual mathematician and its worth is defended solely on the ground that the author is creating beauty. These men regard any application to reality as adulterating or contaminating.

Until about one hundred years ago no mathematician would have had any doubt that the primary purpose of his subject was to understand and control natural phenomena. Gauss, for example, took as his motto, "Thou, nature, art my goddess; To thy laws my services are bound." However, diverging views about the ends of mathematics did arise and controversy flared into the open in a letter which Carl Jacobi wrote to Adrien-Marie Legendre in 1830. Fourier had written in his classic work *The Analytical Theory of Heat:* "The profound study of nature is the most fertile source of mathematical discoveries. This study offers not only the advantage of a well determined goal but the advantage of excluding vague questions and useless calculations. It is a means of building analysis itself and of discovering the ideas which matter most and which science must always preserve. The fundamental ideas are those which represent the natural happenings." To this Jacobi replied, "It is true that Fourier has the opinion that the principal object of mathematics is the public utility and the explanation of natural phenomena; but a scientist like him ought to know that the unique object of science is the honor of the human spirit and on this basis a question of the theory of numbers is worth as much as a question about the planetary system."

There are beautiful chapters of mathematics and there is no doubt that mathematicians derive from doing mathematics the satisfactions which any creative activity affords. But the great mathematicians have been content to accept the beauty of mathematics as a bonus. Their most deep-seated drive has been to aid, through the medium of mathematics, in man's search to understand the universe and his own role in it, and to utilize the forces and phenomena of nature in man's behalf. It is no accident that the men who have contributed most to mathematics—Archimedes, Newton, Lagrange, Laplace, Gauss, Hamilton, Poincaré, and even Jacobi himself—either were primarily physical scientists or at least occupy distinguished places in the history of science. The meaning and purpose of almost all of mathematics do not lie in the series of logically related collections of symbols but in what these collections have to tell us about our world.

Not only the drive to create mathematics but also the concepts and problems derive from the desire to understand and master nature. Science has provided the sustenance and lifeblood of mathematical activity. Talleyrand once remarked that an idealist cannot last long unless he is a realist and a realist cannot last long unless he is an idealist. Applied to mathematics, this remark does speak for the need to idealize real problems and to study them abstractly but it also says that the idealist who ignores reality will not survive. John von Neumann, one of the distinguished mathematicians of our time, issued the same warning. In an article* entitled "The Mathematician" von Neumann said, "As a mathematical discipline travels far from its empirical source, or still more, if it is a second and third generation only indirectly

*In Heywood, Robert B., *The Works of the Mind*, University of Chicago Press, 1947.

inspired by ideas coming from 'reality,' it is beset with very grave dangers. It becomes more and more purely aestheticizing, more and more purely l'art pour l'art. This need not be bad, if the field is surrounded by correlated subjects, which still have closer empirical connections, or if the discipline is under the influence of men with an exceptionally well-developed taste. But there is a grave danger that the subject will develop along the lines of least resistance, that the stream, so far from its source, will separate into a multitude of insignificant branches, and that the discipline will become a disorganized mass of details and complexities. In other words, at a great distance from its empirical source, or after much 'abstract' inbreeding, a mathematical subject is in danger of degeneration."

For this reason Courant, although he points out the vital role that abstractions and generalizations play especially in modern mathematics, stresses in his article that, "Mathematics must take its motivation from concrete specific substance and aim again at some layer of 'reality.' The flight into abstraction must be something more than a mere escape; start from the ground and reentry are both indispensable, even if the same pilot cannot handle all phases of the trajectory."

INNOVATION IN MATHEMATICS

1

PAUL R. HALMOS · September 1958

Everybody knows that for the past 300 years innovations in science and technology have come at a steadily increasing pace. Practically everyone is aware that mathematics has played a central role in this advance. Yet, strangely, many people think of mathematics itself as a static art—a body of eternal truth that was discovered by a few ancient, shadowy figures, and upon which engineers and scientists can draw as needed.

Of course nothing could be further from the truth. Mathematics is improving, changing and growing every day. On its growth depends not only progress in all the other fundamental investigations, but also progress in the crudest, bread-and-butter circumstances of our daily lives.

The late John von Neumann liked to cite this example of the relation between technological development and pure mathematics: A hundred and fifty years ago one of the most important problems of applied science—on which development in industry, commerce and government depended—was the problem of saving lives at sea. The statistics of the losses were frightful. The money and effort expended to solve the problem were frightful too—and sometimes ludicrous. No gadget, however complicated, was too ridiculous to consider—ocean-going passenger vessels fitted out like outrigger canoes may have looked funny, but they were worth a try. While leaders of government and industry were desperately encouraging such crank experiments, mathematicians were developing a tool that was to save more lives than all the crackpot inventors combined dared hope. That tool is what has come to be known as the theory of functions of a complex variable (a variable containing the "imaginary" number i, the square root of minus one). Among the many applications of this purely mathematical notion, one of the most fruitful is in the theory of radio communication. From the mathematician Karl Friedrich Gauss to the inventor Guglielmo Marconi it is only a few steps that almost any pair of geniuses such as James Clerk Maxwell and Heinrich Hertz can take in their stride.

The list of mathematical innovations could be continued almost endlessly. Here are just a few more. The theory of groups, for instance, was developed about 100 years ago. It probably would have seemed an ugly and useless invention to the contemporaries of Gauss. Today it is part of the mathematical repertory of every physicist. As recently as 50 years ago there was not a single professor of statistics in the U. S. Now statistical methods are an imperative tool in such sciences as genetics and experimental psychology. Von Neumann's theory of games, first published in 1928 and revived 20 years later, seems to be finding important applications in economics and operations research. Finally, lest anyone suppose that mathematical ideas spring full-blown and perfect from the brows of their creators, we may recall that Euclid's celebrated geometric proofs were found, after 2,000 years, to contain serious gaps. The holes in his reasoning were finally plugged by the great German mathematician David Hilbert, around the turn of the century.

Admitting, then, that there are innovations in mathematics, let us try to see just what they consist of, and, insofar as it is possible, how they come about. One way to classify a mathematical contribution is this: It may be a new proof of an old fact, it may be a new fact, or it may be a new approach to several facts at the same time.

A large part of the activity of professional mathematicians is a search for new proofs of old facts. One reason for this is pure pleasure: there is esthetic enjoyment in getting a fresh point of view on a familiar landmark. Another is that the original creator hardly ever

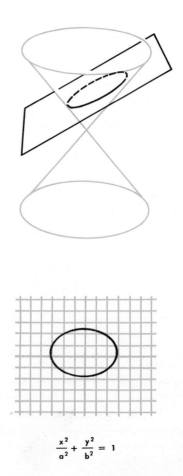

$$\frac{x^2}{a^2} + \frac{y^2}{b^2} = 1$$

GEOMETRY AND ALGEBRA were connected by Descartes's invention of analytic geometry. The first three figures, from left

reached his goal by the shortest, neatest, most efficient route, nor fully appreciated the connections between his brain-child and all other fields of mathematics. This is connected with a third and very practical motive. Mathematics has grown so luxuriantly in the past 2,000 years that it must be continually polished, simplified, systematized, unified and condensed. Otherwise the problem of handing the torch to each new generation would become completely unmanageable. No man alive today can know, even sketchily, all the mathematics published in the last 10 years. In order to give workers in the field enough understanding so that they can move ahead intelligently, it is absolutely imperative to find ever newer, shorter and simpler proofs that at the same time are more illuminating and provide more insight than their predecessors.

Curiously, it is sometimes good to find a new proof more complicated than an old one. If the new proof establishes some previously unsuspected connec-tions between two ideas, it often leads to a generalization that makes the task of future learners far easier than it was for their teachers. René Descartes's co-ordinate, or "analytic," geometry is a good example. One consequence of Descartes's innovation is that it is possi-ble to prove every proposition in Euclid's geometry by algebraic means [*see illustrations on page 10*]. The virtues of ana-lytic geometry are many and they are great, but the simplicity of analytic proofs, when compared with Euclidean ones, is definitely not one of them. In most cases the analytic proof of a Euclid-ean fact about triangles or circles is a messy calculation that teaches us nothing.

The value of analytic geometry is that it reveals a connection between two branches of mathematics—algebra and geometry—which had been thought to be entirely separate. One of the main concerns of the early geometers was conic sections, the curves that are formed by cutting a cone with a plane [*see illustrations below*]. This is obvi-ously a purely spatial way of thinking about the figures. When the conic sec-tions (ellipse, parabola and hyperbola) are plotted on Cartesian coordinates and their algebraic equations are writ-ten down, it turns out that all the equa-tions contain the squares of x and y, but no higher powers. Here is a new fact that provides deeper insight into the nature of the curves. And it also suggests a new question: What about the geomet-ric picture of curves that do involve higher powers of x and y? Now we are led to consider a whole new class of geometric figures to which spatial in-tuition alone would never have led us. Furthermore, by picturing the equations geometrically, we gain new insight into their algebraic structure.

Of course most new proofs represent a gain in simplicity as well as in insight. Consider, for example, the problem of finding the area of the plane region bounded by the parabolic trajectory of a projectile and the line segment joining the gun and the target. This is a problem

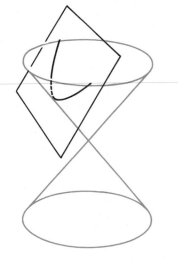

$$y^2 = 2px$$

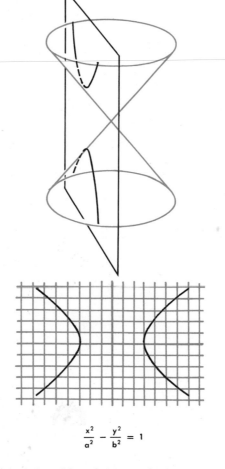

$$\frac{x^2}{a^2} - \frac{y^2}{b^2} = 1$$

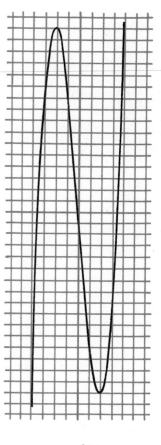

$$y = ax^3 + bx$$

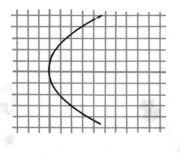

to right, show at top the curves (ellipse, parabola and hyperbola) that can be cut from a cone by a plane. At bottom the same curves are represented as graphical pictures of algebraic equations. These equations turn out to contain the squares of the variables, but no higher powers of the variables. The figure at the right on this page is the graph of an equation in which one of the variables is cubed.

that Archimedes could and did solve; his solution depends on the celebrated "method of exhaustion," a way of finding complicated areas by adding together more and more simple ones. Archimedes' solution is both ingenious and long. The problem can also be solved, in one line of writing, by any mediocre sophomore calculus student. To be sure, the sophomore's efficient solution is the product of the profound thought of many mathematicians over many years.

Individual proofs do become shorter, but only because they become embedded in larger contexts from which it is easy to pluck them. The larger contexts spread and mix with other general concepts, forming a still-larger unified whole. After a couple of centuries 10 of the greatest discoveries of the era are likely to find themselves together between the covers of a slim volume in the pocket of a graduate student who, with luck, will absorb them all in two or three months.

So much for new proofs. What about new facts? In a trivial sense we have all discovered new mathematical facts. We see one every time we add a column of figures on our tax return. The chances are that no one has ever before observed that the sum of just those figures is what it is. A really interesting new mathematical fact has much more breadth and generality. Here is an example that is not exactly brand new (it was proved by Leonhard Euler some 200 years ago), but might be new to nonmathematicians: Every positive whole number is the sum of not more than four squares. The squares are of course 1, 4, 9, 16 and so on. Between them there are larger and larger gaps [see illustration at top left on pages 12 and 13]. If we add the squares two at a time (repetitions such as 4 + 4 are allowed), we get a sequence with fewer gaps. If we fill in all the numbers that are sums of three squares, there will be still fewer gaps.

Euler's theorem says that if we fill in all the numbers that are sums of four squares, there will be no more gaps left.

Another example of a mathematical fact, also no longer new, but which illustrates the powerful role that mathematical innovation can play, is the theory of the solvability of equations. It was created by the young French genius Evariste Galois in the early part of the 19th century. Galois's predecessors had found general formulas for solving equations up to the fourth degree—that is, equations in which the unknown is raised to no higher power than four. (One is the familiar "quadratic formula" of high-school algebra, which solves equations of the second degree.) Naturally they expected that there were also formulas that would solve equations of higher degree, and they spent an enormous amount of time and effort looking for them.

Galois dared to doubt the existence of such generalized formulas. He attacked the problem from a fresh point of view, looking not for tricks that would yield the supposedly hidden formulas, but trying to find more general properties of equations and their solutions. His work led to the important and fruitful concept of groups—sets of entities for which an operation similar to multiplication is defined. An immediate result of his beautiful and deep intellectual construction was to confirm his doubt: there are no general formulas for the solution of all algebraic equations. Thus he discovered a new fact.

The work of Galois exemplifies the third type of innovation also: the new approach. Group theory has proved an invaluable tool for attacking an extremely wide range of mathematical problems. Furthermore, Galois's ideas turned up another surprising connection between algebra and geometry. They show that the famous ancient puzzles of squaring the circle, duplicating the cube and trisecting the angle also have no general solutions. The reverberations of Galois's new approach can still be felt in modern algebra.

Where does a mathematical innovation come from? Sometimes, but by no means always, the source lies outside mathematics. Just as mathematics can make contributions to engineering, physics, psychology, genetics, economics and other disciplines, these other disciplines can keep mathematical creativity alive by asking stimulating questions, pointing to fresh lines of development, and, at the very least, providing suggestive language for the expression of

mathematical ideas. It has happened that when a physicist needed a mathematical theory, it was already sitting there, waiting to be picked up and used. More often it happens that when something new is needed for such applications, the news percolates up to the ivory tower in a few decades (or more), and the answer comes down after a comparable time interval.

New mathematics often comes from plain curiosity. The right kind of mathematical curiosity is a precious possession that usually belongs only to professionals of the highest rank. The hardest problem of a young mathematician is to find a problem. The right question, well asked, is more than half the battle, and often the only part that requires inspiration. The answer itself may be difficult, and it may require ingenuity in the use of known techniques, but it often happens that all the thrill of creation and insight is concentrated in the question.

It should perhaps be mentioned that after the question is formulated, the mathematician does not proceed (as it is often supposed) like a scientific Sherlock Holmes. A mathematician is not a deduction machine, but a human being. New mathematics comes to him not by pure thought and deduction, but by sweat, experiment, induction and, if he is lucky, inspiration. Of course a mathematical experiment does not involve wires, tubes and bubbling liquids; it consists, rather, of a detailed examination of some particular cases or analogues of the desired result. (Example: Write down the first 10 squares, and write down systematically all the numbers that can be obtained as sums of two, or three, or four of them.) On the basis of such experiments the mathematician jumps inductively to bold conclusions. It may then be a difficult task to prove them, but often the purely deductive arrangement of the work serves more to communicate facts than to establish them.

To return to the source of innovations, it should be said that mathematicians share their curiosity, as well as their knowledge, with one another. At the beginning of his career a student often battens off the curiosity of his teachers. Great men do essentially the same thing when they decide to attack a problem that their predecessors could not solve. Galois himself was solving problems that he did not create. There will always be unsolved problems from bygone days: two famous ones that are not quite dead are the four-color map problem and Fermat's last theorem

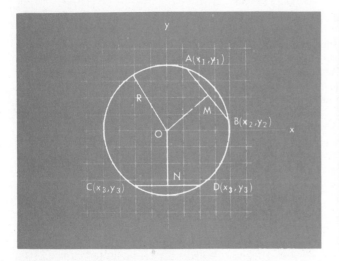

Given the curve $x^2 + y^2 = R^2$, $AB = CD$

To prove $OM = ON$

M is midpoint of AB and its coordinates are

$$\left(\frac{x_1 + x_2}{2} , \frac{y_1 + y_2}{2} \right)$$

$$OM = \sqrt{ \left(\frac{x_1 + x_2}{2} \right)^2 + \left(\frac{y_1 + y_2}{2} \right)^2 }$$

Expanding and substituting R^2

for $x_1^2 + y_1^2$ and $x_2^2 + y_2^2$

$$OM = \sqrt{ \frac{R^2 + x_1 x_2 + y_1 y_2}{2} }$$

But $ON = y_3$, so we must prove

$$y_3 = \sqrt{ \frac{R^2 + x_1 x_2 + y_1 y_2}{2} }$$

$$AB = \sqrt{ (x_2 - x_1)^2 + (y_2 - y_1)^2 }$$

Expanding and substituting as above

$$AB = \sqrt{ 2R^2 - 2x_1 x_2 - 2y_1 y_2 }$$

$CD = 2x_3$, and since $AB = CD$,

$$\sqrt{ 2R^2 - 2x_1 x_2 - 2y_1 y_2 } = 2x_3$$

$$2R^2 - 2x_1 x_2 - 2y_1 y_2 = 4x_3^2$$

$$x_1 x_2 + y_1 y_2 = R^2 - 2x_3^2$$

Substituting in the expression for OM,

$$OM = \sqrt{ \frac{R^2 + R^2 - 2x_3^2}{2} }$$

$$OM = \sqrt{ R^2 - x_3^2 }$$

But $x_3^2 + y_3^2 = R^2$

$$\therefore R^2 - x_3^2 = y_3^2$$

$$\therefore OM = \sqrt{ y_3^2 } = y_3$$

$$\therefore OM = ON$$

ANALYTIC PROOF of a Euclidean theorem is outlined above. The theorem states that equal chords of a circle are equidistant from the center. Proving the statement requires no ingenuity, but the algebraic computations are long, tedious and unilluminating.

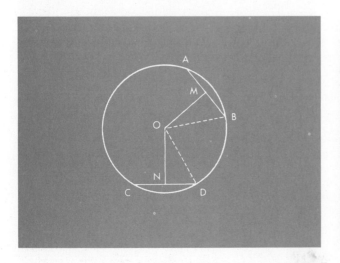

Draw OB and OD

$OB = OD$	Radii of the same $\odot$ are equal
$MB = \tfrac{1}{2} AB$ and $ND = \tfrac{1}{2} CD$	A perpendicular from the center of a circle to a chord bisects the chord
$\therefore MB = ND$	Halves of equals are equal
$\therefore \triangle OND \cong \triangle OMB$	Hypotenuse and leg
$\therefore OM = ON$	

Q.E.D.

EUCLIDEAN PROOF of the proposition that equal chords are equidistant from the center is much shorter and neater than the analytic proof. Analytic geometry is valuable not as a method of grinding out proofs, but as a link between algebra and geometry.

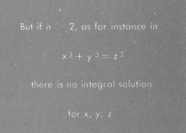

nd look for an
re precisely, a
ic if it is a solu-
as $a + bx = 0$,
r $a + bx + cx^2$
$a, b, c, d, etc.$
numbers (pos-
bly even zero).
gebraic is called

ely many equa-
y different solu-
tely many alge-
question arises:
lental numbers?
(it is yes). But
led along com-
considered the
the set of alge-
n found a way
these infinitely

sets we simply
Thus there is no
at the set of all
larger than the
invented a kind
that can be ap-
e *illustrations at
pages*]. He was
t the set of all
y larger than the
rs. The matter is
numbers must in-

ut numbers and
stems have been
's methods. His
bution, however,
iew, to which al-
natical world has
nstead of consid-
ers or points or
ntor mathemati-
ts of numbers or
ese have proper-
ribed to the indi-
that nevertheless
e elements. A set
ple can walk arm
cannot. And we
out a person from

ed example, imag-
ropean attending
otball game. Be-
e of the bands
ield. You have a
inoculars through
the musicians one
eir blazers means
cannot tell which
. But if you put
d notice that the
the letter P as it

$$x^n + y^n = z^n$$
where
$$x, y, z, n$$
are positive integers

If $n = 2$
the equation reads
$$x^2 + y^2 = z^2$$
and there are
many solutions

For example
$$3^2 + 4^2 = 5^2$$
$$5^2 + 12^2 = 13^2$$
etc.

But if $n > 2$, as for instance in
$$x^3 + y^3 = z^3$$
there is no integral solution
for x, y, z

FERMAT'S LAST THEOREM states that the equation $x^n + y^n = z^n$ has no solutions in which x, y and z are positive whole numbers, if n is a whole number greater than two. Fermat noted in a book that he had "discovered a truly remarkable proof which this margin is too small to contain," but no one has been able to prove the theorem.

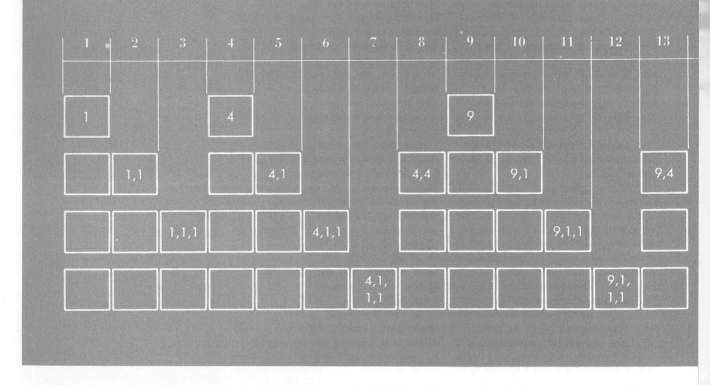

A MATHEMATICAL DISCOVERY of Euler is illustrated in this table. The theorem states that every positive whole number can be expressed as the sum of no more than four squares of other whole numbers. Rectangles in top row represent the squares themselves. Those in succeeding rows represent numbers that can be formed by adding two, three and four squares respectively. Figures

marches out, you can probably decide that they are Princetonians. Of course, it might be the Yale band making a courteous gesture, but the general idea is clear. The structure of a set can tell you something about its members.

The classical mathematician was interested in individual problems. Confronted with a system of equations, he asked: Do they have solutions? If so, what does each solution look like? The modern mathematician also wants to know the answers to these questions, but he approaches the problem differently. He might begin, for instance, by asking: "Is the sum or the product of two solutions also a solution?" This is a question about the structure of the set of all possible solutions. If the answer is yes, he knows that he is dealing with a particular type of set (for instance, a group), and this gives him important information about the individual solutions.

Some problems lead to complicated and difficult sets. Consider a few sets of points that can be chosen from a particular straight line. (Assume that the line is graduated like a thermometer. There is a point marked zero, with positive numbers on one side of it and negative numbers on the other.) Let us start with some simple sets: the set of all points above zero (the positive numbers); the set of all points (we might as well say numbers) between 2 and 7; the set of all points below — 2. All these are easily conceived, everyday sets, and can be readily visualized in geometrical dia-

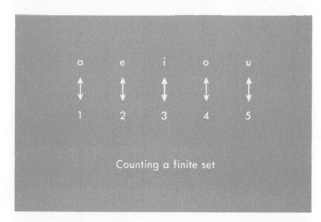

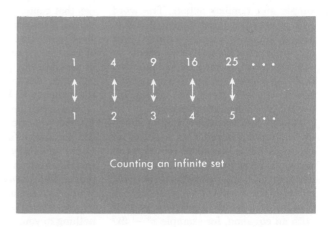

SETS are counted and compared by the method illustrated here. Counting a finite set, such as the vowels (*left*), means matching its members to positive integers. Counting an infinite set, such as the squares of the whole numbers (*middle*), also means matching each of its members to a positive integer. The infinite set of points in a line (*right*) is known to be larger than the infinite set of positive

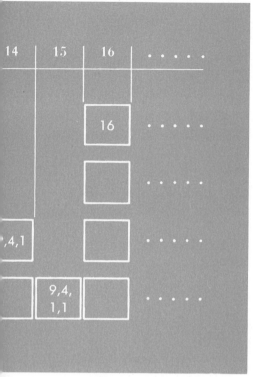

in rectangles are the squares which, when added together, give the number. The theorem is true for all of the positive integers.

grams [*see top three illustrations at right*]. Now suppose we think of the points between the whole numbers as decimals, and construct the set of all those points with a positive odd number to the left of the decimal point. This is still not too bad; with a small mental effort we can imagine it and draw its picture [*bottom illustration at right*]. But what about the set of points in whose decimal representation the digit 6 never appears? It is a perfectly reasonably defined set, and we know quite a

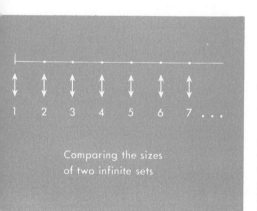

Comparing the sizes
of two infinite sets

integers because, no matter how some of the points are matched up with integers, some other points will always be left unmatched.

lot about it. We know, for instance, that the point 11/20 (.55) and the point 8/7 (1.142857142857 . . .) belong to the set, and the point *pi* (3.14159265 . . .) does not. The geometric diagram of the set is probably impossible to visualize—and even so this set is much simpler than some which mathematicians are regularly forced to study. To show just one possible additional complication, consider the set of points in whose decimal representation the digit 6 may or may not occur, but never six times consecutively. Once again we know something about the set; we know, for instance, that 11/20 and 8/7 still belong to it. There is no one on the face of the earth who can decide whether *pi* belongs to the set or not.

Of course mathematicians long before Cantor had been studying certain kinds of sets (for example, lines, triangles, circles and the like), even if they did not think of them in those terms. In the early days of set theory, many mathematicians took up the idea with more enthusiasm than discretion. Any set was as good as any other. The result was mathematical anarchy. A kind of inverted snobbishness even led some workers to prefer the wildest and most unruly sets to the well-behaved, coherent sets of older days. This radicalism was not welcomed in all quarters. The great French mathematician Henri Poincaré remarked on one occasion: "Later generations will regard set theory as a disease from which one has recovered."

But after its youthful excesses post-Cantorian mathematics settled down to a mature and responsible evaluation of itself and its role in history. The set-theoretic approach is now instilled into young mathematicians virtually in the cradle, and, as a result, it is so much in their bloodstream as to have lost almost all its controversial character. It has proved to be one of the most powerful unifying themes in the history of mathematics, a theme which reveals connections between apparently remote regions of ideas.

What is the mathematics of today that will precipitate the controversies of tomorrow and become the orthodoxy of the next day? No one can say. It may take a decade, or a century, to see a mathematical innovation in its proper light. But of one thing we may be certain: As long as there is a world with mathematicians in it, innovation will continue. The new ideas will be studied, sometimes applied to practical problems, and always enjoyed.

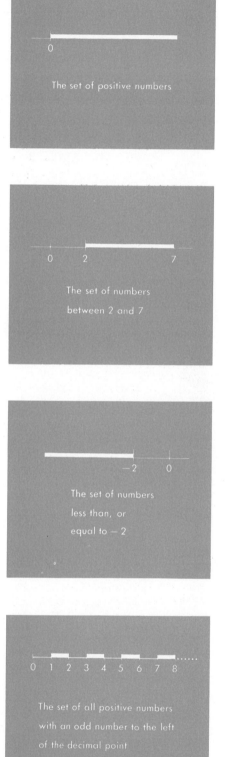

The set of positive numbers

The set of numbers
between 2 and 7

The set of numbers
less than, or
equal to − 2

The set of all positive numbers
with an odd number to the left
of the decimal point

SETS OF NUMBERS such as those in the illustrations above are easy to visualize and to represent diagrammatically. Others that are mentioned in the text are difficult to conceive and also impossible to diagram.

2 MATHEMATICAL CREATION

HENRI POINCARÉ · August 1948
Edited by JAMES R. NEWMAN

How is mathematics made? What sort of brain is it that can compose the propositions and systems of mathematics? How do the mental processes of the geometer or algebraist compare with those of the musician, the poet, the painter, the chess player? In mathematical creation which are the key elements? Intuition? An exquisite sense of space and time? The precision of a calculating machine? A powerful memory? Formidable skill in following complex logical sequences? A supreme capacity for concentration?

The essay below, delivered in the first years of this century as a lecture before the Psychological Society in Paris, is the most celebrated of the attempts to describe what goes on in the mathematician's brain. Its author, Henri Poincaré, cousin of Raymond, the politician, was peculiarly fitted to undertake the task. One of the foremost mathematicians of all time, unrivalled as an analyst and mathematical physicist, Poincaré was known also as a brilliantly lucid expositor of the philosophy of science. These writings are of the first importance as professional treatises for scientists and are at the same time accessible, in large part, to the understanding of the thoughtful layman.

* * *

THE GENESIS of mathematical creation is a problem which should intensely interest the psychologist. It is the activity in which the human mind seems to take least from the outside world, in which it acts or seems to act only of itself and on itself, so that in studying the procedure of geometric thought we may hope to reach what is most essential in man's mind....

A first fact should surprise us, or rather would surprise us if we were not so used to it. How does it happen there are people who do not understand mathematics? If mathematics invokes only the rules of logic, such as are accepted by all normal minds; if its evidence is based on principles common to all men, and that none could deny without being mad, how does it come about that so many persons are here refractory?

That not every one can invent is nowise mysterious. That not every one can retain a demonstration once learned may also pass. But that not every one can understand mathematical reasoning when explained appears very surprising when we think of it. And yet those who can follow this reasoning only with difficulty are in the majority; that is undeniable, and will surely not be gainsaid by the experience of secondary-school teachers.

And further: how is error possible in mathematics? A sane mind should not be guilty of a logical fallacy, and yet there are very fine minds who do not trip in brief reasoning such as occurs in the ordinary doings of life, and who are incapable of following or repeating without error the mathematical demonstrations which are longer, but which after all are only an accumulation of brief reasonings wholly analogous to those they make so easily. Need we add that mathematicians themselves are not infallible? ...

As for myself, I must confess, I am absolutely incapable even of adding without mistakes.... My memory is not bad, but it would be insufficient to make me a good chess-player. Why then does it not fail me in a difficult piece of mathematical reasoning where most chess-players would lose themselves? Evidently because it is guided by the general march of the reasoning. A mathematical demonstration is not a simple juxtaposition of syllogisms, it is syllogisms *placed in a certain order*, and the order in which these elements are placed is much more important than the elements themselves. If I have the feeling, the intuition, so to speak, of this order, so as to perceive at a glance the reasoning as a whole, I need no longer fear lest I forget one of the elements, for each of them will take its allotted place in the array, and that without any effort of memory on my part.

We know that this feeling, this intuition of mathematical order, that makes us divine hidden harmonies and relations, cannot be possessed by every one. Some will not have either this delicate feeling so difficult to define, or a strength of memory and attention beyond the ordinary, and then they will be absolutely incapable of understanding higher mathematics. Such are the majority. Others will have this feeling only in a slight degree, but they will be gifted with an uncommon memory and a great power of attention. They will learn by heart the details one after another; they can understand mathematics and sometimes make applications, but they cannot create. Others, finally, will possess in a less or greater degree the special intuition referred to, and then not only can they understand mathematics

HENRI POINCARE was born in 1854, the son of a civil servant and meteorologist. During his fruitful professional life he devoted himself to pure mathematics and its application to physics and astronomy. Author of several books in these fields, he is also known for his writings in the philosophy of science. Poincaré died in 1912.

even if their memory is nothing extraordinary, but they may become creators and try to invent with more or less success according as this intuition is more or less developed in them.

IN FACT, what is mathematical creation? It does not consist in making new combinations with mathematical entities already known. Anyone could do that, but the combinations so made would be infinite in number and most of them absolutely without interest. To create consists precisely in not making useless combinations and in making those which are useful and which are only a small minority. Invention is discernment, choice.

It is time to penetrate deeper and to see what goes on in the very soul of the mathematician. For this, I believe, I can do best by recalling memories of my own. But I shall limit myself to telling how I wrote my first memoir on Fuchsian functions. I beg the reader's pardon; I am about to use some technical expressions, but they need not frighten him, for he is not obliged to understand them. I shall say, for example, that I have found the demonstration of such a theorem under such circumstances. This theorem will have a barbarous name, unfamiliar to many, but that is unimportant; what is of interest for the psychologist is not the theorem but the circumstances.

For fifteen days I strove to prove that there could not be any functions like those I have since called Fuchsian functions. I was then very ignorant; every day I seated myself at my work table, stayed an hour or two, tried a great number of combinations and reached no results. One evening, contrary to my custom, I drank black coffee and could not sleep. Ideas rose in crowds; I felt them collide until pairs interlocked, so to speak, making a stable combination. By the next morning I had established the existence of a class of Fuchsian functions, those which come from the hypergeometric series; I had only to write out the results, which took but a few hours.

Then I wanted to represent these functions by the quotient of two series; this idea was perfectly conscious and deliberate, the analogy with elliptic functions guided me. I asked myself what properties these series must have if they existed, and I succeeded without difficulty in forming the series I have called theta-Fuchsian.

Just at this time I left Caen, where I was then living, to go on a geologic excursion under the auspices of the school of mines. The changes of travel made me forget my mathematical work. Having reached Coutances, we entered an omnibus to go some place or other. At the moment when I put my foot on the step the idea came to me, without anything in my former thoughts seeming to have paved the way for it, that the transformations I had used to define the Fuchsian functions were identical with those of non-Euclidean geometry. I did not verify the idea; I should not have had time, as, upon taking my seat in the omnibus, I went on with a conversation already commenced, but I felt a perfect certainty. On my return to Caen, for conscience' sake I verified the result at my leisure.

THEN I turned my attention to the study of some arithmetical questions apparently without much success and without a suspicion of any connection with my preceding researches. Disgusted with my failure, I went to spend a few days at the seaside, and thought of something else. One morning, walking on the bluff, the

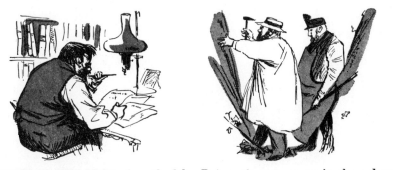

idea came to me, with just the same characteristics of brevity, suddenness and immediate certainty that the arithmetic transformations of indeterminate ternary quadratic forms were identical with those of non-Euclidean geometry.

Returned to Caen, I meditated on this result and deduced the consequences. The example of quadratic forms showed me that there were Fuchsian groups other than those corresponding to the hypergeometric series; I saw that I could apply to them the theory of theta-Fuchsian series and that consequently there existed Fuchsian functions other than those from the hypergeometric series, the ones I then knew. Naturally I set myself to form all these functions. I made a systematic attack upon them and carried all the outworks, one after another. There was one, however, that still held out, whose fall would involve that of the whole place. But all my efforts only served at first the better to show me the difficulty, which indeed was something. All this work was perfectly conscious.

Thereupon I left for Mont-Valérien, where I was to go through my military service; so I was very differently occupied. One day, going along the street, the solution of the difficulty which had stopped me suddenly appeared to me. I did not try to go deep into it immediately, and only after my service did I again take up the question. I had all the elements and had only to arrange them and put them together. So I wrote out my final memoir at a single stroke and without difficulty.

I shall limit myself to this single example; it is useless to multiply them....

Most striking at first is this appearance of sudden illumination, a manifest sign of long, unconscious prior work. The role of this unconscious work in mathematical invention appears to me incontestable, and traces of it would be found in other cases where it is less evident. Often when one works at a hard question, nothing good is accomplished at the first attack. Then one takes a rest, longer or shorter, and sits down anew to the work. During the first half-hour, as before, nothing is found, and then all of a sudden the decisive idea presents itself to the mind....

There is another remark to be made about the conditions of this unconscious work; it is possible, and of a certainty it is only fruitful, if it is on the one hand preceded and on the other hand followed by a period of conscious work. These sudden inspirations (and the examples already cited prove this) never happen except after some days of voluntary effort which has appeared absolutely fruitless and whence nothing good seems to have come, where the way taken seems totally astray. These efforts then have not been as sterile as one thinks; they have set agoing the unconscious machine and without them it would not have moved and would have produced nothing....

Such are the realities; now for the thoughts they force upon us. The unconscious, or, as we say, the subliminal self plays an important role in mathematical creation; this follows from what we have said. But usually the subliminal self is considered as purely automatic. Now we have seen that mathematical work is not simply mechanical, that it could not be done by a machine, however perfect. It is not merely a question of applying rules, of making the most combinations possible according to certain fixed laws. The combinations so obtained would be exceedingly numerous, useless and cumbersome. The true work of the inventor consists in choosing among these combinations so as to eliminate the useless ones or rather to avoid the trouble of making them, and the rules which must guide this choice are extremely fine and delicate. It is almost impossible to state them precisely; they are felt rather than formulated. Under these

CREATIVE PROCESS, described by Poincaré, may go on in the subconscious between periods of conscious work. At work on a problem (*first draw-*

conditions, how imagine a sieve capable of applying them mechanically?

A first hypothesis now presents itself; the subliminal self is in no way inferior to the conscious self; it is not purely automatic; it is capable of discernment; it has tact, delicacy; it knows how to choose, to divine. What do I say? It knows better how to divine than the conscious self, since it succeeds where that has failed. In a word, is not the subliminal self superior to the conscious self? You recognize the full importance of this question. . . .

Is this affirmative answer forced upon us by the facts I have just given? I confess that, for my part, I should hate to

ing), Poincaré went on a geology expedition (*second drawing*). The solution came to him as he stepped into omnibus (*third drawing*), was written later.

accept it. Reexamine the facts then and see if they are not compatible with another explanation.

It is certain that the combinations which present themselves to the mind in a sort of sudden illumination, after an unconscious working somewhat prolonged, are generally useful and fertile combinations, which seem the result of a first impression. Does it follow that the subliminal self, having divined by a delicate intuition that these combinations would be useful, has formed only these, or has it rather formed many others which were lacking in interest and have remained unconscious?

In this second way of looking at it, all the combinations would be formed in consequence of the automatism of the subliminal self, but only the interesting ones would break into the domain of consciousness. And this is still very mysterious. What is the cause that, among the thousand products of our unconscious activity, some are called to pass the threshold, while others remain below? Is it a simple chance which confers this privilege? Evidently not; among all the stimuli of our senses, for example, only the most intense fix our attention, unless it has been drawn to them by other causes. More generally the privileged unconscious phenomena, those susceptible of becoming conscious, are those which, directly or indirectly, affect most profoundly our emotional sensibility.

It may be surprising to see emotional sensibility invoked *à propos* of mathematical demonstrations which, it would seem,

can interest only the intellect. This would be to forget the feeling of mathematical beauty, of the harmony of numbers and forms, of geometric elegance. This is a true esthetic feeling that all real mathematicians know, and surely it belongs to emotional sensibility.

Now, what are the mathematic entities to which we attribute this character of beauty and elegance, and which are capable of developing in us a sort of esthetic emotion? They are those whose elements are harmoniously disposed so that the mind without effort can embrace their totality while realizing the details. This harmony is at once a satisfaction of our esthetic needs and an aid to the mind, sustaining and guiding. And at the same time, in putting under our eyes a well-ordered whole, it makes us foresee a mathematical law. . . . Thus it is this special esthetic sensibility which plays the role of the delicate sieve of which I spoke, and that sufficiently explains why the one lacking it will never be a real creator.

Yet all the difficulties have not disappeared. The conscious self is narrowly limited, and as for the subliminal self we know not its limitations, and this is why we are not too reluctant in supposing that it has been able in a short time to make more different combinations than the whole life of a conscious being could encompass. Yet these limitations exist. Is it likely that it is able to form all the possible combinations, whose number would frighten the imagination? Nevertheless that would seem necessary, because if it produces only a small part of these combinations, and if it makes them at random, there would be small chance that the *good,* the one we should choose, would be found among them.

Perhaps we ought to seek the explanation in that preliminary period of conscious work which always precedes all fruitful unconscious labor. Permit me a rough comparison. Figure the future elements of our combinations as something like the hooked atoms of Epicurus. During the complete repose of the mind, these atoms are motionless, they are, so to speak, hooked to the wall. . . .

On the other hand, during a period of apparent rest and unconscious work, cer-

tain of them are detached from the wall and put in motion. They flash in every direction through the space (I was about to say the room) where they are enclosed, as would, for example, a swarm of gnats or, if you prefer a more learned comparison, like the molecules of gas in the kinematic theory of gases. Then their mutual impacts may produce new combinations.

WHAT IS the role of the preliminary conscious work? It is evidently to mobilize certain of these atoms, to unhook them from the wall and put them in swing. We think we have done no good, because we have moved these elements a thousand different ways in seeking to assemble them, and have found no satisfactory aggregate. But, after this shaking up imposed upon them by our will, these atoms do not return to their primitive rest. They freely continue their dance.

Now, our will did not choose them at random; it pursued a perfectly determined aim. The mobilized atoms are therefore not any atoms whatsoever; they are those from which we might reasonably expect the desired solution. Then the mobilized atoms undergo impacts which make them enter into combinations among themselves or with other atoms at rest which they struck against in their course. Again I beg pardon, my comparison is very rough, but I scarcely know how otherwise to make my thought understood.

However it may be, the only combinations that have a chance of forming are those where at least one of the elements is one of those atoms freely chosen by our will. Now, it is evidently among these that is found what I called the *good combination.* Perhaps this is a way of lessening the paradoxical in the original hypothesis. . . .

I shall make a last remark: when above I made certain personal observations, I spoke of a night of excitement when I worked in spite of myself. Such cases are frequent, and it is not necessary that the abnormal cerebral activity be caused by a physical excitant as in that I mentioned. It seems, in such cases, that one is present at his own unconscious work, made partially perceptible to the over-excited consciousness, yet without having changed its nature. Then we vaguely comprehend what distinguishes the two mechanisms or, if you wish, the working methods of the two egos. And the psychologic observations I have been able thus to make seem to me to confirm in their general outlines the views I have given.

Surely they have need of [confirmation], for they are and remain in spite of all very hypothetical: the interest of the questions is so great that I do not repent of having submitted them to the reader.

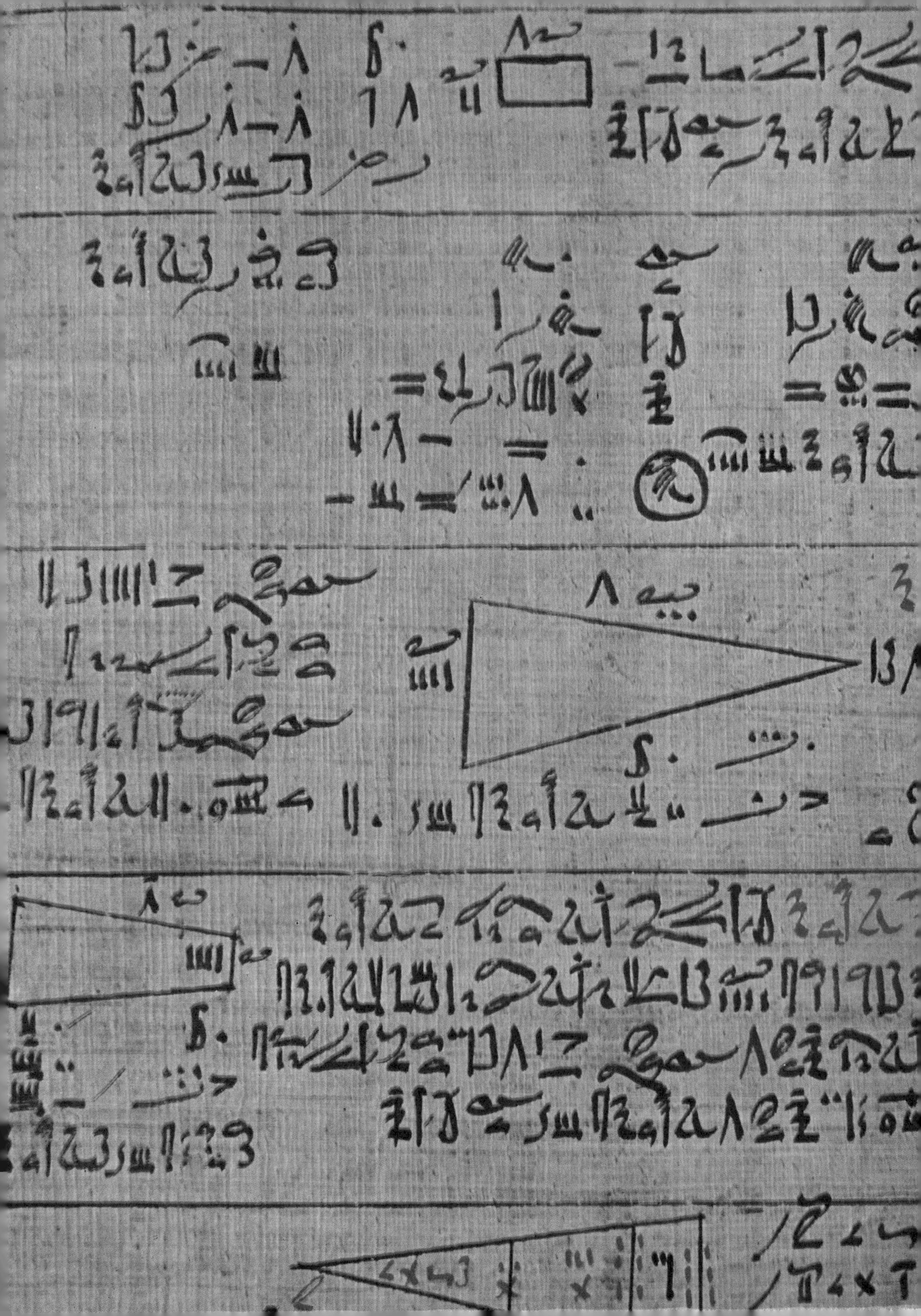

MATHEMATICS IN THE MODERN WORLD

3

RICHARD COURANT · September 1964

The expanding role of mathematics in the modern world is vividly reflected in the proliferation of mathematicians. Since 1900 memberships in the several professional mathematical organizations in the U.S. have multiplied by an estimated 30 times. Today the number qualified by the doctorate stands at 4,800. During the past 25 years the number of mathematicians at work outside the universities in industry and Government has increased twelvefold. Activities of a more or less mathematical character now employ tens of thousands of workers at all levels of competence. In the colleges three times as many undergraduates were majoring in mathematics in 1962 as in 1956. Mathematics is no longer the preoccupation of an academic elite; it is a broad profession attracting talented men and women in increasing numbers. The scope of mathematical research and teaching has been greatly extended in the present period, and mathematical techniques have penetrated deep into

fields outside the mathematical sciences such as physics, into new realms of technology, into the biological sciences and even into economics and the other social sciences. Computing machines and computing techniques have stimulated areas of research with obviously enormous and as yet only partly understood importance for mathematics itself and for all the sciences with inherent mathematical elements.

The contemporary role of mathematics is best appraised, however, by comparison with previous stages in its development. As recently as three centuries ago the main fabric of mathematical thought was supplied by geometry, inherited from the ancients and only meagerly augmented during the intervening 20 centuries. Then began a radical and rapid transformation of mathematics. The rigorous, axiomatic, deductive style of geometry yielded to inductive, intuitive insights, and purely geometric notions gave way to concepts of number and algebraic operations em-

bodied in analytic geometry, the calculus and mechanics. It was the small intellectual aristocracy of the new mathematics that now spearheaded the forward thrust of science. By the time of the French Revolution the accumulated wealth of results and the demonstrated power of the mathematical sciences brought a widening of the narrow human basis of scientific activity, with the writing of textbooks to make the new mathematics more widely accessible, the systematic training of scientists and mathematicians in the universities and the opening up of new careers in the expansion of human knowledge.

The "classical" mathematics that had its beginnings in the 17th century retains its power and central position today. Some of the most fruitful work has come from the clarification and generalization of the two basic concepts of the calculus: that of function, which is concerned with the interdependence of two or more variables, and that of limit, which brings the intuitive notion of continuity within rigorous scrutiny. The concepts of mathematical analysis, including the theory of differential equations for one or more variables, which is an essential tool for dealing with rates of change, pervade the vastly extended territory of modern mathematics. That territory is surveyed in three articles in this volume (see "Number," page 89, "Algebra," page 102, and "Geometry," page 112) from three points of vantage—number, geometry and algebra—

that offer perspectives familiar to the nonmathematician. As will be seen, geometry has had a most fruitful growth, liberated by the concepts of function and of the number continuum; its youngest offspring, topology and differential geometry, rank among the most active and "modern" branches of mathematics. The special field of probability deserves a chapter in itself because it has found such wide application in science and technology and because it gives mathematical expression to some of the deep unsolved problems in the philosophy of science.

Mathematics today also reflects a vigorous trend, started early in the 19th century, toward solidification of the new conquests in the spirit of the mathematical rigor practiced by the ancients. This effort has inspired intense work on the foundations of mathematics, directed at clarifying the structure of mathematics and the meaning of "existence" for the objects of mathematical thought.

Inevitably the expansion of mathematics has enhanced immanent tendencies toward specialization and isolation;

mathematics is threatened with a loss of unity and cohesion. Mutual understanding among representatives of different fields of mathematics has become difficult, and contact of mathematics with other sciences has been weakened. Yet remarkable advances continue to be won, mostly by young talent amply supported by a society that recognizes the increasing importance of mathematics. At the same time the growing volume of mathematical activity has led to a bewildering avalanche of publications, a multiplicity of meetings, administrative tangles and pressures of commercialism. It becomes the urgent duty of mathematicians, therefore, to meditate about the essence of mathematics, its motivations and goals and the ideas that must bind divergent interests together. For this purpose they can find no better occasion than the opportunity to explain their work to a wider public.

The question "What is mathematics?" cannot be answered meaningfully by philosophical generalities, semantic definitions or journalistic circumlocutions. Such characterizations also fail to do

justice to music or painting. No one can form an appreciation of these arts without some experience with rhythm, harmony and structure, or with form, color and composition. For the appreciation of mathematics actual contact with its substance is even more necessary.

With this caution, some remarks of a general nature can nevertheless be made. As is so often said, mathematics aims at progressive abstraction, logically rigorous axiomatic deduction and ever wider generalization. Such a characterization states the truth but not the whole truth; it is one-sided, almost a caricature of the live reality. Mathematics, in the first place, has no monopoly on abstraction. The concepts of mass, velocity, force, voltage and current are all abstract idealizations of physical reality. Mathematical concepts such as point, space, number and function are only somewhat more strikingly abstract.

The model of rigorous axiomatic deduction for so long impressed on mathematics by Euclid's *Elements* constitutes the remarkably attractive form in which

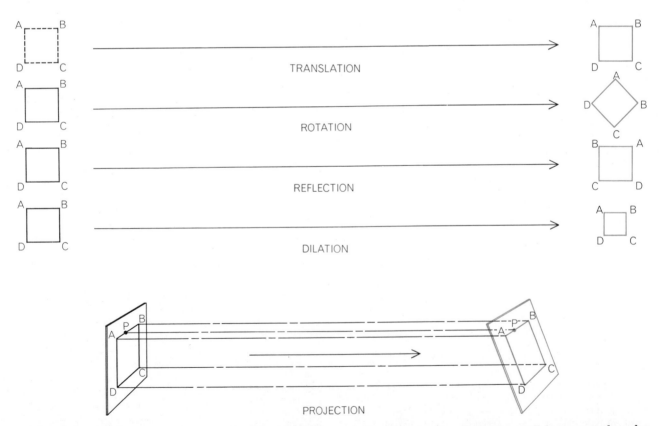

TRANSLATION

ROTATION

REFLECTION

DILATION

PROJECTION

TYPES OF GEOMETRY were classified by Felix Klein according to the invariant properties of figures when they undergo various groups of transformations. Euclidean geometry is represented at top left as the study of properties such as "angle" that are retained when the square *ABCD* is translated, rotated, reflected or dilated. Affine geometry, represented at bottom left, permits all these transformations, and projection by parallel rays to a plane that can be tilted. In this instance the ratio of collinear points is constant. (If *P* is a point on the line *AB*, then the ratio of *AP* to *PB* does not change when the figure is transformed.) At top right is a representation of projective geometry, which permits point-source projection to a randomly tilted screen. An invariant prop-

the end product of mathematical thought can often be crystallized. It signifies ultimate success in penetrating and ordering mathematical substance and laying bare its skeletal structure. But emphasis on this aspect of mathematics is totally misleading if it suggests that construction, imaginative induction and combination and the elusive mental process called intuition play a secondary role in productive mathematical activity or genuine understanding. In mathematical education, it is true, the deductive method starting from seemingly dogmatic axioms provides a shortcut for covering a large territory. But the constructive Socratic method that proceeds from the particular to the general and eschews dogmatic compulsion leads the way more surely to independent productive thinking.

Just as deduction should be supplemented by intuition, so the impulse to progressive generalization must be tempered and balanced by respect and love for colorful detail. The individual problem should not be degraded to the rank of special illustration of lofty general theories. In fact, general theories emerge from consideration of the specific, and they are meaningless if they do not serve to clarify and order the more particularized substance below.

The interplay between generality and individuality, deduction and construction, logic and imagination—this is the profound essence of live mathematics. Any one or another of these aspects of mathematics can be at the center of a given achievement. In a far-reaching development all of them will be involved. Generally speaking, such a development will start from the "concrete" ground, then discard ballast by abstraction and rise to the lofty layers of thin air where navigation and observation are easy; after this flight comes the crucial test of landing and reaching specific goals in the newly surveyed low plains of individual "reality." In brief, the flight into abstract generality must start from and return again to the concrete and specific.

These principles are dramatically and convincingly illustrated in the evolution of the mathematical sciences. Johannes Kepler, with the genius of the true diagnostician, abstracted from the wealth of Tycho Brahe's observations the elliptical shape of the planetary orbits. Isaac Newton, by further abstraction, derived from these models the universal law of gravitation and the differential equations of mechanics. On this elevated level of unencumbered mathematical abstraction mechanics gained an enormous mobility. On descent to concrete and specific earthbound problems it has won success after success in enormous regions outside its original province of celestial dynamics.

Similarly, in electromagnetism Michael Faraday established a body of experimental findings linked by his own ingenious interpretations. From these some mathematical qualitative laws of electromagnetism were soon abstracted. Then, behind the formulations for specific, simple configurations, the genius of James Clerk Maxwell divined a very general quantitative law that combines in a system of differential equations the magnetic and electric forces and their rates of change. These equations, abstracted and cut loose from specific, tangible cases, may at first have seemed

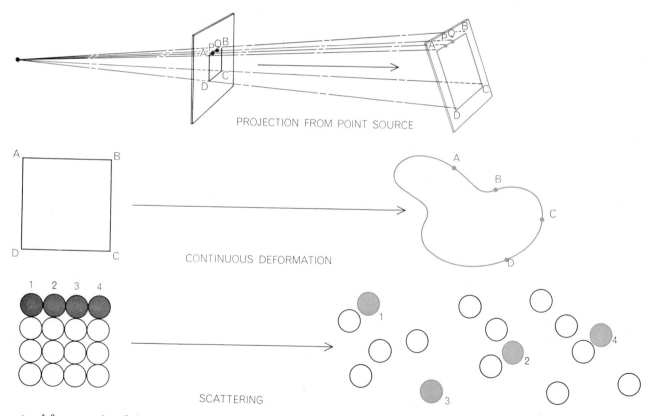

PROJECTION FROM POINT SOURCE

CONTINUOUS DEFORMATION

SCATTERING

erty of figures projected this way is the cross ratio of collinear points. (If P and Q are points on the line AB, the ratio of AP/PQ : AD/PD is unchanged by the transformation.) Topology, a fourth type of geometry that is represented at middle right, studies properties preserved during the bending, stretching and twisting operations called continuous deformation. The order of four points $A, B,$ C and D remains after the deformation. In point-set theory, the type of geometry shown at bottom right, the order of points is not retained during the kind of transformation called "scattering." The scattered points *do* remain conumerous with the points in the original figure. Thus point-set theory can be described as the study of the properties preserved under all one-to-one correspondences.

$$25x_1{}^2 + 22x_2{}^2 + 16x_3{}^2 + 20x_1x_2 - 4x_1x_3 - 16x_2x_3 - 62x_1 - 32x_2 - 44x_3 + 55 = 0$$

$$25x_1'{}^2 + 22x_2'{}^2 + 16x_3'{}^2 + 20x_1'x_2' - 4x_1'x_3' - 16x_2'x_3' - 36 = 0$$

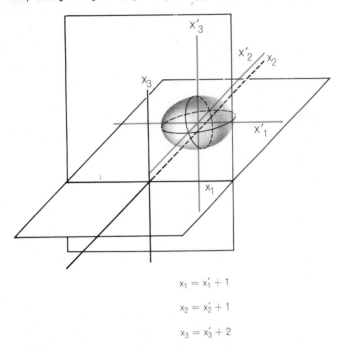

$$x_1 = x_1' + 1$$

$$x_2 = x_2' + 1$$

$$x_3 = x_3' + 2$$

$$x_1' = \tfrac{1}{3}(-x_1'' + 2x_2'' + 2x_3'')$$

$$x_2' = \tfrac{1}{3}(2x_1'' - x_2'' + 2x_3'')$$

$$x_3' = \tfrac{1}{3}(2x_1'' + 2x_2'' - x_3'')$$

ALGEBRA AND GEOMETRY of bringing a quadratic surface into normal form is shown for the case of an ellipsoid with center at point $(1, 1, 2)$ of the coordinate system in which it is considered. By parallel translation the coordinate system can be moved to a new position (*colored axes at left*) so the center of the ellipse is at its origin $(0, 0, 0)$. The algebra of this translation calls for the substitutions yielding the equation above the middle diagram. The principal axes of the ellipsoid can be made coincident with the translated coordinate system by rotation of its axes to the position given by the colored lines in the middle diagram. **Further**

too esoteric for application. It soon became clear, however, that Maxwell's ascent to abstraction had opened the way to further progress in a number of directions. The Maxwell equations illuminated the wave nature of electromagnetic phenomena, inspired the experiments of Heinrich Hertz on the propagation of radio waves, started the growth of an entire new technology and led investigators to new lines of research, including, for example, the now very active field of magnetohydrodynamics.

It cannot be said that Maxwell's equations were the product of systematic deductive thinking. Neither should his achievement be ascribed to purely inductive Socratic processes. Instead Maxwell must be counted among those rare minds that recognize similarities and parallels between seemingly remote, disconnected facts and arrive at a major new insight by combining patently diverse elements into a unified system.

In mathematics proper a corresponding arc of development—from concrete individual substance through abstraction and back again to the concrete and individual—endows a theory with its meaning and significance. To appreciate this basic fact one must bear in mind that the terms "concrete," "abstract," "individual" and "general" have no stable or absolute meaning in mathematics. They refer primarily to a frame of mind, to a state of knowledge and to the character of mathematical substance. What is already absorbed as familiar, for example, is readily taken to be concrete. The words "abstraction" and "generalization" describe not static situations or end results but dynamic processes directed from some concrete stratum to some "higher" one.

Fruitful new discoveries in mathematics sometimes come suddenly with relatively little apparent effort: the view is cleared by abstracting from concrete material and laying bare the structurally essential elements. Axiomatics, irrespective of its Euclidean form, means just that. A recent instance of the fruitful use of abstraction is the generalization by John von Neumann and others of David Hilbert's "spectral" theory, from what proved to be the special case of "bounded" linear operators to "unbounded" ones.

This far-reaching development can be traced in a succession of abstractions upward from the familiar concrete ground of analytic geometry. In the elementary analytic geometry of a three-dimensional space with coordinates x_1, x_2, x_3 a plane is characterized by a linear equation, and a quadratic surface, such as that of a sphere or an ellipsoid, is characterized by a quadratic equation (that is, an equation in which the highest power of an unknown is its square) in the variables x_1, x_2, x_3. For example, an equation of the general form $\lambda_1 x_1{}^2 + \lambda_2 x_2{}^2 + \lambda_3 x_3{}^2 = 1$ describes a quadratic surface centered at the origin of the coordinate system and with its three principal axes pointing in the direction of the coordinate axes. In the case of the ellipsoid the "coefficients" λ_1, λ_2, λ_3 stand for fixed positive numbers; they represent the expressions $1/a_1{}^2$, $1/a_2{}^2$, $1/a_3{}^2$, in which a_1, a_2, a_3 are the semi-axes of the ellipsoid. The ellipsoid consists precisely of those points for which the values of the variables x_1, x_2, x_3 satisfy the equation [*see illustration on these two pages*].

Now, without much ado, the algebraization of geometry permits one to speak of a space of more than three dimensions, say n dimensions, with coordinates x_1, x_2, $x_3 \ldots x_n$. In this space planes are again defined by linear equations and quadratic surfaces by quad-

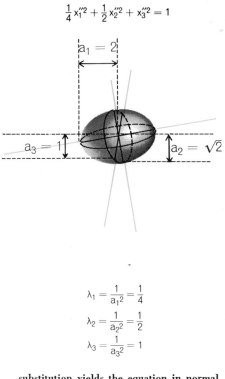

$$\frac{1}{4}x_1''^2 + \frac{1}{2}x_2''^2 + x_3''^2 = 1$$

$$a_1 = 2$$

$$a_3 = 1 \qquad a_2 = \sqrt{2}$$

$$\lambda_1 = \frac{1}{a_1^2} = \frac{1}{4}$$

$$\lambda_2 = \frac{1}{a_2^2} = \frac{1}{2}$$

$$\lambda_3 = \frac{1}{a_3^2} = 1$$

substitution yields the equation in normal form, shown at the right above the ellipsoid it describes. The lengths of the semiaxes (a_1, a_2, a_3) are related to the coefficients of the terms in the equation as indicated.

ratic equations in the variables x_1, x_2, $x_3 \ldots x_n$. It is one of the most important results of "linear algebra" that quadratic surfaces can be brought into the algebraic normal form $\lambda_1 x_1^2 + \lambda_2 x_2^2 + \lambda_3 x_3^2 \ldots \lambda_n x_n^2 = 1$ after a suitable transformation of the coordinate system (or a rigid motion of the figure) that centers the figure at the origin with its principal axes along the coordinate axes. This theorem is the key to many applications; for instance, to the theory of mechanical or electrical systems involving the vibrations of a finite number n of mass points or circuit elements about a state of equilibrium.

Physicists such as Lord Rayleigh did not hesitate to apply this result, without mathematical justification, in a much more general way by letting the number of dimensions n tend to infinity. This step toward greater generalization and abstraction of the underlying mathematics has served well in the study of vibrating systems consisting not of a finite number of mass points or circuit elements but rather of a continuum of matter, such as a string, a membrane or a transmission line.

Hilbert, one of the truly great mathematicians of the past generation, recognized that such quadratic forms of infinitely many variables ought to be secured in a complete mathematical theory. In this endeavor he found it necessary first to restrict the domain of the variables by requiring that the sum of their squares should "converge," that is, have a finite value. Another way of stating this, with the help of a "generalized" Pythagorean theorem, is to say that a point in a "Hilbert space" of infinitely many dimensions must have a finite distance $r = \sqrt{x_1^2 + x_2^2 + \ldots}$ from the origin. Next, Hilbert defined the quadratic form in infinitely many variables—the bounded form—as a double infinite sum of the form

$$a_{11}x_1^2 + a_{12}x_1x_2 + a_{13}x_1x_3 + \ldots$$
$$+ a_{22}x_2^2 + a_{23}x_2x_3 + \ldots$$
$$+ \ldots,$$

where the first index (that is, x_1 in the first row, x_2 in the second row and so on) goes to infinity from row to row and the second index (that is, x_2 in the first row, x_3 in the second row and so on) goes to infinity along the row. This double infinite sum is under the crucial restriction that it must converge at every point in a Hilbert space.

In such a space many concepts relating to the properties of planes and the quadratic surfaces in finite-dimensional geometry remain meaningful. This is true in particular of the theory of the transformation of quadratic forms to their principal axes. Hilbert showed that every quadratic form in this class can be brought into a normal form by a rotation of the coordinate system. By analogy with the finite-dimensional case Hilbert called the set of values λ_1, λ_2, λ_3 appearing in this normal form the "spectrum" of the quadratic form.

In his generalization of the principal-axis theory from ordinary quadratic forms in n variables to forms in infinitely many variables Hilbert discovered many new phenomena, such as the occurrence of continuous mathematical spectra. Moreover, Hilbert's work served well in the emergence of quantum mechanics. His term "mathematical spectra" found a prophetic relevance to the spectra of energy states in atoms and their constituent particles. But Hilbert's theory of quadratic forms was not quite equal to the task of handling quantum mechanics; the forms occurring there turned out to be "unbounded."

At this point von Neumann, inspired by Erhard Schmidt and more inclined toward abstraction than his elders, carried the process of abstraction another crucial stratum upward. By discarding Hilbert's concept of a quadratic form as something that can be expressed concretely as an infinite algebraic expression and instead formulating the concept abstractly, he was able to avoid its earlier limitations. Thus extended, Hilbert's spectral theory was made to answer the tangibly concrete needs of contemporary physics.

The theory of groups, a central concern of contemporary mathematics, has evolved through an analogous progression of abstractions. Group theory traces its origins back to a problem that has fascinated mathematicians since the Middle Ages: the solving of algebraic equations of degree greater than two by algebraic processes, that is, by addition, subtraction, multiplication, division and extraction of roots. The theory of quadratic equations was known to the Babylonians, and the solution of equations of the third and the fourth degree was accomplished by the Renaissance mathematicians Girolamo Cardano and Niccolò Tartaglia. The solution of equations of the fifth degree and higher degrees, however, encountered insurmountable obstacles.

Early in the 19th century a novel and profound attack on these old problems was launched by Joseph Louis Lagrange, P. Ruffini and Niels Henrik Abel and, in a most original way, by Évariste Galois. These new approaches started from the known facts that an algebraic equation of degree n of the form $x^n + a_{n-1}x^{n-1} + \ldots + a_1x + a_0 = 0$ has n roots r_1, $r_2 \ldots r_n$, and that this set of n roots determines the equation uniquely. (For example, if 1 and 3 are roots of a quadratic equation, then $(x-1)(x-3) = x^2 - 4x + 3 = 0$ is the equation determined by the roots 1 and 3.) The coefficients of the equation are symmetric functions of the roots; that is, they depend on the set of roots regardless of the order. (For example, in a cubic equation $x^3 + ax^2 + bx + c = 0$ with roots r_1, r_2, r_3 the coefficients can be written $-a = r_1 + r_2 + r_3$, $b = r_1r_2 + r_2r_3 + r_3r_1$, $c = r_1r_2r_3$, and if r_1, r_2, r_3 are permuted, a, b and c are not changed.)

Over the years work with such equations revealed that the key to the problem of expressing the roots of the equations in terms of the coefficients lies not only in the study of symmetric expressions but also more decisively in the study of not completely symmetric expressions and in the analysis of whatever symmetries they possess. The expression $E = r_1r_2 + r_3r_4$ does not, for example, remain unchanged for all arbitrary permutations of the four symbols r_1, r_2, r_3, r_4. If the indices 1 and 2 or 3 and 4 are interchanged, E is invariant, that is, remains unchanged. If 1 and 3 are interchanged, however, the resulting expression is not E. On the other hand, the succession of two permutations that changes and then restores E amounts to a permutation that clearly leaves E invariant. The set of these permutations, called a "group" by Galois, represents the intrinsic symmetries of the expression E. The understanding of permutation groups was recognized by the ingenious Galois as the key to a deeper theory of algebraic equations.

Soon afterward mathematicians were discovering permutation groups in other fields. The set of six motions that carry an equilateral triangle into itself, for example, forms a group [see illustration on page 103]. Other groups have been uncovered as fundamental structural elements in most of the branches of mathematics.

To embrace such groups, in all their different guises and manifestations, in a single concept and to anticipate the even wider scope of undiscovered possibilities required formulation of the underlying group concept in the most abstract terms. This has been done by calling a set of mathematical objects a group if a rule is given for "combining" two elements so as to obtain again an element S of the set; this rule is required to be associative, that is, $(ST)U = S(TU) = S$. Furthermore, the set must include a "unit" element I that, when combined with any other element S of the set, yields S, that is, $IS = SI = S$. Finally, for every element S in the set there must be an "inverse" element S^{-1} such that the combination SS^{-1} yields the unit element, that is, $SS^{-1} = I$.

The specific "substantial" nature of the group is left wide open, of course, by this abstract definition. The elements may be numbers, rotations of geometric bodies, deformations of space (such deformations may be defined by linear or other transformation of the coordinates) or, as above, the permutations of n objects.

Altogether the group concept and the clarification and unification it brought to the diverse branches of mathematics must be reckoned a major achievement of the past 150 years. Much of the effort has been expended on the intermediate, lofty sector of the arc of development, that is, on the structural analysis of the abstracted concepts. The work has contributed all along, however, to illuminating more specific concrete areas, such as number theory and algebra. One of the remarkable successes along this line was Felix Klein's famous classification in the 1870's of the various branches of geometry according to groups of transformations under which certain geometrical properties remain invariant [see illustration on pages 20 and 21].

Abstract group theory has found significant application in the still more concrete problems of particle physics. Here the occasion is provided by the intricate group of open and hidden symmetries that prevail in the configuration and interaction of the nuclear particles. The success of group theory in bringing order to a great mass of data and predicting the existence of new particles [see "Mathematics in the Physical Sciences," page 249] shows convincingly how abstraction can help in the search for hard facts.

Intuition, that elusive vital agent, is always at work in creative mathematics, motivating and guiding even the most

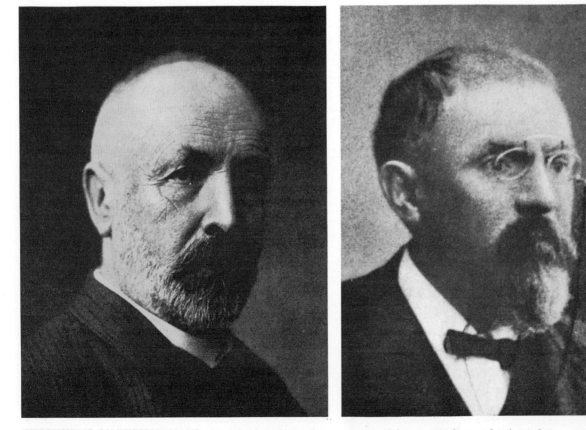

INFLUENTIAL MATHEMATICIANS who helped to direct the course of 20th-century thought are shown on these two pages. Georg

Cantor (left) suggested an order for infinite sets, thus focusing mathematical speculation on set theory. Henri Poincaré (middle)

abstract thinking. In its most familiar manifestation, geometrical intuition, it has figured in the many major recent advances in mathematics that have occurred in or flowed from work in geometry. Yet there is a powerful compulsion in mathematics to reduce the visible role of intuition, or perhaps one may better say to buttress it, by precise and rigorous reasoning.

Topology, the youngest and most vigorous branch of geometry, illustrates in a spectacular way the fruitful working of this tension between intuition and reason. With a few isolated but important earlier discoveries—for example the one-sided Möbius band—as its stock-in-trade, topology emerged as a field of serious study in the 19th century. For a long period it was almost entirely a matter of geometrical intuition, of cutting and pasting together surfaces in an effort to visualize the mathematical substance of topology, that is, the properties of surfaces that do not change under arbitrary continuous deformation. Early in the evolution of the new discipline, however, Georg Friedrich Bernhard Riemann brought it to the center of attention. In his sensational work on the

theory of algebraic functions of a complex variable (a variable incorporating the imaginary number $\sqrt{-1}$) he showed that the topological facts concerning what are now called Riemann surfaces are essential to a real understanding of these functions.

During the 19th century investigators discovered and systematically explored a wide range of topological properties of surfaces of two, three and then of n dimensions. Still on a more or less intuitive basis, early in this century, the great Henri Poincaré and others built a fascinating edifice of topological theory. This work proceeded in close relation to the development of group theory and found uses in other fields of mathematics and in the evolution of the mathematical sciences to higher levels of sophistication. It was put to work, for example, in celestial mechanics, specifically in the construction of planetary orbits in space curved by gravitational fields.

Topologists soon began to feel with urgency the need to sharpen their tools in order to catch the products of geometrical intuition in the vise of modern mathematical precision—without destroying their convincing beauty. This

task was accomplished almost single-handed in the first decades of this century by the Dutch mathematician L. E. J. Brouwer. Thanks to his gigantic effort, topology is now as amenable to rigorous treatment as the geometry of Euclid, and advances in the field proceed on the solid ground of logically impeccable reasoning.

At the center of the difficulties confronting Brouwer was the dilemma presented by the concept of continuity. Everyone has a sure intuitive idea of what continuity is, for example the smoothness of a curve. But the beginning student of calculus loses his assurance at the very outset as he attempts to capture continuity in a precise mathematical formulation. Difficulty is inherent in the task because the geometrical intuition of continuity and the mathematical logical concept do not perfectly match. Rigorous definition brings to the surface whole areas of cases, perhaps marginal, that confound the intuition with paradox. It is easy to construct, for instance, continuous curves (in the exact sense of the definition) that do not have a length [see *lower illustration on page 27*], that have nowhere a direction or that wind around, without any self-intersection, within a square so that they come arbitrarily close to any given point in the square. Such bizarre constructions highlight the need for careful reasoning in proofs of the topological properties of surfaces or other objects subjected to complex continuous deformations.

That need is not at once intuitively apparent to the nontopologist. Consider, for example, C. Jordan's famous theorem stating that any nonintersecting continuous closed curve in a plane bounds two separate domains—the interior and the exterior [see *upper illustration on page 27*]. Every scientist, engineer and student in his naïve right mind will regard the effort to prove such a theorem as an unnecessary, self-imposed, almost masochistic exercise. Yet in writing his classical textbook on analysis Jordan felt strongly the need for a proof and presented one. It is a measure of the subtlety of the problem that Jordan's proof turned out to be not completely correct! Similarly, no one will doubt that the dimensionality of a two-dimensional or three-dimensional geometric figure remains unchanged under any continuous deformation. Yet the precise proof of this fact, under the general assumption of mere abstract continuity, stands as one of Brouwer's major achievements.

It is possible, of course, to evade some

warned against preoccupation with set theory. David Hilbert (right) generalized the principal-axis theory. In 1900 he proposed 23 projects for 20th-century mathematicians.

of the difficulties in the notion of continuity by restricting the group of continuous deformations—by demanding, for example, "smoothness" or differentiability instead of pure continuity. This has been done with great success. Differential topology, as it is called, has recently achieved outstanding results. Investigation of deformations conducted under the requirement of "reasonable" smoothness has produced significantly different classifications of topological structures than would be yielded under a regime of completely general continuity.

These developments may also be welcomed as indicating a healthy deflection of the trend toward boundless generality. Ever since Georg Cantor's achievements in the theory of sets, in the last decades of the 19th century, that trend has occupied many mathematical minds. Some great mathematicians, notably Poincaré, have fought it bitterly as a menace to mathematics, in particular because it leads to unresolved paradoxes. If Poincaré's militant criticism has proved to be overly restrictive and even reactionary, it was nonetheless salutary because it encouraged constructive mathematicians concerned with specific and graspable matters.

Various motivations, in the same individual or in different people, inspire mathematical activity. Certainly the roots in physical reality of large parts of mathematics—especially analysis—supply powerful motivation and inspiration. The situation with respect to other realms of reality is not much different. In number theory and algebra it is the intriguing reality of the world of numbers, so deeply inherent in the human mind. Still more removed from physical reality, one might think, is the reality of the logical processes involved in mathematical thinking. Yet basic ideas from esoteric work in mathematical logic have proved useful for the understanding and even for the design of automatic computing machines.

In brief, mathematics must take its motivation from concrete specific substance and aim again at some layer of "reality." The flight into abstraction must be something more than a mere escape; start from the ground and re-entry are both indispensable, even if the same pilot cannot always handle all phases of the trajectory. The substance of the purest mathematical enterprise may often be provided by tangible physical reality. That mathematics, an emanation of the human mind, should serve so effectively for the description

MAPPING A FUNCTION of a complex variable from an infinitely many-sheeted Riemann surface produces the figure shown at top of this illustration. The circle-arc polygons that grow infinitely small toward the outer circle correspond to straight-line polygons (*bottom*) that extend infinitely without changing size throughout the plane on which they are shown.

and understanding of the physical world is a challenging fact that has rightly attracted the concern of philosophers. Leaving philosophical questions aside, however, the engagement in physical questions or the apparent absence of such engagement must not be taken as a criterion for distinguishing between the kinds of mathematics and mathematicians.

No sharp dividing line can, in fact, be drawn between "pure" and "applied" mathematics. There should not be a class of high priests of unadulterated mathematical beauty, exclusively responsible to their own inclinations, and a class of workers who serve other masters. Class distinctions of this kind are at best the symptom of human limitations that keep most individuals from roaming at will over broad fields of interest.

Although the substance of mathematics is indivisible, distinct differences must be acknowledged in the attitudes that the same scientist or different scientists may bring to a problem. The attitude of the purist, which every scientifically inclined mind will at least sometimes assume, demands uncompromising perfection. No gaps or rough spots can be tolerated in the solution of a problem and the result must flow from an unbroken chain of flawless reasoning. If the attempt encounters insurmountable obstacles, then the purist is inclined to restate his problem or replace it with another in which the difficulty is capable of being managed. He may even "solve" his problem by redefining what he means by a solution; this is, in fact, a not uncommon preliminary step toward a true solution of the original problem.

In the case of applied research the situation is different. The problem, in the first place, cannot be as freely modified or avoided; what is wanted is a believable, humanly reliable answer. If necessary, therefore, the mathematician must accept compromise; he must be willing to interpolate guesswork into the train of reasoning and to make allowance for the uncertainty of numerical evidence. But even the most practically motivated study—the analysis, for instance, of flow involving shock discontinuities—may demand fundamental mathematical investigation to discover how to frame the question. Pure existence proofs may also be significant in applied research; ascertaining that a solution exists may give the needed assurance of the suitability of the mathematical model. Finally, applied mathematics is dominated by approximations; these are inescapable in the attempt to mirror physical processes in mathematical models.

To handle the translation of reality into the abstract models of mathematics and to appraise the degree of accuracy thereby attainable calls for intuitive feeling sharpened by experience. It may also often involve the framing of genuine mathematical problems that are far too difficult to be solved by the available techniques of the science. Such, in part, is the nature of the intellectual adventure and the satisfaction experienced by the mathematician who works with engineers and natural scientists on the mastering of the "real" problems that arise in so many places as man extends his understanding and control of nature.

JORDAN CURVE THEOREM states that any closed curve such as the one shown here bounds interior and exterior domains. A line drawn from inside the curve to the outside will make an odd number of intersections; a line drawn from outside it, an even number.

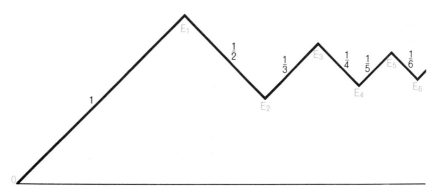

INFINITE ZIGZAG is composed of successive segments with lengths 1, ½, ⅓, ¼, ⅕, ⅙.... The sequence of unit fractions has no finite sum and the curve itself has no finite length.

II

BIOGRAPHY

BIOGRAPHY

INTRODUCTION

Why do we bother to read the biographies of mathematicians when our real interest is presumably in mathematics proper? Surely a knowledge of their personal lives does not help us to understand or create mathematics. One reason, of course, is sheer curiosity. We should like to know something about the men who have contributed to the great intellectual achievements of our civilization. And our curiosity is rewarded. Instead of finding that they were all staid, conservative, conventional men we learn that many were among the most interesting and even exciting characters in history.

They have differed markedly from one another. The special talent, if there is such, that makes a man a mathematician has been lodged in Casanovas and ascetics, in business men and philosophers, in atheists and the profoundly religious, in the retiring and the worldly, in rogues and models of rectitude, and in the naive and the astute. Many were modest; others, extremely egotistical and vain beyond toleration. One finds scoundrels such as Jerome Cardan, and most proper men such as Newton. Some were generous in their recognition of other great minds; others were resentful and jealous and even stole ideas to boost their own reputations. Consequently disputes about priority of discovery abounded.

The creativity of a mathematician is generally believed to be at its height when he is still young. It is doubtful that an exhaustive study of the lives of mathematicians would support this belief. It is true that Blaise Pascal and Karl Gauss were even precocious. Évariste Galois was dead at the age of 21 and Niels Hendrik Abel at 27. But others, such as Pierre Simon Laplace, Karl Weierstrass, David Hilbert, and Henri Poincaré, matured normally and were productive throughout their lives.

Perhaps the most surprising fact is that until 1900 very few were primarily mathematicians. Of the men whose biographies are included in the articles in this section, Newton, Laplace, Hamilton, and Maxwell were physicists; Descartes was a supreme philosopher and far more notable even as a biologist than as a mathematician.

There are reasons more worthy than mere curiosity for studying the biographies of mathematicians. Mathematics is usually regarded as a series of logically ordered subjects, each possessing an impersonal, objective character and each seemingly a complete and exhaustive investigation of its theme. In contrast, philosophy, for example, is recognized to be the work of men and the study of philosophy breaks down into the study of individual, quite varied, and highly personal views. But a serious study of the biographies of mathematicians, which should include some sketch of the nature of their work, shows that mathematics, too, bears the distinctive marks of the men who fashioned it. The work of mathematicians may be likened to the work of men who are set down in various spots of a heavily forested wilderness and are required to build roads in the areas in which they are placed. Like wise men, each first chooses a goal toward which to direct his road. Some project a path leading to minerals; others, to water; and still others, a path to elevated land from which they hope to survey further prospects. The roads are then built but they differ widely in character from one another. Some are reasonably well cut through and need only be broadened, smoothed out, and made more traversable by succeeding workers. Others remain clogged with stumps and boulders and are barely traversable. A few are interrupted by streams which have yet to be bridged. Finally, some are dead ends. These roads bear the marks of the men who carved them out of the wilderness.

This picture of mathematics is not only more accurate than that of a series of exhaustive logically developed branches but it is the one that any man who hopes to contribute to mathematics must acquire. If he is to follow in the footsteps of his predecessors he must know what kind of path he is choosing and just what hazards he will encounter on it. The cleared roads offer no opportunities for further contributions. The dead ends must be avoided unless a man feels strong enough to clear obstacles or overcome hurdles which barred progress earlier. In any case he must know that the roads were built by men and are therefore likely to be subject to impediments or imperfections which other human beings failed to remove.

The history of mathematics gives ample evidence that the subject is indelibly stamped by the outlooks and personal qualities of men. No more striking example can be furnished than the revolution which was effected by Gauss in his work on non-Euclidean geometry. Gauss began his work in mathematics in the 1790's when Kant's philosophy of mathematics dominated the European intellectual scene. Kant had concluded that Euclidean geometry was the only and necessary way in which the human mind can comprehend space and the properties of figures in space. In this sense mathematics was a body of unalterable truths. Kant's thinking epitomized two thousand years of conviction. However, in order to dispose of an undesirable feature in one of the axioms of Euclidean geometry a number of the best mathematicians constructed alternative geometries which they expected to show were self-contradictory or inconsistent and thus render Euclidean geometry incontestable. Gauss was the first man to realize that these alternative or non-Euclidean geometries, as they are called, are equally good descriptions of physical space and that we have no criterion to select which one was the true description. In his work on non-Euclidean geometry Gauss contributed primarily a new viewpoint. This viewpoint forced succeeding generations of mathematicians to abandon the claim that mathematics offers truths, and they had to be content with the position that mathematics offers only rather arbitrary man-made models of reality that more or less describe what happens in the physical world.

How did the idea arise that mathematics offers truths, that the theorems of mathematics exist independently of human beings like diamonds in a mine and that all humans do is unearth the diamonds one by one? An examination of the intellectual environment in which the earlier mathematicians lived and of the ways they responded to that environment explains the growth and acceptance of this view of mathematics. Similarly the change that Gauss wrought — the view that mathematics is a collection of synthetic stones, brilliant enough to bedazzle a few mathematicians, perhaps those already blinded by pride in their own creations, into still believing that they are real — can be understood by examining the atmosphere in which Gauss worked.

There is another value to be derived from the study of biography. While mathematicians produce formulas, no formula produces mathematicians. It is noteworthy that neither the Roman nor the medieval civilization, each of which endured for a thousand years and reached great heights in some areas of culture, produced a single mathematician. Moreover even in the more favorable intellectual climate of post-Renaissance Europe it was pure luck that

Newton and Gauss, two of the three greatest mathematicians, managed to come to the fore. Mathematicians flourish only under particular sociological, physical, and intellectual conditions. A society concerned with the promotion of mathematical activity must learn just what these conditions are and provide them. The knowledge of what must be provided can best be obtained by examining the lives of mathematicians.

Recognition of the decisive role of men not only explains why the progress of the rational subject of mathematics has been so highly irrational but also explains in large measure why the kinds of mathematics produced by the several civilizations differ so sharply from one another. Although no subject has profited as much as mathematics has by the cumulative effect of thousands of efforts, in no subject is the role of great men more discernible.

4 DESCARTES

A. C. CROMBIE · October 1959

"I should consider that I know nothing about physics if I were able to explain only how things *might* be, and were unable to demonstrate that they *could not be otherwise*. For, having reduced physics to mathematics, the demonstration is now possible, and I think that I can do it within the small compass of my knowledge."

With these words René Descartes declared the viewpoint that placed him among the principal revolutionaries in the 17th-century scientific revolution. Against the "forms" and "qualities" of Aristotelian physics, which had proved to be a blind alley, he asserted the "clear and fundamental idea" that the physical world was sheer mechanism and nothing else. Because the ultimate laws of nature were the laws of mechanics, everything in nature could ultimately be reduced to the rearrangement of particles moving according to these laws. In analytical geometry, perhaps Descartes' most enduring achievement, he created a technique for expressing these laws in algebraic equations. He thus put forward the ideal program of all theoretical science: to construct from the smallest number of principles a system to cover all the known facts and to lead to the discovery of new facts.

All subsequent theoretical physics has been aimed at the realization of this ideal of a single theoretical system in which the last details of observable regularities should be shown to be deducible from a minimum number of fundamental equations, written perhaps on a single page. Blaise Pascal and Isaac Newton may certainly be said to have carried on in the 17th century the Cartesian program of looking for the explanation of the physical world in terms of its mechanism. In this century we have witnessed attempts at universal theories by Albert

Einstein and Werner Heisenberg, among others. In the vision of Descartes, however, his indisputable first principles— "nearly all so evident that it is only necessary to understand them in order to assent to them"—were not the end but the beginning of the search.

There can be no doubt of the revolutionary character and influence of Descartes' theoretical insights and program. The paradox is that he should have exercised so profound an influence over men who found his approach essentially distasteful and who rejected some of the most important of his fundamental assumptions and detailed conclusions. Christiaan Huygens, the great Dutch mathematician and astronomer whose father had been an intimate friend of Descartes, admitted late in life that he could no longer accept any but a small part of Cartesian physics. But he said that it was Descartes' *Principles of Philosophy* that first opened his eyes to science. Descartes, he said, had not only exposed the failure of the old philosophy but had offered "in its place causes which one could understand for all that exists in nature." As is so often the case with revolutionists, the legacy of Descartes was not only achievement but also prophecy and vision.

Descartes himself came to recognize that his purely deductive, mathematical ideal for science had failed in the face of the complexities of nature and the enigmas of matter. This failure was especially apparent in physiology, the field into which he ventured most daringly. Out of failure and compromise, however, Descartes extracted another contribution to scientific thinking in many ways as important as the original theoretical program itself. Forced to turn to experiment and hypothesis, he showed himself to be the first great master of the hypothetical

model. This has become an essential tool in all scientific investigation. In his theoretical models of physiological processes Descartes displayed the most ingenious exercises of his imaginative and experimental genius.

René Descartes was born on March 31, 1596, at La Haye, a small and attractive town on the river Creuse in Touraine. His family were of the *petite-noblesse*, long in government service; his father was counselor to the *Parlement* of Brittany. From his mother, who died a month after his birth, he inherited "a dry cough and a pale complexion," which he kept until he was over 20. He also inherited property from her that gave him complete financial independence. Because he was a delicate child, it was thought that he would not live long. But he used his enforced inactivity to indulge an early passion for study.

When he was 10, his father sent him to the newly established Jesuit college of La Flèche, where he remained for eight and a half years and received an excellent education that embraced logic, moral philosophy, physics and metaphysics, classical geometry and modern algebra, as well as an acquaintance with the recent telescopic work of Galileo. All the main characteristics of his mind appeared precociously at La Flèche. Introduced to the classics, he fell in love with poetry. Far from being a "geometer who is only a geometer" (Pascal's description of him), Descartes himself wrote in an early essay, the *Olympica:* "There are sentences in the writings of the poets more serious than in those of the philosophers. The reason is that the poets wrote through enthusiasm and power of imagination. There are in us, as in a flint, seeds of knowledge. Philosophers adduce them through the reason;

poets strike them out from the imagination, and these are the brighter."

Mental facility was one of Descartes' most striking and perhaps more dangerous gifts. A fellow pupil described his prowess in argument. He would first get his opponents to agree on definitions and the meaning of accepted principles, and then he would build up a single deductive argument that was very difficult to shake. At La Flèche he also acquired a habit that persisted throughout his life. He was excused from certain work and allowed to lie late in bed. Here he found it possible to indulge most fully his natural inclination to solitary concentrated thought.

When he was 20, having graduated in law from the University of Poitiers, Descartes went to Paris. Here he became a young man of fashion somewhat

PORTRAIT OF DESCARTES by Frans Hals hangs in the Louvre. Among the fields that he worked in were physiology, psychology, optics and astronomy. Many consider him the father of modern philosophy. He died in 1650 while tutor to the Queen of Sweden.

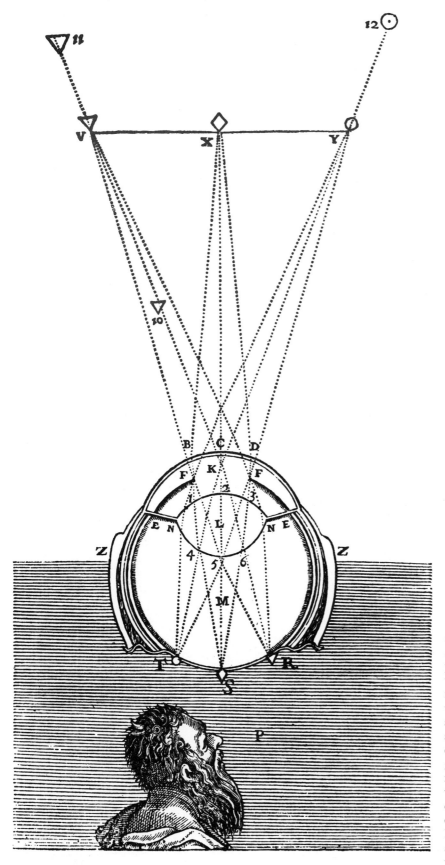

DESCARTES' EYE INVESTIGATIONS included removing the retina from the eye of an ox and replacing it with thin paper or eggshell so that he could study the image. This illustration is reproduced from Descartes' book *Dioptrics*, which was first published in 1637.

at a loose end. Soon, however, his thoughts returned to mathematics and philosophy. He was encouraged by his more serious friends, among them the Minim friar Marin Mersenne, whom Descartes had known at La Flèche. Mersenne was himself a competent mathematician and a skillful experimenter. His cell in the convent of the *Place Royale* was to become the meeting place of *savants*, an antecedent of the Academy of Sciences founded later in the century. Mersenne came to have a vast correspondence, of which only part has been published, and thus became a center of scientific intelligence in the days before there were any scientific journals. He also translated Galileo's *Dialogue* and *Discourses* into French, the former in 1634, the year after Galileo's condemnation. Until the end of his life Mersenne remained Descartes' principal friend, and after Descartes left France for good in 1628 Mersenne kept him posted with scientific news from Paris.

In 1618 Descartes joined the army of Prince Maurice of Nassau (later Prince of Orange) as a gentleman volunteer. He was sent to the garrison at Breda in the Netherlands, there being at that time a truce between the Franco-Dutch forces and the Spaniards, whose rule the Low Countries were throwing off. His scientific interests were such as were appropriate for an officer: ballistics, acoustics, perspective, military engineering, navigation.

One day—November 10, 1618—he came upon a group of people gathered about a notice pinned up in the street. It was in Flemish, and turning to someone in the group, Descartes asked him to translate it into Latin or French. The notice proved to be a challenge inviting all comers to solve the mathematical problem that it proposed. The man whom Descartes had asked to translate it was Isaac Beeckman, one of the country's leading mathematicians. Descartes solved the problem and presented his solution to Beeckman, who at once recognized the young man's mathematical genius and set out to revive his interest in theoretical problems. During that winter Beeckman proposed that Descartes should find the mathematical law of the acceleration of falling bodies. Neither knew that Galileo had in fact already solved this problem; his solution was to appear in his *Dialogue on the Two Principal Systems of the World* in 1632. Descartes produced solutions based on different assumptions. That none of them described the way bodies actually fall did not concern him. He had not yet learned to unite mathematical analysis with experiment.

We are indebted to Beeckman's journal, discovered in 1905, for a flood of light on this period of Descartes' life. It was a time of self-discovery; the young man's mind moved with incredible speed over a broad assortment of questions. Descartes now got on the track of the method by which he was to attempt the unification of human knowledge upon a single, central set of premises.

On March 26, 1619, Descartes reported to Beeckman "an entirely new science which will allow of a general solution of all problems that can be proposed in any and every kind of quantity, continuous or discontinuous, each in accordance with its nature . . . so that almost nothing will remain to be discovered in geometry." This was Descartes' announcement of his discovery of analytical geometry or, as Voltaire was to describe it, "the method of giving algebraic equations to curves." Descartes' 14th-century countryman Nicole Oresme may have contributed something toward this idea. In the 17th century Descartes' contemporary Pierre de Fermat was to make the same discovery quite independently, but he did not follow it up. Descartes did not publish his "new science" until 1637, when he included in his essay *Geometry* both an exposition of the principles and several particular applications. Its generality is there shown in Descartes' demonstration that the conic sections of Apollonius are all contained in a single set of quadratic equations. Since conic sections include the circles of the ancient astronomers, the ellipses of Johannes Kepler, and the parabola used by Galileo to describe the trajectory of a projectile, it is plain that Descartes' first invention placed a powerful tool in the hands of physicists. Without it Newton himself would have suffered a crippling handicap.

Exactly a year after his meeting with Beeckman, Descartes had a celebrated experience, perhaps the most important and certainly the most dramatic of his whole life. He had joined the army of the Duke of Bavaria, another of France's allies in the Thirty Years' War, and found himself in winter quarters at a remote place on the Danube. Much occupied with his thoughts, he spent the whole of November 10 shut up alone in the famous *poêle* (literally "stove," but actually an overheated room). In the course of the day he made two important decisions. First, he decided that he must

methodically doubt everything he knew about physics and all other organized knowledge, and look for self-evident, certain starting points from which he could reconstruct all the sciences. Second, he decided that just as a perfect work of art or architecture is always the product of one master hand, so he must carry out the whole of this program himself.

That night, according to his 17th-century biographer Adrien Baillet, Descartes had three dreams. First he found himself in a street swept by a fierce wind. He was unable to stand because of a weakness in his right leg, but companions near him stood up firmly. He awoke, and fell asleep again; he was reawakened by

dreaming that he had heard a clap of thunder and had found the room full of sparks. He fell asleep once more and dreamt that he had found a dictionary on his table. Then, in another book, his eye "fell upon the words *Quid vitae sectabor iter?* [What way of life shall I follow?]. At the same time a man he did not know presented him with some verses beginning with the words *Est et non*, which he recommended highly to him." These words Descartes recognized as the opening lines of two poems by Ausonius. Even before Descartes had finally awakened he had begun to interpret the first dream as a warning against past errors, the second as the descent of the spirit of truth to take possession of

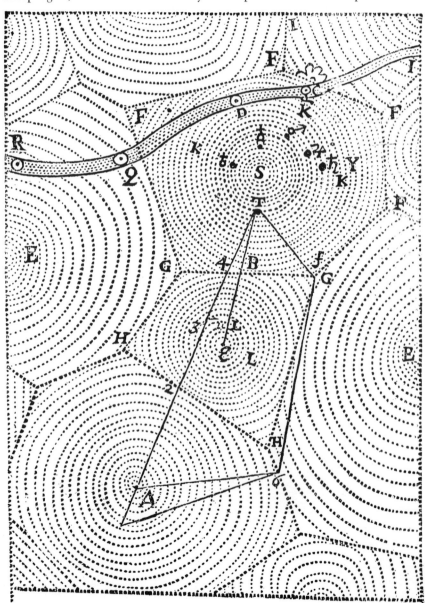

SYSTEM OF VORTEXES with which Descartes sought to account for the motions of the heavenly bodies consisted of whirlpools of "ether." In the case of the solar system the vortex carried the planets around the sun (S). Irregular path across top of the illustration is a comet, the motions of which Descartes believed could not be reduced to a uniform law.

him, and the third as the opening to him of the treasures of all the sciences and the path of true knowledge. However this incident may have been elaborated in the telling by Baillet, it stands as a symbol of Descartes' certainty in the rightness of his approach to true knowledge.

He went on soldiering until 1622, seeing action at the battle of Prague and the sieges of Pressburg and Neuhäusel. Then for a few years he was a traveler, ranging over Europe from Poland to Italy and returning at last to Paris in 1625. There he rejoined the circle round Mersenne, worked at his "universal mathematics," and engaged in speculations on many subjects from moral psychology to the prolongation of life. From such pursuits he was distracted, in the fashion of his leisured contemporaries, by the social whirlpool and by music, idle reading and gambling. His father expressed the opinion that he was "not good for anything but to be bound in buckskin."

Then an incident occurred that turned Descartes' vision into his life's mission. He found himself present, along with a fashionable and impressive audience including his friend Mersenne and the influential Cardinal de Bérulle, at the house of the papal nuncio to hear a certain Chandoux expound his "new philosophy." Descartes alone did not join in the applause. Pressed to give his opinion, he spoke at length, demonstrating how it was possible for a clever man to establish an apparently convincing case for a proposition and also for its opposite, and showing that by using what he called his "natural method" even mediocre thinkers could reach principles that were found to be true. His hearers were astonished. When Descartes visited Bérulle a few days later, the cardinal charged him to devote his life to working out the application of his method in philosophy and in "mechanics and medicine."

In October, 1628, Descartes left for the Netherlands, where he remained for the rest of his life except for three short visits to France and his last journey to Stockholm in 1649. He avoided the company of everyone but his intimate friends and disciples, and dedicated his time to the application of his principles in philosophy, science and mathematics and to the dissemination of his conclusions. Within a year of finally leaving the Netherlands at the invitation of Queen Christina of Sweden, he died in Stockholm in February, 1650.

Descartes may be described as a centrifugal thinker: he moved primarily outward from a firm central theoretical point, in diametrical contrast to thinkers like Francis Bacon or Isaac Newton. The French writer and amateur of science Bernard le Bovier de Fontenelle, in the well-known *Eloge de Newton* written on Newton's death, drew an eloquent contrast between the methods of Newton and Descartes:

"The two great men so placed in opposition had much in common. Both were geniuses of the first order, born to dominate the minds of others and to found empires. Both, being outstanding geometers, saw the need to carry geometry into physics. Both founded their physics on a geometry which they developed almost single-handed. But the one [Descartes] tried in one bold leap to put himself at the source of everything, to make himself master of the first principles by means of certain clear and fundamental ideas, so that he could then simply descend to the phenomena of Nature as to necessary consequences of these principles. The other [Newton], more timid or more modest, began his journey by leaning upon the phenomena in order to mount up unknown principles, resolved to admit them only in such a way that they could yield the chain of consequences. The one set out from what he knew clearly, in order to find the cause of what he saw. The other set out from what he saw, in order to find the cause."

The primary direction and movement of Descartes' philosophical and scientific enterprise are shown by the sequence in which he composed his major works. From 1618 to 1628, during the restless years of military life, travel and dissipation, he worked out his conception of

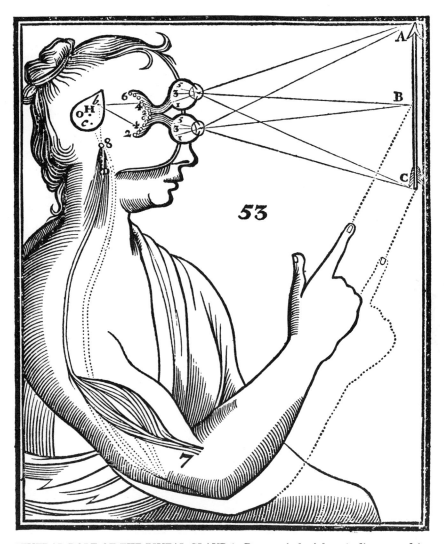

CENTRAL ROLE OF THE PINEAL GLAND in Descartes' physiology is diagrammed in *l'Homme*. Images fall on retinas (*5, 3, 1*) and are conveyed to the cerebral ventricles (*6, 4, 2*); these then form a single binocular image on the pineal gland (*H*), the site from which the soul controls the body. Stimulated by the image, the soul inclines the pineal gland, activating the "hydraulic system" of the nerves (*8*), causing a muscle to move (at *7*).

true science and his highly rationalistic method for attaining it. These he described in his first work, *Rules for the Direction of the Mind*, finished in 1628 but published posthumously, and in the *Discourse on Method*, which he wrote after settling in the Netherlands. Before completing the latter he began work on the *Meteors*, the *Dioptrics* and the *Geometry*, which he presented as three illustrations of the power of the method applied to specific lines of investigation, when they were published with the *Discourse* in 1637. Meanwhile, by 1628, he had turned to the next stage of his investigations, the discovery of first principles. These he propounded in his *Meditations on First Philosophy*, published in 1641. From first principles he moved on quickly to the elaboration of his cosmology, which he completed in *Le Monde* in 1633, but withheld from publication upon the news of Galileo's condemnation. A revised version, with its Copernicanism mitigated by the idea that all motion is relative, was published in 1644 under the title *Principles of Philosophy*. At the same time Descartes was working out his conception of the relationship between the mind and the machinery of the body, and in his last work, *Passions of the Soul* (completed in 1649), he brought psychology within the compass of his system.

Perhaps the most revealing illustration of the power of his method is Descartes' *Dioptrics*. He characteristically announces at the outset that he intends to solve the problem of constructing a telescope on rational scientific principles. Accordingly he undertakes first an analysis of the nature of light: space is filled with fine contiguous globules of matter, forming a kind of "ether"; light is a mechanical phenomenon, an instantane-

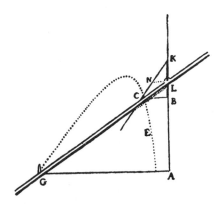

DESCARTES' GEOMETRY is, in Voltaire's words, "a method of giving algebraic equations to curves." Illustration is from a page in which equation for parabola is discussed.

ous pressure transmitted through this "ether" from a luminous source. Descartes then gives an elegant geometrical demonstration of the laws of reflection and refraction. Some years earlier the Dutch physicist Willebrord Snell had discovered the correct sine law of refraction, but he had not published it. Descartes' demonstration of what is now known as Snell's Law was almost certainly independent; he was the first to publish it.

Since the purpose of a telescope is to increase the power of vision, Descartes next makes a detailed analysis of the human eye in both its normal and its pathological states. For this, as his correspondence shows us, he conducted extensive studies and dissections. Repeating an experiment made by Christoph Scheiner, he removed the back of an ox's eye, replaced it with thin white paper or eggshell, and examined the reversed image cast upon it of an object placed in front of the eye. The whole investigation shows considerable anatomical knowledge and experimental skill; Descartes describes the functioning of the iris, the ciliary muscle, binocular vision, optical illusions and various forms of coordination and accommodation.

He now considered himself to be in a position, denied to Kepler and Galileo, to show scientifically what the curvatures of the lenses used in constructing a telescope should be. He concluded that their cross sections should be either hyperbolas or ellipses. He did not of course allow for chromatic aberration, a problem not then understood. Finally he gives a description of a machine designed to cut lenses on these scientific principles.

From a long correspondence between Descartes and a French spectacle-maker named Ferrier we know how this unfortunate man tried and failed to put Descartes' ideas into practice. In the end no actual telescope was constructed on Descartes' theoretical principles.

The essential structure and content of Descartes' physics and cosmology derive from the revolutionary conclusions at which he arrived soon after his retirement to the Netherlands in 1628. He found the basis for the possibility and certainty of knowledge in the fact of thought itself. This elemental fact, apprehended with "clarity and distinctness," became his criterion for determining whether or not anything else was true. The "qualities" of classical philosophy, apprehended by mere sensation, he found not to be clear and distinct. Thus he eliminated from the world outside

everything but extension—the one measurable aspect of things and hence their true nature. This division of the world into the two mutually exclusive and collectively exhaustive realms of thought and extension enabled Descartes to offer what he regarded as a true science of nature. The task of science was now to deduce from these first principles the causes of everything that happens, just as a mathematics is deduced from its premises.

It was the very breadth of this program—which in effect declares that the whole of physical nature may ultimately be reduced to and comprehended by the laws of motion—that gave Descartes' work its revolutionary scientific importance. Descartes himself offered explanations, in terms of the motions of particles of various shapes and sizes, of chemical properties and combinations, taste and smell, heat, magnetism, light, the operation of the heart and nervous system as the source of action of the mechanism of the body, and many other phenomena that he investigated by sometimes rather naive experiments. The vastness of this program was its undoing; Descartes simply had no time to go into all these questions accurately and quantitatively. Coming from the author of a mathematizing program, Descartes' general physics and cosmology are surprisingly almost entirely qualitative. He was forced to fall back on speculation far beyond "the small compass of my knowledge," with the result that he came to fear that he had produced, to use his own phrase, nothing more than a beautiful "romance of nature."

His most disastrous failure occurred in fact at the very center of his program, in the laws of motion themselves. He had reached his conclusion that the essential property of matter was extension in space by a process of purely rational analysis. Since his method *a priori* ruled out other possibilities, it did not leave the question open to empirical test. From this supposedly firm basis he then proceeded to construct a system of mechanics that left out important facts, notably those included in what became the Newtonian notion of "mass." His mechanics certainly contains some valuable conclusions; for example, his account of the conservation of motion and his enunciation of an equivalent of the principle of inertia. But geometrically identical bodies of different masses do not behave identically when they collide or interact in other ways. Descartes' treatment of this subject was disastrously wrong because his antecedent analysis of matter into mere extension was itself mistaken.

In order to explain how the planets were kept in their orbits, Descartes put forward his famous vortex theory, according to which the fine matter of the "ether" forms great whirlpools or vortexes round the stars and the sun. The planets are carried about in the sun's vortex, rather like a set of children's boats in the celestial bathwater, and the moon is carried round the earth in the same way. The astonishing thing is that Descartes did not bother to check whether or not this very important part of his physical system agreed with the facts as expressed by Kepler's laws of planetary motion. It was Newton who destroyed Descartes' famous vortex theory. In fact, he may have chosen the title *Principia Mathematica* to give point to his polemic against Descartes' *Principia Philosophiae*. Newton treated the vortex theory as a serious problem of fluid dynamics and utterly demolished it.

Descartes' subsequent reputation as a mere speculator has been kept going largely by historians of mechanics writing under the influence of Newtonian polemics. But if we turn from Descartes' mechanics to his physiology we can observe him at work in a field where the qualitative hypotheses on which he had fallen back in dealing with other subjects yielded results more worthy of him.

Descartes is rightly ranked with William Harvey as a founder of modern physiology. Harvey was a master of experimental analysis, but Descartes introduced the master-hypothesis on which all subsequent physiology has been based. Having divided the world into extension and thought, Descartes was able to regard biology as a branch of mechanics and nothing else. In modern terms this view asserts that living organisms are in the last analysis explicable in terms of the physics and chemistry of their parts. In man, according to Descartes, the realm of thought makes contact with the extended body at a single point: the pineal gland in the brain.

Descartes' correspondence shows that during his long residence in the Netherlands he spent much time in making anatomical dissections. He found biology the most defeating of all the fields into which he tried to carry his explanations by means of mechanical principles. It is in this field that he found experiment most necessary, both to acquire information and to choose between different possible explanations of the same phenomenon. Although he accepted Harvey's discovery of the circulation of the blood, he engaged somewhat unsuccessfully in a controversy with him over the mechanism of the heart's action, each bringing forward a crucial experiment to establish his explanation. Descartes was wrong in fact, but he made the essential point that a full explanation of the heart's action cannot simply start with the fact that it is beating, but must try to account for this fact in terms of the underlying mechanism—ultimately in terms of the laws of motion common to all matter.

Although Descartes' mechanistic explanation of this still-obscure phenomenon now seems rather naive, the method by which he attacked it and the working of the machine of the body as a whole introduced one of the most powerful tools of all modern physiological research. This was the hypothetical model. Descartes' physiological writings contain many good observations and some brilliant mechanistic explanations of such phenomena as automatic actions like blinking and the coordination of different muscles in complicated movements such as walking. He was inclined to sacrifice real anatomy to the hypothetical anatomy demanded by his mechanism. But he always said explicitly that he was describing a hypothetical body to imitate the actions of the real body, just as a modern investigator will build an electronic machine to imitate the processes of the brain.

Descartes set out to produce a true science of nature in which everything would follow mathematically from self-evident first principles. Modern physicists, of course, reject the idea that the principles of physics can be self-evidently certain. Even in the 17th century Pascal and Huygens made the same criticism. They pointed out that there is an essential difference between physics and abstract mathematics in that the principles of physics, which explores the unknown in the concrete world of fact, are always exposed to complete or partial invalidation by the discovery of new facts.

Descartes, moving outward from his central principles, had himself come to appreciate the point made by Pascal and Huygens, and to realize that his mathematical ideal of unilinear deduction had broken down because of the difficulty of connecting abstract general principles with the particulars of fact. Yet as a positive scientific thinker he was perhaps not so different from his successors in our time. His search was for the causes and meaning of no less than everything that occurs.

5 ISAAC NEWTON

I. BERNARD COHEN • December 1955

The mind and personality of Isaac Newton challenge any historian. Newton was a strange, solitary figure, and the wellsprings of his behavior were hidden even from his contemporaries. A biographer of his time compared Newton to the River Nile, whose great powers were known but whose source had not been discovered. Nevertheless, the few facts we have about his early life do allow some speculation about Newton's character and development.

He was born prematurely, a physical weakling. It is said that he had to wear a "bolster" to support his neck during his first months, that no one expected him to live. Newton later was fond of saying that his mother had said he was so tiny at birth that he could have been put into a quart mug.

Newton's father died three months before he was born. When the boy was less than two years old, his mother remarried, and he was turned over to his aged grandmother. He lived on an isolated farm, deprived of parental care and love, without the friendly companionship and rivalry of brothers and sisters. The late Louis T. More, author of the best-known modern biography of the man, held that much of Newton's "inwardness" could be attributed to his lonely and unhappy childhood.

Born in 1642, Newton grew up in an era when England was still tasting the "terrors of a protracted and bitter civil war." Raiding and plundering parties were common. His grandmother was "suspected of sympathy to the royal forces." In the face of these real terrors and "the frights of his imagination," he could not have received much comfort from his grandmother or the hired laborers on the farm. Naturally enough, as More observed, the boy turned to "the solace of lonely meditation" and developed a strong habit of self-absorption. A girl who knew him in his youth described him as a "sober, silent, thinking lad" who "was never known scarce to play with the boys abroad, at their silly amusements."

He evidently overcame his physical weakness by the time he reached school age, for a schoolmate reported that Newton challenged a bully who had

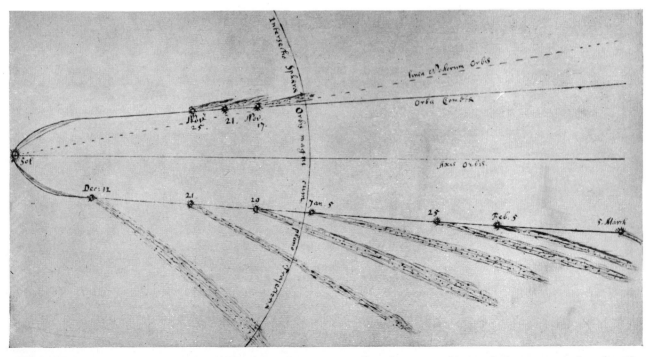

ORBIT of Halley's comet in its appearance of 1682 was bound into the first edition of the *Principia*. Newton pointed out that comets as well as planets are subject to the inverse square law of gravitation. This hand-drawn picture was made by an unknown draftsman.

NEWTON'S "SILENT FACE," behind which Wordsworth saw a "mind voyaging strange seas of thought," appears in this engraving based on a painting by Godfrey Kneller.

an astronomer and an authority in the field of optics. Barrow was one of the first to recognize Newton's genius. Soon after his student had taken a degree, Barrow resigned his professorship so that Newton might have it. Thus at 26 Newton was established in an academic post of distinction and was free to pursue his epoch-making studies.

He had already sown the seeds of his revolutionary contributions to three distinct fields of scientific inquiry: mathematics, celestial mechanics and physical optics. After his graduation from the University he had returned to his home at Woolsthorpe for 18 months of work which can fairly be described as the most fruitful 18 months in all the history of the creative imagination. Newton's subsequent life in science consisted to a large degree in the elaboration of the great discoveries made during those "golden" months. What Newton did at Woolsthorpe is best stated in his words:

"In the beginning of the year 1665 I found the method for approximating series and the rule for reducing any dignity [power] of any binomial to such a series [*i.e.*, the binomial theorem]. The same year in May I found the method of tangents of Gregory and Slusius, and in November [discovered] the direct method of Fluxions [*i.e.*, the elements of the differential calculus], and the next year in January had the Theory of Colours, and in May following I had entrance into the inverse method of Fluxions [*i.e.*, integral calculus], and in the same year I began to think of gravity extending to the orb of the Moon . . . and having thereby compared the force requisite to keep the Moon in her orb with the force of gravity at the surface of the earth, and found them to answer pretty nearly. . . ."

As a by-product of his analysis of light and colors, which he had shyly kept to himself, Newton invented a reflecting telescope, to free telescopes from the chromatic aberration of refracting lenses. He made a small version of his new telescope for the Royal Society of London, and was shortly elected, at the age of 30, as a Fellow of the Royal Society, the highest scientific honor in England.

Newton was understandably overwhelmed by his sudden public recognition. He had been loath to announce his discoveries, but within a week after his election to the Society he asked permission to communicate an account of the "philosophical discovery" which had induced him "to the making of the said telescope." With a disarming lack of false modesty, he said that in his judg-

kicked him in the belly to a fight and "beat him till he would fight no more"— winning out because he had "more spirit and resolution." The bully stood high in the class, and Newton was so determined "to beat him also at his books" that "by hard work he finally succeeded, and then gradually rose to be the first in the school."

When Newton was 14, his mother took the boy back into her home, her second husband having died. She conceived the idea of making him a farmer, but the experiment proved an unquali-

fied failure. Newton found farming totally distasteful. Instead of attending properly to his chores, he would read, make wooden models with his knife, or dream. Fortunately for science, his mother gave up the attempt and allowed him to prepare for Cambridge University.

At the age of 18, Newton entered Trinity College. In his early years at the University he was not outstanding in any way. Then he came under the influence of Isaac Barrow, a professor of mathematics and an extraordinary man. He was an able mathematician, a classicist,

ment he had made "the oddest, if not the most considerable detection, which hath hitherto been made in the operations of nature."

Newton's letter to the Royal Society, "containing his new theory of light and colours," was sent to London on February 6, 1672. This paper can claim a number of "firsts." It was Newton's initial publication; it founded the science of spectroscopy, and it marked the beginning of a sound analysis of color phenomena. Briefly, what Newton showed is that a prism separates white light into its component colors, associated with specific indices of refraction, and that a second prism can recombine the dispersed light and render it white again. These magnificent experiments provided a new departure for the formulation of theories about the nature of color. Yet the paper did not win for Newton the universal applause that he had sought. The Royal Society was bombarded with letters disputing Newton's conclusions. Some of the objectors were unimportant, but others were men of stature: Christian Huygens, Robert Hooke. With as-

tonishing patience, Newton wrote careful letters answering each objection. But he won over only one of his opponents—the French Jesuit Father Pardies.

The controversy had an acid effect on Newton's personality. He vowed that he would publish no further discoveries. As he wrote later to Leibnitz: "I was so persecuted with discussions arising from the publication of my theory of light, that I blamed my own imprudence for parting with so substantial a blessing as my quiet to run after a shadow." And yet he did later continue to publish; he wanted the applause of the scientific world. This ambivalence was not overlooked by Newton's enemies. The astronomer John Flamsteed, who broke with Newton, described him as "insidious, ambitious, and excessively covetous of praise, and impatient of contradiction. . . . I believe him to be a good man at the bottom; but, through his nature, suspicious."

At Cambridge Newton was the very model of an absent-minded professor. His amanuensis, Humphrey Newton (no relative), wrote that he never knew Newton "to take any recreation or pas-

time either in riding out to take the air, walking, bowling, or any other exercise whatever, thinking all hours lost that was not spent in his studies." He often worked until two or three o'clock in the morning, ate sparingly and sometimes forgot to eat altogether. When reminded that he had not eaten, he would go to the table and "eat a bite or two standing." Newton rarely dined in the college hall; when he did, he was apt to appear "with shoes down at heels, stockings untied, surplice on, and his head scarcely combed." It was said that he often delivered his lectures to an empty hall, apparently with as much satisfaction as if the room had been full of students.

After the controversy, Newton withdrew from the public eye as a scientist. He served the University as its representative in Parliament and worked away in private at chemistry and alchemy, theology, physics and mathematics. He became acquainted with Leibnitz, but refused to give his great contemporary any exact information about his discoveries in mathematics. Today it is gen-

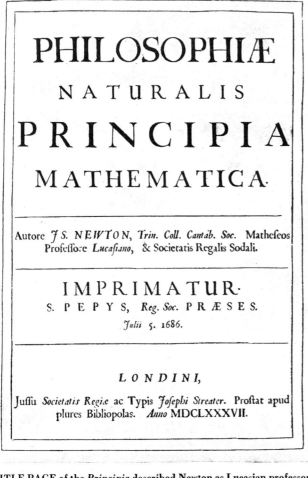

TITLE PAGE of the *Principia* described Newton as Lucasian professor of mathematics at Cambridge. The "imprimatur" was signed by the diarist Samuel Pepys, who was then the president of the Royal Society.

NEWTON'S first communication to the Royal Society announced his discovery that white light is a mixture of many colors which can be separated by a prism and then recombined.

erally agreed that the calculus was discovered more or less independently by both Newton and Leibnitz, but the two men and their partisans quarreled acrimoniously over priority, and Newton accused Leibnitz of plagiarism. Newton conceived a jealous proprietary interest in every subject he studied, and almost every achievement of his creative life was accompanied by some quarrel.

In 1684 came the famous visit to Newton by the astronomer Edmund Halley. He had a problem concerning the gravitational attraction between the sun and the planets. Halley and Hooke had concluded from Johannes Kepler's accounting of planetary motions that the force of attraction must vary inversely with the square of the distance between a planet and the sun. But they had been unable to prove their idea. "What," Halley asked Newton, "would be the curve described by the planets on the supposition that gravity diminished as the square of the distance?" Newton answered without hesitation: "An ellipse." How did he know that? "Why," replied Newton, "I have calculated it." These four words informed Halley that Newton had worked out one of the most fundamental laws of the universe—the law of gravity. Halley wanted to see the calculations at once, but Newton could not find his notes. He promised to write out the theorems and proofs. Under Halley's insistent urging he completed a manuscript for the Royal Society. Thus was born the *Philosophiae Naturalis Principia Mathematica*, known ever since simply as the *Principia*.

Just before its publication a crisis arose when Hooke laid claim to the inverse-square law. Newton threatened to withdraw the climactic chapters of his work, but Halley mollified him and the great classic went to press intact. Halley's credit in this enterprise is enormous. He not only got Newton to write the work but also saw it through the press and paid the costs of publication, although he was not a wealthy man.

The *Principia* is divided into three "books." In the first Newton laid down his three laws of motion and explored the consequences of various laws of force. In the second he explored motion in various types of fluids; here he was somewhat less successful, and much of his work had to be revised in the succeeding decades. In the third he discussed universal gravitation and showed how a single law of force explains at once the falling of bodies on the earth, the motion of our moon or of Jupiter's satellites, the motions of planets and the phenomenon of tides.

One of the most vexing problems for Newton was to find a rigorous proof that a sphere acts gravitationally as if all its mass were concentrated at its center. Without this theorem, the whole theory of gravitation would rest on intuition rather than precise calculation. For instance, in the simple case of an apple falling to the ground—the occasion of the central idea of gravitation according to Newton's own account—what is the "distance between" the earth and the apple? Here the calculus came into play. Newton considered the earth as a collection of tiny volumes of matter, each attracting the apple according to the inverse-square law of gravitation. Then he summed up the individual forces and showed that the result was the same as if the earth were a point mass, as if all the matter of the earth were shrunk into a tiny region at its center.

Newton suffered some kind of "nervous breakdown" after the completion of the *Principia*. He complained that he could not sleep, and said that he lacked the "former consistency of his mind." He wrote angry letters to friends and then apologized; he protested bitterly to John Locke, for example, that the philosopher had attempted to "embroil him with women."

In 1696 Newton abandoned the academic life for the position of Warden, later Master, of the Mint. Honors for his scientific achievements continued to come to him: he was knighted in 1705 and served many years as president of the Royal Society. But the last quarter century of his life produced no major contributions to science. Some say that his creative genius had simply burned out. Others argue that after having founded the science of physical optics, invented the calculus and shown the mechanism of the universe, there just wasn't anything left for him to do in the realm of science.

Although he made no important discoveries, Newton's last years were not barren of ideas. Now famous and honored, he felt secure enough to offer many public speculations on scientific problems. He suggested various possible hypotheses as to the "cause" of gravitation and speculated on the nature of the "aether," the size of the constituent units of matter, the forces of electricity and magnetism, the cause of muscular response to the "commands of the will," the origins of sensation, the creation of the world, the ultimate destiny of man. In the century after Newton physical experimenters followed up many of his bold speculations.

Newton is often described as the inaugurator of the "Age of Reason." Alexander Pope expressed the sentiment of his time in the famous lines:

*Nature and Nature's laws lay hid in
      night:*
*God said, Let Newton be! and all
      was light.*

But the late Lord Keynes called attention to another side of Newton: his quest for an answer to the riddle of existence, his intense interest in alchemy, occult philosophy and religious studies, his unorthodox theological views. Anyone who reads the nonscientific writings of Newton, or even the speculations he published in the *Opticks* toward the end of his life, will not be wholly satisfied with Pope's famous couplet. He will, perhaps, prefer the summary by William Wordsworth, who wrote of Newton:

. . . with his prism and silent face,
. . . a mind forever
*Voyaging through strange seas of
      thought, alone.*

NEWTON'S RINGS are explained in this diagram from the *Opticks*. The lines AB and CD represent the plane and convex surfaces of a pair of lenses which Newton pressed together to obtain the well-known pattern of colored rings. His interpretation of the result was that moving light corpuscles (*slanted lines*) are put into alternate "fits" of reflection and refraction by passing through the varying thicknesses of the air space between the lenses.

PIERRE SIMON DE LAPLACE was born in 1749 and died in 1827. This 19th-century lithograph shows him in the studied posture of reading a volume of his own *Mécanique céleste*, which systematized the gravitational studies of three generations of mathematicians.

6 LAPLACE

JAMES R. NEWMAN · June 1954

Historians of science have rightly called the Marquis de Laplace the Newton of France. He earned the title for his immense work on celestial mechanics, which capped the labors of three generations of mathematical astronomers and produced a universal principle that has been applied to almost every field of physics. Biographers have found Laplace no less interesting—though less impressive—as a person than as a scientist. He was a man of curiously mixed qualities: ambitious but not unamiable, brilliant but not above stealing ideas shamelessly from others, supple enough to be by turns a republican and a royalist in the tempestuous time in which he lived—the era of the French Revolution.

Pierre Simon de Laplace was born at Beaumont-en-Auge, a Normandy village in sight of the English Channel, on March 23, 1749. The facts of his life, of the earlier years especially, are both sparse and in dispute. Most of the original documents essential to an accurate account were burned in a fire which in 1925 destroyed the château of his great great grandson the Comte de Colbert-Laplace; others were lost during World War II in the bombardment of Caen. Many errors about Laplace's life have gained currency: that his father was a poor peasant, that he owed his education to the generosity of prosperous neighbors, that after he became famous he sought to conceal his "humble origins." Recent researches by the mathematician Sir Edmund Whittaker seem to show that whatever Laplace's reasons for reticence about his childhood, poverty of his parents was not among them. His father owned a small estate and was a syndic of the parish; his family belonged to the "good bourgeoisie of the land." One of Laplace's uncles was a surgeon, another a priest. The latter, a member of the teaching staff of the Benedictine Priory at Beaumont, where Laplace had his first schooling, is said to have awakened the boy's interest in mathematics. For a time it was thought that Laplace would follow his uncle's profession as a priest, but at the University of Caen, which he entered at the age of 16, he soon demonstrated his mathematical inclinations. He wrote a paper on the calculus of finite differences which was published in a journal edited by Joseph Louis Lagrange, the great mathematician, 13 years Laplace's senior, with whom he was later to collaborate.

When Laplace was 18, he set out for Paris. He carried enthusiastic letters of recommendation to Jean le Rond d'Alembert, the most prominent mathematician of France. D'Alembert ignored them; Laplace, not an easy fellow to put off, thereupon wrote him a letter on the general principles of mechanics which made so strong an impression that d'Alembert at once sent for the precocious young man and said: "Monsieur, as you see, I pay little enough attention to recommendations; you had no need of them. You made your worth known; that is enough for me; my support is your due." A short while later d'Alembert procured for him an appointment as professor of mathematics in the *Ecole Militaire* of Paris.

Laplace's rise was rapid and brilliant. He submitted to the Academy of Sciences one memoir after another applying his formidable mathematical capabilities to the outstanding questions of planetary theory. "We have never seen," said a spokesman for the usually imperturbable savants of the Academy, "a man so young present in so short a time so many important memoirs on such diverse and difficult problems."

One of the main problems Laplace ventured to attack was the perturbations of the planets. The anomalies of their motion had long been known; the English astronomer Edmund Halley had noted, for instance, that Jupiter and Saturn over the centuries alternately lagged behind and were accelerated ahead of their expected places in a peculiar kind of orbital horse race. The application of Newton's theory of gravitation to the behavior of the planets and their satellites entailed fearful difficulties. The famous three-body problem (how three bodies behave when attracting one another under the inverse square law) is not completely solved today; Laplace tackled the much more complex problem of all the planets cross-pulling on one another and on the sun.

Newton had feared that the planetary melee would in time derange the solar system and that God's help would be needed to restore order. Laplace decided to look elsewhere for reassurance. In a memoir described as "the most remarkable ever presented to a scientific society," he demonstrated that the perturbations of the planets were not cumulative but periodic. He then set out to establish a comprehensive rule concerning these oscillations and the inclination of the planetary orbits. This work bore on the fate of the entire solar system. If it could be shown that disturbances in the machinery were gradually overcome and the status quo restored—a kind of self-healing and self-preserving process

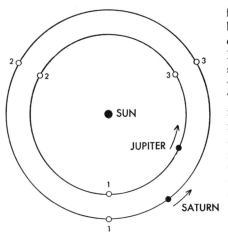

PERTURBATIONS of the planets were mathematically described by Laplace and Lagrange. When Jupiter and Saturn are in conjunction (on a line with the sun), one planet speeds up and the other slows down. Numbers indicate they are in conjunction three times in every five circuits of Jupiter.

analogous to the physiological principle which Walter Cannon has called homeostasis—the future of the cosmic machine, and of its accidental passenger, man, was reasonably secure. If, however, the disturbances tended to accumulate, and each oscillation simply paved the way for a wilder successor, catastrophe was the inevitable end. Laplace worked out a theoretical solution which seemed to fit observation, showing that the outcome would be happy, that the changes of the solar system merely "repeat themselves at regular intervals, and never exceed a certain moderate amount." The period itself is of course tremendously long; the oscillations are those of "a great pendulum of eternity which beats ages as our pendulums beat seconds."

Thus Laplace's theorems gave assurance of the reliability of the stellar clockwork of the universe; its peculiar wobbles and other irregularities were seen to be minor, self-correcting blemishes which in no sense threatened the revolutions of the engine as a whole. Indeed, Laplace regarded the anomalies as a boon to astronomers. He wrote in the *Mécanique céleste:* "The irregularities of the two planets appeared formerly to be inexplicable by the law of universal gravitation; they now form one of its most striking proofs. Such has been the fate of this brilliant discovery, that each difficulty which has arisen has become for it a new subject of triumph—a circumstance which is the surest characteristic of the true system of nature."

Two reservations about this work have to be noted. Laplace's solution did not completely prove the stability of the solar system. His solution would be valid for an idealized solar system undisturbed by tidal friction or other force; but the earth is now known, as it was not in Laplace's day, to be a non-rigid body subject to deformation by tidal friction, which thus acts as a brake on its motion. The effect is very small but acts always in one direction. Consequently we cannot conclude, as Laplace did, that nature arranged the operations of the celestial machine "for an eternal duration, upon the same principles as those which prevail so admirably upon the Earth, for the preservation of individuals and for the perpetuity of the species."

The second point concerns Laplace's failure to mention his indebtedness to Lagrange. Almost everything that Laplace accomplished in physical astronomy owes a debt to Lagrange's profound mathematical discoveries. It is impossible in many instances to separate their contributions. Lagrange was the greater mathematician; Laplace, for whom mathematics was only a means to an objective, was primarily a mathematical physicist and astronomer. Others have severely censured Laplace for his lack of acknowledgment of his collaborator's contributions, but Lagrange, obviously a saintly soul, did not; the two always remained on the best of terms.

Laplace's *Mécanique céleste* appeared in five immense volumes between 1799 and 1825. He described its scope as follows:

"We have given, in the first part of this work, the general principles of the equilibrium and motion of bodies. The application of these principles to the motions of the heavenly bodies has conducted us, by geometrical reasoning, without any hypothesis, to the law of universal attraction; the action of gravity, and the motion of projectiles, being particular cases of this law. We have then taken into consideration a system of bodies subjected to this great law of nature; and have obtained, by a singular analysis, the general expressions of their motions, of their figures, and of the oscillations of the fluids which cover them. From these expressions we have deduced all the known phenomena of the flow and ebb of the tide; the variations of the degrees, and of the force of gravity at the surface of the earth; the precession of the equinoxes; the libration of the moon; and the figure and rotation of Saturn's rings. We have also pointed out the cause why these rings remain permanently in the plane of the equator of Saturn. Moreover, we have deduced, from the same theory of gravity, the principal equations of the motions of the planets; particularly those of Jupiter and Saturn, whose great inequalities have a period of above 900 years."

Napoleon, on receiving a copy of the *Mécanique céleste*, protested to Laplace that in all its vast expanse God was not mentioned. The author replied that he had no need of this hypothesis. Napoleon, much amused, repeated the reply to Lagrange, who is said to have exclaimed: "Ah, but it is a beautiful hypothesis; it explains many things."

To mathematicians the work is especially memorable. The Irish mathematician William Rowan Hamilton is said to have begun his mathematical career by discovering a mistake in the *Mécanique céleste*. George Green, the English mathematician, derived from it a mathematical theory of electricity. Perhaps the greatest single contribution of the work was the famous Laplace equation:

$$\frac{\partial^2 u}{\partial x^2} + \frac{\partial^2 u}{\partial y^2} + \frac{\partial^2 u}{\partial z^2} = 0$$

Laplace's expression is a field equation, which is to say it can be used to describe what is happening at every instant of time at every point in a field produced by a gravitational mass, an electric charge, fluid flow and so on. Another way of saying this is that the equation deals with the value of a physical quantity, the potential, throughout a continuum. The potential function u, introduced in the first instance as a purely mathematical quantity, later acquired a physical meaning. The difference between the values of the potential function at two different points of a field measures the amount of work required to move a unit of matter from one of these points to the other; the rate of change of potential in any direction measures the force in that direction.

By giving u different meanings (*e.g.*, temperature, velocity potential and so on) the equation is found to have an enormous range of applications in the theories of electrostatics, gravitation, hydrodynamics, magnetism, sound, light, conduction of heat. In hydrodynamics, where u is the velocity potential (distance squared divided by time), the rate of change of potential is the measure of the velocity of the fluid. The equation applies to a fluid which is incompressible and indestructible; if as much fluid flows out of any tiny element of volume as flows in, the potential function satisfies Laplace's equation. A rough explanation of why this equation serves as an almost universal solvent of physical problems is that it describes a characteristic economy of natural behavior—"a general tendency toward uniformity so that local inequalities tend to be smoothed out." Thus a metal rod heated at one end tends to become of uniform temperature throughout; a solute in a liquid tends to distribute itself evenly.

The *Mécanique céleste* is a book whose difficulties are proportional to its bulk. Laplace made no concession to the reader. He bridged great gaps in the argument with the infuriating phrase "it is easy to see." The U. S. mathematician and astronomer Nathaniel Bowditch, who translated four of the volumes into English, said he never came across this expression "without feeling sure that I have hours of hard work before me to fill up the chasm." Laplace himself, when required to reconstruct some of his reasoning, confessed he found it not at all *aisé à voir* how his conclusions had been reached. Nor is it a modest or entirely honorable writing. "Theorems and formulae," wrote Agnes Mary Clerke, the noted historian of astronomy, "are appropriated wholesale without acknowledgment, and a production which may be described as the organized result of a century of patient toil presents itself to the world as the offspring of a single brain." The biographer Eric Temple Bell has remarked that it was Laplace's practice to "steal outrageously, right and left, wherever he could lay his hands on anything of his contemporaries and predecessors which he could use."

For those unable to follow the formidable abstractions of the *Mécanique* Laplace wrote in 1796 the *Exposition du système du monde*, one of the most charming and lucid popular treatises on astronomy ever published. In this masterpiece Laplace put forward his famous nebular hypothesis (which had been anticipated by Immanuel Kant in 1755). Its gist is that the solar system evolved from a rotating mass of gas, which condensed to form the sun and later threw off a series of gaseous rings that became the planets. While still in the gaseous state the planets threw off rings which became satellites. The hypothesis has had its ups and downs since Kant and Laplace advanced it. In Laplace's theory revolution in a retrograde direction by a member of the solar system was impossible; yet before Laplace died Sir William Herschel found that the satellites of Uranus misbehaved in this way, and others have since been discovered. Yet the theory was an intellectual landmark, and much of its basic reasoning is still accepted by some cosmologists as valid for astronomical aggregates larger than the solar system.

Another subject upon which Laplace bestowed his attention, both as a mathematician and as a popularizer, is the theory of probability. His comprehensive treatise *Théorie analytique des probabilités* described a useful calculus for assigning a "degree of rational" belief to propositions about chance events. Its framework was the science of permutations and combinations, which might be called the mathematics of possibility.

The theory of probability, said Laplace, is at bottom nothing more than common sense reduced to calculation. But his treatise seemed to indicate that the arithmetic of common sense is even more intricate than that of the planets. No less a mathematician than Augustus De Morgan described it as "by very much the most difficult mathematical work we have ever met with," exceeding in complexity the *Mécanique céleste.*

Laplace's contributions to probability are perhaps unequaled by any other single investigator; nevertheless the *Théorie analytique*, like the *Mécanique*, failed to acknowledge the labors of other mathematicians, on which many of its conclusions depended. De Morgan said of Laplace: "There is enough originating from himself to make any reader wonder that one who could so well afford to state what he had taken from others, should have set an example so dangerous to his own claims."

In a companion work, the *Essai philosophique sur les probabilités*, presenting a nontechnical introduction to the laws of chance, Laplace wrote a passage which is regarded as the most perfect statement of the deterministic interpretation of the universe, a symbol of that happy and confident age which supposed that the past could be described and the future predicted from a single snapshot of the present:

"We ought then to regard the present state of the universe as the effect of its anterior state and as the cause of the one which is to follow. Given for one instant an intelligence which could comprehend all the forces by which nature is animated and the respective situation of the beings who compose it—an intelligence sufficiently vast to submit these data to analysis—it would embrace in the same formula the movements of the greatest bodies of the universe and those of the lightest atom; for it, nothing would be uncertain and the future, as the past, would be present to its eyes. The human mind offers, in the perfection which it has been able to give to astronomy, a feeble idea of this intelligence. Its discoveries in mechanics and geometry, added to that of universal gravity, have

enabled it to comprehend in the same analytical expressions the past and future states of the system of the world. Applying the same method to some other objects of its knowledge, it has succeeded in referring to general laws observed phenomena and in foreseeing those which given circumstances ought to produce. All these efforts in the search for truth tend to lead it back continually to the vast intelligence which we have just mentioned, but from which it will always remain infinitely removed. This tendency, peculiar to the human race, is that which renders it superior to animals; and their progress in this respect distinguishes nations and ages and constitutes their true glory."

Together with the great chemist Antoine Lavoisier, Laplace engaged in experiments to determine the specific heats of a number of substances. They designed the instrument known as Laplace's ice calorimeter, which measures heat by the amount of ice melted, a method employed earlier by the Scottish chemist Joseph Black and the German Johann Karl Wilke.

Laplace prospered financially and politically; Lavoisier died on the guillotine. In 1784 Laplace was appointed "examiner to the royal artillery," a lucrative post and one in which he had the good fortune to examine a promising 16-year-old candidate named Napoleon Bonaparte. The relationship was to blossom forth 20 years later, much to Laplace's advantage. With Lagrange, Laplace taught mathematics at the *Ecole Normale*, became a member and then president of the Bureau of Longitudes, aided in the introduction of the decimal system and suggested, in keeping with the reform spirit of the Revolution, the adoption of a new calendar based on certain astronomical calculations.

There is some reason to believe that for a brief period during the Revolution Laplace fell under suspicion; he was removed from the commission of weights and measures. But he managed not only to hold on to his head but to win new honors. He had a knack for riding the waves of his turbulent era. Under the Republic he was an ardent Republican and declared his "inextinguishable hatred to royalty." The day following the 18th Brumaire (November 9, 1799), when Napoleon seized power, he shed his Republicanism and formed an ardent attachment for the first consul, whom he had helped earlier to form a Commission for Egypt. Almost immediately Napoleon rewarded Laplace with the portfolio of the Interior. The evening of his appointment the new minister demanded a pension of 2.000 francs for the widow of the noted scholar Jean Bailly, executed during the Terror, and early the next morning Madame Laplace herself brought the first half-year's income to "this victim of the passions of the epoch." It was a "noble beginning," as Laplace's protégé François Arago wrote, but it is hard to discover any other noble accomplishment gracing Laplace's ministerial career. His tenure of office was brief—six weeks. Napoleon wrote tartly of Laplace's shortcomings in his St. Helena memoirs: "He was a worse than mediocre administrator who searched everywhere for subtleties, and brought into the affairs of government the spirit of the infinitely small." But to soothe the hurt of his dismissal the deposed minister was given a seat in the Senate and in 1803 became its Chancellor.

Historians have amused themselves describing Laplace's skill in running with the hare and hunting with the hounds. The neatest evidence appears in his introductions to successive editions of his books. He inscribed the first edition of the *Système du monde* in 1796 to the Council of Five Hundred, and in 1802 prefixed the third volume of the *Mécanique céleste* with a worshipful paean to Napoleon, who had dispersed the Council. Laplace dedicated the 1812 edition of the *Théorie analytique des probabilités* to "Napoleon the Great"; in the 1814 edition he suppressed this dedication and wrote "that the fall of empires which aspired to universal dominion could be predicted with very high probability by one versed in the calculus of chances." Napoleon had made Laplace a count; this gave him the opportunity to join in the 1814 decree of forfeiture banishing the man who had made him a count. When the Bourbons returned, Laplace was one of the first to fall at their feet; for this genuflection he received a marquisate.

Laplace was not an evil or a malicious man. He gave a hand up to many younger scientists. At his country home in Arcueil he surrounded himself with "adopted children of his thought": Arago, an astronomer and physicist; the physicist Jean Biot, noted for his investigations of the polarization of light; Baron Alexander von Humboldt, the celebrated German naturalist and traveler; Joseph Gay-Lussac, the great chemist and physicist; Siméon Poisson, the brilliant mathematician. Biot related that after he had read a paper on the theory of equations, Laplace took him aside and showed him "under a strict pledge of secrecy papers yellow with age in which he had long before obtained the same results." Having soothed his ego, Laplace told the young man to say nothing about the earlier work and to publish his own.

The almost universal admiration for Laplace's scientific genius did not mitigate the widespread distrust inspired by his political adaptability. The more tolerantly cynical of his contemporaries referred to his "suppleness." The stock appraisal is to compare him to the Vicar of Bray. The Vicar, an accommodating man who was twice a Papist and twice a Protestant, is said to have defended the charge of being a time-server by replying: "Not so, neither, for if I changed my religions, I am sure I kept true to my principle, which is to live and die the Vicar of Bray." Laplace could have made similar answer.

About his family life and personal habits there is a strange lack of information. Laplace's marriage with Charlotte de Courty de Romanges, contracted in 1788, was apparently a happy one. They had a daughter and a son, Emile, who rose to the rank of general in the artillery. In later years Laplace passed much of his time at Arcueil, where he had a house next to the chemist Count de Berthollet. There in his study, where the portrait of Racine, his favorite author, hung opposite that of Newton, he pursued his studies with "unabated ardor" and received "distinguished visitors from all parts of the world." He died on March 5, 1827, a few days before his 78th birthday. Illustrious men are required to say deathless things on their deathbeds. Laplace is said to have departed after expressing the reasonable opinion, "What we know is very slight; what we don't know is immense." De Morgan, observing that "this looks like a parody on Newton's pebbles," claimed to have learned on close authority that Laplace's very last words were: "Man follows only phantoms."

ASTRONOMICAL DECORATION is from the title page of Laplace's *Théorie du mouvement et de la figure elliptique des planètes*.

7 WILLIAM ROWAN HAMILTON

SIR EDMUND WHITTAKER · May 1954

After Isaac Newton, the greatest mathematician of the English-speaking peoples is William Rowan Hamilton, who was born in 1805 and died in 1865. His fame has had some curious vicissitudes. During his lifetime he was celebrated but not understood; after his death his reputation declined and he came to be counted in the second rank; in the 20th century he has become the subject of an extraordinary revival of interest and appreciation.

About his ancestry there is not much to be said. His father was a Dublin solicitor who defended the outlawed Irish patriot Archibald Hamilton Rowan and obtained a reversal of his sentence. From Rowan, who acted as sponsor at the baptism of the infant William, the boy received his second Christian name. The child was not brought up by his own parents. When he was about a year old, they decided to entrust his education to Mr. Hamilton's brother James, a clergyman settled at Trim, a small town 30 miles north of Dublin. Young William lived in Trim, with occasional visits to Dublin, until he was of age to enter the University.

Whether the credit must be given to his uncle's methods of education or to his own natural gifts, it is recorded that by the age of three William could read English easily; at five he was able to read and translate Latin, Greek and Hebrew; at eight he had added Italian and French; before he was 10 he was studying Arabic and Sanskrit. At the age of 14 he wrote a letter in Persian to the Persian ambassador, then on a visit to Dublin.

The boy loved the classics and the poets, but at the age of 15 his interests, and the course of his life, were completely changed when he met one Zerah Colburn, an American youngster who gave an exhibition in Dublin of his powers as a lightning calculator. "For a long time afterwards," wrote Hamilton later, "I liked to perform long operations in arithmetic in my mind; extracting the square and cube root, and everything that related to the properties of numbers." William resolved upon a life of mathematics. "Nothing," he declared, "so exalts the mind, or so raises a man above his fellow-creatures, as the researches of Science. Who would not rather have the fame of Archimedes than that of his conqueror Marcellus? . . . Mighty minds in all ages have combined to rear the vast and beautiful temple of Science, and inscribed their names upon it in imperishable characters; but the edifice is not completed; it is not yet too late to add another pillar or another ornament. I have yet scarcely arrived at its foot, but I may aspire one day to reach its summit."

In his diary there presently appeared such entries as "read Newton's *Life*" and "began Newton's *Principia*." At the age of 16 he made the acquaintance of Laplace's *Mécanique céleste*. (An entry in his journal around this time recounted: "We have been getting up before five for several mornings—that is, my uncle and I; he pulls a string which goes through the wall and is fastened to my shirt at night.") In 1823, preceded by rumors of his intellectual prowess, "Hamilton the prodigy" entered Trinity College at Dublin. There his progress was brilliant, not only on the examinations but also in original research. When he was only 21 years old he submitted to the Royal Irish Academy a paper entitled *A Theory of Systems of Rays* which in effect made a new science of mathematical optics.

In this paper Hamilton's aim was to remodel the geometry of light by establishing one uniform method for the solution of all problems in that science. He started from the already established principles that a ray of light always travels by the path that takes the least time (according to the wave theory) or the least "action" (according to the corpuscular theory) in going from one point to another; this is true whether the path is straight or bent by refraction. Hamilton's contribution was to consider the action (or time) as a function of the positions of the points between which the light passes, and to show that this quantity varied when the coordinates of these points varied, according to a law which he called the law of varying action. He demonstrated that all researches on any system of optical rays can be reduced to the study of this single function. Hamilton's discovery of this "characteristic function," as he called it, was an extraordinary achievement of scientific genius. He had originally projected it when he was 16 and he brought it to a form approaching completeness in his 21st year.

The communication of the paper was soon followed by a great change in Hamilton's circumstances. The chair of professor of astronomy at Trinity College, which paid an annual salary of 250 pounds and conferred on its occupant the title of Royal Astronomer of Ireland, was vacated in 1826 when its holder, the Reverend John Brinkley, was appointed to the Bishopric of Cloyne, once held by the great philosopher George Berkeley. Hamilton was elected as Brinkley's successor a few months later. The election of an undergraduate to a professorial chair was an astonishing event, and it led to some curious consequences. For instance, the Royal Astronomer was by virtue of his office an examiner for the Bishop Law Prize, a mathematical distinction open to candidates of junior bachelor standing, and thus came to pass the anomalous proceeding of an undergraduate examining graduates in the highest branches of mathematics.

While everyone acknowledged the unprecedented honor of Hamilton's appointment to the chair, opinion was sharply divided as to whether he was wise to have accepted it. In another year or two he would undoubtedly have been elected a fellow of Trinity College, with better financial and other prospects. What determined his choice was the consideration that the Royal Astronomership was practically a research appointment, involving very little in the way of fixed duties, while a fellow was required to become a clergyman and must soon have developed into a tutor and lecturer, with duties occupying most of his time. To be sure, the research equipment of the astronomical observatory was poor in the extreme, but what really was in the minds both of Hamilton and of the electors was not astronomy but an arrangement by which he could continue the theoretical researches of which the paper on *Systems of Rays* was such a glorious beginning.

Hamilton did have the duty of giving a course of lectures on astronomy. In these it was his custom to discuss the relations of astronomy to physical science in general, to metaphysics and to all related realms of thought. His lectures were so poetic and learned that they attracted crowded audiences of professors and visitors as well as his class of undergraduates; when in 1831 there was some talk of his being transferred to the chair of mathematics, the Board insisted that he remain where he was. As inducement the Board raised his salary to 580 pounds a year and gave him permission to devote his research principally to mathematics.

In 1832 Hamilton announced to the Royal Irish Academy a remarkable discovery in optics which followed up his theory of systems of rays. It had been known for some time that certain biaxial crystals, such as topaz and aragonite, gave rise to two refracted rays, producing a double image. Augustin Fresnel of France had worked out the rules of double refraction. Now Hamilton, investigating by his general method the law of Fresnel, was led to conclude that in certain cases a single ray of incident light in a biaxial crystal should give rise to not merely two but an infinite number of refracted rays, forming a cone, and that in certain other cases a single ray within such a crystal would emerge as a different cone. He therefore proposed from

theory two new laws of light, which he called internal and external conical refraction. They were soon verified experimentally by his friend Humphrey Lloyd, a Dublin physicist.

In 1834 Hamilton, then 29, wrote to his uncle: "It is my hope and purpose to remodel the whole of dynamics, in the most extensive sense of the word, by the idea of my characteristic function." He proceeded to apply this principle to the motion of systems of bodies, and in the following year he expressed the equations of motion in a form which showed the duality between the components of momentum of a dynamical system and the coordinates of its position. Only a century later, with the development of quantum theory, did physicists and mathematicians fully realize the importance of this duality.

In 1835 Hamilton received the honor of knighthood, and two years later he was elected president of the Royal Irish Academy. But his private life was less happy. Upon becoming a professor he had set up house with three of his sisters at the Dunsink Observatory on a hill five miles from Dublin. At the age of 26 he fell in love with Helen Maria Bayly, the daughter of a former rector in County Tipperary. She at first refused to entertain his proposal of marriage but ultimately accepted him, and the wedding took place on April 9, 1833. He had remarked in a letter to a friend on her "extreme timidity and delicacy"; these qualities were only too fully confirmed after the marriage. Lady Hamilton bore two sons and a daughter in six years, but she found herself unequal to the work of home administration and left Dunsink for two years to live with a married sister in England. She returned in 1842, but things became no better. Hamilton henceforth had no regular times for his

William Rowan Hamilton

HAMILTON was portrayed by a contemporary artist with his mace of office as President of the Royal Academy of Ireland. He was Royal Astronomer of Ireland from 1826 to 1865.

MERIDIAN ROOM of the Dunsink Observatory, home of the Royal Astronomer, was depicted in 1845. The equipment was poor. Hamilton spent nearly all his time on mathematics.

meals, and he began to use alcoholic stimulants to a dangerous extent.

When I held Hamilton's chair, to which I had the honor of being appointed in 1906, many years after his death, I met many people who had known him. The countryside was full of stories about him. One of them concerns his administration of the 17 acres of farmland around Dunsink Observatory, of which the Royal Astronomer has control. Hamilton, who was town-bred, knew nothing of farming, but in order to supply his household with milk he bought a cow. After some time, in the ordinary course of nature, the yield of milk began to fall off. Hamilton went to consult a neighboring farmer. The farmer, knowing with whom he had to deal, said that the cow, as the solitary occupant of 17 acres, was suffering from loneliness. Thereupon Hamilton inquired whether it would be possible to provide her with companions, and the farmer graciously agreed, in recognition of a payment by Hamilton, to allow his cattle to graze on the rich pastures of Dunsink.

In spite of the unfavorable conditions of his life, Hamilton's scientific work went on. In 1843 he made a great discovery—the Calculus of Quaternions.

He was led to this discovery by long thought on the problem of finding a general rule for computing the fourth proportional to three straight line segments when the directions of those lines were taken into account. A line segment with a specified direction is called a vector. It was well known that a vector in a plane could be represented by a complex number; that is, a number formed of both real and imaginary numbers, or

$x + y\sqrt{-1}$. (The square root of -1, an imaginary number, is usually written i, so that the expression becomes $x + yi$.) If we represent real numbers by distances on the x axis of a graph, then multiplication of any number by -1, changing it to the negative number, may be thought of as rotating the line segment 180 degrees, while multiplication by i, the square root of -1, may be thought of as a 90-degree rotation [see *illustrations on page 86*]. Thus imaginary numbers are represented on the y axis, and i may be considered a unit on that axis, or a "unit vector." Any vector in a plane may then be specified by a complex number giving its x and y components. Such a pair of numbers, known as a doublet, obeys the same algebraic laws as a single number: doublets can be added, subtracted, multiplied and divided according to the usual rules. Thus it is possible to calculate the fourth proportional to three vectors in a common plane: $V_1 : V_2 = V_3 : x$.

Hamilton conjectured that in three-dimensional space a vector might be represented by a set of three numbers, a triplet, just as a vector in a plane was expressed by a doublet. He sought to find the fourth proportional by multiplying triplets, but encountered difficulties. The younger members of the household at Dunsink shared affectionately in the hopes and disappointments of their illustrious parent as the investigation proceeded. William Edwin (aged nine) and Archibald Henry (eight) used to ask at breakfast: "Well, Papa, can you multiply triplets?" Whereto he was obliged to reply, with a sad shake of the head, "No, I can only add and subtract them."

One day, while walking from Dunsink into Dublin, Hamilton suddenly realized the answer: the geometrical operations of three-dimensional spaces required for their description not triplets but *quadruplets*. To specify the operation needed to convert one vector into another in space, one had to know four numbers: (1) the ratio of the length of one vector to the other, (2) the angle between them, and (3) the node and (4) the inclination of the plane in which they lie.

Hamilton named the set of four numbers a quaternion, and found that he could multiply quaternions as if they were single numbers. But he discovered that the algebra of quaternions differed from ordinary algebra in a crucial respect: it was *non-commutative*. This word calls for some explanation. When we multiply 2 by 3 we obtain the same product as when we multiply 3 by 2. This *commutative* law of multiplication, as it is called, is embodied in the algebraic formula ab=ba. It applies to imaginary numbers as well as to real numbers. It does not, however, hold for the calculus of quaternions, because the latter describes geometrical operations such as rotations. The illustration on page 87 shows why. It represents three mutually perpendicular axes, the y and z axes lying in the plane of the paper and the x axis extending toward the reader. The characters i, j and k represent unit vectors along the x, y and z axes respectively. Multiplication by i is defined as a 90-degree counterclockwise rotation in the plane of the paper; multiplication by j and k, as rotations in planes perpendicular to that plane. Now multiplication of j by i rotates j to k; that is, $ij=k$. But multiplication of i by j rotates i to $-k$; that is, $ji=-k$. Thus ij does not equal ji.

The surrender of the commutative law was a tremendous break with tradition. It marked the beginning of a new era. The news of the discovery spread quickly, and led, in Dublin at any rate, to a wave of interest amongst people of rank and fashion like the later boom in General Relativity in London, when Lord Haldane invited Einstein to meet the Archbishop of Canterbury at luncheon. Hamilton was buttonholed in the street by members of the Anglo-Irish aristocracy with the question: "What the deuce are the quaternions?" To satisfy them he published the delightful *Letter to a Lady*, in which he explained that the term "occurs, for example, in our version of the Bible, where the Apostle Peter is described as having been delivered by Herod to the charge of four quaternions of soldiers. . . . And to take a lighter and more modern instance from the pages of *Guy Mannering*, Scott represents Sir Robert Hazelwood of Hazelwood as loading his long sentences with 'triads and quaternions.' "

From this time until his death 22 years later, Hamilton's chief interest was to de-

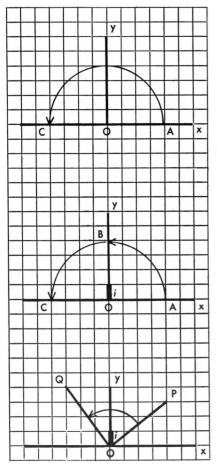

COMPLEX NUMBER, made up of a real number and an imaginary one, the square root of —1, is used to describe the length and direction of a line segment. When complex numbers are added, subtracted or multiplied, the process is equivalent to a geometrical operation, *e.g.*, rotation. In the diagram at the top the line segment OA, representing the number +4, is multiplied by —1, which changes it to the line segment OC, or —4. Thus multiplication by —1 is equivalent to rotation through 180 degrees. In the middle diagram multiplication by —1 is done in two steps, *i.e.*, multiplication by $\sqrt{-1}$ and by $\sqrt{-1}$ again. (The square root of —1 is usually written *i*.) Consequently multiplication by *i* can be considered rotation through 90 degrees. This leads to the idea of measuring imaginary distances on the y axis, as is indicated by making *i* the "unit vector" on that axis. The diagram at the bottom demonstrates that multiplication by *i* has the effect of a 90-degree rotation even if the starting point is not the x axis. The line segment from point O (x=0, y=0) to point P (x=4, y=3) is represented in complex-number notation as $4+3i$. Multiplying this number by *i* gives $4i+3i^2$, or $3-4i$. The latter number represents the line segment OQ (x= —3, y=4), or a 90-degree rotation of the line OP.

velop the new calculus. They were mostly sad and lonely years, owing to the frequent illnesses and absences of his wife. He worked all day in the large dining room of the Observatory house, into which from time to time his cook passed a mutton chop. (After his death scores of mutton chop bones on plates were found sandwiched among his papers.)

Hamilton's discovery was quickly followed by other new algebras, such as the Theory of Matrices, which is likewise non-commutative. Thus he started a glorious school of mathematics, though it was not to come into full flower for another half-century. I remember discussing in 1900 with Alfred North Whitehead whether quaternions and other non-commutative algebras had much of a future as regards applications to physics. Whitehead remarked that while all the physics then known could be treated by ordinary algebra, it was possible that new fields in physics might some day be discovered for which non-commutative algebra would be the only natural representation. In that very year this anticipation was started on the road to fulfillment. Max Planck introduced the quantum *h*, the beginning of the quantum theory. Now *h* is a quantum of action, and action was a central conception in Hamilton's system of dynamics. Thus the Hamiltonian ideas on dynamics began to come into prominence. But very slowly. When my book *Analytical Dynamics* was published in 1904, I was criticized severely for devoting a large part of it to such topics as the coordinates-momentum duality, action and other Hamiltonian ideas. The critics called them mere mathematical playthings.

The good work went on, however. The discovery of special relativity brought quaternions to the fore, because Arthur Cayley of Cambridge University had shown in 1854 that quaternions could be applied to the representation of rotations in four-dimensional space. His result yielded a particularly elegant expression for the most general Lorentz transformation. Moreover, the new discoveries again emphasized the importance of action, which preserves its form in different reference systems and is therefore fundamental in relativity physics.

Meanwhile, the workers in quantum theory were coming to realize that Hamilton's dynamical conceptions must form the basis of all rules of quantification. And in 1925 the other side of his work—his non-commutative algebra—was brought into quantum theory by Werner Heisenberg, Max Born and Pas-

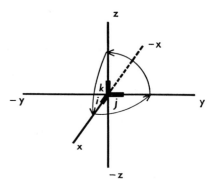

NON-COMMUTATIVE ALGEBRA is used to represent geometrical operations in three dimensions. A vector in three dimensions is represented in a system of coordinates with three mutually perpendicular axes (x points toward the reader, y and z are in the plane of the page) in terms of the unit vectors *i*, *j* and *k*. Multiplication by *i* is arbitrarily defined as meaning a rotation of 90 degrees in the plane perpendicular to the *i* vector, *i.e.*, the plane of y and z. Multiplication by *j* and *k* are similarly defined, as indicated by the arrows. Now it can be seen that applying *i* to *j*, which is to say $i \times j$, has the effect of rotating *j* into *k*. On the other hand, applying *j* to *i*, or $j \times i$, has the effect of rotating *i* into —*k*. So $i \times j = k$, and $j \times i = -k$. In other words, the multiplication is non-commutative: $i \times j$ does not equal $j \times i$.

cual Jordan, who showed that the ordinary Hamiltonian equations of dynamics were still valid in quantum theory, provided the symbols representing the coordinates and momenta in classical dynamics were interpreted as operators whose products did not commute.

Time has amply vindicated Hamilton's intuition of the duality between generalized coordinates and generalized momenta. This was strikingly shown in 1927, when Heisenberg discovered the Principle of Uncertainty, which is usually stated in this way: the more accurately the coordinates of a particle are determined, the less accurately can its momentum be known, and vice versa, the product of the two uncertainties being of the order of Planck's constant *h*.

Quantum-mechanical workers have generally tended to regard matrices rather than quaternions as the type of non-commutative algebra best suited to their problems, but the original Hamiltonian formulae keep cropping up. Thus the "spin matrices" of Wolfgang Pauli, on which the quantum-mechanical theory of rotations and angular momenta depends, are simply Hamilton's three quaternion units *i*, *j*, *k*. Arthur Conway has shown that quaternion methods may be used with advantage in the discussion of P. A. M. Dirac's equation for the spinning electron. Hamilton's formulae of 1843 may even yet prove to be the most natural expression of the new physics.

THE STRANGE LIFE
OF CHARLES BABBAGE

8

PHILIP AND EMILY MORRISON • April 1952

DURING last summer's Festival of Britain the center of the stage in a section of the Exhibition of Science at the South Kensington Science Museum was held by a glowing, streamlined computer called Nimrod. A visitor who wandered away from the main attractions might have found, tucked away in a remote gallery, a dust-covered ancestor of Nimrod. It is a complicated collection of wheels and rods labeled Babbage's Difference Engine. Made in 1833, it was the work of a designer who consumed his years and his fortune in the attempt to build mathematical machines for which his age was not ready but which have now been realized.

Charles Babbage is a name known to some mathematicians today. Few of his own contemporaries recognized the value of his work, and he was held a crackpot by his London neighbors, who knew him chiefly as a crotchety crusader against street organ-grinders; indeed, when he died the London *Times* identified him in the first paragraph of its obituary as a man who had lived to almost 80 "in spite of organ-grinding persecutions." Today mathematicians recognize him as a man far ahead of his time. To an article on one of the modern U. S. calculating machines the British magazine *Nature* gave the title "Babbage's Dream Comes True."

Babbage was a versatile fellow. He wrote a book, *On the Economy of Manufactures and Machinery*, which foreshadowed what is now known as operations research; he made a determined campaign for government subsidy of scientific research at a time when research was still to a large extent a gentleman's hobby; he published a widely-used table of logarithms from 1 to

108,000; he plotted mortality tables and made a pioneering attempt to popularize life insurance; he designed machine tools; he proposed a number of inventions, from schemes for preventing railroad wrecks to a system of lighthouse-signaling; he wrote papers on physics, geology, astronomy and archaeology. But mathematical machines were his great lifelong passion.

BABBAGE was born in Devonshire in 1792, the son of a banker, from whom he eventually inherited a considerable fortune. Because of poor health he was educated by private teachers until he entered Trinity College at Cambridge in 1810. Already passionately fond of mathematics, he was discouraged to find that he knew more than his tutor. His most intimate friends at the University were John Herschel, son of the eminent astronomer William Herschel, and George Peacock. The three undergraduates entered into a compact to "do their best to leave the world wiser than they found it." In 1812, as their first step in this direction, they founded the Analytical Society, primarily to encourage English mathematicians to replace the Newtonian mathematical notation with the Leibnitz scheme used on the Continent. Newton denoted a rate of change by placing a dot over the symbol in question; Leibnitz, by placing a d in front of it. Babbage founded the Society, he once remarked, to advocate the "principles of pure 'd-ism' as opposed to the 'dot-age' of the University." In spite of considerable opposition, the Society had a profound effect on the future development of mathematics in England.

Babbage, believing that he was certain to be beaten in the tripos by both

Herschel and Peacock, transferred from Trinity College to Peterhouse in his third year, preferring to be first at Peterhouse rather than third at Trinity. He did, indeed, graduate first from Peterhouse, and went on to take his M.A. in 1817. Babbage, Herschel and Peacock continued to be friends after they left school. Each in his own way lived up to their joint compact, though their careers were very different. Peacock joined the ministry and soon became Dean of Ely. Herschel, after a brief apprenticeship at law, decided to follow his father into astronomy. Not only did he distinguish himself in astronomy, but he was knighted by the Crown, served as master of the mint, avoided all scientific feuds, and his biographers report that his life was full of serenity and innocence.

Babbage, in contrast, was to spend a life of bitter frustration on his mathematical machines. Toward the end of his life he remarked once to friends that he had never had a happy day in his life, and spoke "as though he hated mankind in general, Englishmen in particular, and the English Government and organ-grinders most of all." Actually it was not as bad as that: for much of his life he was a most social and gregarious man with a sense of humor. Once, on a visit to France with Herschel, Babbage ordered two eggs for each of them for breakfast by telling the waiter "pour chacun deux." The waiter called out to the kitchen, "Il faut faire bouillir cinquante deux oeufs pour Messieurs les Anglais." They succeeded in stopping the cook in time, but the story preceded them to Paris and quickly ran through several editions. Asked by a guest at a dinner party soon afterward whether he thought the tale of two young Englishmen who had eaten 52 eggs and a pie for breakfast was probable, Babbage replied soberly that "there was no absurdity a young Englishman would not occasionally commit." An Edinburgh professor who was once asked to dinner by Babbage reported that "it was with the greatest difficulty that I escaped from him at two in the morning after a most delightful evening." On his frequent trips to the Continent Babbage constantly sought the company of all sorts of people: members of the aristocracy, mathematicians, skilled mechanics.

NONETHELESS, Babbage's obsession with his machines transformed him from a cheerful young man into a bitter old one. He was first seized with this obsession, according to the most credible of his own differing versions, as the result of a chance conversation with his friend Herschel. The latter had brought in some calculations made for the Astronomical Society. In their tedious checking of the figures Herschel and Babbage found a number of errors, and at one point Babbage said, "I wish to God these calculations had been executed by steam." "It is quite possible," remarked Herschel. The more Babbage thought about it, the more convinced he became that it was possible to make machinery to compute and print mathematical tables. He set down a rough outline of his first idea, and made a small model consisting of 96 wheels and 24 axes, which he later reduced to 18 wheels and 3 axes. In 1822 he wrote a letter about his idea to Sir Humphry Davy, the president of the Royal Society, pointing out the advantages of his "Difference Engine" and proposing to construct one for the Government's use. The Royal Society reported favorably on his project, and the Chancellor of the Exchequer made a vague verbal agreement to underwrite the enterprise with Government funds.

Babbage had expected the project to take three years, but he was constantly having new ideas about the machine and scrapping all that had been done, and at the end of four years he was not yet in sight of his goal. The Government built him a fireproof building and workshops next to his home. After a visit by the Duke of Wellington himself to inspect the shops, it made a further liberal grant to continue the work. After a time Babbage and his very excellent engineer Joseph Clement had a "misunderstanding" about salary payments. Clement abruptly dissolved the workshop, dismissed his men and departed with all the tools, of which he was legally the owner, and all the drawings.

At this critical juncture Babbage had a brand-new idea: an Analytical Engine, which would be simpler to build, would operate more rapidly and would have

BABBAGE was born in 1792 and died in 1871. This drawing of him was made from a photograph in his son's book *Babbage's Calculating Engines*.

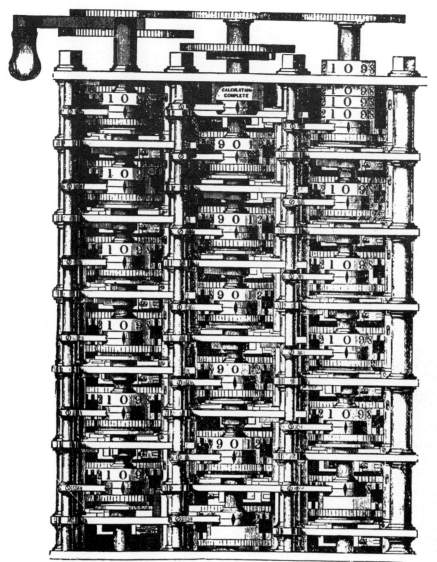

DIFFERENCE ENGINE was Babbage's first great conception. This wood-cut is described in *Babbage's Calculating Engines* as "a portion of Mr. Babbage's Difference Engine. . . . It was commenced 1823 . . . abandoned 1842."

us take a problem the engine was designed to solve, namely, to compute the squares of the successive numbers: 1^2, 2^2, 3^2, 4^2, and so on. The squares of all whole numbers, as far as we have the patience to go, can be obtained by the simple process of addition, with the use of the number 2 as the constant difference. We set up three columns. In the first we always set down the constant 2 (representing the second power). The second column starts with 1 and adds the constant 2 at each successive step. This sum is fed into the third column, which starts with 1, and then gives the answer. For example, 1 plus 2 plus the square of 1 gives 4, the square of 2; 3 plus 2 plus 4 gives 9, the square of 3; 5 plus 2 plus 9 gives 16, the square of 4; and so on. The table looks like this:

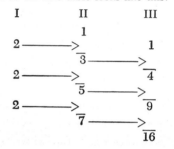

I	II	III
	1	
2	→	1
	3	→
2	→	4
	5	→
2	→	9
	7	→
		16

Now these simple operations can easily be performed by a machine, in much the same manner as the mileage indicator on an automobile, which adds by turning wheels with numbers on them. Babbage's first preliminary model for the Difference Engine, made with toothed wheels on shafts that were turned by a crank, could produce a table of squares up to five places. But the engine he proposed to build was to be on a much grander scale. Babbage's plans called for no less than 20-place capacity, up to differences of the sixth order, instead of only the second. Furthermore, each number as it appeared in the answer column was to be transmitted through a set of levers and cams to a collection of steel punches, which would stamp the number on a copper engraver's plate.

Mechanically all this was an enormous order. Imagine the variety and number of bolts and nuts, claws, ratchets, cams, links, shafts and wheels that would be needed, and remember that standardized machine parts, not requiring hand-fitting, were practically non-existent! Babbage attacked the problem with great skill. He and his assistants designed each part with great care, providing supplementary mechanisms to minimize wear. He became an expert technician, developing tools which were superior for the time, and methods which foreshadowed some of the modern practices of instrument design. But perhaps the very care and thoroughness of the design were its greatest weakness. If the machine had ever been finished, it would have comprised some two tons

far more extensive powers than the Difference Engine. He put the scheme enthusiastically to the Government, asking whether he should continue with the Difference Engine or work on the new idea. For eight years he pressed for an official decision; at last he was advised that the Government must regretfully abandon the project. The Government had already spent £17,000 on it; Babbage had also spent a comparable amount from his own pocket. Now the unfinished Difference Engine, in which he had lost interest, was deposited in the Museum of King's College, London; eventually the bones of his dream went to the South Kensington Museum, where they are now.

For several years Babbage worked on his analytical engine, using his own funds. Then he dropped it and decided to design a second difference engine, which would include all the improvements and simplifications suggested by

his work on the analytical engine. He again asked for Government support, but the Chancellor of the Exchequer declined. Babbage bitterly denounced him as "the Herostratus of Science, [who] if he escapes oblivion, will be linked with the destroyer of the Ephesian Temple."

IN THE END Babbage never completed a working engine. His vision was greater than the means then available for achieving it. Babbage aimed at something higher than a mere desk calculator; he planned to make a machine that could compute lengthy mathematical tables and set them up directly in type. He remarked: "Machinery which will perform . . . common arithmetic . . . will never be of that utility which must arise from an engine which calculates tables."

His Difference Engine was to be based on the principle of constant differences. To illustrate the principle let

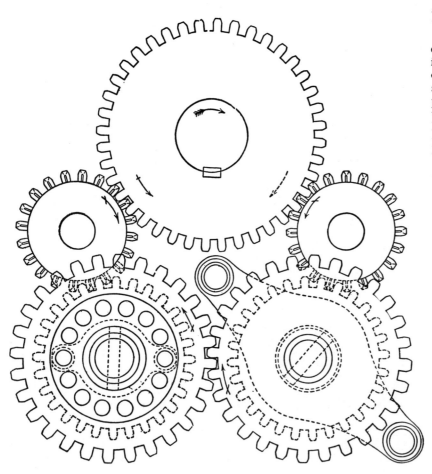

ANALYTICAL ENGINE was designed to carry out any mathematical operation. This part of it is described in Babbage book as a device which "performs the operation of multiplying or dividing a number by any power of ten."

adopted in today's big electronic computers.

Besides the concept itself, Babbage originated many mechanical devices of immediate practical use. Just as a team designing mathematical machines today soon becomes involved in a welter of problems about the properties of vacuum tubes and electronic circuits, so Babbage became deeply involved in the problems of the machine shop and the drafting room. He and his group invented a number of new tools to use with a lathe. Among the highly skilled workmen who worked in his shop was one J. Whitworth, later Sir Joseph Whitworth, Bart., who became the foremost manufacturer of precision tools in England. Babbage's drawings for his various machines, covering altogether more than 400 square feet of paper, were described by contemporary experts as perhaps the best specimens of mechanical drawing ever executed.

Babbage's operations-research book, *On the Economy of Manufactures and Machinery*, ran through several editions, was reprinted in the U. S. and was translated into German, French, Italian and Spanish. In it he took to pieces the manufacture of pins—the operations involved, the kinds of skill required, the expense of each process—and suggested improvements in the current practices. He proposed some general methods for analyzing factories and processes and finding the proper size and location of factories. Babbage treasured as one of the best compliments he ever received a remark by an English workman who told him: "That book made me think."

of novel brass, steel and pewter clockwork, made as nothing before it to gauged standards.

WHAT Babbage saw when he went on from the Difference to the Analytical Engine idea was a really grand vision. He had early conceived a notion which he picturesquely described as "the Engine eating its own tail." By this he meant that the results appearing in the answer column might be made to affect the earlier columns, and thus change the instructions set into the machine. The Analytical Engine was to be capable of carrying out *any* mathematical operation. The instructions set into it would tell it what operations to carry out, and in what order. It would be able to add, subtract, multiply and divide; it would have a memory with a capacity of 1,000 50-digit numbers; it would draw on auxiliary functions such as logarithm tables, of which it would possess its own library. It could compare numbers, and act upon its judgments, thus proceeding on lines not uniquely specified in advance by the machine's instructions.

All or much of this, of course, has come to pass in modern computers. But Babbage was limited to trying to carry it out mechanically; his design did not envision any help from electrical circuits, to say nothing of electronic tubes. He proposed to do it all with punched cards—not the fast-shuffled Hollerith cards moving over handy electrical-switch feelers that we have today, but cards modeled on those used in the Jacquard loom. The instructions and numerical constants would be punched in the cards as coded columns of holes. When the cards were fed into the machine, feeler wires would brush over them. Whenever the holes were in the appropriate pattern, the wires would pass through them and link together the motion of "chains" of columns and whole subassemblies. In this manner the machine would carry out all its operations. The great complexity of the system did not discourage Babbage, for he owned a colored portrait of Joseph Jacquard, woven in silk, in the weaving of which some 20,000 punched cards had been employed!

This is the barest sketch of the machine. Charles Babbage would be proud to see how completely the logical structure of his Analytical Engine has been

WHEN he was past 70, Babbage wrote an autobiography which he titled *Passages from the Life of a Philosopher*. A peevish but not humorless book, it bears on the title page a staggering list of learned societies (chiefly foreign) after his name. His autobiography is as much a record of his disappointments as of his achievements. He wrote it, he said, "to render . . . less unpalatable" the history of his calculating machines.

But there was no need for apology. The conception of the engines was genius. His whole story bears witness to the strong interaction between purely scientific innovation, on the one hand, and the social fabric of current technology, public understanding, and support on the other. His great engines never cranked out answers, for ingenuity can transcend but not ignore its context. His monument is not the dusty controversy of books, nor priority in a mushrooming branch of science, nor the few wheels in a museum. His monument, by no means wholly beautiful but very grand, is the kind of research that is epitomized today by the big digital computers.

9 WILLIAM KINGDON CLIFFORD

JAMES R. NEWMAN · February 1953

A FEW YEARS ago I was asked to prepare a new edition of a small 19th-century classic in mathematics: *The Common Sense of the Exact Sciences*. Seeking details about its author, William Kingdon Clifford, for the introduction to the volume, I discovered to my surprise that very few were available. The only published material on Clifford's life was a few scattered articles and obituaries and a brief biographical preface to his collected lectures and essays written by a contemporary, the barrister and legal historian Sir Frederick Pollock.

This neglect of Clifford is difficult to explain. He was not only one of the great mathematicians of his century but an original philosopher and a leader of British intellectual life in the Victorian age. Much of Clifford's thinking was ahead of his time. His mathematical work was prophetic, and its merit is still untouched after three quarters of a century of immense progress in mathematics; his philosophical ideas were rational and humane; he possessed an art of clarity, as Bertrand Russell has said, "that comes of profound and orderly understanding by virtue of which principles become luminous and deductions look easy." An inspiring faith in the power of reason and in human progress guided Clifford's remarkably productive but tragically short life of 35 years.

He was born in Exeter May 4, 1845. His father was a man of status in the town, serving as justice of the peace. His mother, a sensitive woman of intellectual tastes and delicate health, died when he was a boy—of the same disease to which Clifford was to fall victim. Clifford, a precocious youngster, produced at the age of 18 two original papers in geometry which led his tutor at Cambridge University to prophesy that he would gain a place among the leaders of science. As an undergraduate in Trinity College he read widely in philosophy, classical literature and modern history; he enjoyed companionship and participated in endless debates with his fellows and tutors on subjects ranging from Catholic doctrine to chemistry,

from Thomas Aquinas to Darwin and Spencer. It was Clifford's good fortune to be a student at a time when long-accepted beliefs in science and logic were beginning to crumble under the assaults of new theories and discoveries. Cambridge was a center of this revolution, and Clifford shared in its excitement and its "daring" talk. At first a High-churchman, "fond of supporting Catholic doctrines by ingenious scientific analogies," he turned gradually into a bitter enemy of organized religion, especially what he called "priestcraft." Clifford was a whirlwind in argument; when he let loose his tongue, "the pace was tremendous." His brilliance in conversation in the Grote Club at Cambridge was remembered half a century later by Alfred Marshall, a fellow member who became a famous economist. Marshall wrote of him with immense admiration, though he felt that Clifford was "too fond of astonishing people."

Clifford enthusiastically studied French, German and Spanish (to help him in his work); Arabic, Greek and Sanskrit (because they were difficult); hieroglyphics (because they were a riddle); shorthand and the Morse code (because he was interested "in all methods of conveying thought"). Every branch of mathematical and scientific literature appealed to his eclectic appetite. He won an assortment of literary, scientific and oratorical prizes. He was proudest, however, of his athletic achievements: the crown of his undergraduate career was hanging by his toes from the crossbar on the weathercock of a church steeple—a quaint Cambridge antic not usually fatal in its consequences. He also finished second in the arduous competitive examinations known as the tripos, thus matching the achievement, in their day, of Lord Kelvin and the incomparable James Clerk Maxwell.

H IS TRAINING had been good and his record outstanding, and in 1868 he was elected to a fellowship at Trinity. He was already turning out a steady output of three or four first-class mathematical papers a year. His first

important public lecture was called "Conditions of Mental Development." Like every other important scientist, philosopher and man of letters in the 19th century, he took to the lecture platform to help popularize learning. Clifford excelled in making hard concepts understandable, and he enjoyed the effort. His ability to turn the abstract into the concrete gave his lectures a lucidity and charm which even the lapse of time and transfer to print do not diminish.

Clifford spent two years as a fellow at Cambridge teaching, doing research, developing his ideas—alone and in commerce with other original and provocative minds. Then in 1870 he joined an English expedition to observe an eclipse. The ship carrying the party was wrecked off Sicily, but fortunately all hands and even the instruments were saved. Clifford took the mishap with his customary good humor. Shortly after the shipwreck he wrote from Florence to Lady Pollock, the wife of his friend Sir Frederick:

"At Catania, orange groves and telescopes; thence to camp at Augusta; Jonadab, son of Rechab, great fun, natives kept off camp by a white cord; 200 always to see us wash in the morning—a performance which never lost its charm—only five seconds totality free from cloud, found polarisation on moon's disc, agree with Pickering, other people successful. . . . At Rome 2½ days, pictures, statues, Coliseum by moonlight. Both of us sneezed awfully next morning. This morning arrived in Florence—Pitti Palace—spent all my money, and shall get stranded between Cologne and Ostend unless I can live on one egg every other day, and thereout suck no small advantage—be better off in Paris."

Clifford left Cambridge in 1871 to be professor of applied mathematics at University College, London. Clerk Maxwell was among those who strongly recommended him for the post, stressing the freshness and breadth of his research, as opposed to the "mere elaboration of abstruse theorems by ingenious calculation." In the next two years Clifford gave several of his best-known lectures and published a considerable number of mathematical articles, including a paper on biquaternions, dealing with the generalized conceptions of space, which stands high in the literature of mathematics. Two of these lectures, before the British Association for the Advancement of Science in 1872 and before the Royal Institution in 1873, afford admirable examples of Clifford's singular powers.

THE FIRST was "On the Aims and Instruments of Scientific Thought." It touched upon the profound re-evaluation of Euclidean geometry which had been forced by the researches of mathematicians who were taking a fresh look at the foundations of geometry. Up to that time the universality and the eternal verity of Euclid's theorems had never been doubted, just as they had never been tested. The non-Euclidean heresy put an end to this placid confidence.

Clifford illuminated the problem in masterly fashion. Advance in scientific thought, he said, depends on the hypothesis that the order we see in natural events holds good beyond our experience. Although human observation is limited, with the aid of the hypothesis of uniformity we can "infer things that we have not seen from things that we have seen." The hypothesis must be sharply defined, however; we must decide whether the uniformity on which inferences are based is mathematically exact. The mechanistic interpretation of the universe, magnificently elaborated in the 18th century, rested on the conviction that "if we knew all about it, Nature would be found universally subject to exact numerical laws." But the mathematicians themselves had shown that the issue as to whether nature obeyed such laws was far from settled.

"I shall be told, no doubt," said Clifford, "that we do possess a great deal of knowledge of this [exact] kind, in the form of geometry and mechanics; and that it is just the example of these sciences that has led men to look for exactness in other quarters. If this had been said to me in the last century, I should not have known what to reply. But it happens that at about the beginning of the present century the foundations of geometry were criticized independently by two mathematicians, Lobachevski and the immortal Gauss, whose results have been extended and generalized more recently by Riemann and Helmholtz. And the conclusion to which these investigations lead us is that, although the assumptions which were very properly made by the ancient geometers are practically exact—that is to say, more exact than experiment can be—for such finite things as we have to

Clifford among his students

BERNARDA
BRYSON

deal with, and such portions of space as we can reach; yet the truth of them for very much larger things, or very much smaller things, or parts of space which are at present beyond our reach, is a matter to be decided by experiment, when its powers are considerably increased. I want to make as clear as possible the real state of this question at present, because it is often supposed to be a question of words or metaphysics, whereas it is a very distinct and simple question of fact."

Clifford thus firmly allied himself with Georg Friedrich Riemann, one of the greatest mathematicians of the century, in the view that geometry as applied to the world of experience is an experimental science, a proper part of physics. Geometry according to this view remains an exact science but ceases to be a universal one. For a law is true universally only if it is true of all cases whatever, "and this is what we do not know of any law at all." Therefore geometry is an exact science only within a limited field.

Today this is a familiar idea—that geometry is a formal exercise in logic when considered as a pure science of ideal space, and that when it is considered as applied mathematics, purporting to describe actual space (within the atom or out towards Betelgeuse) it is an experimental discipline like cooking or entomology, subject to verification and change as we probe further. But in 1870 this idea was neither familiar nor generally acceptable; indeed, it flagrantly contradicted the main body of accredited mathematics and philosophy. Clifford's opinions were a challenge to the belief that Euclidean geometry was the perfect description, for all times, of all parts of actual space—and the challenge eventually led to the modern conceptions of space, time, energy and matter. From the standpoint of philosophy Clifford's view contested the doctrine, advanced in Kant's transcendental esthetic, that the long-accepted notions of space were immutable because they were determined by our mode of perception, or by the structure of the mind.

CLIFFORD'S second lecture, "The Philosophy of the Pure Sciences," offers a penetrating, at times almost lyrical, survey of the revolution in science, the "changes in the conception of the Cosmos" wrought by the inventors of non-Euclidean geometry.

"What Vesalius was to Galen, what Copernicus was to Ptolemy, that was Lobachevski to Euclid. . . . Before the time of Copernicus, men knew all about the Universe. They could tell you in the schools, pat off by heart, all that it was, and what it had been, and what it would be. There was the flat earth, with the blue vault of heaven resting on it like the dome of a cathedral, and the bright cold stars stuck into it; while the sun and planets moved between. Or, among the better informed, the earth was a globe in the center of the universe, heaven a sphere concentric with it; intermediate machinery as before. At any rate, if there was anything beyond heaven, it was a void space that needed no further description. The history of all this could be traced back to a certain definite time, when it began; behind that was a changeless eternity, which was fully accounted for and described. But in any case the Universe was a known thing. Now the enormous effect of the Copernican system, and of the astronomical discoveries that have followed it, is that, in place of this knowledge of a little, which was called knowledge of the Universe, of Eternity and Immensity, we have now got knowledge of a great deal more; but we only call it the knowledge of Here and Now. We can tell a great deal about the solar system; but, after all, it is our house, and not the city. We can tell something about the star system to which our sun belongs; but, after all, it is our star system, and not the Universe. We are talking about Here with the consciousness of a There beyond it, which we may know some time, but do not at all know now.

"This, then, was the change effected by Copernicus in the idea of the Universe. But there was left another to be made. For the laws of space and motion . . . implied an infinite space and infinite duration, about whose properties as space and time everything was accurately known. The very constitution of those parts of it which are at an infinite distance from us, 'geometry upon the plane at infinity,' is just as well known, if the Euclidean assumptions are true, as the geometry of any portion of this room. . . . So that here we have real knowledge of something at least that concerns the Cosmos; something that is true throughout the Immensities and Eternities. That something Lobachevski and his successors have taken away. The geometer of today knows nothing about the nature of actually existing space at an infinite distance; he knows nothing about the properties of this present space in a past or future eternity. He knows, indeed, that the laws assumed by Euclid are true with an accuracy that no direct experiment can approach . . . but he knows this as of Here and Now; beyond his range is a There and Then of which he knows nothing at present, but may ultimately come to know more. So, you see, there is a real parallel between the work of Copernicus and his successors on the one hand, and the work of Lobachevski and his successors on the other."

THE ORDINARY Euclidean conception of space rests on four fundamental postulates, and Clifford lucidly analyzes each in turn. The first states that space is continuous, without breaks or gaps of any kind. But continuity, Clifford points out, is an impression gathered from our senses, and they may deceive us. With the instruments of physics and chemistry we can see that objects which seem smooth and unbroken break down into atoms or other separate units. What proof have we that space is not of the same nature, smooth in appearance but actually crisscrossed, say, by a lacework of tiny fissures? The Euclidean postulate of continuous space therefore waits upon experience.

The second postulate assumes "the flatness of space in its smallest parts," which is to say that if we take three points in space very close to one another and join them by the shortest possible lines, the triangular figure so formed will lie very nearly in a plane. Clifford doubts the universality of this postulate also, following Riemann's opinion that the ordinary rules of geometry do not hold for "the metric relations of space in the infinitely small."

The third Euclidean postulate is that a body can be moved about in space without altering its size or shape; in other words, that "all parts of space are alike." The fourth postulate is that "any figure may be magnified or diminished in any degree without altering its shape" (which implies Euclid's rule that parallel lines never meet). The third and fourth postulates, taken together, are equivalent to the assumption that space is uniformly of zero curvature. Clifford finds these two postulates vulnerable on the side of the "very great," just as the first two could be attacked on the side of the "very small." That is to say, just as very small regions of space might turn out to be discontinuous, very large regions might turn out to be curved. Extraordinarily complicated *ad hoc* geometries may be required to describe any deviations of a given space from the standard of elementary flatness. These are closely tied to modern concepts of physics, suggesting that all phenomena, even matter itself, may consist of wrinkles or changes of curvature in space.

If the fourth postulate of "similarity," insofar as it relates to parallels, is abandoned, the way is open for a non-Euclidean geometry, such as the hyperbolic, which holds that the sum of the angles of every triangle is less than 180 degrees, or the elliptic, which makes the sum of the angles greater than 180 degrees. The space of elliptic, or Riemannian, geometry, proposing a large but curved and finite universe, appealed to Clifford: "I do not mind confessing that I personally have often found relief from the dreary infinities of homaloidal space in the consoling hope that, after all, this other may be the true state of things."

IN 1874 Clifford was elected a Fellow of the Royal Society, having declined to have his name put forward earlier on the ground that he "did not want to be respectable yet." He was in good health, energetically occupied with teaching and turning out papers on his latest researches, yet not too busy to continue his lectures on popular science as well as on social and ethical philosophy. He put forward some metaphysical theories of "mind-stuff" and the "tribal self" which are obscure and lifeless. But his ethical precepts embody all the warmth, the hatred of intolerance and the faith in reason that characterized his personality. The framework of his ethics was founded on the new doctrines of evolution. Freedom, independence, acting from "one's own inner conviction," he held, were the essential values of society: "There is one thing in the world more wicked than the desire to command, and that is the will to obey." He attempted to develop his ethical theories on the same objective basis as underlay his philosophy of science. It would not have entered his head that moral and religious values could be supported by any arguments other than reason and the teachings of experience. He was no more prepared to accept eternal values in ethics than in geometry.

In Clifford's personal life there was never a trace of cant, hypocrisy or self-righteousness. Writing to Lady Pollock on his "ideal theory" of behavior, he concluded: "All this, by the way, is only theory; my practice is just like other people's." Free from pretentiousness himself, Clifford was sharp in criticizing it in others. Of an acquaintance about to undertake a work in philosophy he remarked:

"He is writing a book on metaphysics, and is really cut out for it; the clearness with which he thinks he understands things and his total inability to express what little he knows will make his fortune as a philosopher."

But he was incapable of malice or personal enmity. Once he wrote:

"A great misfortune has fallen upon me; I shook hands with ————. I believe if all the murderers and all the priests and all the liars in the world were united into one man, and he came suddenly upon me round a corner and said, 'How do you do?' in a smiling way, I could not be rude to him upon the instant."

On April 7, 1875, Clifford married Lucy Lane. When he took leave from University College on this occasion, he informed his class that "he was obliged to be absent on important business which would probably not occur again." His wife became a well-known novelist and playwright, writing under the name Lucy Clifford, and she outlived him by half a century. Two daughters were born to them and brought Clifford great joy. He loved all children and delighted in making up games, fairy tales and poems. Some of his fables he contributed to a collection, *The Little People*. He had a

Clifford at the blackboard

scheme to issue a series of little school manuals whose lessons would be designed to help "kids find out things for themselves."

Clifford's happiness with children and his deep concern with their problem of learning and growing up stand in poignant contrast to the brief period he lived to spend with his own. In 1876 the first alarming signs of tuberculosis appeared. All his life he had taxed his physical powers; he was athletic but essentially frail in constitution. Despite the symptoms of his grave illness Clifford did not let up in his work. In 1876 he published no fewer than nine mathematical papers and various other writings. One of the papers was a remarkable contribution to the Cambridge Philosophical Society "On the Space Theory of Matter," in which he suggested that small portions of space are "analogous to little hills on a surface which is on the average flat . . . that this property of being curved or distorted is

continually being passed on from one portion of space to another after the manner of a wave; that this variation of the curvature of space is what really happens in the *motion of matter* . . . that in the physical world nothing else takes place but this variation, subject (possibly) to the law of continuity. . . ." These words were published 40 years before Einstein announced his theory of gravitation.

IN THE FALL of 1876 Clifford agreed reluctantly to take a six months' leave of absence for his health, and spent it traveling with his wife in Algeria and Spain. He returned to England somewhat improved and in the next year and a half accelerated his work, issuing two of his most celebrated papers, along with other mathematical memoirs, an excellent volume on dynamics, a number of essays, lectures and reviews. Again there came a collapse, and he passed the spring and summer of 1878 in Italy, then returned to England, still looking very ill and feeble. At the beginning of 1879 he sailed for Madeira and there had a few days of peace in the fine sunshine. On March 3, 1879, he died.

"And this," wrote Sir Frederick Pollock, "is the witness of his ending, that as never man loved life more, so never man feared death less. He fulfilled well and truly that great saying of Spinoza, often in his mind and on his lips: *Homo* *liber de nulla re minus quam de morte cogitat* [There is nothing over which a free man ponders less than death]."

Clifford was not only a great professional mathematician, a distinguished philosopher and a brilliant writer, but a citizen of science. He ceaselessly strove to strengthen its foundations and organic unity and, by preaching the widest applicability of its methods, to promote the rational and confound the irrational. His was the spacious outlook of an elevated man: "Remember then that [scientific thought] is the guide of action; that the truth which it arrives at is not that which we can ideally contemplate without error, but that which we may act upon without fear; and you cannot fail to see that scientific thought is not an accompaniment or condition of human progress, but human progress itself." It is a maxim which our age, often mistaking valves and levers for science, would do well to recall.

10 JAMES CLERK MAXWELL

JAMES R. NEWMAN · June 1955

James Clerk Maxwell, the greatest theoretical physicist of the 19th century, opened a new epoch of science, and much of what distinguishes our world from his is due to his work. Because his most spectacular discoveries were the fruits of theoretical rather than experimental researches, he is often cited as an outstanding example of a scientist who built his systems entirely with pencil and paper. This notion is false. Maxwell combined a profound physical intuition with a formidable mathematical capacity to gain insights into physical phenomena, never losing sight of the observations to be explained. This blending of the concrete and the abstract was the chief characteristic of almost all his researches.

Maxwell was born in Edinburgh on November 13 in 1831, the same year Michael Faraday announced his famous discovery of electromagnetic induction. Descended of an old Scots family whose members were distinguished no less for their individuality, "verging on eccentricity," than for their talents (they included eminent judges, politicians, mining speculators, merchants, poets, musicians), he was the only son of a member of the Scottish bar who took little interest in the grubby pursuits of an advocate but instead managed his small estates, took part in county affairs and gave loving attention to the education of his son. Maxwell's father was a warm and rather simple man with a nice sense of humor and a practical interest in mechanical contrivances. His mother is described as having a "sanguine, active temperament."

Jamesie, as the boy was called, passed his early childhood on the family estate at Glenlair, two days' carriage ride from Edinburgh. He was a nearsighted, lively, affectionate little boy, as persistently inquisitive as his father and as fascinated by machines. To discover of anything "how it doos" was his constant aim. "What's the go of that?" he would ask, and if the answer did not satisfy him, he would add, "But what's the *particular* go of that?" His own first creation was a set of figures for a "wheel of life," a scientific toy which produced the illusion of continuous movement; he was fond of making things with his hands, and in later life knew how to design models embodying the most complex motions and other physical processes.

When Maxwell was nine, his mother died of cancer, the disease that was to

ENGRAVING OF MAXWELL appears in *The Collected Papers of James Clerk Maxwell.* This illustration and those appearing on the next three pages are from the Burndy Library.

kill him 40 years later. Her death brought the father and son even more closely together. The boy began his schooling a year later as a day student at the Edinburgh Academy. His early school experiences were painful. The master, a dryish Scotsman whose reputation as a pedagogue derived from a book he had written on the irregular Greek verbs, expected his students to be orderly, well-grounded in the usual subjects and unoriginal. Maxwell was deficient in all these departments. He created something of a sensation because of his clothes, which had been designed by his strong-minded father and included such items as "hygienic" square-toed shoes and a lace-frilled tunic. The boys nicknamed him "Dafty" and mussed him up, but he was a stubborn child and in time won the respect of his classmates even if he continued to puzzle them.

Mathematical Years

At school Maxwell experienced a gradual awakening of mathematical interests. He wrote his father that he had made a "tetra hedron, a dodeca hedron, and two more hedrons that I don't know the wright names for." In his 14th year he won the Academy's mathematical medal and wrote a paper on a method for constructing perfect oval curves with pins and thread. Another prodigious little boy, René Descartes, had anticipated him in this field, but Maxwell's contributions were original. It was a wonderful day for father and son when they heard the boy's paper on ovals read before the Royal Society of Edinburgh by Professor James Forbes. "Met," the father wrote of the event in his diary, "with very great attention and approbation generally."

After six years at the Academy Maxwell entered the University of Edinburgh. He was 16, a restless, enigmatic, brilliantly talented adolescent who wrote not very good but strangely prophetic verse about the destiny of matter and energy:

When earth and sun are frozen clods,
When all its energy degraded
Matter to aether shall have faded

His friend and biographer Lewis Campbell records that he was completely neat in his person, "though with a rooted objection to the vanities of starch and gloves," and that he had a "pious horror of destroying anything—even a scrap of writing paper." He read voraciously and passed much time in mathematical speculations and in chemical,

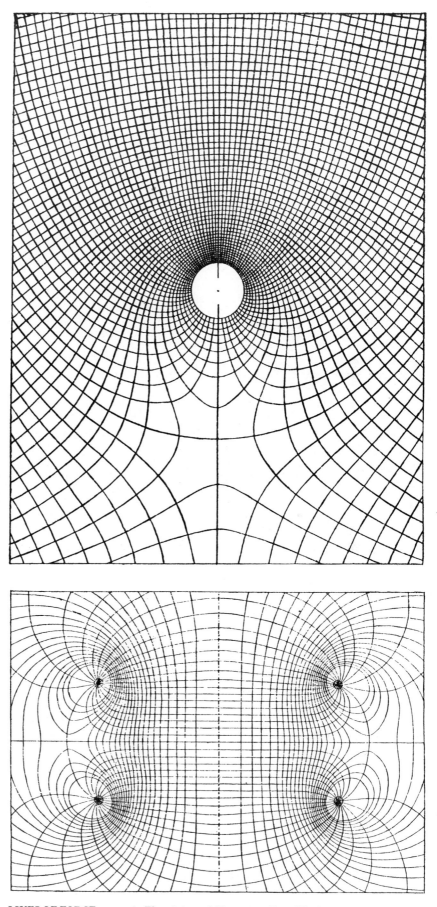

LINES OF FORCE appear in *Electricity and Magnetism.* **Top:** "Uniform magnetic field disturbed by an electric current in a straight conductor." **Bottom:** "Two circular currents."

magnetic and optical experiments. "When at table he often seemed abstracted from what was going on, being absorbed in observing the effects of refracted light in the finger glasses, or in trying some experiment with his eyes—seeing around a corner, making invisible stereoscopes, and the like. Miss Cay [his aunt] used to call his attention by crying, 'Jamesie, you're in a prop [an abbreviation for mathematical proposition].'"

While at Edinburgh, Maxwell regularly attended meetings of the Royal Society, and two of his papers, "On the Theory of Rolling Curves" and "On the Equilibrium of Elastic Solids," were published in the *Transactions*. The papers were read before the Society by others, "for it was not thought proper for a boy in a round jacket to mount the rostrum there." During vacations at Glenlair he wrote long letters reporting his multifarious doings to friends. Many of his letters exhibit an intense interest

in moral philosophy, reflecting his social sympathy, his Christian earnestness, the not uncommon 19th-century mixture of rationalism and simple faith. It was a period when men still believed that questions of wisdom, happiness and virtue could be studied as one studies optics and mechanics.

In 1850 Maxwell went on to the University of Cambridge. There he became a private pupil of William Hopkins, considered the ablest mathematics coach of his time, who prepared him for the mathematical tripos, the stiff competitive examinations in which the brightest students competed. Hopkins at once recognized the talents of the black-haired young Scotsman, describing him as "the most extraordinary man I have ever met," and adding that "it appears impossible for [him] to think incorrectly on physical subjects." Besides working hard on his studies, Maxwell joined fully in social and intellectual activities at the University. He was elected to the Apostles, a club of 12 members which for many years included the outstanding young men at Cambridge. A contemporary described Maxwell as "the most genial and amusing of companions, the propounder of many a strange theory, the composer of many a poetic *jeu d'esprit*." Not the least strange of his theories related to economy of sleep. He would sleep from 5 in the afternoon to 9:30, read very hard from 10 to 2, exercise by running along the corridors and up and down stairs from 2 to 2:30 a.m. and sleep again from 2:30 to 7. The dormitory inhabitants were not pleased, but Maxwell persisted in his bizarre experiments. Another of his investigations was a study of the process by which a cat always lands on her feet. He demonstrated that a cat could right herself even when dropped upside down on a table or bed from a height of about two inches.

In the summer of 1853 a "sort of brain fever" seized Maxwell. For weeks he was totally disabled, and he felt the effects of his illness long afterward. This episode was undoubtedly an emotional crisis, but its causes remain obscure. All that is known is that his illness strengthened Maxwell's religious conviction—a deep, earnest piety, leaning to Scottish Calvinism yet never completely identified with any particular system or sect. "I have no nose for heresy," he used to say.

In January, 1854, Maxwell took the tripos in the Cambridge Senate House, with a rug wrapped around his feet and legs (as his father had advised) to mitigate the perishing cold. His head was

ILLUMINATED LETTER was written by Maxwell to his father in 1843, when the younger Maxwell was 11. The letter refers to a lecture by the American frontier artist George Catlin.

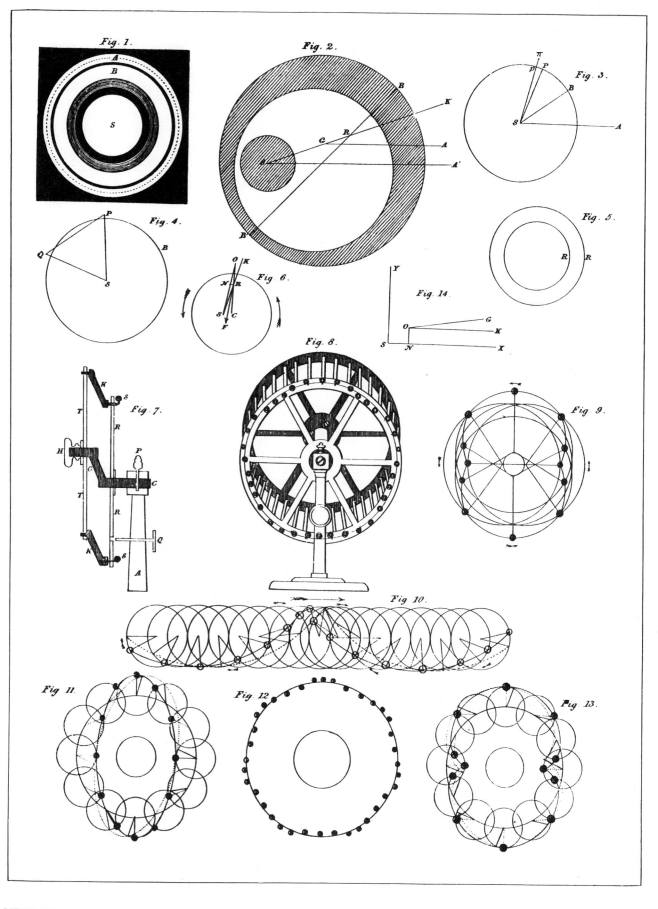

MECHANICAL MODEL is depicted in Figure 7 and Figure 8 of this page from Maxwell's essay "On the Stability of the motion of Saturn's Rings." In this essay Maxwell demonstrated that the rings were neither liquid nor solid but were composed of particles.

warm enough. He finished second wrangler behind the noted mathematician Edward Routh. (In another competition, at Cambridge, for "Smith's prize," where the subjects were more advanced, Maxwell and Routh tied for first.)

Questions and Answers

After getting his degree Maxwell stayed on for two years at Trinity, studying, lecturing, taking private pupils and doing some experiments in optics. He designed a top with colored paper disks to study the mixing of colors, and he was able to show that suitable combinations of three primary colors—red, green and blue—produced "to a very near degree of approximation" almost every color of the spectrum. For this work in color sensation he later won the Rumford medal of the Royal Society.

Maxwell's most significant activity during the two postgraduate years at Trinity, however, was his reading of Faraday's *Experimental Researches* and entrance upon the studies of electricity which were to lead to his greatest discoveries. Before he left Trinity, he published his first major contribution, the beautiful paper "On Faraday's Lines of Force." In 1856 Maxwell was appointed to the chair of natural philosophy at

Marischal College in Aberdeen; he had applied for the post partly to be near his father, whose health had been failing, but his father died a few days before he obtained the appointment. It was an irreparable personal loss to Maxwell; they had been as close as father and son could be. At Aberdeen Maxwell continued his work on electricity. His teaching load was rather light. Although he took teaching seriously, it cannot be said that Maxwell was a great teacher. With classes that were "not bright" he found it difficult to hit a suitable pace. He was unable to heed himself the advice he once gave a friend whose duty it was to preach to a country congregation: "Why don't you give it them thinner?"

Maxwell's electrical studies at Aberdeen were interrupted by a task which engrossed him for almost two years. He entered a competition for a University of Cambridge prize on the subject of Saturn's rings. Were the rings solid? Were they fluid? Did they consist of masses of matter "not mutually coherent?" The problem was to demonstrate which type of structure adequately explained the motion and permanence of the rings. In a brilliant 68-page essay which Sir George Airy, the Astronomer Royal, described as one of the most remarkable applications of mathematics he had ever seen, Maxwell demonstrated

that the only stable structure would be one composed of disconnected particles. His essay won the prize and established him as a leader among mathematical physicists.

His research on Saturn excited his interest in the kinetic theory of gases. Maxwell's predecessors in this field—Rudolf Clausius, Daniel Bernoulli, James Joule and others—had been successful in explaining many of the properties of gases, such as pressure, temperature and density, on the hypothesis that a gas is composed of swiftly moving particles. However, in order to simplify the mathematical analysis they had assumed that all the particles of a gas move at the same speed. Maxwell realized that this was an altogether implausible assumption, for collisions among the molecules must give them various velocities. If the science of gases was to be developed on "strict mechanical principles," it was necessary, he said, to incorporate this fact into the mathematical formulation of the laws of motion of the particles.

Maxwell's Law of Gases

Maxwell proceeded to examine mathematically the behavior of an assemblage of colliding particles as if they were "small, hard and perfectly elastic spheres acting on one another only during impact." Since the many molecules could not be treated individually, he introduced the statistical method for dealing with them. He supposed that the distribution of velocities among the molecules in a gas would follow the famous bell-shaped frequency curve, which applies to so many phenomena, from the pattern of shots on a target to groupings of men according to height. Thus while the velocity of an individual molecule might elude description, the velocity of a crowd of molecules would not. Having arrived at a quantitative description of the speeds of molecules composing a gas, Maxwell was able to write a precise formula for gas pressure. Curiously enough this expression did not differ from that based on the assumption that the velocity of all the molecules was the same, but at last the right conclusion had been won by correct reasoning. Moreover the generality and elegance of Maxwell's mathematical methods led to the extension of their use into almost every branch of physics.

Maxwell went on to consider another factor which needed to be determined for precise formulation of the laws of gases: namely, the distance a molecule travels, on the average, between colli-

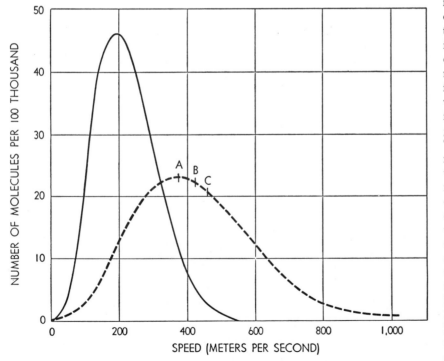

MAXWELL DISTRIBUTION is plotted for the molecules in a gas at 200 degrees centigrade (*solid curve*) and at 0 degrees centigrade (*broken curve*). Each point on the curves indicates the number of molecules in the gas moving at that speed. The speed corresponding to Point A is the most probable velocity of the molecules. The speed corresponding to Point B is the average velocity. The speed corresponding to Point C is the root mean square velocity

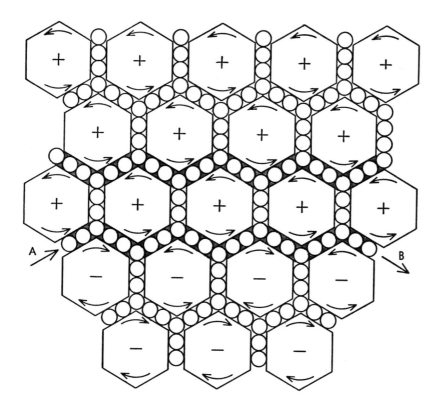

MODEL OF AN ELECTROMAGNETIC FIELD used by Maxwell visualized "molecular vortices" rotating in space. In this illustration the vortices are slender cylinders seen from the end. (Maxwell gave the cylinders a hexagonal cross section to simplify the geometry of the model.) Between the vortices are small "idle wheels." If a row of the idle wheels is moved from A toward B, they cause the adjacent vortices to rotate in opposite directions.

proof. He showed that the Maxwell distribution of velocities was the only possible equilibrium state of a gas. This equilibrium state, as both men realized, is the thermodynamic condition of maximum entropy—the most disordered state, in which the least amount of energy is available for useful work.

The concept of entropy led Maxwell to one of the celebrated images of modern science, namely that of the sorting demon. Increasing entropy is man's fate because we are not very bright. But a demon more favorably endowed could sort out the slow- and fast-moving particles of a gas, thereby changing disorder into order and converting unavailable into available energy. Maxwell imagined one of these small, sharp fellows "in charge of a frictionless, sliding door in a wall separating two compartments of a vessel filled with gas. When a fast-moving molecule moves from left to right, the demon opens the door; when a slow-moving molecule approaches, he (or she) closes the door. The fast-moving molecules accumulate in the right-hand compartment, and slow ones in the left. The gas in the first compartment grows hot and that in the second cold." Thus the demon would thwart the second law of thermodynamics. Living organisms, it has been suggested, achieve an analogous process; as Erwin Schrödinger has phrased it, they suck negative entropy from the environment in the food they eat and the air they breathe.

Maxwell and Boltzmann, working independently and in a friendly rivalry, at first made notable progress in explaining the behavior of gases by statistical mechanics. After a time, however, formidable difficulties arose. For example, they were unable to write accurate theoretical formulas for the specific heats of certain gases (the quantity of heat required to raise the temperature of a body of the gas by a given amount). Explanation of the discrepancies they found had to await the development of quantum theory, which showed that the spin and vibration of molecules were restricted to certain values. But neither quantum theory nor relativity, nor the other modes of thought constituting the 20th-century revolution in physics, would have been possible had it not been for the brilliant labors of these natural philosophers in applying statistical methods to the study of gases.

Marriage

In February, 1858, Maxwell wrote his aunt, Miss Cay: "This comes to tell you that I am going to have a wife." "Don't

sions—*i.e.*, its mean free path. He reasoned that the mean free path of molecules in a given gas could be measured by the viscosity of that gas. Assume that a gas is composed of groups of molecules with different velocities which slide over one another, thus creating friction. This would account for the viscosity of gases. Now the mean free path of molecules would be related to viscosity in the following way. Imagine two layers of molecules sliding past each other. If a molecule passing from one layer to the other travels only a short distance before colliding with another molecule, the two particles do not exchange much momentum, because near the boundary the difference of velocity between the two layers is small. But if the molecule penetrates deep into the other layer before a collision, the velocity differential will be greater; hence the exchange of momentum between the colliding particles is greater. This amounts to saying that in any gas with high viscosity the molecules must have a long mean free path. Maxwell deduced further the paradoxical fact that the viscosity of a gas is independent of its density, for the increased probability of collisions in a dense gas is offset by the fact that in such a gas a molecule will not

travel far into a different layer before colliding. On balance, then, the momentum conveyed across each unit area per second remains the same regardless of density.

Thus Maxwell constructed a mechanical model of a gas as an assemblage of crowds of particles "carrying with them their momenta and their energy," traveling certain distances, colliding, changing their motion, resuming their travels, and so on. His picture made it possible to account in precise quantitative terms for a gas's various properties—viscosity, diffusion, heat conduction. Altogether it was a scientific achievement of the first rank. The model has since been criticized, on the grounds, for example, that molecules are not hard nor perfectly elastic, like billiard balls, nor is their interaction confined to the actual moment of impact. Yet despite the inadequacies of the model and errors of reasoning, the results, which, as Sir James Jeans said, "ought to have been hopelessly wrong," turned out to be exactly right, and Maxwell's law for the behavior of gases is in use to this day.

The German physicist Ludwig Boltzmann, who recognized at once the significance of these discoveries, set to work refining and generalizing Maxwell's

be afraid," he added, "she is not mathematical, but there are other things besides that, and she certainly won't stop mathematics." His bride was Katherine Mary Dewar, daughter of the Principal of Marischal College. Their union became very close: they enjoyed doing things together—horseback riding, reading aloud to each other, traveling—and he even found useful tasks for her in his experimental work. The marriage was childless, but this very fact increased the couple's dependency and devotion.

In the summer of 1860 Maxwell moved to London as professor of natural philosophy at King's College. He remained there for five years. Living in London offered him the opportunity to see something of Faraday, with whom, up to this time, Maxwell had had only correspondence, and to make the acquaintance of other scientists. He was no solitary. "Work is good, and reading is good, but friends are better," he wrote to his friend Litchfield. Despite social distractions and arduous teaching duties at King's, the five years in London were the most productive of Maxwell's life. He continued his work on gases. In the large garret of his house in Kensington he measured the viscosity of gases and obtained practical confirmation of his theoretical work. (To maintain the necessary temperature a fire had to be kept up in the midst of very hot weather and kettles kept boiling to produce steam which would be allowed to flow into the room. Mrs. Maxwell acted as stoker.) But his major work was in the theory of electricity, from which he had been diverted and to which he now returned.

A Model for Electricity

Faraday's experiments had crowned a century of researches (by Coulomb, Oersted, Ampère and others) which had established many facts about the behavior of electricity and its link with magnetism. They had shown that electric charges attracted and repelled each other according to a law like that of gravitation (in proportion to the product of the charges and in inverse proportion to the square of the distance between the charges); that a current produces a magnetic field, and a moving magnet produces a current; that an electric current in one circuit can induce a current in another.

What absorbed Maxwell was the attempt to explain these phenomena. What was a field? How did electricity and magnetism exert their influence through space? Faraday had suggested a new concept to answer these questions, and it was his idea that excited Maxwell's interest.

Most theorists had pursued the analogy of electricity to gravitation and had sought to explain the phenomena in terms of "action at a distance." They imagined a charge (or mass) situated at one point in space mysteriously influencing a charge (or mass) at another point, with no linkage or connection of any kind between the charges (or masses). Faraday proposed to explain electricity as a mechanical system. He asserted that the instrumentality of electric and magnetic action was lines of force running through space—not merely imaginary lines but actual, physical entities, with properties of tension, attraction, repulsion, motion and so on.

Maxwell admirably summarized the cleavage between the two views: "Faraday, in his mind's eye, saw lines of force traversing all space, where the mathematicians saw centres of force attracting at a distance; Faraday saw a medium where they saw nothing but distance; Faraday sought the seat of the phenomena in real actions going on in the medium, they were satisfied that they had found it in a power of action at a distance impressed on the electric fluids."

Maxwell believed in Faraday's concept, and he set out to develop it. In his first paper, "On Faraday's Lines of Force," he tried to imagine a physical model, embodying Faraday's lines, whose behavior could be reduced to formulas and numbers. He did not suggest that the model represented the actual state of things, but he felt that it was important "to lay hold of a clear physical conception, without being committed to any theory founded on the physical science from which that conception is borrowed." Such a method would protect the investigator against being led into a blind alley of abstractions or being "carried beyond the truth by a favorite hypothesis."

Maxwell proposed a hydrodynamic model, in which he incorporated Faraday's lines of force in the form of "tubes of flow" carrying an incompressible fluid such as water. The fluid moving through the tubes represented electricity in motion; the form and diameter of the tubes gave information as to the strength and direction of the flow. The velocity of the fluid was the equivalent of electrical force; differences of fluid pressure were analogous to differences of electrical pressure or potential; pressure transmitted from tube to tube by way of the elastic tube surfaces furnished an analogue to electric induction. By applying the established equations of hydrodynamics to such a system, Maxwell was able to account for many of the observed facts concerning electricity.

It was a wonderful paper, and Faraday expressed his appreciation. "I was at first almost frightened," he wrote Maxwell, "when I saw such mathematical force made to bear upon the subject, and then wondered to see that the subject stood it so well." Other students, however, thought the subject stood it not at all well. Electricity was mysterious enough without adding tubes and incompressible fluids. But Maxwell, who had had good training in being considered queer, went on with the task of extending Faraday's ideas.

Cylinders and Balls

Maxwell's second great memoir, "On Physical Lines of Force," was published after he returned to the subject of elec-

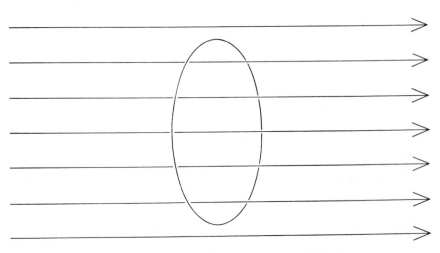

CURL of Maxwell's equations is suggested by this diagram. The arrows are a moving magnetic field. The circle is the electric field which "curls" around the magnetic lines of force.

tricity in London. He now constructed a more elaborate model to account not only for electrostatic effects but also for magnetic attraction and electromagnetic induction. In the new model "molecular vortices" rotating in space were the agents that produced magnetic fields. A molecular vortex may be thought of as a slender cylinder which rotates around the lines of magnetic force. The velocity of rotation depends on the intensity of the magnetic force. Two mechanical effects are associated with the cylinders: tension in the direction of the lines of force, and lateral pressure arising from the centrifugal force produced by the rotating cylinders. Combined, these effects mechanically reproduce magnetic phenomena: magnetism is a force exerted both along the axis and outward from the axis.

Maxwell proceeded to show how this curious arrangement might explain the production of a magnetic field by an electric current and of a current by a changing field. He supposed first that a uniform magnetic field consists of a portion of space filled with cylinders rotating at the same velocity and in the same direction "about axes nearly parallel." But immediately a puzzle confronted him. Since the cylinders are in contact, how can they possibly rotate in the same direction? As everyone knows, a rotating wheel or cylinder causes its neighbor to rotate in the opposite direction. Maxwell hit upon a pretty idea. He supposed that rows of small spheres, like layers of ball bearings, lay between the cylinders and acted as gears (in Maxwell's words, "idle wheels"). Thus the cylinders all rotated in the same direction.

And now, as just reward for his ingenuity, Maxwell found that the spheres could be made to serve another even more valuable purpose. Think of them as particles of electricity. Then by purely mechanical reasoning it can be shown that their motions in the machine of which they are a part serve to explain many electrical phenomena.

Consider these examples. In an unchanging magnetic field the cylinders all rotate at the same constant rate. The little rotating spheres keep their position; there is no flow of particles, hence no electric current. Now suppose a change in the magnetic force. This means a change in the velocity of rotation of the cylinders. As each cylinder is speeded up, it transmits the change in velocity to its neighbors. But since a cylinder now rotates at a slightly different speed from its neighbor, the spheres between them are torn from their positions by a kind of shearing action. This

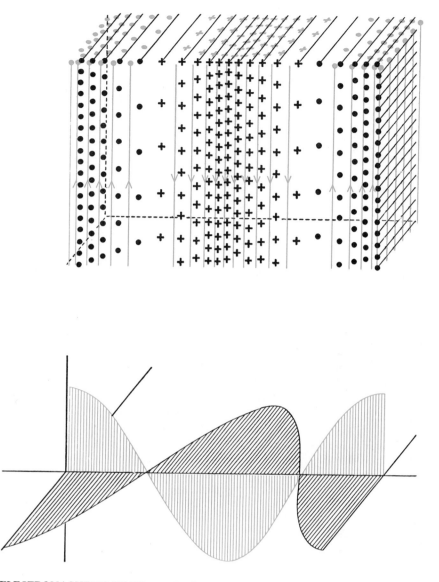

ELECTROMAGNETIC WAVE was visualized by Maxwell as a moving disturbance which tended to separate positive (*plus sign*) and negative (*dot*) charges. In the drawing at the top magnetic lines of force (*arrows*) lie at right angles to the direction in which the disturbance is moving. The drawing at the bottom depicts the two components of the electromagnetic wave. The electrical component is shown in black; the magnetic component, in color.

motion of translation of the particles is an electric current.

Observe now how the model begins to live a life of its own. Though designed primarily to demonstrate how magnetic changes produce electric currents, it also suggested to Maxwell a mechanism whereby a change in electric force might produce magnetism. Assume the spheres and cylinders are at rest. If a force is applied to the spheres of electricity, causing them to move, the cylinders of magnetism with which they are in contact will begin to rotate, thereby producing a magnetic force. Moreover, the model holds up even as to details. Take a single illustration. An examination of Maxwell's model shows that the cylinders will rotate in the direction perpendicular to the motion of the spheres, thus bearing out

the observation that a magnetic field acts at right angles to the flow of a current!

"I do not bring it forward," Maxwell wrote of his system, "as a mode of connection existing in Nature. . . . It is, however, a mode of connection which is mechanically conceivable and easily investigated, and it serves to bring out the actual mechanical connections between the known electromagnetic phenomena." Among the other "mechanical connections" Maxwell was able to demonstrate were electrical repulsion between two parallel wires carrying currents in opposite directions (ascribed to the centrifugal pressures of the revolving cylinders on the electrical particles in the model) and the induction of currents (the result of communication of rotary velocity from one cylinder to another).

Maxwell was not done with the model. It had yet to pass the supreme test: that is, to supply a mechanical explanation of the origin of electromagnetic waves. To orient ourselves in this matter we must examine briefly the question of condensers and insulators.

Faraday in his experiments had come upon a curious fact. The type of insulating material used in a condenser made a considerable difference in the condenser's capacity to take or to hold a charge. This was difficult to understand if all insulators were equally impermeable to an electric current. With the help of his model, Maxwell advanced a bold hypothesis. In an insulating material the little electrical particles somehow are unable to move freely from cylinder to cylinder; hence no current can flow. However, it was known that "localized electric phenomena" did occur in insulators. Maxwell suggested that these phenomena were currents of a special kind. When an electric force acts on an insulator, the particles of electricity are "displaced" but not torn loose; that is, they behave like a ship riding at anchor in a storm. They move only a limited distance, to the point where the force pushing them is balanced by the resistance of the elastic cylinders. As soon as the impelling force ceases to act, the particles snap back to their original positions. When a particle snaps back, it overshoots and oscillates about its fixed position. The oscillation is transmitted through the insulator as a wave. Thus for a brief instant a displacement current flows, for the wave is the current. If the electric force applied to the insulator is varied continually, it will produce a continually varying displacement wave: in other words, a continuing current.

Maxwell next arrived at an epoch-making conclusion. It had to do with the relation of the velocity of the displacement wave, or current, to that of light. For the point of departure we must go back to earlier work by the German physicists Wilhelm Weber and Friedrich Kohlrausch on the relationship between electrostatic and electrodynamic forces. The electrostatic unit of charge was defined as the repulsion between two like unit charges at unit distance apart. The electrodynamic unit was defined as the repulsion between two measured lengths of wire carrying currents "which may be specified by the amount of charge which travels past any point in unit time." In order to compare the repulsion between static charges with that between moving charges, a factor of proportionality must be introduced, since the units are different. This factor turns out to be a

velocity, for since the length of the wires is fixed, and the number of units of electricity passing a given point in a given time can be measured, what the investigator must consider is length divided by time, or velocity. Weber and Kohlrausch had found that the velocity of propagation of an electric disturbance along a perfectly conducting wire was close to 3×10^{10} centimeters per second. This was an astonishing coincidence, for the figure was about the same as the velocity of light, determined a few years earlier.

Maxwell pursued the coincidence. He himself confirmed the Weber-Kohlrausch results, using an ingenious torsion balance to compare the repulsion between two static charges and two wires carrying currents, and at about the same time he calculated the velocity of displacement currents in a dielectric (nonconductor). The resulting values tallied closely. In other words, currents in a wire, displacement currents in a dielectric, and light in empty space (which of course is a dielectric) all traveled with the same velocity. With this evidence at hand Maxwell did not hesitate to assert the identity of the two phenomena—electrical disturbances and light. "We can scarcely avoid the inference," he said, "that light consists in the transverse undulations of the same medium which is the cause of electric and magnetic phenomena."

Maxwell's Equations

Maxwell now had to outgrow his model. In "A Dynamical Theory of the Electromagnetic Field," published in 1864, he displayed the architecture of his system, as Sir Edmund Whittaker has said, "stripped of the scaffolding by aid of which it had first been erected." The particles and cylinders were gone; in their place were the field and the aether, a special kind of "matter in motion by which the observed electromagnetic phenomena are produced." The matter composing the aether had marvelous properties. It was very fine and capable of permeating bodies; it filled space with an elastic medium. It was the vehicle of "the undulations of light and heat."

For all its refinements and subtleties the aether was no less a mechanical rig than the cylinders and balls. It could move, transmit motions, undergo elastic deformations, store potential (mechanical) energy and release it when the deforming pressures were removed. As a mechanism, Maxwell said, it "must be subject to the general laws of dynamics, and we ought to be able to work out all

the consequences of its motion, provided we know the form of the relation between the motions of the parts." Applying himself to this task, he devised the famous Maxwellian equations of the electromagnetic field. In their most finished form they appear in his *Treatise on Electricity and Magnetism*, which presents the results of 20 years of thought and experiment.

Maxwell based the equations on four principles: (1) that an electric force acting on a conductor produces a current proportional to the force; (2) that an electric force acting on a dielectric produces displacement proportional to the force; (3) that a current produces a magnetic field at right angles to the current's lines of flow and proportional to its intensity; (4) that a changing magnetic field produces an electric force proportional to the intensity of the field. The third and fourth principles exhibit a striking symmetry. The third is Faraday's law of electromagnetic induction, according to which "the rate of alteration in the number of lines of magnetic induction passing through a circuit is equal to the work done in taking unit electric charge round the circuit." Maxwell's complementary law, the fourth principle, is that "the rate of alteration in the number of lines of electric force passing through a circuit is equal to the work done in taking a unit magnetic pole round it."

On this foundation two sets of symmetrical equations can be erected. One set expresses the continuous nature of electric and magnetic fields; the second set tells how changes in one field produce changes in the other.

How does the concept of the field enter the theory? We have followed Maxwell as he stripped his model of its particles and cylinders and reduced it to an aethereal medium. Now he robs the medium of almost all its attributes other than form. Its properties are all purely geometric. The grin is left but the cat is gone. It is a perfect example of mathematical abstraction.

The aether is a thing that quivers when it is prodded, but does nothing on its own. An electromagnetic field consists of two kinds of energy: electrostatic, or potential, energy, and electrodynamic, or kinetic, energy. The aether, like a universal condenser, may be conceived as storing energy—in which case, being elastic, it is deformed. Since the aether fills all space and therefore penetrates conductors as well as dielectrics, it no longer makes any difference whether we deal with a conduction current or a displacement current; in either case the aether is set in motion. This motion is communicated mechanically from one part of the medium to the next and is apprehended by us as heat, light, mechanical force (as in the repulsion between wires) or other phenomena of magnetism and electricity. The ruling principle of all such phenomena, it should be observed, is that of least action. This is the grand overriding law of the parsimony of nature: every action within a system is executed with the least possible expenditure of energy. It was of the first importance to Maxwell that electrical phenomena should satisfy the principle, for otherwise his mechanical explanation of the phenomena would not have been possible.

Div and Curl

With these points in mind, we may examine a set of Maxwell's equations in a form which describes the behavior of an electromagnetic field in empty space. No conductors or free charges are present; the source of the field is some other region of space.

The first equation then reads:

$$\text{div } E = 0$$

E represents the electric field strength, which varies in time and from place to place. Div is an abbreviation for divergence. It signifies a mathematical operation which gives a rate of change. The equation says that the number of electric lines of force (representing the field strength) which enter any tiny volume of space must equal the number leaving it. That is, the rate of change in the number of lines is zero, and they can neither be created nor destroyed.

The second equation reads:

$$\text{div } H = 0$$

It makes the same assertion for the magnetic field H as the first equation makes for the electric field.

The third equation is:

$$\text{curl } E = -\frac{1}{c}\frac{\partial H}{\partial t}$$

This is Maxwell's statement of Faraday's law of induction: it describes what happens in a changing magnetic field. The expression $\partial H/\partial t$ simply states the rate of change of the magnetic field. The changing magnetic field creates an electric field, and this fact is expressed on the left side of the equation, where the term "curl" signifies a mathematical operation dealing with rotation. The equation is more than analytic; it actually gives a

picture of the event. A simple diagram may help make it clear [see illustration on page 68]. Suppose the existence of a magnetic field uniform over a region of space. A bundle of parallel lines represents the intensity and direction of this field. If the field is changed (by motion or by increase or reduction of strength), it produces an electric field which acts in a circle around the lines of magnetic force. By summing the work done in moving unit electric charge around the circle we obtain what is called the net electromotive force around the circle. If the circle were made of wire, the changing magnetic lines would of course induce the flow of a current; but even without a wire a force would be induced. Dividing this force by the area enclosed by the circle gives the net electromotive force (per unit area) which "curls" around the circle. Now imagine the circle growing smaller and smaller and shrinking finally to the point P. By this limiting process we obtain a limiting value of the net electromotive force per unit area: this is curl E at P. Thus the equation says that the limiting value of electromotive force per unit area equals the rate of change of H at the point P, multiplied by the tiny negative fraction, -1/c. The symbol c here stands for the ratio of the electrostatic to the electromagnetic units of electricity. It is required to translate E (an electrostatic phenomenon) and H (an electrodynamic phenomenon) into the same system of units. The equation explains how Maxwell was able to connect electrical and magnetic phenomena with the velocity of light, for c is in fact that velocity.

The last equation is:

$$\text{curl } H = \frac{1}{c}\frac{\partial E}{\partial t}$$

It says that except for the change of algebraic sign (which has to do with the directions of the fields), the roles of E and H in the preceding equation may be reversed. At any given point and instant the magnetic force per unit of area created by a changing electric field is equal to the time rate of change of the electric field multiplied by the tiny positive fraction 1/c. Now this rate of change is none other than Maxwell's displacement current. For since the changes are taking place in the dielectric known as empty space, the only currents that can flow are displacement currents. Prior to Maxwell it was thought that a magnetic field could be produced only by currents which flowed in wires. It was Maxwell's great discovery, deduced mechanically from his model and expressed mathematically in this equation, that a time-

varying electric field produced a magnetic force even in an insulator or empty space.

According to Maxwell's theory the introduction of a time-varying electric force in a dielectric produces displacement waves with the velocity of light. These periodic waves of electric displacement are accompanied by a periodic magnetic force. The wave front itself comprises electric vibrations at right angles to the direction of propagation, and a magnetic force at right angles to the electric displacement. The compound disturbance is therefore called an electromagnetic wave. A light wave (a displacement wave), as Henri Poincaré later elaborated, is "a series of alternating currents, flowing in a dielectric, in the air, or in interplanetary space, changing their direction 1,000,000,000,000,000 times a second. The enormous inductive effect of these rapid alternations produces other currents in the neighboring

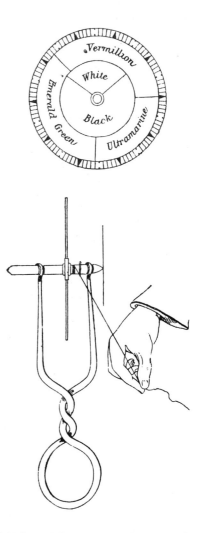

COLOR WHEEL is depicted in Maxwell's essay "Experiments on Colour, as perceived by the Eye, with remarks on Colour-Blindness." The wheel is shown at the top. The apparatus for rotating it is at the bottom.

portions of the dielectric, and thus the light waves are propagated from place to place."

The electromagnetic theory of light was testable experimentally, and stood up remarkably well in laboratory trials. There were also other ways of testing Maxwell's theory. If his reasoning was correct, different sources of disturbance should produce other electrical waves at frequencies different from those of light. They would not be visible; yet it should be possible to detect them with appropriate instruments. Maxwell did not live to see their discovery, but 10 years after his death Heinrich Hertz won the race to demonstrate their existence. In a series of brilliant experiments he succeeded in generating electric radio waves. He concluded that the connection "between light and electricity . . . of which there were hints and suspicions and even predictions in the theory, is now established. . . . Optics is no longer restricted to minute aether waves, a small fraction of a millimetre in length; its domain is extended to waves that are measured in decimetres, metres and kilometres. And in spite of this extension, it appears merely . . . as a small appendage of the great domain of electricity. We see that this latter has become a mighty kingdom."

Construction Work

Maxwell completed his great work on electromagnetic theory while "in retirement" at Glenlair. It drew only part of his energy. As a "by-work" during the same period he wrote a textbook on heat and a number of papers on mathematics, color vision and topics of physics. He maintained a heavy scientific and social correspondence, enlarged his house, studied theology, composed stanzas of execrable verse, rode his horse, went on long walks with his dogs, visited his neighbors and played with their children, and made frequent trips to Cambridge to serve as moderator and examiner in the mathematical tripos.

In 1871 a chair in experimental physics was founded at Cambridge. It is hard to realize that at the time no courses in heat, electricity and magnetism were being taught there, and no laboratory was available for the pursuit of these arcane matters. The University, as a contemporary scholar delicately observed, "had lost touch with the great scientific movements going on outside her walls." A committee of the faculty began to bestir itself, a report was issued, and the lamentable facts fell under the gaze of the Duke of Devonshire,

chancellor of the University. He offered the money for the building and furnishing of the famous Cavendish Laboratory. Maxwell, though at first reluctant to leave Glenlair, yielded to the urging of his friends to offer himself as a candidate for the chair. He was promptly elected.

He now devoted himself to the task of designing and superintending the erection of the laboratory. His aim was to make it the best institution of its kind, with the latest apparatus and the most effective arrangements for research. He presented to the laboratory all the apparatus in his own possession and supplemented the Duke's gift by generous money contributions. With so many details to be taken care of, the structure and its appointments were not completed until 1874. The delay, while inevitable, was inconvenient. "I have no place," wrote Maxwell, "to erect my chair, but move about like the cuckoo, depositing my notions in the Chemical Lecture Room in the first term, in the Botannical in Lent and in the Comparative Anatomy in Easter." His "notions" were the courses he gave on heat, electricity and electromagnetism.

Maxwell's classic *Matter and Motion,* "a small book on a great subject," was published in 1876. About this time he contributed articles on various subjects —"Atom," "Aether," "Attraction," "Faraday," among others—to the famous ninth edition of the Encyclopaedia Britannica. His public lectures include a charming discourse "On the Telephone," which, though delivered when he was already very ill, is not only as clear as his best expositions but filled with gay, amusing asides. Speaking of "Professor Bell's invention," he commented on "the perfect symmetry of the whole apparatus—the wire in the middle, the two telephones at the ends of the wire, and the two gossips at the ends of the telephones. . . ." Maxwell spent five years editing 20 packets of unpublished scientific papers of Henry Cavendish. This splendid two-volume work, published in 1879, did much to fix the reputation of the immensely gifted 18th-century investigator, whose important work on electricity was unknown to his contemporaries because the results were confided only to his manuscripts. Maxwell repeated Cavendish's experiments and showed that he had anticipated major discoveries in electricity, including Ohm's law.

Glenlair

As Maxwell grew older, friends remarked on his "ever-increasing soberness" of spirit. He continued to see his

many friends, to write light verse and parodies, to promenade with his dog Toby, to play small practical jokes. But he became somewhat more reticent, and more and more concealed his feelings and reflections beneath an ironical shell. The tough, rational, Scotch commonsense cord of his nature had always been intertwined with threads of mysticism. He had faith in science; yet he was at bottom skeptical as to how much could be learned from science alone about nature and meaning. His contemporaries described him as both modest and intellectually scornful, tentative in his scientific opinions and dogmatic when others seemed to him to be immoderately self-assured.

The most striking of Maxwell's traits was his gentleness. An extraordinary selflessness characterized his relationship to those close to him. When his brother-in-law came to London to undergo an operation, Maxwell gave up the ground floor of his house to the patient and nurse and lived in a room so small that he frequently breakfasted on his knees because there was no room for a chair at the table. Mrs. Maxwell had a serious and prolonged illness in the last years of Maxwell's life, and he insisted on nursing her. On one occasion it is reported that he did not sleep in a bed for three weeks. But his work went on as usual and he was as cheerful as if he enjoyed the ordeal—which may indeed have been the case. Nor did he give the slightest sign of being downcast or show self-pity when his own fatal illness seized him.

In the spring of 1877 he began to be troubled with pain and a choking sensation on swallowing. For some strange reason he consulted no one about his symptoms for almost two years, though his condition grew steadily worse. His friends at Cambridge observed that he was failing, that the spring had gone out of his step. When he went home to Glenlair for the summer of 1879, he was so obviously weakening that he called for medical help. He was in terrible pain, "hardly able to lie still for a minute together, sleepless, and with no appetite for the food which he so required." He understood thoroughly that his case was hopeless, yet his main concern seemed to be about the health of his wife. On November 5 he died. "No man," wrote his physician, Dr. Paget, "ever met death more consciously or more calmly." When Maxwell was buried in Parton Churchyard at Glenlair, the world had not yet caught up with his ideas. Even today it has not fully explored the kingdom created by his imagination.

11 SRINIVASA RAMANUJAN

JAMES R. NEWMAN · June 1948

I HAVE here set down, from the scanty materials available, a brief account of the poor Indian boy who became, as one eminent authority has written, "quite the most extraordinary mathematician of our time." Srinivasa Ramanujan died in India of tuberculosis on April 26, 1920, at the age of 33. Except among mathematicians, his name is almost unknown. He was a mathematician's mathematician, and as such, did not attract wide attention outside his field. But his work has left a memorable imprint on mathematical thought.

There are two points which will provide the background for this sketch. The first is that, despite a very limited formal education, Ramanujan was already a brilliant mathematician when he came to England to study in 1914. On the foundation of a volume known as Carr's *Synopsis of Pure Mathematics*, the only book on higher mathematics to which he had access, he had built "an astounding edifice of analytical knowledge and discovery." The nature of Ramanujan's achievement is made clear on examining this one text at his disposal. While a work of real merit and scholarship, it was in fact no more than a synopsis of some 6,000 theorems of algebra, trigonometry, calculus and analytical geometry, with proofs "which are often little more than cross-references." In general the mathematical knowledge contained in Carr's book went no further than the 1860's. Yet in areas that interested him, Ramanujan arrived in England abreast, and often ahead of contemporary mathematical knowledge. Thus in a lone, mighty sweep he had succeeded in recreating in his field, through his own unaided powers, a rich half century of European mathematics. One may doubt that so prodigious a feat had ever before been accomplished in the history of thought.

The second noteworthy point is that Ramanujan was a particular kind of mathematician. He was not as versatile as Karl Friedrich Gauss or Henri Poincaré. He was not a geometer; he cared nothing for mathematical physics, let alone the possible "usefulness" of his mathematical work in other disciplines. Instead, Ramanujan's intuition was most at ease in the bewildering interstices of the number system. Numbers, as will appear, were his friends; in the simplest array of digits he detected wonderful properties and relationships which escaped the notice of even the most gifted mathematicians. The modern theory of numbers is at once one of the richest, most elusive and most difficult branches of mathematics. Some of its principal theorems, while self-evident and childishly simple in statement, defy the most strenuous efforts to prove them. A good example is Goldbach's Theorem, which states that every even number is the sum of two prime numbers. Any fool, as one noted mathematician remarked, might have thought of it; it is altogether obvious and, indeed, no even number has ever been found which does not obey it. Yet no proof which demonstrates its application to *every* even number has ever been adduced. It was in dealing with such problems as this that Ramanujan showed his greatest gifts.

The late G. H. Hardy of Cambridge, a leading mathematician of his time, was professionally and personally closest to Ramanujan during his fruitful five years in England. I have taken from Hardy's well-known obituary of Ramanujan and from his notable course of Ramanujan lectures at Harvard the bulk of the material to be found here; the rest comes from a brief biographical sketch by P. V. Seshu Aiyar and R. Ramachandra Rao to be found in Ramanujan's *Collected Works*. Some of the material is understandable only to the professional mathematician. There is enough, I think, of general interest to justify bringing before the interested layman even this inadequate notice of a true genius' life and work.

*　　　　*　　　　*

SRINIVASA Ramanujan Aiyangar, according to his biographer Seshu Aiyar, was a member of a Brahman family in somewhat poor circumstances in the Tanjore district of the Madras presidency. His father was an accountant to a cloth merchant at Kumbakonam, while his mother, a woman of "strong common sense," was the daughter of a Brahman petty official in the Munsiff's (or legal judge's) Court at Erode. For some time after her marriage she had no children, "but her father prayed to the famous goddess Namagiri, in the neighboring town of Namakkal, to bless his daughter with offspring. Shortly afterwards, her eldest child, the mathematician Ramanujan, was born on 22nd December 1887."

He first went to school at five and was transferred before he was seven to the Town High School at Kumbakonam, where he held a scholarship. His extraordinary powers appear to have been recognized almost immediately. He was quiet and meditative and had an extraordinary memory. He delighted in entertaining his friends with theorems and formulae, with the recitation of complete lists of Sanskrit roots and with repeating the values of *pi* and the square root of two to any number of decimal places.

When he was 15 and in the sixth form at school, a friend of his secured for him the loan of Carr's *Synopsis of Pure Mathematics* from the library of the local Government College. Through the new world thus opened to him Ramanujan ranged with delight. It was this book that awakened his genius. He set himself at once to establishing its formulae. As he was without the aid of other books, each solution was for him a piece of original research. He first devised methods for constructing magic squares. Then he branched off to geometry, where he took up the squaring of the circle and went so far as to get a result for the length of the equatorial circumference of the earth which differed from the true length by only a few feet. Finding the scope of geometry limited, he turned his attention to algebra. Ramanujan used to say that the goddess of Namakkal inspired him with the formulae in dreams. It is a remarkable fact that, on rising from bed, he would frequently note down results and verify them, though he was not always

RAMANUJAN, wrote a friend, was "a short uncouth figure...with one conspicuous feature—shining eyes..."

able to supply a rigorous proof. This pattern repeated itself throughout his life.

He passed his matriculation examination to the Government College at Kumbakonam at 16, and secured the "Junior Subrahmanyam Scholarship." Owing to weakness in English—for he gave no thought to anything but mathematics—he failed in his next examination and lost his scholarship. He then left Kumbakonam, first for Vizagapatam and then for Madras. Here he presented himself for the "First Examination in Arts" in December 1906, but failed and never tried again. For the next few years he continued his independent work in mathematics. In 1909 he was married and it became necessary for him to find some permanent employment. In the course of his search for work he was given

a letter of recommendation to a true lover of mathematics, Diwan Bahadur R. Ramachandra Rao, who was then Collector at Nelore, a small town 80 miles north of Madras. Ramachandra Rao had already seen one of the two fat notebooks kept by Ramanujan into which he crammed his wonderful ideas. His first interview with Ramanujan is best described in his own words.

"Several years ago, a nephew of mine perfectly innocent of mathematical knowledge said to me, 'Uncle, I have a visitor who talks of mathematics; I do not understand him; can you see if there is anything in his talk?' And in the plenitude of my mathematical wisdom, I condescended to permit Ramanujan to walk into my presence. A short uncouth

figure, stout, unshaved, not overclean, with one conspicuous feature—shining eyes—walked in with a frayed notebook under his arm. He was miserably poor. He had run away from Kumbakonam to get leisure in Madras to pursue his studies. He never craved for any distinction. He wanted leisure; in other words, that simple food should be provided for him without exertion on his part and that he should be allowed to dream on.

"He opened his book and began to explain some of his discoveries. I saw quite at once that there was something out of the way; but my knowledge did not permit me to judge whether he talked sense or nonsense. Suspending judgment, I asked him to come over again, and he did. And then he had gauged my ignorance and

$$(1.1)\quad 1-\frac{3!}{(1!2!)^3}x^2+\frac{6!}{(2!4!)^3}x^4-\cdots$$

$$=\left(1+\frac{x}{(1!)^3}+\frac{x^2}{(2!)^3}+\cdots\right)\left(1-\frac{x}{(1!)^3}+\frac{x^2}{(2!)^3}-\cdots\right)$$

$$(1.2)\quad 1-5\left(\tfrac{1}{2}\right)^3+9\left(\frac{1\cdot3}{2\cdot4}\right)^3-13\left(\frac{1\cdot3\cdot5}{2\cdot4\cdot6}\right)^3+\cdots=\frac{2}{\pi}$$

$$(1.3)\quad 1+9\left(\tfrac{1}{4}\right)^4+17\left(\frac{1\cdot5}{4\cdot8}\right)^4+25\left(\frac{1\cdot5\cdot9}{4\cdot8\cdot12}\right)^4+\cdots=\frac{2^{\frac{3}{2}}}{\pi^{\frac{1}{2}}\left[\Gamma(\frac{3}{4})\right]^2}$$

$$(1.4)\quad 1-5\left(\tfrac{1}{2}\right)^5+9\left(\frac{1\cdot3}{2\cdot4}\right)^5-13\left(\frac{1\cdot3\cdot5}{2\cdot4\cdot6}\right)^5+\cdots=\frac{2}{\left[\Gamma(\frac{3}{4})\right]^4}$$

$$(1.5)\quad \int_0^\infty \frac{1+\left(\frac{x}{b+1}\right)^2}{1+\left(\frac{x}{a}\right)^2}\cdot\frac{1+\left(\frac{x}{b+2}\right)^2}{1+\left(\frac{x}{a+1}\right)^2}\cdots dx=\frac{1}{2}\pi^{\frac{1}{2}}\frac{\Gamma(a+\frac{1}{2})\Gamma(b+1)\Gamma(b-a+\frac{1}{2})}{\Gamma(a)\Gamma(b+\frac{1}{2})\Gamma(b-a+1)}$$

$$(1.6)\quad \int_0^\infty \frac{dx}{(1+x^2)(1+r^2x^2)(1+r^4x^2)\cdots}=\frac{\pi}{2(1+r+r^3+r^6+r^{10}+\cdots)}$$

$$(1.7)\quad \text{If}\quad \alpha\beta=\pi^2\quad \text{then}$$

$$\alpha^{-\frac{1}{4}}\left(1+4\alpha\int_0^\infty\frac{xe^{-\alpha x^2}}{e^{2\pi x}-1}dx\right)=\beta^{-\frac{1}{4}}\left(1+4\beta\int_0^\infty\frac{xe^{-\beta x^2}}{e^{2\pi x}-1}dx\right)$$

$$(1.8)\quad \int_0^\infty e^{-x^2}dx=\frac{1}{2}\pi^{\frac{1}{2}}-\frac{e^{-t}}{2t+}\frac{1}{t+}\frac{2}{t+}\frac{3}{2t+}\frac{4}{t+}\cdots$$

$$(1.9)\quad 4\int_0^\infty\frac{xe^{-x\sqrt{5}}}{\cosh x}dx=\frac{1}{1+}\frac{1^2}{1+}\frac{1^2}{1+}\frac{2^2}{1+}\frac{2^2}{1+}\frac{3^2}{1+}\frac{3^2}{1+}\cdots$$

$$(1.10)\quad \text{If}\quad \mu=\frac{x}{1+}\frac{x^5}{1+}\frac{x^{10}}{1+}\frac{x^{15}}{1+}\cdots,\quad v=\frac{x^{1/5}}{1+}\frac{x}{1+}\frac{x^2}{1+}\frac{x^3}{1+}\cdots$$

then

$$v^5=\mu\frac{1-2\mu+4\mu^2-3\mu^3+\mu^4}{1+3\mu+4\mu^2+2\mu^3+\mu^4}$$

$$(1.11)\quad \frac{1}{1+}\frac{e^{-2\pi}}{1+}\frac{e^{-4\pi}}{1+}\cdots=\left(\sqrt{\frac{5+\sqrt5}{2}}-\frac{\sqrt5+1}{2}\right)e^{\frac{2\pi}{5}}$$

$$(1.12)\quad \frac{1}{1+}\frac{e^{-2\pi\sqrt5}}{1+}\frac{e^{-4\pi\sqrt5}}{1+}\cdots=\left[\frac{\sqrt5}{1+\sqrt[5]{5^{\frac{3}{2}}\frac{\sqrt5-1}{2}}}-\frac{\sqrt5+1}{2}\right]e^{\frac{2\pi}{\sqrt5}}$$

$$(1.13)\quad \text{If}\quad F(k)=1+\left(\tfrac{1}{2}\right)^2k+\left(\frac{1\cdot3}{2\cdot4}\right)^2k^2+\cdots\quad \text{and}\quad F(1-k)=\sqrt{210}\,F(k)$$

then

$$k=(\sqrt2-1)^2(2-\sqrt3)(\sqrt7-\sqrt6)^2(8-3\sqrt7)(\sqrt{10}-3)^2$$

$$\times(4-\sqrt{15})(\sqrt{15}-\sqrt{14})(6-\sqrt{35})^2$$

THEOREMS of Ramanujan's letter (*here copied from original*) astounded the mathematician Hardy.

---

showed me some of his simpler results. These transcended existing books and I had no doubt that he was a remarkable man. Then, step by step, he led me to elliptic integrals and hypergeometric series and at last his theory of divergent series not yet announced to the world converted me. I asked him what he wanted. He said he wanted a pittance to live on so that he might pursue his researches."

RAMACHANDRA RAO undertook to pay Ramanujan's expenses for a time. After a while, other attempts to obtain a scholarship having failed and Ramanujan being unwilling to be supported by anyone for any length of time, he accepted a small appointment in the office of the Madras Port Trust.

But he never slackened his work in mathematics. His earliest contribution was published in the *Journal of the Indian Mathematical Society* in 1911, when Ramanujan was 23. His first long article was on "Some Properties of Bernoulli's Numbers" and was published in the same year. In 1912 he contributed two more notes to the same journal and also several questions for solution.

By this time Ramachandra Rao had induced a Mr. Griffith of the Madras Engineering College to take an interest in Ramanujan, and Griffith spoke to Sir Francis Spring, the chairman of the Madras Port Trust, where Ramanujan was employed. From that time on it became easy to secure recognition of his work. Upon the suggestion of Seshu Aiyar and others, Ramanujan began a correspondence with G. H. Hardy. then Fellow of Trinity College, Cambridge. His first letter to Hardy, dated January 16, 1913, which his friends helped him put in English, follows:

"Dear Sir,

"I beg to introduce myself to you as a clerk in the Accounts Department of the Port Trust Office at Madras on a salary of only £20 per annum. I am now about 23 years of age. [*He was actually 25—Ed.*] I have had no University education but I have undergone the ordinary school course. After leaving school I have been employing the spare time at my disposal to work at Mathematics. I have not trodden through the conventional regular course which is followed in a University course, but I am striking out a new path for myself. I have made a special investigation of divergent series in general and the results I get are termed by the local mathematicians as 'startling'. . . .

"I would request you to go through the enclosed papers. Being poor, if you are convinced that there is anything of value I would like to have my theorems published. I have not given the actual investigations nor the expressions that I get but I have indicated the lines on which I proceed. Being inexperienced I would very highly value any advice you give me. Requesting to be excused for the trouble I give you.

I remain, Dear Sir, Yours truly,
S. Ramanujan."

To the letter were attached about 120 theorems, of which the 13 here presented (*see box*) were part of a group selected by Hardy as "fairly representative." Hardy commented on these:

"I should like you to begin by trying to reconstruct the immediate reactions of an ordinary professional mathematician who receives a letter like this from an unknown Hindu clerk.

"The first question was whether I could recognise anything. I had proved things rather like (1.7) myself, and seemed vaguely familiar with (1.8). Actually (1.8) is classical; it is a formula of Laplace first proved properly by Jacobi; and (1.9) occurs in a paper published by Rogers in 1907. I thought that, as an expert in definite integrals, I could probably prove (1.5) and (1.6), and did so, though with a good deal more trouble than I had expected. . . .

"The series formulae (1.1)-(1.4) I found much more intriguing, and it soon became obvious that Ramanujan must possess much more general theorems and was keeping a great deal up his sleeve. The second is a formula of Bauer well known in the theory of Legendre series, but the others are much harder than they look. . . .

"The formulae (1.10)-(1.13) are on a different level and obviously both difficult and deep. An expert in elliptic functions can see at once that (1.13) is derived somehow from the theory of 'complex multiplication,' but (1.10)-(1.12) defeated me completely; I had never seen anything in the least like them before. A single look at them is enough to show that they could only be written down by a mathematician of the highest class. They must be true because, if they were not true, no one would have had the imagination to invent them. Finally . . . the writer must be completely honest, because great mathematicians are commoner than thieves or humbugs of such incredible skill. . . .

"While Ramanujan had numerous brilliant successes, his work on prime numbers and on all the allied problems of the theory was definitely wrong. This may be said to have been his one great failure. And yet I am not sure that, in some ways, his failure was not more wonderful than any of his triumphs. . . ."

Ramanujan's notation of one mathematical term in this area, wrote Hardy, "was first obtained by Landau in 1908. Ramanujan had none of Landau's weapons at his command; he had never seen a French or German book; his knowledge even of English was insufficient to qualify for a degree. It is sufficiently marvellous that he should have even dreamt of problems such as these, problems which it has taken the finest mathematicians in Europe a hundred years to solve, and of which the solution is incomplete to the present day."

AT last, in May of 1913, as the result of the help of many friends, Ramanujan was relieved of his clerical post in the Madras Port Trust and given a special scholarship. Hardy had made efforts from the first to bring Ramanujan to Cambridge. The way seemed to be open, but Ramanujan refused at first to go because of caste prejudice and lack of his mother's consent.

"This consent," wrote Hardy, "was at last got very easily in an unexpected manner. For one morning his mother announced that she had had a dream on the previous night, in which she saw her son seated in a big hall amidst a group of Europeans, and that the goddess Namagiri had commanded her not to stand in the way of her son fulfilling his life's purpose."

When Ramanujan finally came. he had a scholarship from Madras of £250, of which £50 was allotted to the support of his family in India, and an allowance of £60 from Trinity.

"There was one great puzzle," Hardy observes of Ramanujan. "What was to be done in the way of teaching him modern mathematics? The limitations of his knowledge were as startling as its profundity. Here was a man who could work out modular equations, and theorems of complex multiplication, to orders unheard of, whose mastery of continued fractions was, on the formal side at any rate, beyond that of any mathematician in the world, who had found for himself the functional equation of the Zeta-function and the dominant terms of many of the most famous problems in the analytic theory of numbers; and he had never heard of a doubly periodic function or of Cauchy's theorem, and had indeed but the vaguest idea of what a function of a complex variable was. His ideas as to what constituted a mathematical proof were of the most shadowy description. All his results, new or old, right or wrong, had been arrived at by a process of mingled argument, intuition, and induction, of which he was entirely unable to give any coherent account.

"It was impossible to ask such a man to submit to systematic instruction, to try to learn mathematics from the beginning once more. I was afraid too that, if I insisted unduly on matters which Ramanujan found irksome, I might destroy his confidence or break the spell of his inspiration. On the other hand there were things of which it was impossible that he should remain in ignorance. Some of his results were wrong, and in particular those which concerned the distribution of primes, to which he attached the greatest importance. It was impossible to allow him to go through life supposing that all

the zeros of the Zeta-function were real. So I had to try to teach him, and in a measure I succeeded, though obviously I learnt from him much more than he learnt from me....

"I should add a word here about Ramanujan's interests outside mathematics. Like his mathematics, they shewed the strangest contrasts. He had very little interest, I should say, in literature as such, or in art, though he could tell good literature from bad. On the other hand, he was a keen philosopher, of what appeared, to followers of the modern Cambridge school, a rather nebulous kind, and an ardent politician, of a pacifist and ultra-radical type. He adhered, with a severity most unusual in Indians resident in England, to the religious observances of his caste; but his religion was a matter of observance and not of intellectual conviction, and I remember well his telling me (much to my surprise) that all religions seemed to him more or less equally true. Alike in literature, philosophy, and mathematics, he had a passion for what was unexpected, strange, and odd; he had quite a small library of books by circle-squarers and other cranks...He was a vegetarian in the strictest sense—this proved a terrible difficulty later when he fell ill—and all the time he was in Cambridge he cooked all his food himself, and never cooked it without first changing into pyjamas....

"It was in the spring of 1917 that Ramanujan first appeared to be unwell. He went to a Nursing Home at Cambridge in the early summer, and was never out of bed for any length of time again. He was in sanatoria at Wells, at Matlock. and in London, and it was not until the autumn of 1918 that he shewed any decided symptom of improvement. He had then resumed active work, stimulated perhaps by his election to the Royal Society. and some of his most beautiful theorems were discovered about this time. His election to a Trinity Fellowship was a further encouragement; and each of those famous societies may well congratulate themselves that they recognized his claims before it was too late."

Early in 1919 Ramanujan went home to India, where he died in the following year.

FOR an evaluation of Ramanujan's method and work in mathematics we must again quote from Hardy. "I have often been asked whether Ramanujan had any special secret; whether his methods differed in kind from those of other mathematicians; whether there was anything really abnormal in his mode of thought. I cannot answer these questions with any confidence or conviction; but I do not believe it. My belief is that all mathematicians think, at bottom, in the same kind of way, and that Ramanujan was no exception. He had, of course, an extraordinary memory. He could remember the idiosyncrasies of numbers in an

almost uncanny way. It was Mr. Littlewood (I believe) who remarked that 'every positive integer was one of his personal friends.' I remember once going to see him when he was lying ill at Putney. I had ridden in taxi-cab No. 1729, and remarked that the number seemed to me rather a dull one, and that I hoped it was not an unfavourable omen. 'No,' he replied, 'it is a very interesting number; it is the smallest number expressible as a sum of two cubes in two different ways.' I asked him, naturally, whether he knew the answer to the corresponding problem for fourth powers; and he replied, after a moment's thought, that he could see no obvious example, and thought that the first such number must be very large. His memory, and his powers of calculation, were very unusual, but they could not reasonably he called 'abnormal.' If he had to multiply two large numbers, he multiplied them in the ordinary way; he could do it with unusual rapidity and accuracy, but not more rapidly or more accurately than any mathematician who is naturally quick and has the habit of computation.

"It was his insight into algebraical formulae, transformations of infinite series, and so forth, that was most amazing. On this side most certainly I have never met his equal, and I can compare him only with Euler or Jacobi. He worked, far more than the majority of modern mathematicians, by induction from numerical examples; all of his congruence properties of partitions, for example, were discovered in this way. But with his memory, his patience, and his power of calculation, he combined a power of generalisation, a feeling for form, and a capacity for rapid modification of his hypotheses, that were often really startling, and made him, in his own field, without a rival in his day.

"It is often said that it is much more difficult now for a mathematician to be original than it was in the great days when the foundations of modern analysis were laid; and no doubt in a measure it is true. Opinions may differ as to the importance of Ramanujan's work, the kind of standard by which it should be judged, and the influence which it is likely to have on the mathematics of the future. It has not the simplicity and the inevitableness of the very greatest work; it would be greater if it were less strange. One gift it has which no one can deny—profound and invincible originality. He would probably have been a greater mathematician if he had been caught and tamed a little in his youth; he would have discovered more that was new, and that, no doubt, of greater importance. On the other hand he would have been less of a Ramanujan, and more of a European professor and the loss might have been greater than the gain."

12 "NICOLAS BOURBAKI"

PAUL R. HALMOS • May 1957

His name is Greek, his nationality is French and his history is curious. He is one of the most influential mathematicians of the 20th century. The legends about him are many, and they are growing every day. Almost every mathematician knows a few stories about him and is likely to have made up a couple more. His works are read and extensively quoted all over the world. There are young men in Rio de Janeiro almost all of whose mathematical education was obtained from his works, and there are famous mathematicians in Berkeley and in Göttingen who think that his influence is pernicious. He has emotional partisans and vociferous detractors wherever groups of mathematicians congregate. The strangest fact about him, however, is that he does not exist.

This nonexistent Frenchman with the Greek name is Nicolas Bourbaki (rhymes with *Pooh-Bah key*). The fact is that Nicolas Bourbaki is a collective pseudonym used by an informal corporation of mathematicians. (The charming French phrase for corporation, "anony-mous society," is quite apt here.) The pseudonymous group is writing a comprehensive treatise on mathematics, starting with the most general basic principles and to conclude, presumably, with the most specialized applications. The project got under way in 1939, and 20 volumes (almost 3,000 pages) of the monumental work have appeared.

Why the authors chose to call themselves Bourbaki is shrouded in mystery. There is reason to think that their choice was inspired by an army

NICOLAS BOURBAKI is fancifully represented by this milling throng of French mathematicians. Bourbaki appears to consist of 10 to 20 men at any one time. Any resemblance between these men and the individuals in the drawing is entirely coincidental.

officer of some importance in the Franco-Prussian War. General Charles Denis Sauter Bourbaki was quite a colorful character. In 1862, at the age of 46, he was offered a chance to become the King of Greece, but he declined the opportunity. He is remembered now mainly for the unkind way the fortunes of war treated him. In 1871, after fleeing from France to Switzerland with a small remnant of his army, he was interned there and then tried to shoot himself. Apparently he missed, for he is reported to have lived to the venerable age of 83. There is said to be a statue of him in Nancy. This may establish a connection between him and the mathematicians who are using his name, for several of them were at various times associated with the University of Nancy.

One of the legends surrounding the name is that about 25 or 30 years ago first-year students at the Ecole Normale Supérieure (where most French mathematicians get their training) were annually exposed to a lecture by a distinguished visitor named Nicolas Bourbaki, who was in fact an amateur actor disguised in a patriarchal beard, and whose lecture was a masterful piece of mathematical double-talk.

It is necessary to insert a word of warning about the unreliability of most Bourbaki stories. While the members of this cryptic organization have taken no blood oath of secrecy, most of them are so amused by their own joke that their stories about themselves are intentionally conflicting and apocryphal. Outsiders, on the other hand, are not likely to know what they are talking about: they can only report an often-embellished legend. The purpose of this article is to describe Bourbaki's scientific accomplishments and relate a few samples of the stories told about him (them). Some of the stories are unverifiable, to say the least, but that doesn't make them any less entertaining.

Scientific publication under a pseudonym is not, of course, original with this group. The English statistician William Sealy Gosset published his pioneering work on the theory of small samples under the name of "Student," probably to avoid embarrassing his employers (the brewers of Guinness). At about the time Bourbaki was starting up, another group of wags invented E. S. Pondiczery, a purported member of the Royal Institute of Poldavia. The initials (E.S.P., R.I.P.) were inspired by a projected but never-written article on extrasensory perception. Pondiczery's main work was on mathematical curiosa. His

GENERAL BOURBAKI, whose name was not Nicolas but Charles Denis Sauter, is depicted in this drawing based on an engraving. He was once offered the crown of Greece.

proudest accomplishment was the only known use of a second-degree pseudonym. Submitting a paper on the mathematical theory of big-game hunting to *The American Mathematical Monthly*, Pondiczery asked in a covering letter that he be allowed to sign it with a pseudonym, because of the obviously facetious nature of the material. The editor agreed, and the paper appeared (in 1938) under the name of H. Pétard.

Primitive tribes, and occasionally scientists, may find magic in a name. This accounts for a publication which would never have been conceived if the authors' names had been different. George Gamow and his friend Hans Bethe saw and took advantage of a wonderful opportunity when a bright young physicist with an unusual name appeared on the scene. On April 1, 1948, they published in *The Physical Review* a perfectly straight-faced paper on the origin of chemical elements whose only unusual feature was the by-line. It read, of course, Alpher, Bethe and Gamow.

While we are on the subject of articles appearing under strange names, it is appropriate to mention the case of Maurice de Duffahel. This gentleman achieved mathematical immortality by the very simple device of publishing, under his own name, some of the classical papers of the great masters. He made only the feeblest attempt to disguise his activities. In 1936 he republished as his own a paper which had been published only 24 years earlier by Charles Emile Picard. Duffahel's version was identical with Picard's, word for word, symbol for symbol, except for one omission: he left out, for understandable reasons, a footnote in which Picard had referred to one of his earlier papers. Scholarship eventually caught up with Duffahel. You can fool some editors some of the time, but you can't fool all reviewers all of the time. A reviewer of the Picard-Duffahel paper happened to know the works of Picard well enough to recognize the repetition, and Duffahel's publishing career came to an abrupt end.

The works of Bourbaki do not have to be concealed from the executives of a brewery, they are not mere innocent merriment but serious mathematics, and they are definitely not plagiarized from anyone else. The group originally adopted the pseudonym half in jest and half to avoid a boringly long list of authors on the title page; they continue its use more as a corporate name than as a disguise. The names of the members are an open secret to most mathematicians. The membership of Bourbaki, like that of most corporations, changes from time to time, but the style and the spirit of the work stay the same. It is handy to be able to describe a certain style and spirit by one adjective (the accepted term is *Bourbachique*) rather than by a reference to the "young French school" or a similar circumlocution.

Bourbaki's first appearance on the scene was in the middle 1930s, when they began to publish notes, reviews and other papers in the *Comptes Rendus* of the French Academy of Sciences and elsewhere. The major treatise on which they later embarked was explained in a paper which was translated into English and printed (in 1950) in *The American Mathematical Monthly* under the title "The Architecture of Mathematics." A footnote reads: "Professor N. Bourbaki, formerly of the Royal Poldavian Academy [shades of Pondiczery!], now residing in Nancy, France, is the author of a comprehensive treatise

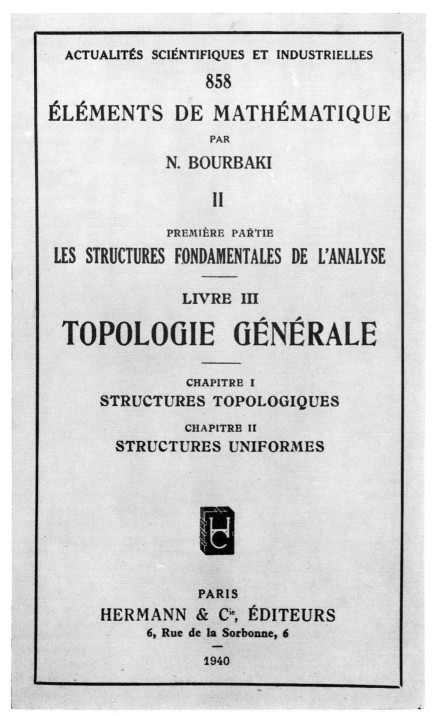

PAPER-BACKED BOOK, of which this is both the title page and the cover, is only a part of Book III of Part I of the Bourbaki treatise. Book III is entitled *General Topology*.

of modern mathematics, in course of publication under the title *Eléments de Mathématique* (Hermann et Cie., Paris, 1939–), of which 10 volumes have appeared so far." The paper, by the way, is an interesting statement of Bourbaki's view of the concept of "structure" in mathematics; it is a masterful description of the Bourbaki spirit. Another paper, which appeared in *The Journal of Symbolic Logic* for 1949, has the ambitious title "Foundations of Mathematics for the Working Mathematician." It is quite technical, but the authors' personality shows through the symbolism. It concludes: "On these foundations I state that I can build up the whole of the mathematics of the present day; and if there is anything original in my procedure, it lies solely in the fact that, instead of being content with such a statement, I proceed to prove it in the same way as Diogenes proved the existence of motion; and my proof will become more and more complete as my treatise grows."

This paper gives the author's home institution as the "University of Nancago" (Nancy plus Chicago). The main reason for the combination is that one of the founding fathers is now on the staff of the University of Chicago. His name is André Weil (and he is, by the way, the brother of the well-known religious mystic Simone Weil). Although André Weil is not known to the general public, many of his colleagues are prepared to argue that he is the world's greatest living mathematician. His work on algebraic number theory and algebraic geometry is profound and important; his influence on the development of 20th-century mathematics is great, and even some of his more offhand contributions (for example, uniform structures and harmonic analysis on topological groups) have opened up new directions and inspired further researches. Nancago, incidentally, crops up again in a new series of advanced mathematical books which is being published under the impressive heading *Publications de l'Institut Mathématique de l'Université de Nancago.*

According to one of the Bourbaki legends, their major work, whose general title is *Elements of Mathematics*, owes its origin to a conversation between Weil and Jean Delsarte on how calculus should be taught. Whatever the motivation of the work may originally have been, its present purpose is certainly not elementary pedagogy. It is as if a discussion of the best way to teach an understanding of popular music gave rise

S-CURVE in the Bourbaki treatise indicates a "dangerous turn" in the argument.

to a complete treatise on harmony and musicology. (Mathematicians consider the calculus to be as "trivial" as musicians consider the music of Victor Herbert.) Bourbaki's treatise (written in French) is a survey of all mathematics from a sophisticated point of view.

The whole will presumably consist of several parts, but the 20 volumes that have appeared so far do not even complete Part I, titled *The Fundamental Structures of Analysis*. The names of the six subdivisions of Part I are a mild shock to the layman (or the classical mathematician) who thinks of mathematics in terms of arithmetic, geometry and other such old-fashioned words. They are: (1) Set Theory, (2) Algebra, (3) General Topology, (4) Functions of a Real Variable, (5) Topological Vector Spaces and (6) Integration.

Each volume comes provided with a loose insert of four pages constituting a set of directions on the proper use of the treatise. They go into detail about the necessary prerequisites for reading the treatise (about two years of university mathematics), describe the organization of the work and specify the "rigorously fixed logical order" in which the chapters, books and parts must be read. The directions also explain the authors' pedagogical tricks, and some of them are very good tricks indeed. One trick, which other authors could profitably copy, is to warn the reader whenever the subject becomes especially slippery, that is, when he is likely to fall into an error: the slippery passages are flagged by a conspicuous S-curve ("dangerous turn") in the margin.

A less admirable Bourbachique trick is their slightly contemptuous attitude toward the substitution of what they call "abuses of language" for technical terms. It is generally admitted that strict adherence to rigorously correct terminology is likely to end in being pedantic and unreadable. This is especially true of Bourbaki, because their terminology and symbolism are frequently at variance with commonly accepted usage. The amusing fact is that

often the "abuse of language" which they employ as an "informal" replacement for a technical term is actually conventional usage: weary of trying to remember their own innovation, the authors slip comfortably into the terminology of the rest of the mathematical world.

Almost every Bourbaki volume contains an excellent set of exercises. Mathematics cannot be learned passively, and the Bourbaki exercises are a challenge to activity. The authors used a lot of ingenuity in inventing new exercises, and in rephrasing and rearranging old ones. As a matter of policy they usually do not give credit to the original authors of the exercises they have revised, but no one seems to mind. A mathematician is even likely to consider it an honor to have one of his papers "stolen" by Bourbaki and used as an exercise.

The Bourbaki gadgetry includes foldout sheets that summarize important definitions and assumptions, a dictionary for each book that serves also as a comprehensive index and a guide to both non-Bourbachique terminology and basic Bourbakese. The only important thing missing is adequate bibliographical guidance. The Bourbaki presentation of each subject is systematic and thorough, and often includes a brilliant historical review of the subject. But the historical essays make only a few grudging references to the classics and fail almost entirely to mention the sources of the modern contributions. No deception is intended (Bourbaki does not claim to have discovered all of modern mathematics), but the practice may have the effect of confusing the future mathematical historian.

These are the external trappings of Bourbaki. The Bourbaki style and spirit, the qualities that attract friends and repel enemies, are harder to describe. Like the qualities of music, they must be felt rather than understood.

One of the things that attracted students to Bourbaki from the start was that they gave the first systematic account of some subjects (for example, general topology and multilinear algebra) which were not available anywhere else in book form. Bourbaki pioneered in reducing to orderly form a large mass of papers which had appeared over several decades in many journals and in several languages. The main features of the Bourbaki approach are a radical attitude about the right order for doing things, a dogmatic insistence on a privately invented terminology, a clean and economical organization of ideas and a style of presentation which is so bent on saying everything that it leaves nothing to the imagination and has, consequently, a watery, lukewarm effect.

A typical sample of the thoroughness and leisurely pace of the Bourbaki treatment is their approach to defining the number "1." They devote almost 200 pages to preparation before they get to the definition itself. They then define the number 1 in terms of highly condensed abbreviating symbols, explaining in a footnote that the unabbreviated form of the definition in their system of notation would require several tens of thousands of symbols. In all fairness to Bourbaki it must be said that modern mathematical logicians have known for some time that concepts such as the number 1 are not so elementary as they look.

How does a cooperative work of this magnitude ever get written? A large part of the credit goes to Jean Dieudonné (originally from Nancy, now at Northwestern University) who has been Bourbaki's chief scribe almost from the beginning. Since Dieudonné is a prolific writer on mathematics under his own name, there is a certain difficulty about distinguishing his private work from his efforts for Bourbaki. According to one story, he manages to keep the record straight in a truly remarkable manner. The story is that Dieudonné once published, under Bourbaki's name, a note which later was found to contain a mistake. The mistake was corrected in a paper entitled "On an Error of M. Bourbaki" and signed Jean Dieudonné.

The membership of Bourbaki seems to vary between 10 and 20. With one conspicuous exception all the members have always been French. The exception is Samuel Eilenberg (originally from Warsaw, now at Columbia University). Known to the friends of his youth as S^2P^2 (for Smart Sammy the Polish Prodigy), Eilenberg is a charming extrovert who learned more about the U. S. within six months of his arrival than most Americans ever find out. (One of the first things he did was to go on an extended hitchhiking tour.) Since he speaks French like a native and knows more about algebraic topology than any Frenchman, the unwritten rule restricting Bourbaki to Frenchmen was waived to admit him.

The French orientation of Bourbaki is not mere chauvinism but a linguistic necessity (since Frenchmen started it). When a collection of prima donnas such as Weil, Dieudonné, Claude Chevallier and Henri Cartan get together with their colleagues, the rate and volume of the flow of French is impressive. To follow

and take part in the conversation under such circumstances you must not only speak French fast and loud, but you must know the latest Parisian student slang. Even if everyone in the room fulfills these conditions, it is difficult to see how any work ever gets done at the famous Bourbaki congresses. But it does get done. The members convene each year, usually in some pleasant French vacation spot, to make major policy decisions. Since their treatise has proved a commercial success (to Bourbaki's considerable surprise), there is ample royalty money to pay travel expenses and to provide the French food and wines that lubricate the proceedings. (The commercial success, by the way, is due mainly to the American market. Four of the five senior members of Bourbaki are now residents in the U. S.)

A lot of work goes into the preparation of a Bourbaki volume. Once a particular project has been decided on, some member agrees to write the first draft. In so doing he gets himself in for a trying experience. When his draft is finished, it is duplicated and copies are sent around to the others. At the next congress the draft is mercilessly criticized, and, quite possibly, completely rejected. The first draft of the Bourbaki book on integration, for instance, was written by Dieudonné and became known as "Dieudonné's monster." Rumor has it that in spirit and content Dieudonné's monster was very similar to a well-known American book on the subject, written by an author whose name we shall simply give here as Blank. Dieudonné's monster was never published; his confreres hooted it down. What settled the matter was Weil's snort: "If we're going to do that sort of thing, let's just translate Blank's book into French and have done with it."

After the first draft has been dealt with, a second draft is begun, possibly by a different member. The process goes on and on: six or seven drafts are not unknown. The result of this painstaking work is not a textbook that it is safe to put into a beginner's hands (even Bourbaki admit that), but it is a reference book, almost an encyclopedia, without which 20th-century mathematics would be, for better or for worse, quite different from what it is.

Bourbaki's youthful exuberance augurs well for the future of their labors, but it is one of the main annoyances to their enemies. The officials of the American Mathematical Society were not amused when they received an application for membership signed N. Bourbaki. They considered the joke sophomoric,

and they rejected the application. The secretary of the Society coldly suggested that Bourbaki might apply for an institutional membership. Since the dues for institutional membership are substantially higher than those for individuals, and since Bourbaki did not wish to admit that he does not exist, nothing more was heard of the matter.

Yes, the joke may be sophomoric, but sophomores are young, and mathematics is a young man's profession. Bourbaki's emphasis on youth is laudable. Upon reaching the age of 50 recently, Dieudonné and Weil, though founding fathers of Bourbaki, announced their retirement from the group. They had declared their intention to get out at 50, and they kept their promise.

It is appropriate to conclude by warning the reader to be on the lookout for Bourbaki-inspired rumors about the author of this article, and to be prepared to take such rumors with a generous grain of salt. The corporation does not like to have its secrets told in public, and it has demonstrated its ability to take effective measures against informers. To be sure, the fiction has been exposed in print before this. In 1949 André Delachet, in his little book on mathematical analysis, referred to the "polycephalic mathematician" N. Bourbaki, and went so far as to mention some of the heads by name. A year or two before that, the *Book of the Year* of the *Encyclopaedia Britannica* had a brief paragraph about Bourbaki as a group. The author of the paragraph was Ralph P. Boas, then executive editor of the journal *Mathematical Reviews*, now a colleague of Dieudonné at Northwestern. Soon afterward the editors of the *Britannica* received an injured letter signed by N. Bourbaki, protesting against Boas's allegation of Bourbaki's nonexistence. The editors' confusion and Boas's embarrassment were not reduced when a member of the University of Chicago mathematics department wrote a truthful but shrewdly worded letter, implying, but not saying, that Bourbaki did indeed exist. The situation was cleared up for the editors by a letter from the secretary of the American Mathematical Society (the same secretary who had refused to approve Bourbaki's membership application).

Bourbaki got its revenge. Calling forth all its polycephalic, international resources, the corporation circulated a rumor that *Boas* did not exist. Boas, said Bourbaki, is the collective pseudonym of a group of young American mathematicians who act jointly as the editors of *Mathematical Reviews*.

III

SOME
CHAPTERS
OF
MATHEMATICS

SOME CHAPTERS OF MATHEMATICS

INTRODUCTION

Like Gaul, mathematics is divided into three parts. Although in the past these three domains were often at odds with each other, today not only has all hostility vanished but the relationships are even intimate. One consequence of the intimacy is the creation of some mathematical topics or subjects that belong as much to one of the three parts as to another.

The three divisions of mathematics, algebra, geometry, and analysis, do not have the same logical status. Whereas geometry and algebra are independent subjects, each having its own axiomatic foundation, analysis is an extension of algebra. The distinguishing feature of analysis, as opposed to algebra, is that it utilizes the notion of a limit, that is, a number which is approached more and more closely by a set of numbers just as the numbers $1/2, 3/4, 7/8, 15/16, \cdots$ approach the number 1 as a limit.

Where is arithmetic in this scheme? It is part of algebra, or we may say that algebra is generalized arithmetic. If one wishes to discuss any expression of the form $6 - 4$, such as $7 - 3$, $12 - 8$ and $.2 - .1$, he writes $a - b$, where a refers to any one of the first numbers and b to the second, and discusses $a - b$. The transition to letters marks the transition from arithmetic to algebra. Thus arithmetic, algebra, and analysis deal basically with numbers, whether particular numbers, such as 3 and $\sqrt{2}$, or classes of numbers denoted by a, b, or some other letter.

This description of the subdivisions of mathematics is an aerial view. Closer inspection reveals that there are many arithmetics, many algebras, geometries rather than geometry, and analyses rather than analysis.

How can there be many arithmetics? Doesn't $2 + 2$ always equal 4? And how can there be many geometries? Isn't the sum of the angles of a triangle always equal to 180 degrees? The answers to these questions are a bit lengthy but vital to understanding the nature, content, and role of mathematics. Elementary mathematics is a response to the immediate realities. Whole numbers were introduced to represent the quantity of cows in a herd, and fractions to represent the portion of a man's income that was to be given to the church or state as taxes. A straight line was just an idealization of the boundary of a field or of a stretched rope, and the moon's shape suggested the sphere. The mathematics that was erected on the basis of these physically familiar and real concerns is extensive and marvelously adapted to the exploration of nature, engineering uses, and commercial needs. In this domain of mathematics, $2 + 2$ always equals 4 and the sum of the angles of a triangle always equals 180 degrees. In this phase of mathematical thought, in this innocent state of nature, to borrow Rousseau's phrase, mathematical concepts and operations were regarded as merely abstracted from nature, and mathematicians by reasoning on the basis of obvious physical truths learned more about nature than was immediately apparent or attainable through physical means such as measurement and experimentation. But mathematics expressed no more than the reality in nature.

Several events were decisive in bringing about a rude awakening. A minor jolt was the introduction of negative numbers by the Hindus. However, although it took the mathematicians many hundreds of years, they finally reconciled themselves to these numbers by using them to distinguish distances in one direction from distances in another. Because they had ascribed a kind of reality to negative numbers, they made peace with them, even if a trace of uneasiness remained as late as the middle of the nineteenth century.

By indulging in their propensity to generalize, the mathematicians jolted themselves far more severely. Some of the simplest real problems lead to the solution of equations such as $x^2 = 2$ or $x^2 - 5x + 6 = 0$. The roots of these equations are positive and negative numbers. However, the mathematicians were not satisfied to solve only these particular problems. Hence they considered the general second degree equation $ax^2 + bx + c = 0$, where a, b, and c stand for any positive or negative number. We need not consider the general equation to see that the mathematicians had let themselves in for trouble. What are the solutions of $x^2 + 2 = 0$ or $x^2 = -2$? By analogy with what they did when they solved $x^2 = 2$ and wrote $x = +\sqrt{2}$ and $x = -\sqrt{2}$, the mathematicians now wrote $x = +\sqrt{-2}$ and $x = -\sqrt{-2}$. They had created a monster. What is $\sqrt{-2}$? It should be, according to the meaning of square root, a number which when multiplied by itself yields -2. But the positive and negative numbers that the mathematicians knew were such that the product of any one with itself yielded a positive number. Hence there was no known number which equalled $\sqrt{-2}$. To make matters worse in solving equations such as $x^2 - 6x + 11 = 0$, by applying the very same process they used to solve $x^2 - 5x + 6 = 0$ they were led to "numbers" such as $3 + \sqrt{-2}$ and $3 - \sqrt{-2}$. These "numbers" made even less sense.

The mathematicians' resolution of the difficulty raised by the appearance of these strange "numbers" was to ignore them. They called them imaginary numbers (they are called complex numbers today) and, having libeled them, ostracized them. Their consciences were disturbed but consciences are more elastic than rational thought.

The event which forced the hand of the mathematicians was non-Euclidean geometry. The story of this development will be found in Kline's article on Geometry. However let us note here some additional history, not related in the Kline article, that is especially relevant for the concept of mathematics as a whole. Euclid's geometry contains an axiom to the effect that, given a line and a point, there is one and only one line, through the point and in the plane determined by the given line and point, that does not meet the given line. Until the year 1800 no one doubted the *physical* truth of this axiom but quite a few men objected to the introduction of this fact as an axiom because, especially as Euclid worded it, it did not seem quite as self-evident as an axiom should be. To avoid the introduction of this axiom a number of men, notably Girolamo Saccheri, pursued an ingenious plan. There are two alternatives to Euclid's axiom. The first is that through the given point more than one line can be drawn that does not meet the given line; the second, that no line can be drawn that does not meet the given line. The plan was to adopt, first, one of these axioms in place of Euclid's axiom and to use it in conjunction with the remaining Euclidean axioms to deduce theorems. These men fully expected that contradictory theorems would result and this outcome would show that the substituted axiom could not be true. The same procedure was then to be pursued with the second of the alternative axioms and with the same expected outcome. The final argument was to be that if the only two possible alternatives led to contradictions, Euclid's statement must be true. In fact, because it would be a logical consequence of the other axioms it would not be an axiom but a theorem.

Unfortunately the adoption of these alternative axioms did not lead to contradictions (we omit a detail here about the second alternative) and the mathematicians were faced with totally new geometries. Moreover—and this was the great contribution of Gauss, which was described in the Introduction to Section II—these new geometries applied to nature as accurately as did Euclidean geometry insofar as measurement could determine.

Now the mathematicians had to face the question, "Which one of these geometries, Euclidean and non-Euclidean, is the truth about nature?" There was no criterion that pointed to one rather than another. Yet several geometries differing radically from one another could not all be true. Slowly and reluctantly the mathematicians grasped the implication. There was no reason to believe that any of the geometries was true.

But if Euclidean geometry, one of the basic branches of mathematics, was not necessarily true, then it behooved mathematicians to reconsider their understanding of the nature of all mathematics. They had believed that they had started with truths evident in nature and that by reasoning they had deduced further truths about nature. But the import of non-Euclidean geometry was that they had rather superficially selected only seemingly correct facts about nature and had deduced consequences which fortunately were applicable. It was possible to start with assertions quite different from the previous Euclidean assertions and still produce useful results.

The vital point was that mathematics was man-made. It was artificial. Neither the basic axioms nor the theorems deduced from them were written into the universe. Begrudgingly the mathematicians granted that they had been deceived for two thousand years about the nature of what they were doing.

But the mathematicians managed to turn defeat into victory. If the ordinary algebra and ordinary geometry were contrived and yet useful, perhaps other artifices would prove equally so. Thus it was not necessary to delay the acceptance of imaginary numbers until they were related to immediate experience. The very fact that they arose from a sound mathematical theme, namely, the solution of second degree equations, was some assurance that they were worthy of investigation if only to learn more about such a vital subject. Moreover imaginary numbers were in a very significant sense no more artificial than ordinary whole numbers and fractions, because it was now clear that these, too, although historically suggested by experience, were really creations of the human mind.

Mathematics experienced a new birth of freedom, the freedom to explore creations of the human mind as opposed to being tied to concepts abstracted directly from the real world. By the end of the nineteenth century, Georg Cantor, one of the great mathematicians of recent times, was able to say, "The essence of mathematics is its freedom." However his contemporary, Felix Klein, warned that freedom must be accompanied by responsibility, responsibility to the serious purposes of mathematics.

Whether mathematicians have lived up to their responsibilities we shall not undertake to discuss here. What is relevant is that during the last hundred years mathematicians have created many new types of numbers whose properties, compared to those of the familiar number system, are strange. In his article Davis discusses several of these newer types and their properties. Of course the properties of the familiar whole numbers continued to intrigue the mathematicians, and Herwitz' article gives some of the reasons.

Just as ordinary algebra is a generalized manner of working with ordinary numbers, so new algebras which generalize the treatment of these various new number systems were created. The existence of many algebras in turn led to the study of the structure or properties of classes of algebras. Some of the recently developed algebras and the modern notions of classes of algebras, such as groups and fields, are explained by Sawyer in his article.

Geometry, too, has expanded enormously in the last hundred years. Beyond the non-Euclidean geometries already referred to in this introduction, many new and more general non-Euclidean geometries, called Riemannian and non-Riemannian, were created. Mathematicians have also plunged boldly into n-dimensional geometry and into the study of complicated curves, surfaces and higher dimensional figures. Within practically this century still another branch of geometry called topology has been introduced. Kline's article "Geometry" is a survey of the major developments throughout the history of geometry. A number of the other articles explain the nature of particular geometries. Kline's second article discusses the nature of projective geometry and its relation to Euclidean geometry. Le Corbeiller's article treats Riemannian geometry. Tucker and Bailey present the concept of topology. Two special topics of topology are elaborated upon in the selection from Euler, the greatest mathematician of the eighteenth century, and in the article by Shinbrot.

In this century the disciplines of statistics and probability, which had served in ancillary roles, have been not only highly developed but applied far more widely and to more diverse fields than any other branch of mathematics. The articles by Ayer, Kac, and Weaver explain the mathematics and cover many of the uses.

Not all of the exposition of mathematics proper is to be found in this section. For example, in Section I, Halmos' article contains a fine presentation of the basic idea of analytic geometry, and Courant sketches many topics of modern abstract mathematics. Whittaker's article in Section II presents Hamilton's work on quaternions and their relation to complex numbers. Pfeiffer, in Section IV, gives a fine introduction to symbolic or mathematical logic. In Section V, Ulam's article on computers contains some work on the theory of numbers and combinatorial analysis.

One part of mathematics, analysis, is not well represented in Section III, but it is not neglected in this volume. Analysis, as we have pointed out, is an extension of algebra. Several factors complicate the task of securing either a bird's-eye view or some insight into analysis. The basic subject of this part of mathematics, the calculus, is built upon new concepts such as the limit concept, which are somewhat more subtle than those of algebra and geometry, as well as upon a mass of new techniques. Beyond the calculus are a number of distinct subjects, such as ordinary differential equations, partial differential equations, differential geometry, the calculus of variations, and functions of a complex variable, all of which employ the calculus but are not readily encompassed in one unified approach. Furthermore, of the three major domains of mathematics, analysis is the one whose concepts and techniques are most significant for the investigation of nature, so that an account of the mathematics itself remains bleak.

Nevertheless much can be gleaned about analysis from the many articles in this volume. For example, in this section Le Corbeiller's article provides a fine introduction to Riemann's geometry, which is a part of differential geometry and indeed that part used in the theory of relativity. This use is discussed by Einstein and Gamow in their articles in Section V. Some inkling of how differential equations are used may be obtained from Newman's biographies of Laplace and Maxwell, in Section II, and from Dirac's article in Section V.

However, mathematics is a cumulative development and no marvels of exposition can elucidate in depth topics which presuppose an extensive background. If there is any handicap to the learning of mathematics it consists only in the necessity to take account of the sequential order of the ideas, and not in the intrinsic difficulty of the ideas. Hence the reader who masters elementary mathematics may confidently undertake other readings in analysis, such as those suggested in the bibliographies of many of the articles.

13 NUMBER

PHILIP J. DAVIS · September 1964

By popular definition a mathematician is a fellow who is good at numbers. Most mathematicians demur. They point out that they have as much difficulty as anybody else in reconciling their bank statements, and they like to refer to supporting anecdotes, such as that Isaac Newton, who was Master of the Mint, employed a bookkeeper to do his sums. They observe further that slide rules and electronic computers were developed as crutches to help mathematicians.

All of this is obviously irrelevant. Who, if not the mathematician, is the custodian of the odd numbers and the even numbers, the square numbers and the round numbers? To what other authority shall we look for information and help on Fibonacci numbers, Liouville numbers, hypercomplex numbers and transfinite numbers? Let us make no mistake about it: mathematics is and always has been the numbers game par excellence. The great American mathematician G. D. Birkhoff once remarked that simple conundrums raised about the integers have been a source of revitalization for mathematics over the centuries.

Numbers are an indispensable tool of civilization, serving to whip its activities into some sort of order. In their most primitive application they serve as identification tags: telephone numbers, car licenses, ZIP-code numbers. At this level we merely compare one number with another; the numbers are not subjected to arithmetical operations. (We would not expect to arrive at anything significant by adding the number of Leonard Bernstein's telephone to Elizabeth Taylor's.) At a somewhat higher level we make use of the natural order of the positive integers: in taking a number for our turn at the meat counter or in listing the order of finish in a race. There is still no need to operate on the numbers; all we are interested in is whether one number is greater or less than another. Arithmetic in its full sense does not become relevant until the stage at which we ask the question: How many? It is then that we must face up to the complexities of addition, subtraction, multiplication, division, square roots and the more elaborate dealings with numbers.

The complexity of a civilization is mirrored in the complexity of its numbers. Twenty-five hundred years ago the Babylonians used simple integers to deal with the ownership of a few sheep and simple arithmetic to record the motions of the planets. Today mathematical economists use matrix algebra to describe the interconnections of hundreds of industries [see "Mathematics in the Social Sciences," page 284], and physicists use transformations in "Hilbert space"—a number concept seven levels of abstraction higher than the positive integers—to predict quantum phenomena [see "Mathematics in the Physical Sciences," page 249].

The number systems employed in mathematics can be divided into five principal stages, going from the simplest to the most complicated. They are: (1) the system consisting of the positive integers only; (2) the next higher stage, comprising the positive and negative integers and zero; (3) the rational numbers, which include fractions as well as the integers; (4) the real numbers, which include the irrational numbers, such as π; (5) the complex numbers, which introduce the "imaginary" number $\sqrt{-1}$.

The positive integers are the numbers a child learns in counting. They are usually written 1, 2, 3, 4..., but they can and have been written in many other ways. The Romans wrote them I, II, III, IV...; the Greeks wrote them α, β, γ, δ...; in the binary number system, containing only the digits 0 and 1, the corresponding numbers are written as 1, 10, 11, 100.... All these variations come to the same thing: they use different symbols for entities whose meaning and order are uniformly understood.

Early man needed only the first few integers, but with the coming of civilization he had to invent higher and higher numbers. This advance did not come readily. As Bernard Shaw remarked in *Man and Superman:* "To the Bushman who cannot count further than his fingers, eleven is an incalculable myriad." As late as the third century B.C. there appears to have been no systematic way of expressing large numbers. Archimedes then suggested a cumbersome method of naming them in his work *The Sand Reckoner.*

Yet while struggling with the names of large numbers the Greek mathematicians took the jump from the finite to

---

NEW-WORLD NUMBERS, in dot-and-bar notation, record the date of a fragmentary Olmec stela from the state of Vera Cruz in Mexico. Each dot equals one unit; each bar equals five. Restored, these numbers show seven periods of 400 "years" (*missing from top*), plus 16 periods of 20 "years" (*the topmost surviving numeral, dot eroded*), plus six "years" of 360 days each, plus 16 "months" of 20 days each, plus 18 days: a total elapsed time of nearly 3,127 "years" since the mythical start of the system. By one method of correlation with the Christian calendar, this is the equivalent of November 4, 291 B.C., and is the second oldest recorded date in the Western Hemisphere.

```
                              1     2     3     4 . . .
_____

  . . . −4    −3    −2    −1    0    1     2     3     4 . . .
_____

  . . . −4    −3    −2    −1    0    1     2     3     4 . . .

                                   1/2

                                   1/3

                                   1/4
                                    .
                                    .

  . . . −4    −3    −2    −1    0    1     2     3     4 . . .

                                   1/2                     3.14159265535 . . .

                                   1/3

                                   1/4
                                    .
                                    .
_____

                                    .
                                    .
              4√−1

              3√−1

              2√−1

               √−1

  . . . −4    −3    −2    −1    0    1     2     3     4 . . .

             −√−1    1/2                     3.14159265535 . . .

            −2√−1    1/3

            −3√−1    1/4
                      .
            −4√−1     .
                      .
```

NUMBER CONCEPTS can be arrayed in such a way that each succeeding system embraces all its predecessors. The most primitive concept, consisting of the positive integers alone, is succeeded by one extended to include zero and the negative integers. The next two additions are the rational and the irrational numbers, the latter recognizable by their infinitely nonrepetitive sequence of integers after the decimal. This completes the system of real numbers. The final array represents complex numbers, which began as a Renaissance flight of fancy and have since proved vital to the mathematics of physics and engineering. The complex numbers consist of real numbers combined with the quantity $\sqrt{-1}$, or i.

the infinite. The jump is signified by the three little dots placed after the 4 in the series above. They indicate that there is an integer after 4 and another after the successor to 4 and so on through an unlimited number of integers. For the ancients this concept was a supreme act of the imagination, because it ran counter to all physical experience and to a philosophical belief that the universe must be finite. The bold notion of infinity opened up vast possibilities for mathematics, and it also created paradoxes. Its meaning has not been fully plumbed to this day.

Oddly the step from the positive to the negative integers proved to be a more difficult one to make. Negative numbers seem altogether commonplace in our day, when 10 degrees below zero is a universally understood quantity and the youngest child is familiar with the countdown: "...five, four, three, two, one...." But the Greeks dealt with negative numbers only in terms of algebraic expressions of the areas of squares and rectangles, for example $(a - b)^2 = a^2 - 2ab + b^2$ [see illustration at top of pages 92 and 93]. Negative numbers were not fully incorporated into mathematics until the publication of Girolamo Cardano's Ars Magna in 1545.

Fractions, or rational numbers (the name they go by in number theory), are more ancient than the negative numbers. They appear in the earliest mathematical writings and were discussed at some length as early as 1550 B.C. in the Rhind Papyrus of Egypt. The present way of writing fractions (for instance 1/4, 1/5, 8/13) and also the present way of doing arithmetic with them date from the 15th and 16th centuries. Today most people probably could not be trusted to add 1/4 and 1/5 correctly. (Indeed, how often do they need to?) The handling of fractions, however, is by no means a dead issue. It recently became a matter of newspaper controversy as a result of the treatment of fractions in some of the new school mathematics courses, with the cancellation school pitted against the anticancellation school. The controversy stemmed from a divergence of opinion as to what the practical and aesthetic goals of school mathematics should be; the mystified layman, reading about it over his eggs and coffee, may have been left with the impression that everything he had once been taught about fractions was wrong or immoral.

The irrational numbers also have a long history. In the sixth century B.C. the mathematical school of Pythag-

	0	1	2	3	4	5	6	7	8	9	10	11	12	13	14	15	16
ABACUS PRINCIPLE																	
EGYPTIAN		I	II	III	IIII	III II	III III	IIII III	IIII IIII	IIII III IIII	∩	∩I	∩II	∩III	∩IIII	∩ III II	∩ III III
MAYAN		•	••	•••	••••	—	·—	··—	•••—	••••—	=	·=	··=	•••=	••••=	≡	·≡
GREEK		A	B	Γ	Δ	E	F	Z	H	Θ	I	IA	IB	IΓ	IΔ	IE	IF
ROMAN		I	II	III	IV	V	VI	VII	VIII	IX	X	XI	XII	XIII	XIV	XV	XVI
ARABIC	0	1	2	3	4	5	6	7	8	9	10	11	12	13	14	15	16
BINARY	00000	00001	00010	00011	00100	00101	00110	00111	01000	01001	01010	01011	01100	01101	01110	01111	10000

ANCIENT AND MODERN NOTATIONS for the numerals from 1 to 16 are arrayed beneath the equivalent values set up on a two-rod abacus. Of the six examples all but two have a base of 10; these are repetitive above that number regardless of whether the symbol is tally-like or unique for each value. The Mayan notation has a base of 20 and is repetitive after the numeral 5. The binary system has a base of 2 and all its numbers are written with only a pair of symbols, 0 and 1. Thus two, or 2^1, is written 10; four, or 2^2, is written 100, and eight, or 2^3, is written 1000. Each additional power of 2 thereafter adds one more digit to the binary notation.

oras encountered a number that could not be fitted into the category of either integers or fractions. This number, arrived at by the Pythagorean theorem, was $\sqrt{2}$: the length of the diagonal of a square (or the hypotenuse of a right triangle) whose sides are one unit long. The Greeks were greatly upset to find that $\sqrt{2}$ could not be expressed in terms of any number a/b in which a and b were integers, that is, any rational number. Since they originally thought the only numbers were rational numbers, this discovery was tantamount to finding that the diagonal of a square did not have a mathematical length! The Greeks resolved this paradox by thinking of numbers as lengths. This led to a program that inhibited the proper development of arithmetic and algebra, and Greek mathematics ran itself into a stone wall.

It took centuries of development and sophistication in mathematics to realize that the square root of two can be represented by putting three dots after the last calculated digit. Today we press the square-root button of a desk calculator and get the answer: $\sqrt{2} = 1.41421\ldots$. Electronic computers have carried the specification of the digits out to thousands of decimal places. Any number that can be written in this form—with one or more integers to the left of a decimal point and an infinite sequence of integers to the right of the point—is a "real" number. We can express in this way the positive integers (for example, $17 = 17.0000\ldots$), the negative integers ($-3 = -3.0000\ldots$) or the rational numbers ($17\frac{1}{5} = 17.20000\ldots$). Some rational numbers do not resolve themselves into a string of zeros at the right; for instance, the decimal expression of one-seventh is $1/7 = 0.142857$ 142857 $142857\ldots$. What makes these numbers "rational" is the fact that they contain a pattern of digits to the right of the decimal point that repeats itself over and over. The numbers called "irrational" are those that, like the square root of two, have an infinitely nonrepeating sequence of decimal digits. The best-known examples of irrationals are: $\sqrt{2} = 1.4142135623\ldots$ and $\pi = 3.1415926535\ldots$. The irrational

numbers are of course included among the real numbers.

It is in the domain of the "complex numbers" that we come to the numbers called "imaginary"—a term that today is a quaint relic of a more naïve, swashbuckling era in arithmetic. Complex numbers feature the "quantity" $\sqrt{-1}$, which, when multiplied by itself, produces -1. Since this defies the basic rule that the multiplication of two positive or negative numbers is positive, $\sqrt{-1}$ (or i, as it is usually written) is indeed an oddity: a number that cannot be called either positive or negative. "The imaginary numbers," wrote Gottfried Wilhelm von Leibniz in 1702, "are a wonderful flight of God's Spirit; they are almost an amphibian between being and not being."

From Renaissance times on, although mathematicians could not say what these fascinating imaginaries were, they used complex numbers (which have the general form $a + b\sqrt{-1}$) to solve equations and uncovered many beautiful identities. Abraham de Moivre discovered the formula $(\cos\theta + \sqrt{-1}\sin\theta)^n$

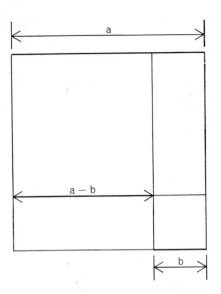
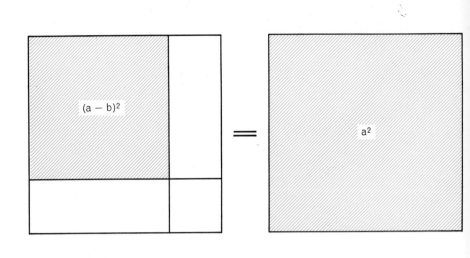

NEGATIVE NUMBERS were visualized by the Greeks in terms of lines and bounded areas. Thus they realized that the square erected on the line $a - b$ was equal in area, after a series of manipulations, to the square on the entire line a. The first manipula-

$= \cos\ n\theta + \sqrt{-1}\ \sin\ n\theta$. Leonhard Euler discovered the related formula

$$e^{\pi\sqrt{-1}} = -1$$

(e being the base of the "natural logarithms," $2.71828\ldots$).

The complex numbers remained on the purely manipulative level until the 19th century, when mathematicians began to find concrete meanings for them. Caspar Wessel of Norway discovered a way to represent them geometrically [see illustration on page 94], and this became the basis of a structure of great beauty known as the theory of functions of a complex variable. Later the Irish mathematician William Rowan Hamilton developed an algebraic interpretation of complex numbers that represented each complex number by a pair of ordinary numbers. This idea helped to provide a foundation for the development of an axiomatic approach to algebra.

Meanwhile physicists found complex numbers useful in describing various physical phenomena. Such numbers began to enter into equations of electrostatics, hydrodynamics, aerodynamics, alternating-current electricity, diverse other forms of vibrating systems and eventually quantum mechanics. Today many of the productions of theoretical physics and engineering are written in the language of the complex-number system.

In the 19th century mathematicians invented several new number systems. Of these modern systems three are particularly noteworthy: quaternions, matrices and transfinite numbers.

Quaternions were Hamilton's great creation. For many years he brooded over the fact that the multiplication of complex numbers has a simple interpretation as the rotation of a plane. Could this idea be generalized? Would it be possible to invent a new kind of number and to define a new kind of multiplication such that a rotation of three-dimensional space would have a simple interpretation in terms of the multiplication? Hamilton called such a number a triplet; just as Wessel represented complex numbers by a point on a two-dimensional plane, the triplets were to be represented by a point in three-dimensional space.

The problem was a hard nut to crack. It was continually on Hamilton's mind, and his family worried over it with him. As he himself related, when he came down to breakfast one of his sons would ask: "Well, Papa, can you multiply triplets?" And Papa would answer dejectedly: "No, I can only add and subtract them."

One day in 1843, while he was walking with his wife along a canal in Dublin, Hamilton suddenly conceived a way to multiply triplets. He was so elated that he took out a penknife then and there and carved on Brougham Bridge the key to the problem, which certainly must have mystified passersby who read it: "$i^2 = j^2 = k^2 = ijk = -1$."

The letters i, j and k represent hypercomplex numbers Hamilton called quaternions (the general form of a quaternion being $a + bi + cj + dk$, with a, b, c and d denoting real numbers). Just as the square of $\sqrt{-1}$ is -1, so

$i^2 = -1$, $j^2 = -1$ and $k^2 = -1$. The key to the multiplication of quaternions, however, is that the commutative law does not hold [see table on page 95]. Whereas in the case of ordinary numbers $ab = ba$, when quaternions are reversed, the product may be changed: for example, $ij = k$ but $ji = -k$.

The second modern number concept mentioned above, that of the matrix, was developed more or less simultaneously by Hamilton and the British mathematicians J. J. Sylvester and Arthur Cayley. A matrix can be regarded as a rectangular array of numbers. For example,

$$\begin{pmatrix} 1 & 6 & 7 \\ 2 & 0 & 4 \end{pmatrix}$$

is a matrix. The entire array is thought of as an entity in its own right. Under the proper circumstances it is possible to define operations of addition, subtraction, multiplication and division for such entities. The result is a system of objects whose behavior is somewhat reminiscent of ordinary numbers and which is of great utility in many provinces of pure and applied mathematics.

The third modern concept, that of transfinite numbers, represents a totally different order of idea. It is entertainingly illustrated by a fantasy, attributed to the noted German mathematician David Hilbert and known as "Hilbert's Hotel." It would be appreciated by roomless visitors to the New York World's Fair. A guest comes to Hilbert's Hotel and asks for a room. "Hm," says the manager. "We are all booked up, but that's not an unsolvable problem

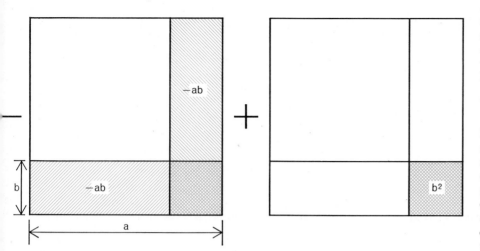

tions require the subtraction of two rectangles of length a and width b from a^2. But these rectangles overlap, and one quantity has been subtracted twice. This is b^2, which is restored.

here; we can make space for you." He puts the new guest in room 1, moves the occupant of room 1 to room 2, the occupant of room 2 to room 3 and so on. The occupant of room N goes into room $N + 1$. The hotel simply has an infinite number of rooms.

How, then, can the manager say that the hotel is "all booked up?" Galileo noted a similar paradox. Every integer can be squared, and from this we might conclude that there are as many squares as there are integers. But how can this be, in view of the known fact that there are integers that are not squares, for instance 2, 3, 5, 6...?

One of the endlessly alluring aspects of mathematics is that its thorniest paradoxes have a way of blooming into beautiful theories. The 19th-century German mathematician Georg Cantor turned this paradox into a new number system and an arithmetic of infinite numbers.

He started by defining an infinite set as one that can be put into a one-to-one correspondence with a part of itself, just as the integers are in a one-to-one correspondence with their squares. He noted that every set that can be put into such correspondence with the set of all the integers must contain an infinite number of elements, and he designated this "number" as $\aleph$ (aleph, the first letter of the Hebrew alphabet). Cantor gave this "first transfinite cardinal" the subscript zero. He then went on to show that there is an infinity of other sets (for example the set of real numbers) that cannot be put into a one-to-one correspondence with the positive integers because they are larger than that set. Their

sizes are represented by other transfinite cardinal numbers ($\aleph_1$, $\aleph_2$ and so on). From such raw materials Cantor developed an arithmetic covering both ordinary and transfinite numbers. In this arithmetic some of the ordinary rules are rejected, and we get strange equations such as $\aleph_0 + 1 = \aleph_0$. This expresses, in symbolic form, the hotel paradox.

The transfinite numbers have not yet found application outside mathematics itself. But within mathematics they have had considerable influence and have evoked much logical and philosophical speculation. Cantor's famous "continuum

hypothesis" produced a legacy of unsolved problems that still occupy mathematicians. In recent years solutions to some of these problems have been achieved by Alfred Tarski of the University of California at Berkeley and Paul J. Cohen of Stanford University.

We have reviewed the subject matter (or dramatis personae) of the numbers game; it now behooves us to examine the rules of the game. To nonmathematicians this may seem to be an exercise in laboring the obvious. The geometry of Euclid is built on "self-evident" axioms, but rigorous examination of the axioms in the 19th century disclosed loopholes, inconsistencies and weaknesses that had to be repaired in order to place geometry on firmer foundations. But, one may ask, what is there about the simple rules of arithmetic and algebra that needs examination or proof? Shaken by the discoveries of the shortcomings of Euclid's axioms, and spurred by the surprising features of the new number concepts such as the quaternions, many mathematicians of the 19th century subjected the axioms of number theory to systematic study.

Are the laws of arithmetic independent, or can one be derived logically from another? Are they really fundamental, or could they be reduced to a more primitive, simpler and more elegant set of laws? Answers to questions such as these have been sought by the program of axiomatic inquiry, which is

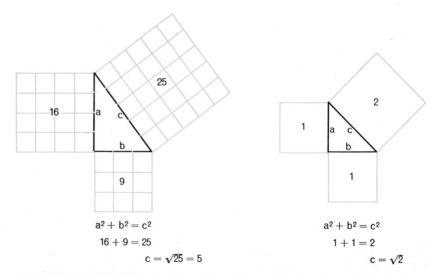

$$a^2 + b^2 = c^2$$
$$16 + 9 = 25$$
$$c = \sqrt{25} = 5$$

$$a^2 + b^2 = c^2$$
$$1 + 1 = 2$$
$$c = \sqrt{2}$$

IRRATIONAL NUMBERS seemed paradoxical to the Greeks, who could not imagine numbers that were neither integers nor rational fractions but who could nonetheless express such numbers geometrically. In a right triangle with two sides of unit length 3 and 4 respectively, the hypotenuse is 5 units in length. But no rational fraction is equal to $\sqrt{2}$, the length of the hypotenuse of a right triangle that has sides of length 1. In effect, this says that an easily constructed line of quite tangible length is nonetheless "immeasurable."

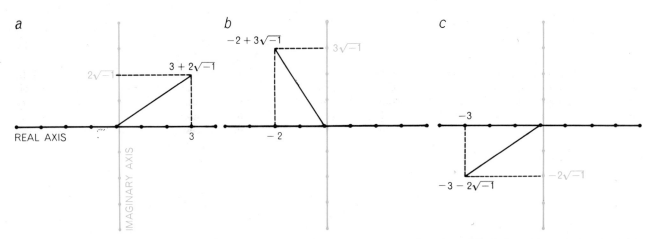

COMPLEX NUMBERS can be represented and even manipulated in a geometric fashion. On the real, or *x*, axis each unit is 1 or −1. On the imaginary, or *y*, axis each unit is *i*, or $\sqrt{-1}$, or else −*i*. Thus all points on the plane can be given complex numbers of the form *x* + *yi*. If a line through both the origin and any point on the plane (*as shown in "a"*) is rotated through 90 degrees (*as in "b"*), the result is the multiplication of the original complex number by $\sqrt{-1}$. A second rotation, and multiplication by *i*, appears in *c*.

still going on. It has yielded rigorous and aesthetically appealing answers to some of them, and in the process it has brought forth new concepts such as "rings," "fields," "groups" and "lattices," each with its own set of rules of operation and its own characteristic theory.

One of the major accomplishments, achieved in the 1870's, was the establishment of a set of axioms for the real numbers. It is summed up in the statement that the real-number system is a "complete ordered field." Each of these words represents a group of rules that defines the behavior of the numbers.

First of all, the word "field" means a mathematical system in which addition and multiplication can be carried out in a way that satisfies the familiar rules, namely (1) the commutative law of addition: $x + y = y + x$; (2) the associative law of addition: $x + (y + z) = (x + y) + z$; (3) the commutative law of multiplication: $xy = yx$; (4) the associative law of multiplication: $x(yz) = (xy)z$; (5) the distributive law: $x(y + z) = xy + xz$.

Furthermore, a field must contain a zero element, 0, characterized by the property that $x + 0 = x$ for any element x. It contains a unit element, 1, that has the property that $1 \cdot x = x$. For any given element x of a field there is another element $-x$ such that $-x + x = 0$. This is the foundation on which subtraction is built. Another axiomatic property of a field is the cancellation rule of multiplication, that is, if $xy = xz$, then $y = z$ (provided that x is not equal to zero). Finally, for any element x (other than zero) a field must contain an element $1/x$ such that $x(1/x) = 1$. This is the basis for division. Briefly,

then, a field is a system (exemplified by the rational numbers) whose elements can be added, subtracted, multiplied and divided under the familiar rules of arithmetic.

Considering now the second word, a field is "ordered" if the sizes of its elements can be compared. The shorthand symbol used to denote this property is the sign >, meaning "greater than." This symbol is required to obey its own set of rules, namely (1) the trichotomy law: for any two elements x and y, exactly one of these three relations is true, $x > y$, $x = y$ or $y > x$; (2) the transitivity law: if $x > y$ and $y > z$, then $x > z$; (3) the law of addition: if $x > y$, then $x + z > y + z$; (4) the law of multiplication: if $x > y$ and $z > 0$, then $xz > yz$.

Finally, what do we mean by the word "complete" in describing the system of real numbers as a "complete ordered field"? This has to do with the problem raised by a number such as $\sqrt{2}$. Practically speaking, $\sqrt{2}$ is given by a sequence of rational numbers such as 1, 1.4, 1.41, 1.414... that provide better and better approximations to it. That is to say, $1^2 = 1$, $(1.4)^2 = 1.96$, $(1.41)^2 = 1.9981$, $(1.414)^2 = 1.999$-396.... Squaring these numbers yields a sequence of numbers that are getting closer and closer to 2. Notice, however, that the numbers in the original sequence (1, 1.4, 1.41...) are also getting closer and closer to one another. We would like to think of $\sqrt{2}$ as the "limiting value" of such a sequence of approximations. In order to do so we need a precise notion of what is meant by saying that the numbers of a sequence are getting closer and closer to one an-

other, and we need a guarantee that our system of numbers is rich enough to provide us with a limiting number for such a sequence.

Following the path taken by Cantor, we consider a sequence of numbers in our ordered field. We shall say that the numbers of this sequence are getting closer and closer to one another if the difference of any two numbers sufficiently far out in the sequence is as small as we please. This means, for example, that all terms sufficiently far out differ from one another by at the most 1/10. If one wishes to go out still further, they can be made to differ by at most 1/100, and so forth. Such a sequence of numbers is called a "regular sequence." An ordered field is called a "complete" ordered field if, corresponding to any regular sequence of elements, there is an element of the field that the sequence approaches as a limiting value. This is the "law of completeness": the "gaps" between the rational numbers have been completed, or filled up. It is the final axiomatic requirement for the real-number system.

All these rules may seem so elementary that they hardly need stating, let alone laborious analysis. The program of systematizing them, however, has been vastly rewarding. Years of polishing the axioms have reduced them to a form that is of high simplicity. The rules I have just enumerated have been found to be necessary, and sufficient, to do the job of describing and operating the real-number system; throw any one of them away and the system would not work. And, as I have said, the program of axiomatic inquiry has answered some fundamental questions about numbers and produced enormously fruitful new concepts.

The spirit of axiomatic inquiry pervades all modern mathematics; it has even percolated into the teaching of mathematics in high schools. A high school teacher recently said to me: "In the old days the rules of procedure were buried in fine print and largely ignored in the classroom. Today the fine print has been parlayed into the main course. The student is in danger of knowing that $2 + 3 = 3 + 2$ by the commutative law but not knowing that the sum is 5." Of course anything can be overdone. Exclusive attention to axiomatics would be analogous to the preoccupation of a dance group that met every week and discussed choreography but never danced. What is wanted in mathematics, as in anything else, is a sound sense of proportion.

We have been considering how numbers operate; ultimately we must face the more elementary question: What *are* numbers, after all? Nowadays mathematicians are inclined to answer this question too in terms of axiomatics rather than in terms of epistemology or philosophy.

To explain, or better still to create, numbers it seems wise to try the method of synthesis instead of analysis. Suppose we start with primitive, meaningful elements and see if step by step we can build these elements up into something that corresponds to the system of real numbers.

As our primitive elements we can take the positive integers. They are a concrete aspect of the universe, in the form of the number of fingers on the human hand or whatever one chooses to count. As the 19th-century German mathematician Leopold Kronecker put it, the positive integers are the work of God and all the other types of number are the work of man. In the late 19th century Giuseppe Peano of Italy provided a primitive description of the positive integers in terms of five axioms: (1) 1 is a positive integer; (2) every positive integer has a unique positive integer as its successor; (3) no positive integer has 1 as its successor; (4) distinct positive integers have distinct successors; (5) if a statement holds for the positive integer 1, and if, whenever it holds for a positive integer, it also holds for that integer's successor, then the statement holds for all positive integers. (This last axiom is the famous "principle of mathematical induction.")

Now comes the *fiat lux* ("Let there be light") of the whole business. Axiom: There exists a Peano system. This stroke creates the positive integers, because the Peano system, or system of objects that fulfills the five requirements, is essentially equivalent to the set of positive integers. From Peano's five rules all the familiar features of the positive integers can be deduced.

Once we have the positive integers at our disposal to work with and to mold, we can go merrily on our way, as Kronecker suggested, and construct extensions of the number idea. By operations with the positive integers, for example, we can create the negative integers and zero. A convenient way to do this is by operating with *pairs* of positive integers. Think of a general pair denoted (a,b) from which we shall create an integer by the operation $a - b$. When a is greater than b, the subtraction $a - b$ produces a positive integer; when b is greater than a, the resulting $a - b$ integer is negative; when a is equal to b, then $a - b$ produces zero. Thus pairs of positive integers can represent all the integers—positive, nega-

tive and zero. It is true that a certain ambiguity arises from the fact that a given integer can be represented by many different pairs; for instance, the pair (6,2) stands for 4, but so do (7,3), (8,4) and a host of other possible combinations. We can reduce the ambiguity to unimportance, however, simply by agreeing to consider all such pairs as being identical.

Using only positive integers, we can write a rule that will determine when one pair is equal to another. The rule is that $(a,b) = (c,d)$ if, and only if, $a + d = b + c$. (Note that the latter equation is a rephrasing of $a - b = c - d$, but it does not involve any negative integers, whereas the subtraction terms may.) It can easily be shown that this rule for deciding the equality of pairs of integers satisfies the three arithmetical laws governing equality, namely (1) the reflexive law: $(a,b) = (a,b)$; (2) the symmetric law: if $(a,b) = (b,c)$, then $(b,c) = (a,b)$; (3) the transitive law: if $(a,b) = (c,d)$ and $(c,d) = (e,f)$, then $(a,b) = (e,f)$.

We can now proceed to introduce

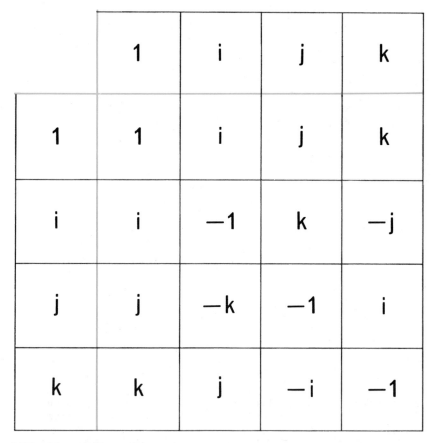

	1	i	j	k
1	1	i	j	k
i	i	−1	k	−j
j	j	−k	−1	i
k	k	j	−i	−1

MULTIPLICATION TABLE for the quaternions, devised by William Rowan Hamilton, demonstrates the noncommutative nature of these imaginary quantities. For example, the row quantity *j*, multiplied by the column quantity *k*, produces *i*, but row *k* times column *j* produces −*i* instead. Each of the three quantities, multiplied by itself, is equal to −1.

conventions defining the addition and the multiplication of pairs of positive integers, again using only positive terms. For addition we have $(a,b) + (c,d) = (a + c,\ b + d)$. Since (a,b) represents $a - b$ and (c,d) represents $c - d$, the addition here is $(a - b) + (c - d)$. Algebraically this is the same as $(a + c) - (b + d)$, and that is represented by the pair $(a + c,\ b + d)$ on the right side of the equation. Similarly, the multiplication of pairs of positive integers is defined by the formula $(a,b) \cdot (c,d) = (ac + bd,\ ad + bc)$. Here $(a,b)(c,d)$, or $(a - b)(c - d)$, can be expressed algebraically as $(ac + bd) - (ad + bc)$, and this is represented on the right side of

the equation by the pair $(ac + bd,\ ad + bc)$.

It can be shown in detail that all the familiar operations with integers (positive, negative and zero), when performed with such pairs of positive integers, will produce the same results.

Having constructed all the integers (as pairs of positive integers), we can go on to create all the other real numbers and even the complex numbers. The rational numbers, or fractions, which are pairs of integers in the ordinary system, can be represented as pairs of pairs of positive integers. For the real numbers, made up of infinite sequences

of integers, we must set up infinite sequences of rationals rather than pairs. When we come to the complex numbers, we can again use pairs; indeed, it was for these numbers that the device of number pairs was first employed (by Hamilton). We can think of a complex number, $a + b\sqrt{-1}$, as essentially a pair of real numbers (a,b), with the first number of the pair representing the real element and the second representing the imaginary element of the complex number. Now, pairs will be considered equal only if they contain the same numbers in the same order; that is, $(a,b) = (c,d)$ only if $a = c$ and $b = d$. The rule for addition will be

a

$$\begin{bmatrix} a_1 & a_2 & a_3 \\ a_4 & a_5 & a_6 \\ a_7 & a_8 & a_9 \end{bmatrix} + \begin{bmatrix} b_1 & b_2 & b_3 \\ b_4 & b_5 & b_6 \\ b_7 & b_8 & b_9 \end{bmatrix} = \begin{bmatrix} a_1 + b_1 & a_2 + b_2 & a_3 + b_3 \\ a_4 + b_4 & a_5 + b_5 & a_6 + b_6 \\ a_7 + b_7 & a_8 + b_8 & a_9 + b_9 \end{bmatrix}$$

$$\begin{bmatrix} 7 & 0 & 0 \\ -3 & 1 & -6 \\ 4 & 0 & 7 \end{bmatrix} + \begin{bmatrix} -8 & 0 & 1 \\ 4 & 5 & -1 \\ 0 & 3 & 0 \end{bmatrix} = \begin{bmatrix} 7 - 8 & 0 + 0 & 0 + 1 \\ -3 + 4 & 1 + 5 & -6 - 1 \\ 4 + 0 & 0 + 3 & 0 + 7 \end{bmatrix} = \begin{bmatrix} -1 & 0 & 1 \\ 1 & 6 & -7 \\ 4 & 3 & 7 \end{bmatrix}$$

b

$$\begin{bmatrix} a_1 & a_2 & a_3 \\ a_4 & a_5 & a_6 \\ a_7 & a_8 & a_9 \end{bmatrix} \times \begin{bmatrix} b_1 & b_4 & b_7 \\ b_2 & b_5 & b_8 \\ b_3 & b_6 & b_9 \end{bmatrix} = \begin{bmatrix} a_1b_1 + a_2b_2 + a_3b_3 & a_1b_4 + a_2b_5 + a_3b_6 & a_1b_7 + a_2b_8 + a_3b_9 \\ a_4b_1 + a_5b_2 + a_6b_3 & a_4b_4 + a_5b_5 + a_6b_6 & a_4b_7 + a_5b_8 + a_6b_9 \\ a_7b_1 + a_8b_2 + a_9b_3 & a_7b_4 + a_8b_5 + a_9b_6 & a_7b_7 + a_8b_8 + a_9b_9 \end{bmatrix}$$

$$\begin{bmatrix} 6 & 0 & -1 \\ 1 & -3 & 2 \\ 8 & 5 & 6 \end{bmatrix} \times \begin{bmatrix} 4 & 2 & 3 \\ 0 & 1 & 6 \\ -5 & -1 & 7 \end{bmatrix} = \begin{bmatrix} 24 + 0 + 5 & 12 + 0 + 1 & 18 + 0 - 7 \\ 4 + 0 - 10 & 2 - 3 - 2 & 3 - 18 + 14 \\ 32 + 0 - 30 & 16 + 5 - 6 & 24 + 30 + 42 \end{bmatrix} = \begin{bmatrix} 29 & 13 & 11 \\ -6 & -3 & -1 \\ 2 & 15 & 96 \end{bmatrix}$$

MATRICES are rectangular arrays of numbers, themselves without numerical value, that nonetheless can be treated as entities and thus can be added, subtracted, multiplied or divided in the proper circumstances. Such arrays offer a particularly convenient method for calculating simultaneous changes in a series of related variables. Addition is possible with any pair of matrices having the same number of columns and rows; row by row, each element in each column of the first matrix is added to the corresponding element in the corresponding column of the next, thus forming a new matrix. (The process is shown schematically at the top of the illustration and then repeated, with numerical values, directly below.) Multiplication is a more complex process, in which the two matrices need not be the same size, although they are in the illustration; a 3 × 2 matrix could multiply a 2 × 3 one. Each term in the upper row of the left matrix successively multiplies the corresponding term in the first column of the right matrix; the sum of these three multiplications is the number entered at column 1, row 1 of the product matrix. The upper row of the left matrix is now used in the same way with the second column of the right matrix to find a value for column 2, row 1 of the product matrix, and then multiplies the third column of the right matrix. The entire operation is repeated with each row of the left matrix.

the same as in the case of the real numbers: $(a,b) + (c,d) = (a + c, b + d)$. This parallels the "ordinary" outcome of the addition of two complex numbers: $(a + b\sqrt{-1}) + (c + d\sqrt{-1}) = (a + c) + (b + d)\sqrt{-1}$. The multiplication formula for complex numbers, $(a,b) \cdot (c,d) = (ac - bd, ad + bc)$, also corresponds to the ordinary multiplication of such numbers: $(a + b\sqrt{-1})(c + d\sqrt{-1}) = (ac - bd) + (ad + bc)\sqrt{-1}$. Pairs of real numbers manipulated according to these rules reproduce all the familiar behavior of the complex numbers. And the mysterious $\sqrt{-1}$, that "amphibian between being and not being," emerges from the sea of axiomatics as the number pair $(0,1)$.

Thus, by four steps of construction and abstraction, we have advanced from the primitive positive integers to the complex numbers. Pairs of positive integers, combined in a certain way, lead to the set of all the integers. Pairs of integers (that is to say now, pairs of pairs of positive integers), combined in a different way, lead to the rational numbers. Infinite sequences of rational numbers lead to real numbers. Finally, pairs of real numbers lead to the complex numbers.

Looking back over the 2,500 years that separate us from Pythagoras, we can make out two streams of thinking about numbers. There is the stream of synthesis, which began with tally marks and went on to build up number concepts of increasing complexity, in much the same way that a complex molecule is built up from atoms. On the other hand, there is a stream of analysis whereby mathematicians have sought to arrive at the essence of numbers by breaking down the complexities to their most primitive elements. Both streams are of enormous importance. Professional mathematicians today tend to play down number as such, favoring the qualitative aspects of their science and emphasizing the logical structure and symbolic potentialities of mathematics. Nevertheless, new ideas about number keep making their way into the mathematics journals, and the modern number theories are just now diffusing rapidly throughout our educational system, even down to the elementary schools. There are programs and committees for teaching advanced number concepts, from set theory to matrices, to students in high school. It seems safe to say that the coming generation will be imbued with an unprecedented interest in the fascinating uses and mysteries of numbers.

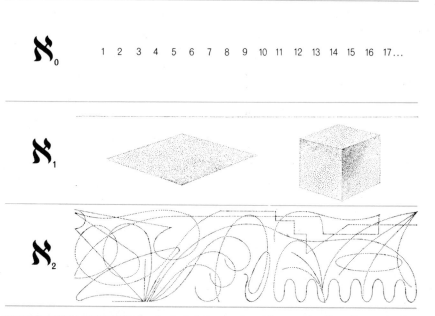

TRANSFINITE CARDINALS exist in infinite number. The most familiar, $\aleph_0$, symbolizes the "number," or the cardinality, of the positive integers or of any set that can be put into a one-to-one correspondence with the positive integers. These are the sets that are countable. The cardinality of the real numbers is larger than the cardinality of the positive integers. It is identical with the cardinality of the points on a line, in a plane or in any portion of a space of higher dimension. These noncountable sets are symbolized by $\aleph_1$. The "number" of all possible point sets is a still larger transfinite cardinal and is symbolized by $\aleph_2$.

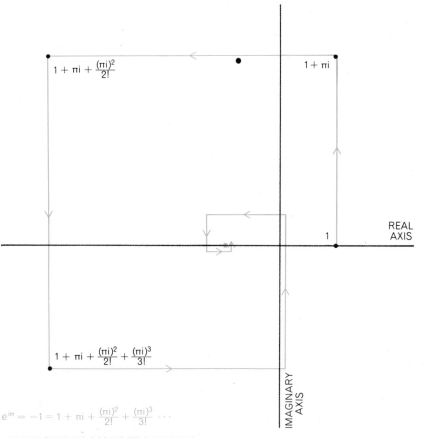

VIRTUOSITY OF COMPLEX NUMBERS is demonstrated by conversion into geometrical form of the formula that relates e (the natural base of logarithms), π and $\sqrt{-1}$. The equation (color) can be expressed as the sum of a series of vectors. When these are added and plotted on a complex plane, they form a spiral that strangles the point equal to -1.

14 THE THEORY OF NUMBERS

PAUL S. HERWITZ · July 1951

THREE shipwrecked sailors found themselves on an island where the only food was coconuts. They gathered a large number of coconuts and decided to get some needed sleep before they divided the pile into three equal shares. During the night one of the sailors awakened and, not trusting his companions, decided to take his share of the collection without waiting until morning. He found that after throwing away one of the coconuts he could divide those remaining into three equal shares. He buried his share, left the rest in a pile and went back to sleep. Later one of the other sailors awakened and proceeded to go through the same routine: he threw away one coconut, took one third of the remainder and buried them, then went back to sleep. Still later the third sailor, no less suspicious than his mates, went through exactly the same procedure. What is the least number of coconuts the sailors must have collected originally so that there would be a whole number of coconuts left after all this? (We leave to the psychologists the problem of deciding how the sailors reacted to the shrinkage of the pile in the morning.)

Let x represent the number of coconuts collected by the sailors. The first sailor, after burying his share of them, left $2/3(x-1)$, the second left $2/3[2/3(x-1)-1]$; the final equation is $2/3\{2/3[2/3(x-1)-1]-1\}=y$, the number of coconuts left in the morning. This simplifies to $8x-27y=38$. As a general equation this has an infinite number of possible solutions for varying values of x, but we know from the terms of our particular problem that x and y must be positive whole numbers and that x must be the smallest positive in-teger that will permit y to be a positive integer. The last condition gives us one, and only one, answer, namely, the least number of coconuts the sailors originally collected was 25, and the next morning there would have been six left in the pile.

Had four sailors landed on the island and suffered the same mutual mistrust, our problem would have reduced to the equation $81x-256y=525$. If we generalize the problem to apply to any number of sailors, n (where n is more than 1), the final equation is $(n-1)^n x - n^n y = (n-1)^n + n(n-1)^{n-1} + n^2(n-1)^{n-2} + \ldots + n^{n-1}(n-1)$. (The series of dots indicates that there may be more terms, or fewer terms, than we have written.) This equation is itself a specific instance of the general equation $ax+by=c$, where all the numbers are integers and c is a constant. Many problems lead to

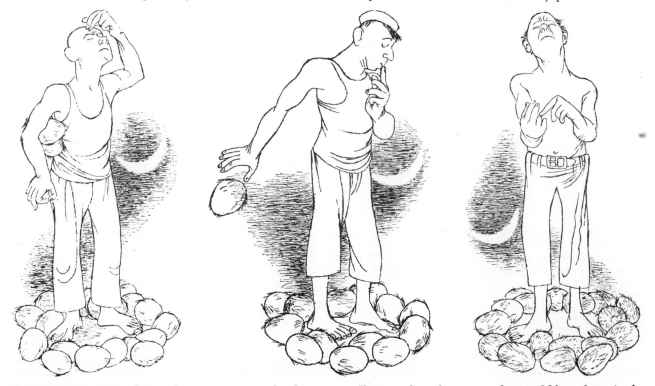

SUSPICIOUS SAILORS awoke one by one to divide a pile of coconuts into three equal shares. What is the smallest number of coconuts that could have been in the original pile? The drawings do not show all the coconuts.

equations which are special cases of this general equation. Such an equation is called Diophantine, after the Greek mathematician Diophantus, who first discussed it around A.D. 250.

THE Diophantine equation is one of the cornerstones of the Theory of Numbers. This branch of study has as its aim the discovery of properties of the integers. The fact that these principles are frequently illustrated by application to the solution of puzzles and brain-teasers, such as that of the sailors and the coconuts, should not mislead anyone into thinking that the Theory of Numbers is nothing but a scientific curiosity. Simple as many properties of the integers may appear, their proofs have often entailed many years of study by numerous fine mathematicians, and number theory has long been an important branch of mathematics.

Pierre de Fermat, the celebrated 17th-century French mathematician, is considered to be the father of the modern theory of numbers. Fermat uncovered many interesting properties which are by no means obvious or superficial. Probably as famous as the ancient problem of trisecting an angle is what is known as Fermat's Last Theorem. Fermat was accustomed to write remarks and theorems, without their proofs, in the margins of his books. In his copy of Diophantus' *Arithmetica* he stated the following "theorem": *The equation* $x^n + y^n = z^n$ *has no nontrivial solution in integers for n greater than 2.* By a trivial solution is meant a solution such as x, y and z all equal to zero. Fermat claimed to have a proof of this "theorem," but to this day no general proof of it has been found for all values of n, although many proofs are known for particular values of n. The best known special case of Fermat's equation is the Pythagorean theorem, in which $n = 2$. Pythagoras' principle can be stated as follows: If x and y represent the lengths of the sides of a right triangle and z the length of the hypotenuse, then $x^2 + y^2 = z^2$. This is a Diophantine equation, since there are more unknowns than equations, and integral solutions are desired.

OF first importance in the study of the Theory of Numbers is the concept of prime and composite numbers. A prime number of course is one that is evenly divisible only by plus or minus itself and by $+1$ and -1. All other integral numbers are composite, which means that they can be divided by some number other than themselves or 1 and yield a whole number as the quotient. A composite number can always be written as a product of two or more primes. The first few primes are 2, 3, 5, 7, 11, 13, 17, 19, 23. The composite number 12 can be written as the product of three primes: $2 \times 2 \times 3$. Many unsuccessful

BERNARDA BRYSON

FERMAT wrote a baffling theorem about numbers on the margin of a book. Generations of mathematicians have sought the proof, without success.

attempts have been made to find a simple algebraic formula that will yield only prime numbers. One of the best known was suggested by Fermat: he believed that $2^{2^n} + 1$ was a prime for all positive integral values of n. For $n = 1, 2, 3$ and 4 we have respectively the primes 5, 17, 257 and 65,537. But the 18th-century Swiss mathematician Leonhard Euler showed that when $n = 5$, the result is not a prime number; $2^{2^5} + 1 = 4,294,967,297$, which is a composite number that can be factored into $641 \times 6,700,417$. In fact, it has not been proved that $2^{2^n} + 1$ is a prime for any value of n greater than 4. The formula is laborious and difficult to investigate, because even relatively small values of n produce very large numbers: for instance, if $n = 7$, Fermat's number is greater than 34×10^{37}, that is, 34 followed by 37 zeros. There are other formulas that yield primes up to a certain point, such as $n^2 - n + 41$, which is prime for integral values of n less than 41, and $n^2 - 79n + 1,601$, prime for integral values of n less than 80. But no one has found a formula that produces primes for all values of n.

The distribution of the primes among the integers is highly irregular. The 19th-century German mathematician Peter Gustav Lejeune Dirichlet proved that in every arithmetic progression there are an infinite number of primes. An arithmetic progression is a sequence of numbers each of which is obtained from the preceding one by addition of a certain number; for example, 1, 3, 5, 7 is a progression formed by adding 2 in each case. Dirichlet's proof falls into the branch of mathematics known as analytic number theory—as contrasted to algebraic number theory. The analytic theory applies the calculus and the theory of functions to properties of the integers. The truth of Dirichlet's theorem is readily demonstrable by relatively simple considerations in certain particular cases, but for the general arithmetic progression a, $a + d$, $a + 2d$ and so on it has been necessary until recently to apply highly technical methods to prove the theorem. In 1949 the young mathematician Atle Selberg, of the Institute for Advanced Study, published a proof which has placed Dirichlet's problem in a new light. Selberg's work has revived interest in this problem and, along with several related proofs, has brought him international recognition.

An unsolved problem concerning the distribution of the primes is the problem of prime pairs. All primes larger than 2 are odd numbers, since any even number is divisible by 2. In the sequence of all odd numbers (1, 3, 5, 7, 9, 11 and so on) it has been noted that certain pairs of consecutive numbers are pairs of primes, as 3 and 5, 5 and 7, 11 and 13, 17 and 19, 29 and 31. Although it is thought that the number of such prime pairs is infinite, no one has yet succeeded in proving this to be so.

Another type of problem concerning the primes was posed in a letter that Christian Goldbach, a German teacher of mathematics, wrote to Euler in 1742. Goldbach said he believed that every even integer could be written as the sum of two primes and asked Euler whether he could prove this or could find an example to disprove it. Though Goldbach's only importance in the history of mathematics lies in this conjecture, his name will be remembered, for the problem has never been solved.

NO DISCUSSION of the Theory of Numbers could be considered complete without mention of the great German mathematician Carl Friedrich Gauss (1777-1855). In his *Disquisitiones arithmeticae* Gauss made monumental contributions to the theory. We shall consider here only one of the many subjects he discussed in this work. This is the notion of congruence of numbers, which Gauss defined somewhat as follows: If the difference of two integers, a—b, is divisible by a third integer c, then we say a is congruent to b with respect to the modulus c, or simply a is congruent to b modulo c. For example, 19 is congruent to 7 modulo 3, since $19-7=12$ and 12 is divisible by 3. The meanings of the words "congruence" and "modulus" give a hint as to the significance of this concept. The former word comes from the Latin *congruere*, meaning to coincide or agree, and the latter from the Latin *modulus*, a small measure. The number c acts as a measure of the "sameness" of the numbers a and b, in a certain sense.

Now when one number is divisible by another, the first of course is a multiple of the second; thus the number 6, divisible by 3, is a multiple of 3 obtained by multiplying 3 by 2. The notion of congruence, therefore, may be expressed by the equation $a-b=kc$, in which k represents the multiplier. This in turn can be written $a=b+kc$. So far we have nothing essentially new. The importance of Gauss' work springs from an implication inherent in a slight modification of notation which he introduced. Gauss wrote the second of the above equations as $a\equiv b$ (mod c), which reads: a is congruent to b modulo c. From this we may infer that the importance in the relationship between a and b is that they differ by a multiple of c, and the value of that multiplier (k in the original equation) is relatively unimportant.

From a slightly different standpoint, if in the equation $a=b+kc$ the integer b is less than c, but greater than or equal to zero, then b represents the remainder upon division of a by c. For example, 19 is congruent to 1 modulo 3 may be written $19/3=6+1/3$, or $19=1+6\times3$. Here $a=19, b=1, c=3, k=6$, and the division of 19 by 3 leaves the remainder 1. Again, 18 is congruent to zero modulo 3 may be written $18/3=6$, or $18=0+6\times3$. In this case $a=18, b=0, c=3, k=6$, and the remainder of the division of 18 by 6 is 0. In the same way 20 is congruent to 2, 21 is congruent to zero, 22 is congruent to 1, all taken modulo 3. In other words, with respect to the modulus 3, all numbers are congruent to one of the numbers 0, 1 or 2. If the modulus is represented by the general term c, then with respect to c every number is congruent to some

number from 0 up to $c-2$ and $c-1$. In effect this manner of considering the integers places every integer in one of c *classes*, each class represented by one of the numbers 0, 1, and so on, up to $c-1$. For example, modulo 3 the numbers 18, 21, 24, etc., would be placed in the class represented by the number 0, since zero is the remainder left when each of these numbers is divided by 3; the numbers 17, 20, 23, 26, etc., would be placed in the class represented by the number 2, since 2 is their remainder after division by 3, and so on. The gain from this treatment is that we need not consider an infinite number of integers but only a finite number of classes. In a sense all members of a particular class are essentially the same, since they leave

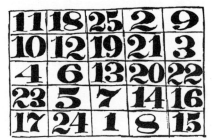

MAGIC SQUARE adds up to 65 in each row, column and two diagonals.

the same remainder upon division by their modulus.

Although this way of dealing with numbers may seem somewhat involved, actually we make use of it every day without examining the process. Suppose, for example, we had been telling the time of day from the year zero by giving each hour a new number. At the time of writing of this article it would be some time after 17,093,328 o'clock. That would be a pretty cumbersome way of telling time. But modulo 24, it is shortly after midnight. What we do is to consider the hours of the day as members of 24 classes modulo 24, represented by the names one o'clock, two o'clock and so on up to 24 o'clock. (In practice we break the day into two halves and use a 12-hour clock, distinguishing one half from the other by a.m. and p.m.) Thus there are 24 "hour-classes" in a day, or two sets of 12 "hour-classes" each. Similarly, there are seven "day-classes" in a week and 12 "month-classes" in a year. Consideration of the day and month classes and certain astronomical data permitted Gauss to state congruences and rules for their use which enable us to determine easily the dates of Easter and other holidays, depending upon both the lunar and solar calendars. Similar congruences assist us in finding the day of the week on which any given date falls in any year, so that we can tell in what years January 13 will fall on a Friday, when the 4th of July will next give us a long week-end, and so on.

There is a well-known rule of arithmetic that a number is divisible by 9 only if the sum of its digits is divisible by 9. This rule, and similar rules, may be proved easily by means of the concept of congruence. Let us take the number 234, the sum of whose digits is $2+3+4=9$. The number 234 may be written $2\times10^2+3\times10+4$. We represent this expression by N, and the expression $2+3+4$ by n. Then N—n is $(2\times10^2+3\times10+4)-(2+3+4)$. This may be written $(2\times10^2-2)+(3\times10-3)+(4-4)$, and this simplifies to $2\times99+3\times9$. Since 9 and 99 are both divisible by 9, the difference N—n is divisible by 9; in other words, N is congruent to n modulo 9. When the sum of the digits of a number is 9, as in our example, the remainder after dividing the number by 9 is zero. When the sum is a number greater than zero but less than 9, this sum represents the remainder that will be left after division by 9. When the sum of digits is greater than 9, we may apply the process to determine whether or not this new number is divisible by 9. For example, the number 73,506,816 is congruent to 36 (the sum of its digits), which is congruent to 9 modulo 9. Therefore, this number is divisible by 9. On the other hand, the number 73,506,818 is congruent to 38; 38 is congruent to 11; 11 is congruent to 2 modulo 9. Thus 73,506,818 leaves the remainder 2 when divided by 9.

Any number divisible by 9 is also divisible by 3, since 3 divides 9. We may state, then, a new rule: a number is divisible by 3 only if the sum of its digits is divisible by 3. Similar considerations allow us to state other rules: a number is divisible by 2 if its last digit on the right is divisible by 2; a number is divisible by 4 or 25, respectively, if the number formed by its last two digits is divisible by 4 or 25, respectively; a number is divisible by 5 if its last digit is zero or 5.

A check on multiplication called "Casting Out Nines" has as its basis the rule for division by 9. The check proceeds in this way: to find out whether the product c is correct in the multiplication $a\times b=c$, we find the remainder after dividing a by 9 and the remainder after dividing b by 9 and multiply the two remainders together. This product must equal the remainder after dividing c by 9. If it does not, the value of c obtained in the original multiplication was in error. What makes the check easy is that to obtain the remainders we need only add up the digits of the respective numbers. As an example let us check the multiplication $6,743\times826=5,569,-718$. The sum of the first number's digits is $6+7+4+3=20$. Dividing 20 by 9 gives a remainder of 2, as can be shown by adding its digits: $2+0=2$. Similarly the second number yields $8+2+6=16$, which divided by 9 gives a remainder of

7. Multiplying the remainders, $2 \times 7 = 14$. The sum of these digits is $1+4=5$. The sum of the digits in the product, 5,569,718, is 41, and its digits also add up to 5, so the answer is probably correct. As a practical method the device of casting out nines was probably known in India before A.D. 800; it came into use in Europe in the Middle Ages. But the mathematical theory behind the method could not be explained easily until the arrival of modern number theory; imagine the difficulty of explaining the theoretical basis of these manipulations without using the ideas of congruence.

A VERY interesting modern application of the Theory of Numbers is made in the field of electronic computing machinery. Some of these machines use the binary instead of the decimal system of numbers. We have noted that 234 can be written $2 \times 10^2 + 3 \times 10 + 4$; this is a sum of multiples of powers of 10 (4 may be written as 4×10^0). The number 234 can also be written as a sum of multiples of powers of 2, thus: 1×2^7 (128) $+1 \times 2^6$ (64) $+1 \times 2^5$ (32) $+ 0 \times 2^4$ (0) $+1 \times 2^3$ (8) $+0 \times 2^2$ (0) $+ 1 \times 2$ (2) $+0 \times 2^0$ (0). Here we use the "base" 2 instead of 10 as in the decimal system. Instead of writing down a long string of powers of 2 we can "suppress the base" and write only the multipliers of the powers of 2, which in order from left to right are 11101010. (The reader should notice that he has been doing exactly the same thing in the decimal system whenever he has written a number larger than 10; he has suppressed the base 10.) Then decimal 234 is the same as binary 11101010; similarly, decimal 15 is binary 1111 and decimal 2 is binary 10. In an electronic computing machine the binary system has this great advantage: the only digits used are 0 and 1. In the "language" of the machine each 1 can be represented by an electrical impulse and each 0 by the absence of an impulse. In this way an electronic computing machine can handle operations with numbers very rapidly.

To return to the realm of games and puzzles, we might mention two typical problems that have been investigated by number theorists. The first is the familiar wine-jug problem, one version of which goes: A man has a five-gallon jug and a three-gallon jug. He wishes to purchase four gallons of wine from an innkeeper who has only a full eight-gallon jug. How does the man measure exactly four gallons without spilling a drop? With some thought you may figure out that he measures out three gallons in the three-gallon jug and pours this into the five-gallon jug, pours three more into the three-gallon jug and fills the five-gallon jug from this, leaving one gallon in the three-gallon jug, then empties the five-gallon jug into the eight-gallon jug and pours into the five-gallon jug the one gallon plus three more measured in the three-gallon jug. This problem has been solved by number theory in general terms for jugs holding A, B and C gallons, with D gallons to be measured out. That is, it is known for what values of A, B, C and D the problem has a solution, and a systematic way of measuring can be stated.

The second problem is the so-called magic square. A magic square is an array of n^2 integers arranged in n rows and n columns in such a way that the sum of the numbers in each row, column or principal diagonal (upper left to lower right and upper right to lower left) is magic; that is, each of these sums is equal to $n/2(n^2+1)$. Magic squares have fascinated man for ages, and many mathematicians have studied them. One method of constructing magic squares is based on notions of congruence. A simple method of constructing such squares, applicable to any square of odd n, is illustrated on the opposite page. In one of the squares shown, for example, $n=5$ and the magic sum is 65.

Each box in the square (known as a cell) contains a number from 1 up to n^2, in this case $n^2=25$. The numbers are placed in the cells in their consecutive order according to the following rules:

Begin by placing the number 1 in the middle cell of the bottom row; after filling a cell in the bottom row, place the next number in the cell at the top of the next column on the right; as far as possible fill the cells in a downward diagonal line from left to right; upon filling a cell in the last right-hand column of the square, place the next number in the cell at the extreme left of the next lower row; if the next cell on the left-to-right downward diagonal is occupied, place the next number in the cell immediately above the one last filled; after filling the cell in the lower right-hand corner, place the next number in the cell immediately above.

MAGIC squares and wine jugs, calculating machines, prime numbers and congruences, Diophantine equations and shipwrecked sailors—all these furnish reasons that help to explain why the Theory of Numbers has interested so many people. Professionals and amateurs alike have been attracted by the subtle fascination of these problems, and the mark of their work has been felt in nearly every branch of mathematics. Problems in the Theory of Numbers are among the most challenging in mathematics, possibly because some of them are so difficult. Fortunately in mathematics as in all other scientific endeavors the difficulty experienced in solving a problem drives man to a continuing search for its solution. For he believes that the science of mathematics is a logical discipline, and as such is subject to complete understanding.

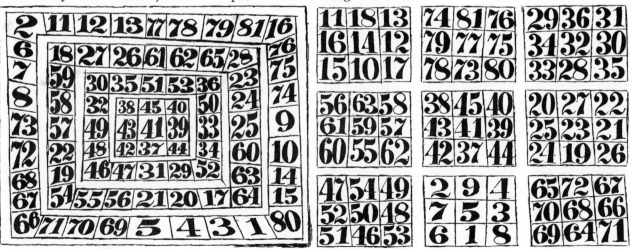

BORDERED SQUARE is magic overall, and each square formed by throwing away a border is also magic.

COMPOSITE SQUARE is similarly magic overall and at the same time magic for each of its smaller squares.

15 ALGEBRA

W. W. SAWYER • September 1964

The history of the branch of mathematics known as algebra can be divided into two main epochs. The first lasted from the time of the ancient Egyptian and Babylonian civilizations until about A.D. 1800; the second extends from 1800 to the present. During the earlier epoch men thought about mathematics exclusively in terms of the things with which it dealt: geometry was about shapes, arithmetic was about numbers and algebra was about the relations and properties of numbers in general (as expressed by arbitrary symbols, usually letters of the alphabet). Trigonometry did not fit very neatly into this scheme, since it applied both arithmetic and algebra to geometric problems; nor did analytic geometry, which made geometry a branch of algebra. Nonetheless, the role of algebra appeared more or less clear throughout the epoch: x *always* stood for a number.

The older algebra provided a versatile tool for many practical and scientific enterprises. Archaeological evidence indicates that algebraic formulas for finding the volumes of cylinders and spheres may have been used in ancient Egypt to compute the amount of grain a peasant owed in taxes to the central government. Before the advent of the calculus and celestial mechanics in the late 17th century, algebra and geometry were the twin mainstays of all astronomical reckoning. The essential operations of the older algebra are familiar to anyone who has studied the traditional curriculum at a good high school. In fact, a person who has mastered elementary algebra and geometry in high school is in a good position to learn without any great mental readjustment most of the mathematics discovered prior to 1800. The reason is that mathematics before 1800 was essentially concerned with only two commonsense ideas, number and shape.

Early in the 19th century this whole view of mathematics began to change. Two new ideas were introduced that profoundly expanded the domain of mathematics. The first was that mathematics did not need to restrict itself to numbers and shapes but could deal effectively with anything (although "anything" often continued to be related in some way to numbers and shapes). The second idea carried the process of abstraction a step further: mathematics could at times be regarded merely as a logical procedure, having no relation to anything in particular.

Scientists, as distinct from mathematicians, are attracted to the first idea; it suggests that mathematics may have a much wider sphere of application than had ever been imagined in the earlier epoch. The second idea appeals more to pure mathematicians, who have come to regard mathematics simply as the study of beautiful patterns. There is no real conflict between the two viewpoints. A pattern conceived for its beauty by a pure mathematician may well prove to fit some aspect of the physical world; conversely, some of the mathematical patterns discovered in nature by the scientist have turned out to be remarkably beautiful.

It would of course be beyond the scope of any one article to attempt to trace all or even most of the effects of these two new ideas on the course of modern algebra. For one thing, algebra itself has become so compartmentalized that each separate branch would have to be treated more or less in isolation. On the other hand, isolated snippets of information are unlikely to satisfy the general reader, who would remain ignorant of the overall framework that gives these fragments their significance. The only satisfactory solution seems to be to cut off a rather large chunk of one

ALGEBRA OF GROUPS is applied to a hypothetical phenomenon in the physical world in the illustration on the opposite page. Imagine a wall with three holes through which three different colors appear (*a*). The order of the colors can be changed in six different ways (*b*) by pushing the six buttons at the bottom of the wall. These changes, or operations, occur in a pattern that fulfills the four basic requirements of a group: (1) If one operation is followed by another, the result is the same as if one operation were performed alone. (2) Any series of operations follows the associative rule, which can be expressed in symbols as $x(yz) = (xy)z$. (3) For every operation there is an inverse operation. (Operations 3 and 5 are the inverses of each other; the other operations are their own inverses.) (4) There is one identity operation, which leaves the original order unchanged (operation 1). The consequences of any pair of operations appear in table *c* (the table is called a matrix). The "simplest" physical explanation of the observed phenomenon would be to postulate the existence of a suitably colored triangular block behind the wall (*d*). Keeping the same orientation in the plane, the triangle can be rotated or turned over in only six different ways, which correspond exactly to the six color arrangements seen through the holes in the wall. This particular group is called a finite, noncommutative group: finite because the number of operations is finite, noncommutative because the sequence in which operations are performed can affect the outcome (xy does not necessarily equal yx). A demonstration of the noncommutative nature of the group is given in *e* and *f*, which show that operation 3 followed by operation 4 does *not* produce the same result as operation 4 followed by operation 3.

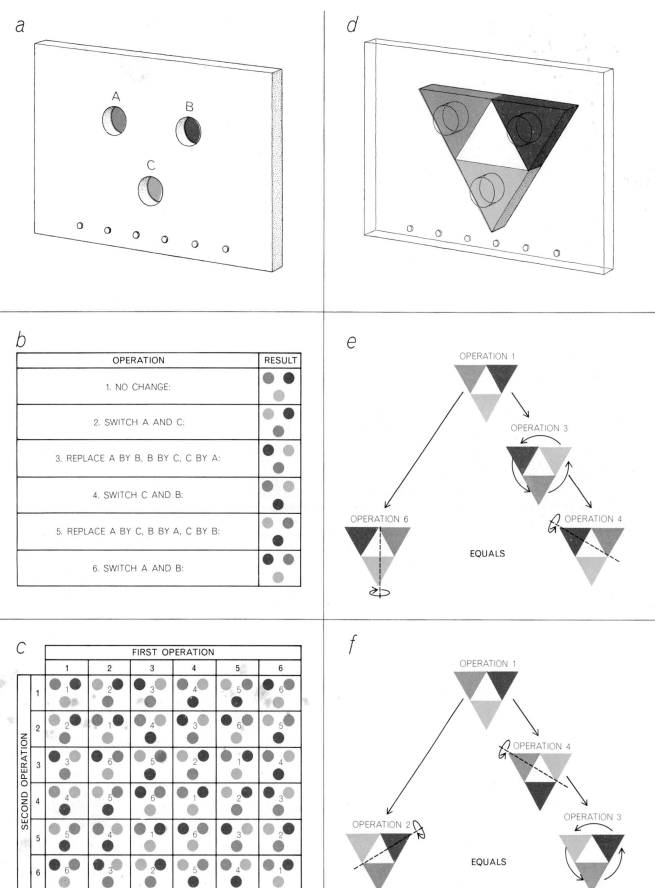

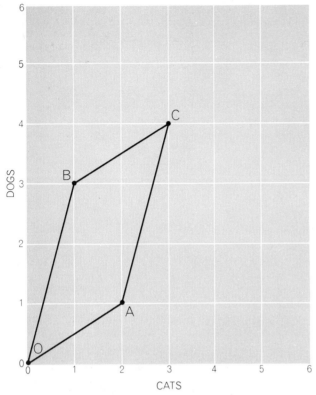

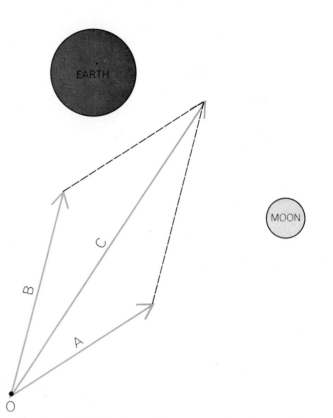

ADDITION involved in statement "Two cats and one dog + one cat and three dogs = three cats and four dogs" can be illustrated by means of a parallelogram. Since point C represents the sum of the quantities represented by A and B, one can write $C = A + B$.

VECTOR ADDITION also involves construction of a parallelo gram. A diagonal of the parallelogram (*Vector C*) represents the total gravitational force exerted on observer at O by the earth (*Vector B*) and the moon (*Vector A*). Again one can write $C = A + B$.

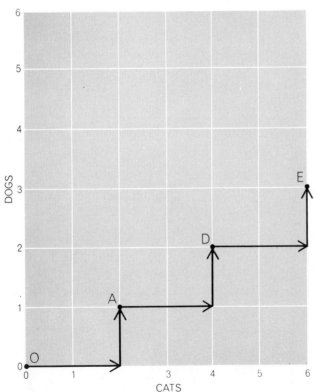

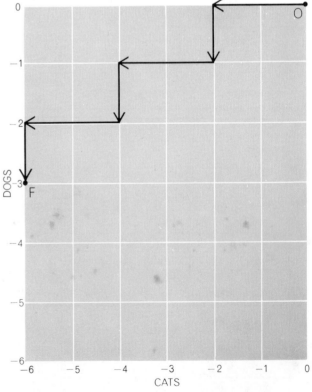

MULTIPLICATION involved in statement $E = 3A$ can be interpreted in several different ways. If A signifies two cats and one dog, E equals six cats and three dogs. Geometrically point E lies in the same direction from O as A but is three times farther away.

NEGATIVE NUMBERS are needed to represent a debt that obliged us, say, to deliver six cats and three dogs (F). The transition from O to F could also represent a three-stage journey, each stage of which has the same specification: two units west and one south.

branch of modern algebra and explain it in detail. The reader will then be able to gain some idea of the general direction in which algebra is moving from a consideration of how this particular branch has developed in the years since 1800. I have chosen to devote most of this article to a detailed discussion of vector algebra and matrix algebra, two subjects that are just beginning to find their way into the high school curriculum. Both subjects have already made significant contributions both to pure mathematics and to science. Finally, I shall sketch more briefly several of the other departments of modern algebra in which interesting and significant work is in progress.

The new ideas about algebra that emerged at the beginning of the 19th century grew naturally out of the older algebra. One stimulus was the concept of the square root of minus one, customarily denoted by i, which was used to solve a wide range of problems in the 17th and 18th centuries but which no one seemed able to explain satisfactorily as a number. In the early 19th century two different solutions to this dilemma were proposed. The first employed what is called the abstract method, in which i was interpreted as a series of rather arbitrary operations on pairs of numbers [see "The Foundations of Mathematics," page 191]. The second solution gave i a concrete interpretation, identifying it with the geometrical operation "Rotate through a right angle in a plane."

Both explanations suggested further exploration. Since excellent dividends had accrued from the introduction of i into the procedures of elementary algebra, might it not be profitable to bring in a few more meaningless symbols? The rules governing these symbols could then be tailored to meet the demands of the situation. If i was interpreted as a rotation in a plane, why not consider rotations in three-dimensional space and see if these could contribute anything to algebra? This whole line of inquiry led eventually to the discovery of quaternions in 1843 by William Rowan Hamilton. In quaternion algebra two new symbols, i and j, were introduced, with the rules $i^2 = -1$, $j^2 = -1$ and the surprising $ji = -ij$ [see "Number," page 89].

Many prominent British mathematicians of Hamilton's day were completely swept off their feet by the discovery of quaternions, which they regarded as the last word in mathematics and the ideal method for solving most algebraic prob-

lems. Actually quaternions were a first rather than a last word. A barrier had been crossed; an algebra had been developed that disregarded several of the basic conventions of the older algebra. Mathematicians soon began to look for other ways in which ordinary numbers could be supplemented by new symbols to produce what came to be known as "hypercomplex numbers." Eventually the question was bound to arise: Why start with ordinary numbers? Why not consider any collection of symbols and lay down rules for combining them? The word "algebra" was gradually being expanded to include any system of handling symbols according to prescribed rules. Anyone was now free to invent his own algebra. Of course this did not mean that anyone who did so earned a right to immortality; the problem has always been to invent a system that yields interesting and fruitful results and contributes significantly to the rest of mathematics and to science.

Algebra thus ceased to be about anything in particular, although this did not rule out the possibility that a particular system of algebra could be ap-

plied to a particular topic. Such a topic would then be said to have an algebraic aspect.

In elementary algebra the symbols stand for numbers and the sign + indicates that the numbers are to be added. It may surprise the reader to learn that after algebra had ceased to be exclusively occupied with numbers the sign + continued to be used. How can one add things that are not numbers? The explanation is that in modern algebra the sign + does not indicate that addition is being carried out in any real sense. It merely means that some operation is being carried out according to rules that remind a mathematician of the rules for addition. The resemblance is one of pattern, not of content.

Let us now consider an example of this broadening of the meaning of the sign + We shall begin with a situation clearly related to addition and from it derive another situation in which the connection with addition is much less apparent.

"Adding" in arithmetic is generally associated with the idea of "putting to-

CATS

MATRIX is used to find the yields of a hypothetical animal "banking scheme" that offers the following interest rates: For each cat deposited now, one will be entitled to two cats and a dog a year from now; for each dog deposited now, one will be entitled to a cat and three dogs a year from now. The light numbers signify deposits; darker numbers signify yields.

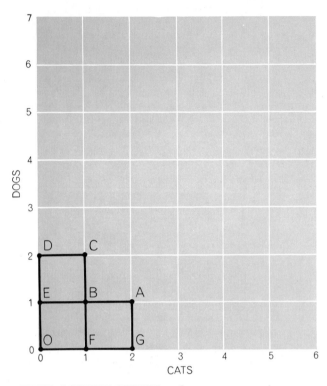

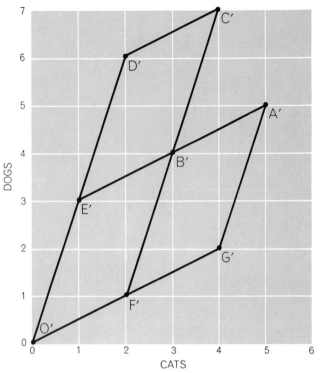

ANIMAL BANKING SCHEME used to construct matrix on pre-ceding page can also be shown graphically. Lettered points in graph at left signify specific deposits; corresponding points in graph at right represent yields from these deposits. The shift from squares representing deposits to parallelograms representing yields is characteristic of any algebraic "banking scheme" of this general type.

gether." In cooking one speaks of adding water to a mixture. Most people would find no difficulty in following the addition involved in the statement: "Two cats and one dog + one cat and three dogs = three cats and four dogs." They would regard this as a legitimate use of the sign +.

The operation of addition in the foregoing statement can be illustrated graphically [*see illustration at top left on page 104*]. Here cats are indicated horizontally and dogs vertically. Point *A* represents two cats and one dog; that is, *A* is two units across and one up from the point of origin (*O*). By the same token point *B* corresponds to one cat and three dogs. Since point *C* represents the sum of these two pairs of numbers (three cats and four dogs) we might be led to write $C = A + B$.

Suppose we were to show this graph to someone who did not know anything about the cat-and-dog story and ask the person to describe what he saw. The chances are he would say: "There is some graph paper with four points, *O*, *A*, *C* and *B*, marked on it so as to form a parallelogram." Thus it is possible to give a purely geometric description of how to get point *C* from *A* and *B*: one simply chooses *C* so that together with *O*, *A* and *B* it completes a parallelogram.

Clearly the graph derived from the statement "Two cats and one dog + one cat and three dogs = three cats and four dogs" can be approached from at least two different viewpoints. In the context of the cat-and-dog story the situation clearly involves addition from the start and the graph is simply a device to illustrate addition. From a purely geometric point of view *C* is the point needed to complete the parallelogram *OACB*. In the latter case it would seem highly unnatural to write $C = A + B$, or indeed to expect any connection at all with algebra. But since the graph itself remains one and the same thing no matter how we view it, it is clear that the geometry of the parallelogram must have a strong algebraic aspect related in some way to addition.

Anyone who has studied mechanics or electricity and magnetism is familiar with the fact that nature often uses the parallelogram as a means of addition. In the illustration at top right on page 104 the letter *O* represents an observer somewhere in space. The line *OB* represents the gravitational pull of the earth, that is, the force that would act on the observer if the earth were the only massive body in his vicinity. Similarly, the line *OA* represents the gravitational pull of the moon by itself. In fact, both the earth and the moon are pulling at the observer simul-taneously, so that to calculate the actual force acting on the observer we must combine, or "add," the effects the earth and the moon would produce separately. This combined force can be represented by the line *OC*, which turns out to be a diagonal of the parallelogram *OACB*.

If we now wished to take into account the force exerted by the sun, we would have to "add" the pull of the sun to the force represented by *OC*, again employing the parallelogram technique. At this point one of the important analogies to the addition of ordinary numbers becomes apparent. If one adds any three numbers, the sequence in which one adds them is immaterial. If one has to pays bills, say, of $3, $5 and $6, one cannot economize by paying them in some special order. In whatever order one pays one is bound to part with the same total sum: $14. This is called the commutative rule of addition. (Strictly speaking, the associative rule of addition, which in symbols states that $a + (b + c) = (a + b) + c$, is also involved here.) Mathematicians would find it misleading to use the sign + for any procedure in which the sequence of the operations affected the final outcome.

Obviously the sequence of operations does not affect our gravitational problem, since the observer at *O* is simul-taneously acted on by the earth, the moon and the sun. In our computation of the total gravitational effect on the observer we can first combine the pull of the earth and the pull of the moon and then "add" this result to the pull of the sun. We could just as well start by combining the effects of the sun and the moon and then "add" this sum to the pull of the earth. If the two procedures were to result in different answers, our purely geometric technique would obviously be unsatisfactory. The physics of the situation demands that the commutative and associative rules apply. Insofar as our procedure for combining forces must obey these rules, it resembles the addition of ordinary numbers.

The parallelogram technique described in the last two examples is known as vector addition. In both examples the lines OA, OB and OC are called vectors and are usually drawn as arrows.

Another way to interpret the cat-and-dog graph is in terms of journeys. The distance from O to A corresponds to a journey of two units to the east and one unit to the north; similarly, the distance from O to B corresponds to a journey of one unit to the east and three units to the north. If we combine these journeys, traveling first two units east and one north and then one east and three north, we find that in all we have journeyed three units east and four north, or the distance from O to C. The story is different, but once again we find that C can be interpreted as the sum of A and B.

We have seen that several different meanings can be attached to the expression $A + B$. What are some of the ways in which we can interpret the expression $3 \times A$, or $3A$?

If A signifies two cats and one dog, there should be little doubt about the meaning of $3A$; the product is obviously six cats and three dogs. In the illustration at bottom left on page 104 this product is indicated by the point E; thus we can write the equation $E = 3A$. Geometrically we see that E lies in the same direction from O as A does, but that it is three times farther away. In addition to this purely geometric interpretation of $E = 3A$, the interpretation as journeys is again helpful; the journey from O to E can be broken into three stages—O to A, A to D and D to E—each of which has the same specification: two units east and one north.

Let us now introduce the symbols c and d as abbreviations for cats and dogs respectively. We have seen that the expression $6c + 3d$ can be interpreted in at least three different ways: (1) in its original meaning of six cats and three dogs, (2) as a way of specifying the position of the point E in the graph at bottom left on page 104 and (3) as describing the stepwise journey from O to E in the same illustration.

Our symbolism still suffers from one restriction. We have no difficulty in writing $6c + 3d$ for the overall journey from O to E, but what about a journey in the opposite direction? For this we need negative numbers; thus the expression $-6c - 3d$ could be interpreted as a journey of six units west and three south. The same expression could also be used to specify the position of the point F in the graph at bottom right on page 104. Or it could represent minus six cats and minus three dogs, that is, a debt that obliged us to deliver six cats and three dogs.

We are now able to specify the position of any point in a plane by a pair of algebraic symbols such as $6c + 3d$. Moreover, we can translate a number of geometric constructions into simple algebraic operations on these symbols; for example, drawing a parallelogram corresponds to addition. Many theorems in elementary plane geometry can be proved without reference to geometric constructions simply by carrying out the appropriate algebraic calculations with c and d.

The illustration on the next page shows a few geometric distortions that can be performed on a rectangular picture. In B the original picture (A) is tilted, or rotated counterclockwise around its bottom left corner; in C it is enlarged; in D it is reflected as in a mirror; in E it is stretched vertically and shrunk horizontally; in F it leans to the right. Do these operations have an algebraic aspect? Can we add and multiply them? For instance, can we add a rotation to a reflection and state the procedure as $B + D$? It may appear to be unlikely and yet it can be done. Such operations have in fact a remarkably simple algebraic aspect.

In order to illustrate the preceding statement let us return to the cat-and-dog story. Imagine a society in which cats and dogs represent wealth, as sheep and cattle do in some primitive societies. In our hypothetical society a bank might offer the following interest rates: For each cat deposited now, one will be entitled to two cats and a dog a year from now; for each dog deposited now, one will be entitled to a cat and three dogs a year from now. In symbols this could be expressed $c \rightarrow 2c + d$; $d \rightarrow c + 3d$. (The arrow signifies "yields.") It is fairly easy to work out the yield for a deposit of any given number of cats and dogs. A deposit of a cat and a dog, for instance, would yield three cats and four dogs ($c + d \rightarrow 3c + 4d$). A deposit of two cats and a dog, on the other hand, would yield five cats and five dogs ($2c + d \rightarrow 5c + 5d$). The yields for various other combinations of cat-and-dog deposits are indicated in the table on page 105. A table of this type is called a matrix and the branch of mathematics that employs such tables is called matrix algebra.

Let us now translate all our symbols

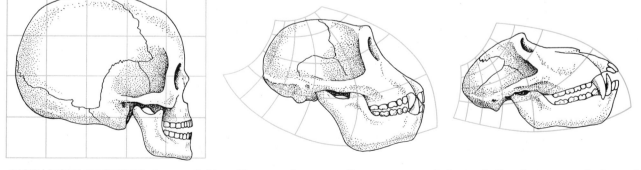

COMPARISON OF SKULLS of a man (*left*), a chimpanzee (*center*) and a baboon (*right*) can be said to have an algebraic aspect. As in the case of the animal banking schemes, the rectangular co-ordinate system over the human skull can be progressively distorted by means of the appropriate algebraic operations. Diagrams of this type have been used in a wide range of morphological studies.

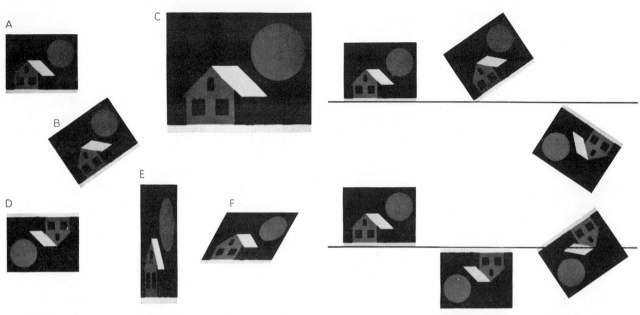

SOME GEOMETRIC DISTORTIONS that can be performed on a rectangular picture (A) are depicted at left. The distortions all have an algebraic aspect: distortion F corresponds to the algebraic banking scheme that converts squares to parallelograms; the other dis-

tortions correspond to similar banking schemes. Any combination of distortions is noncommutative; the illustration at right shows that rotating a reflected picture does *not* produce the same result as reflecting a rotated picture (in symbols, $B + D \neq D + B$).

into geometry. In the graphs on page 106 point A represents a deposit of $2c + d$ and A' represents the yield of this deposit, or $5c + 5d$. Some other points have been marked in; B, for instance, represents the deposit $c + d$ and B' the corresponding yield $3c + 4d$. By the same token C' represents the yield that would result from the deposit C, D' the yield from the deposit D and so on. It is apparent that the points in both graphs are arranged in orderly patterns: the original points (A, B, C, D, E, F and G) form squares and the corresponding primed points (A', B', C', D', E', F' and G') form parallelograms.

This shift from squares to parallelograms is not fortuitous. In fact, any algebraic "banking scheme" of this general type will produce graphs in which squares representing deposits become parallelograms representing yields. Conversely, any geometric distortion that converts squares to parallelograms in this manner can be produced by means of a suitable algebraic "banking scheme." The distortion designated F in the illustration above is an example of this type of square-to-parallelogram distortion. All the other distortions shown in the same illustration correspond to similar "banking schemes." Thus the scheme $c \to 2c$, $d \to 2d$ would yield an enlargement corresponding to distortion C, whereas the scheme $c \to \frac{1}{2}c$, $d \to 2d$ would yield distortion E. Slightly more complicated algebraic schemes are required to produce the distortions shown on the preceding page, in which

the skulls of a man, chimpanzee and a baboon are compared geometrically. Comparative diagrams of this type have been used to study a wide range of morphological characteristics, which can be said to have an algebraic aspect.

Is it possible to "add" two such banking schemes? Suppose in our hypothetical society three banks, X, Y and Z, were to offer three different interest rates; what then could we understand by $X + Y = Z$? It could mean that scheme Z yields as much as schemes X and Y put together. By calculating the yield of scheme X for a given deposit and then adding this quantity to the calculated yield of scheme Y for the same deposit, we can determine what scheme Z would yield for that deposit. Similarly, we could interpret the equation $A = 3B$ as meaning that the yield of scheme A is equal to three times the yield of scheme B for the same deposit.

By combining the last two ideas we can now interpret an expression such as $4A + 5B$. The yield of this combined scheme, for any deposit, would equal four times the yield of scheme A added to five times the yield of scheme B.

It is possible to go on to discuss the multiplication of "banking schemes." The expression AB would indicate that one first invested in scheme B and then reinvested the yield in scheme A. That it is not unreasonable to call this process "multiplication" can be seen from the following example. Suppose the effect of scheme B is to double one's de-

posit and the effect of scheme A is to treble the deposit. If one invests first in scheme B and then reinvests the proceeds in scheme A, the total effect is to multiply the initial investment by six. Since six equals three times two, it is not unreasonable to associate reinvestment with multiplication.

What do all these examples prove? First, the various cat-and-dog stories have demonstrated that algebra can be made to apply to a number of geometric situations that at first sight appear to be in no way related to algebra. Second, the algebra involved is remarkably straightforward; most of the expressions we have used have been simple ones, such as $6c + 3d$, that are familiar from elementary algebra. Third, the broadening of the meaning of the word "algebra" has many important implications. We have been talking about the way in which forces are exerted, the way shapes are distorted under stress, the way things change their position—all topics of obvious importance in science and engineering. There are many less obvious applications both in science and in higher mathematics.

In the preceding discussion of vector and matrix algebra we have dealt largely with models; that is, we have examined certain actual situations and operations—collections of animals, journeys, investments, rotations and reflections—and have found in these situations and operations elements that reminded us of the addition and multiplication of ordinary numbers. The requirement of "reminding us," however, is somewhat vague. How closely must something remind us of addition to deserve being represented by the sign $+$? Clearly more specific rules are needed if there is not to be a great deal of confusion about symbolism.

We have already mentioned a few of the requirements for an operation to be recognized as a generalization of addition. The commutative rule, for example, states that whatever objects a and b might stand for and however complicated the operation of combining them might be, we are always entitled to expect that $a + b$ will mean the same as $b + a$.

In ordinary arithmetic multiplication is also commutative: 3×4 always means the same as 4×3. In fact, the properties of multiplication resemble those of addition very closely. It is only by virtue of this fact that we are able to construct tables of logarithms, which convert multiplication to addition. Since it would be wasteful to have two symbols with the same implications, the convention has arisen among mathematicians that the sign $+$ may be used only for commutative systems, but the sign $\times$ need not carry this restriction. In some branches of algebra $a \times b$ and $b \times a$ may denote the same object, but they are not obliged to. When $a \times b$ and $b \times a$ have different meanings, the algebra is said to be noncommutative.

We do not have to look far for an example of noncommutative algebra: our previous discussion of matrix algebra provides several. In the illustration on the opposite page the sequence in which the operations "rotate" (B) and "reflect" (D) are performed on the original picture can be seen to have an effect on the outcome. Reflecting the rotated picture does *not* produce the same result as rotating the reflected picture; in symbols, $B + D$ does *not* equal $D + B$. It is also possible to construct various "animal-investment banking schemes" in which the sequence of investment and reinvestment affects the final outcome. (This is not the case in ordinary banking, in which reinvestment is always commutative.)

Another important property of addition and multiplication in ordinary arithmetic is that these operations are associative. In other words, if one has to work out $3 + 4 + 5$, it does not matter whether one obtains the answer by considering $7 + 5$ or by considering $3 + 9$. In the case of multiplication the associative rule requires that $3 \times 4 \times 5$ can be found by means of 12×5 or by

means of 3×20. There is perhaps some subtlety involved in this concept. The reader may ask: Are we not saying simply that the system is commutative, that the order in which one adds or multiplies is immaterial? The distinction may be elucidated by considering the phrases "fat-cattle merchant" and "fat cattle-merchant." The order of the words is the same but the meaning is different. What has been changed is the manner in which the words have been grouped together. The associative property deals with the effect of punctuation, not of order. That the two properties are genuinely distinct can be further appreciated by considering the fact that matrix algebra is not commutative but is associative. The majority of algebraic systems that have proved productive so far have been associative, although the theory of nonassociative algebra has recently attracted the attention of some mathematicians.

A third basic property of ordinary arithmetic is expressed by the distributive rule, which in symbols states that $a(b + c) = ab + ac$. The distributive property has a way of turning up in unexpected situations. For example, the boundary of the area covered by California and Illinois is the boundary of California added to the boundary of Illinois. It is not difficult to see a connection between this statement and the equation $b(C + I) = bC + bI$, in which b stands for "the boundary of" and C and I are the initials of the states involved. It is interesting to note that the distributive rule ceases to apply if the states in question have a com-

mon boundary [*see illustration below*].

The concept of boundaries occurs in topology and in certain areas of the calculus. What is important to realize here is that algebra can play a role inside other branches of mathematics, and not merely because numbers are involved in these branches. In fact, the branches of mathematics interact to a surprising degree.

In algebra the word "field" is used to describe a system that closely resembles ordinary arithmetic. The operations of addition, subtraction, multiplication and division occur in a field and are much like the corresponding operations in arithmetic. For instance, there is in every field an element designated by the letter "O" that resembles zero (it makes no difference if you add O) and an element I that resembles one (it makes no difference if you multiply by I). A large variety of fields exist. The tables on the next page specify a field in which there are only four elements: O, I, A and B. Within this system we operate by essentially the same rules as we do in arithmetic and elementary algebra; in it the commutative, associative and distributive properties all hold. The possibility of a field with a finite number of elements was discovered by the French mathematician Évariste Galois in 1830. This particular field is called a Galois field with four elements.

Take any formula from high school algebra and you will find that it remains true in the Galois field. For example, elementary algebra leads us to believe that $A + B$ multiplied by $A - B$ should

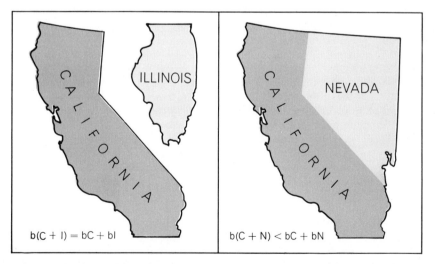

$b(C + I) = bC + bI$

$b(C + N) < bC + bN$

DISTRIBUTIVE RULE of ordinary arithmetic states in symbols that $a(b + c) = ab + ac$. In this example of the distributive rule the boundary of the area covered by California and Illinois is the boundary of California added to the boundary of Illinois; in symbols, $b(C + I) = bC + bI$. The distributive rule does not apply in the case of California and Nevada, which have a common boundary. Since the concept of boundaries occurs both in topology and in calculus, algebra is brought into these branches in cases that do not involve numbers.

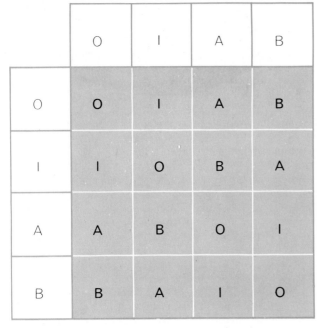
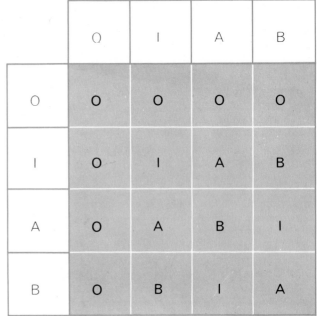

	O	I	A	B
O	O	I	A	B
I	I	O	B	A
A	A	B	O	I
B	B	A	I	O

	O	I	A	B
O	O	O	O	O
I	O	I	A	B
A	O	A	B	I
B	O	B	I	A

GALOIS FIELD is an abstract algebraic system containing only four elements, O, I, A and B, which can be added, subtracted, multiplied and divided by essentially the same rules that hold in arithmetic and elementary algebra. Table at left is for addition; table at right, for multiplication. Galois fields have recently been applied to error-free transmission of information by high-speed machines.

be the same as $A^2 - B^2$. This is also true for the Galois field. Using the tables to work out these two results, you will find that both give the same answer: I.

At this point we have reached a completely abstract stage. There is no suggestion that O, I, A and B have any meaning. We are no longer talking about collections of animals or movements of bodies. We have simply found a pattern that has interesting analogies with the patterns of ordinary arithmetic. A very pure mathematician would say that this is the whole object of mathematics—to discover beautiful and interesting patterns. An applied mathematician, a scientist or an engineer would be interested in knowing if this pattern is one that occurs in nature and can therefore be given an interpretation and an application. Although conceived as an abstract mathematical exercise, Galois fields have recently found a rather unexpected application: they have been studied in connection with error-free codes for the transmission of information by high-speed machines.

In a field we can add, subtract, multiply and divide (except that division by O is barred). Not all algebraic systems have as comprehensive a list of operations. In a ring, for instance, we can add, subtract and multiply but not necessarily divide. A familiar example of a ring is the whole numbers, both

positive and negative. If a person were conversant only with numbers such as ...−4, −3, −2, −1, 0, 1, 2, 3, 4..., he would be able to solve any problem that involved the addition, subtraction or multiplication of these numbers. If asked to divide 3 by 4, however, he would be powerless.

Even more restricted than a ring is the concept of a group. When we say that some system is a group, we promise only the existence in it of one operation, which can be thought of as a kind of generalized multiplication. This operation must be associative: an expression such as XYZ must have a definite meaning regardless of punctuation. The group must also contain an element I that resembles the number one in arithmetic. Furthermore, division must be possible. An example of a group with six elements appears on page 103.

To qualify as a group an algebraic system must pass a surprisingly small number of tests. It is therefore all the more remarkable that such an elaborate theory of groups has been developed, with such widespread ramifications in higher mathematics and physics [see "Mathematics in the Physical Sciences," page 249].

Many new algebraic systems have arisen out of particular problems in other branches of mathematics. Near the end of the 19th century the Norwegian mathematician Sophus Lie completed a comprehensive classification of

differential equations in calculus. Certain patterns in this classification system have since been extracted and now constitute a separate subject, known as Lie groups. Similarly certain problems in topology have led to the new subject of homological algebra, which has also proved to have important applications outside of topology.

In the late 1840's the English mathematician and logician George Boole developed a system of symbolic logic in which the propositions of Aristotelian logic were reduced to equations that were closely analogous to those in elementary algebra. The system follows many of the rules of ordinary arithmetic, including the commutative, the associative and the distributive rules. Boolean algebra has recently been applied to the design of telephone circuits and electronic computers.

Algebra, like every other branch of mathematics and science, continues to proliferate with the vitality and expansiveness of a tropical forest. It is a difficult situation. To know everything is clearly impossible, yet each specialist assures you that you must know the particular part of algebra he finds interesting. The scientist who uses mathematics should be aware that much new mathematical knowledge is being discovered; nearly all of it will be irrelevant to his own research, but he should keep his eyes open for the small piece that may be of great value to him.

16 GEOMETRY

MORRIS KLINE • September 1964

The evolution of mathematics depends on advances in both number and geometry. It cannot be said, however, that these key elements of mathematics have always advanced side by side. Frequently they have competed, and the advance of one has been at the expense of the other. The history of this sometimes strained relation between two disciplines that actually have a common purpose is reminiscent of contrapuntal themes in music.

The first genuine stride of mathematics was taken by geometry. Some primitive mathematics was created by Egyptian and Babylonian carpenters and surveyors in the 4,000 years preceding the Christian era, but it was the classical Greek philosophers who, between 600 B.C. and 300 B.C., gave mathematics its definitive architecture of abstraction and deductive proof, erected the vast structure of Euclidean geometry and dedicated the subject to the understanding of the universe.

Of the several forces that turned the Greeks toward geometry, perhaps the most important was the difficulty Greek scholars had with the concept of the irrational number: a number that is neither a whole number nor a ratio of whole numbers. The difficulty arose in connection with the famous Pythagorean theorem that the length of the hypotenuse of a right triangle is the square root of the sum of the squares of the two sides. In a right triangle with sides of one unit each the hypotenuse must then be $\sqrt{2}$, an irrational number. Such a concept was beyond the Greeks; number to them had always meant whole number or ratio of whole numbers. They resolved the difficulty by banishing it, producing a geometry that affirmed theorems and offered proofs without reference to number. Today this geometry is known as pure geometry or synthetic geometry, the latter an unfortunate term that has only historical justification.

Since the mathematics of the classical Greeks was devoted to deducing truths of nature, it had to be founded on truths. Fortunately there were some seemingly self-evident truths at hand, among them the following: two points determine a line; a straight line extends indefinitely far in either direction; all right angles are equal; equals added to equals yield equals; figures that can be made to coincide are congruent. Some of these axioms make assertions primarily about space itself; others pertain to figures in space.

From these axioms Euclid, in his *Elements*, deduced almost 500 theorems. In other works he and his successors, notably Archimedes and Apollonius, deduced many hundreds more. Because the Greeks chose to work purely in geometry, many of the theorems stated results now regarded as algebraic. For example, the solution of second-degree equations in one unknown ($x^2 - 8x + 7 = 0$ is such an equation) was carried out geometrically and the answer given by Euclid was not a number but a line segment. Thus Euclidean geometry embraced the algebra known at that time.

The welter of theorems might suggest that the Greeks drifted from topic to topic. That would be a false impression. The figures they chose were basic: lines and curves in one category and surfaces in another. In the first category are such figures as the triangle and the conic sections: circle, parabola, ellipse and hyperbola. In the second category are such figures as the cube, sphere, paraboloid, ellipsoid and hyperboloid [*see illustration on page 114*]. Then the Greek geometers tackled basic problems concerning those figures. For instance, what must one know about two figures

to assert that they are congruent (identical except for position in space), similar (having the same shape if not the same size) or equivalent (having the same area)? Thus congruence, similarity and equivalence are major themes of Euclidean geometry, and the majority of the theorems deal with these questions.

The classical Greek civilization that gave rise to Euclidean geometry was destroyed by Alexander the Great and rebuilt along new lines in Egypt. Alexander moved the center of his empire from Athens to the city he modestly named Alexandria, and he proclaimed the goal of fusing Greek and Near Eastern civilizations. This objective was ably executed by his successors, the Ptolemys, who ruled Egypt from 323 B.C. until the last member of the family, Cleopatra, was seduced by the Romans. Under the influence of the Near Eastern civilizations, notably the Egyptian and the Persian, the culture of the Alexandrian Greek civilization became more engineering-minded and more practically oriented. The mathematicians responded to the new interests.

Applied science and engineering must in large part be quantitative. What the Alexandrians appended to Euclid's geometry in order to obtain quantitative results was number: arithmetic and algebra. The disturbing fact about these

RAPHAEL'S "SPOSALIZIO," or "Marriage of the Virgin," part of which is reproduced on the opposite page, indicates how Renaissance painters solved problems of perspective and so contributed to the evolution of projective geometry. The superimposed white lines show how the artist depicted as converging on a "principal vanishing point" lines that in actuality were horizontal, parallel and receding directly from the viewer.

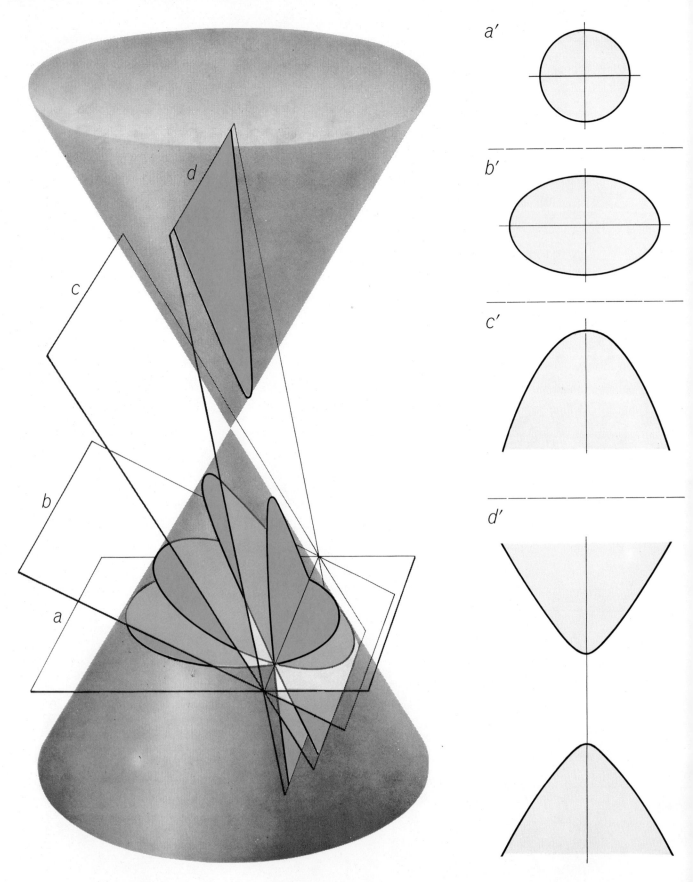

CONIC SECTIONS provide the basic curves with which geometry deals. By following each series of letters, such as *a, a'* and *a''*, one can see at left a plane intersecting a cone to produce a curve, at center the resulting curve and at right the corresponding surface. Thus *a'* is a circle and *a''* a sphere, *b'* an ellipse and *b''* an ellipsoid, *c'* a parabola and *c''* a paraboloid, *d'* a hyperbola and *d''*

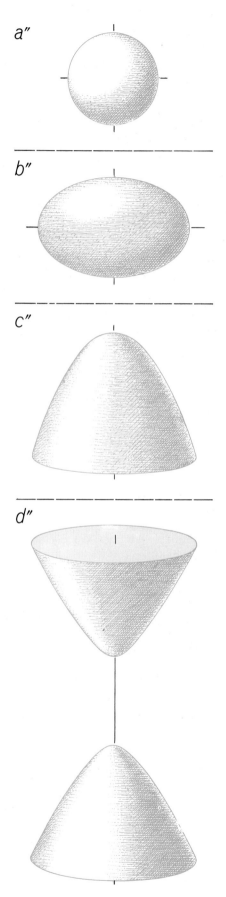

a″

b″

c″

d″

a hyperboloid. Definitions and properties of conic sections were worked out by ancient Greek scholars, notably Apollonius.

subjects was that they did not have a logical foundation; the Alexandrians merely took over the empirically based arithmetical knowledge built up by the Egyptians and Babylonians. Because Euclidean geometry offered the security of proof, it continued for centuries to dominate mathematics. Not until late in the 19th century did mathematicians solve the problem of providing an axiomatic basis for arithmetic and algebra.

Actually geometry consists of several geometries. The first break in the direction of a new geometry was made by Renaissance painters who sought to solve the problem of depicting exactly what the eyes see. Because real scenes are three-dimensional, whereas a painting is flat, it would appear to be impossible to paint realistically. The painters solved their problem by recognizing a fundamental fact about vision. Suppose a man, using one eye, looks through a window at some real scene. He sees the scene because light rays from various points in it travel to his eye. This collection of light rays is called a projection. Since the rays pass through the window, it is possible to mark a point on the window where each light ray pierces it. This collection of points is called a section. What the painters discovered is that the section creates the same impression on the eye as the scene itself does. This is physically understandable [*see top illustration on next page*]. Whether the light rays emanate from particles in the real scene or from points on the window, the same light rays reach the eye. Hence the canvas could contain what appears on the window. Even though this is a one-eye scheme and sight involves two eyes, the painters compensated for the restriction by using diminution of light intensity with distance and by using shadows. How well they succeeded in solving the problems of perspective can be judged by the painting reproduced on page 113.

The use of projection and section raised a basic geometrical question, first voiced by the painters and later taken up by mathematicians. What geometrical properties do an original figure and its section have in common that enable them to create the same impression on the eye? The answer to this question led to new concepts and theorems that ultimately constituted a new branch of geometry called projective geometry [see the article by Morris Kline, "Projective Geometry," page 122 in this volume]. Some of the concepts and theorems are as follows. It is ap-

parent from the top illustration on the next page that the section of the projection of a line is a line and that, if two lines intersect, then a section of the projection of these two intersecting lines will also be two intersecting lines, although the angle between the two lines of the section will generally not be the same as the angle between the two lines in the original figure. It follows that a triangle will give rise to a triangular section and a quadrilateral will give rise to a quadrilateral section.

A more significant example of the properties common to a figure and a section was furnished in the 17th century by the self-educated French architect and engineer Gérard Desargues. In what is now known as Desargues's theorem he showed that for any triangle and any section of any projection of that triangle any pair of corresponding sides will meet in a point and the three points of intersection of the three pairs of corresponding sides lie on one straight line [*see bottom illustration on next page*]. The significance of this and other theorems of projective geometry is that this geometry no longer discusses congruence, similarity, equivalence and other concepts of Euclidean geometry but instead deals with collinearity (points that lie on a line), concurrency (lines that go through a point) and other notions stemming from projection and section.

Projective geometry flourished rather briefly and then was pushed aside temporarily by a rival geometry that appeared on the scene. The rival, which embodied an algebraic approach to geometry, is now called analytic geometry or coordinate geometry. It was motivated by a series of events and discoveries that in the 16th and 17th centuries launched the scientific age in western Europe and brought to the fore the problem of deriving and using the properties of curves and surfaces.

For one thing, the creation by Nicolaus Copernicus and Johannes Kepler of the heliocentric theory of planetary motion made manifest the need for effective methods of working with the conic sections; these curves are the paths of the celestial bodies in such a system. Moreover, by invalidating classical Greek mechanics, which presupposed a stationary earth, the heliocentric theory necessitated a completely new science of motion and therefore the study of curves along which objects move.

Several other forces pushed geometry

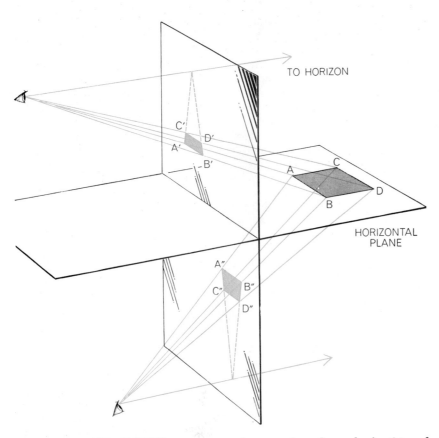

PROJECTION AND SECTION were concepts that arose from the work of artists and helped lead to projective geometry. Projections of a square, such as *ABCD*, to two observers form sections (*color*) on an intersecting plane. In a drawing the square must be represented as a section in order to appear realistic to an observer looking at the drawing.

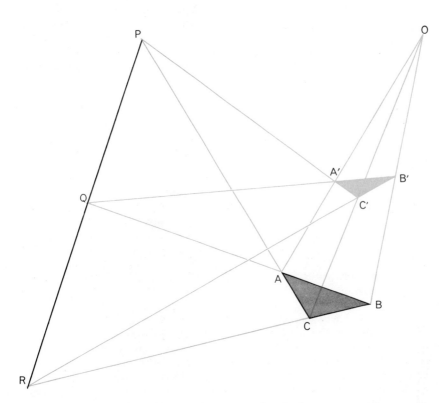

DESARGUES'S THEOREM illustrates the concern of projective geometry with properties common to a figure and its sections. The theorem states that any pair of corresponding sides of a triangle (*ABC*) and a section (*color*) will meet in a point—as, for example, the sides *BC* and *B'C'* meet in point *R*—and that the three points *P, Q* and *R* will lie on a line.

in the same direction. The gradually increasing use of gunpowder raised problems of projectile paths. The discovery of the telescope and the microscope motivated the study of lenses. Geographical exploration called for maps and in particular for the correlation of paths on the globe with paths on flat maps. All these problems not only increased the need for knowledge of properties of familiar curves but also introduced new curves. As René Descartes and Pierre de Fermat realized, the Euclidean synthetic methods were too limited to deal with these problems.

Descartes and Fermat, both major contributors to the fast-growing discipline of algebra, saw the potentialities in that subject for supplying methodology to geometry. The analytic geometry they developed replaced curves by equations through the device of a coordinate system. Such a system locates points in a plane or in space by numbers. In a plane the system uses two numbers, an abscissa and an ordinate [*see illustration on opposite page*]. The abscissa expresses the distance of a point from a fixed vertical line, called the *Y* axis; the ordinate expresses the distance of the point from a fixed horizontal line, called the *X* axis. Distances to the right of the *Y* axis or above the *X* axis are positive; distances in the opposite directions are negative.

How does this device enable one to represent curves algebraically? Consider a circle with a radius of five units. A circle, like any other curve, is just a particular collection of points. And if the circle is placed on a coordinate system, then each point on the circle has a pair of coordinates. Since the circle is a particular collection of points, the coordinates of these points are special in some way. The specialized nature is expressed by the equation $x^2 + y^2 = 5^2$. What this equation states is that if one takes the abscissa of any point on the curve and substitutes that for *x*, and if one takes the ordinate of that same point and substitutes it for *y*, then the number obtained for $x^2 + y^2$ will be 25. One says that the coordinates of any point on the curve satisfy the equation. Moreover, the coordinates of only those points that do lie on the curve satisfy the equation. In the case of surfaces an equation in three coordinates serves. For example, the equation of a sphere with a five-unit radius is $x^2 + y^2 + z^2 = 25$.

Thus under the Descartes-Fermat scheme points became pairs of numbers, and curves became collections of pairs of numbers subsumed in equations. The properties of curves could be deduced by algebraic processes applied to the equations. With this development the relation between number and geometry had come full circle. The classical Greeks had buried algebra in geometry, but now geometry was eclipsed by algebra. As the mathematicians put it, geometry was arithmetized.

Descartes and Fermat were not entirely correct in expecting that algebraic techniques would supply the effective methodology for working with curves. For instance, those techniques could not cope with slope and curvature, which are fundamental properties of curves. Slope is the rate at which a curve rises or falls per horizontal unit; curvature is the rate at which the direction of the curve changes per unit along the curve. Both rates vary from point to point along all curves except the straight line and the circle. To calculate rates of change that vary from point to point the purely algebraic techniques of Descartes and Fermat are not adequate; the calculus, particularly the differential calculus, must be employed. Indeed, the distinguishing feature of the calculus is its power to yield such rates.

With the aid of the differential calculus the study of curves and surfaces was expedited so much that a new term, differential geometry, was introduced to designate this study. Differential geometry considers a variety of problems beyond the calculation of slope and curvature. It considers in particular the all-important problem of geodesics, or the

shortest distance between two points on a surface. Given a surface such as the surface of the earth, what curve joining two given points P and Q on the surface is the shortest distance from P to Q along the surface? If one takes the surface of the earth to be a sphere, the answer is simple. The geodesics are arcs of great circles. (A great circle cuts the sphere in half; the Equator is a great circle but a circle of latitude is not.) If one more accurately takes the surface of the earth to be an ellipsoid, however, the geodesics are more complicated curves and depend on which points P and Q one chooses. The concerns of differential geometry include the curvature of surfaces, map making and surfaces of least area bounded by curves in space, the last of which are so handsomely realized by soap films [see bottom illustration on page 119].

From the standpoint of pure geometry the methodologies of analytic geometry and differential geometry were far too successful. Although these subjects treated geometry, the representations of curves were equations and the methods of proof were algebraic or analytic (that is, they involved the use of the calculus). The beautiful geometrical reasoning was abandoned and geometry was submerged in a sea of formulas. The spirit of geometry was banished.

For 150 years the pure geometers remained in the shadows. In the 19th century, however, they found the courage and the vitality to reassert themselves. The revival of geometry was

launched by Gaspard Monge (1746–1818), a leading French mathematician and adviser to Napoleon. Monge thought the analysts had sold geometry short and had even handicapped themselves by failing to interpret their analysis geometrically and to use geometrical pictures to help them think. Monge was such an inspiring teacher that he gathered about him a number of very bright pupils, among them L. N. M. Carnot (1753–1823), Charles J. Brianchon (1785–1864) and Jean Victor Poncelet (1788–1867). These men, imbued by Monge with a fervor for geometry, went beyond the intent of their master and sought to show that geometric methods could accomplish as much and more than the algebraic and analytic methods. To defeat Descartes or, as Carnot put it, "to free geometry from the hieroglyphics of analysis," became the goal.

The geometers, led by Poncelet, turned back to projective geometry, which had been so ruthlessly abandoned in the 17th century. Poncelet, serving as an officer in Napoleon's army, was captured by the Russians and spent the year 1813–1814 in a Russian prison. There he reconstructed without the aid of any books all he had learned from Monge; he then proceeded to create new results in projective geometry.

Projective geometry was actively pursued throughout the 19th century. Curiously an algebraic method, essentially an extension of the method of coordinate geometry, was developed to prove

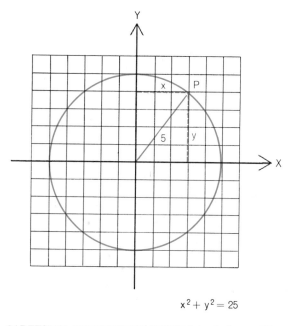

$$x^2 + y^2 = 25$$

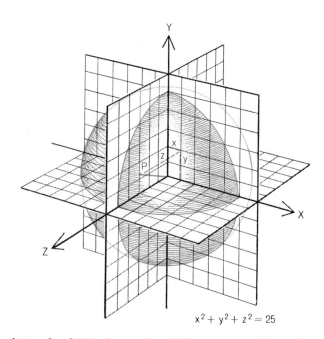

$$x^2 + y^2 + z^2 = 25$$

CARTESIAN COORDINATE SYSTEM made it possible to express any shape as an equation. For the circle at left, with a radius of five units, the equation is $x^2 + y^2 = 25$. Any values of x and y that produced 25 in the equation would represent a point on this circle; for the point P, $x = 3$ and $y = 4$. At right is a visualization of the sphere represented by the equation $x^2 + y^2 + z^2 = 25$.

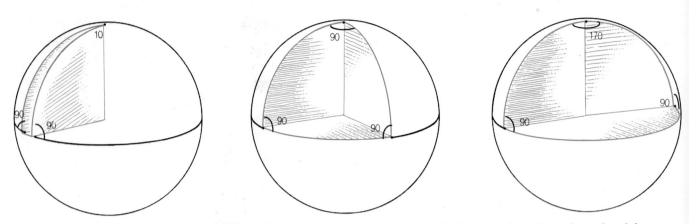

SPHERICAL TRIANGLES can have angles that sum to more than 180 degrees. On the sphere at left the triangle has angles sum-ming to 190 degrees. On the succeeding spheres the angles of the triangles sum respectively to 270 degrees, 350 degrees and 510 de-

its theorems, and to this extent the interests of the pure geometers who launched the revival were subverted. But projective geometry was again put in the shade by another development as dramatic and as weighty as the creation of mathematics by the classical Greeks: the creation of non-Euclidean geometry.

Throughout the long reign of Euclidean geometry many mathematicians were troubled by a slight blemish that seemed to mar the collection of axioms. Apropos of parallel lines, by which is meant two lines in the same plane that do not contain any points in common, Euclid formulated an axiom that reads as follows: If the straight line n cuts the lines l and m so as to make corresponding angles with each line that total less than 180 degrees, then l and m will meet on that side of the line n on which the angles lie. This axiom is essential to the derivation of the most important theorems, among them the theorem that the sum of the angles of a triangle is 180 degrees. The axiom is a bit involved, and there are reasons to believe Euclid himself was not too happy about it. Neither he nor any of the later mathematicians up to about 1800 really doubted the truth of the statement; that is, they had no doubt that it was a correct idealization of the behavior of actual, or physical, lines. What bothered Euclid and his successors was that the axiom was not quite so self-evident as, say, the axiom that any two right angles are equal.

From Greek times on mathematicians sought to replace the axiom on parallels by an equivalent one: an axiom that, together with the other nine axioms of Euclid, would make it possible to deduce the same body of theorems Euclid deduced. Many equivalent axioms were proposed. One of these, which was suggested by the mathematician John Play-

fair (1748–1819) and is the one usually taught in high schools, states that given a line l and a point P not on l, there is only one line m in the plane of P and l that passes through P and does not meet l.

Playfair's axiom is not only equivalent to Euclid's axiom but it is also simpler and appears to be intuitively convincing; that is, it does seem to state an unquestionable or self-evident property of lines in physical space. Later mathematicians, however, were not satisfied with Playfair's axiom or any of the other proposed equivalents of Euclid's axiom. The reason they were not satisfied was that every proposed substitute directly or indirectly involved an assertion about what happens far out in space. Thus Playfair's axiom asserts that l and m will not meet, no matter how far out these lines are extended. As a matter of fact, Euclid's axiom is superior in this respect because all it asserts is a condition under which lines will meet at some finite distance.

What is objectionable about axioms that assert what happens far out in space? The answer is that they transcend experience. The axioms of Euclidean geometry were supposed to be unquestionable truths about the real world. How can one be sure that two straight lines will extend indefinitely far out into physical space without ever being forced to meet? The problem the mathematicians faced was that Euclid's parallel axiom was not quite self-evident, and that the equivalent axioms, which were seemingly more self-evident, proved on closer examination to be somewhat suspect also.

The problem of the parallel axiom or, as the French mathematician Jean Le Rond d'Alembert put it, "the scandal of geometry," engaged the mathematicians of every period from Greek times up to 1800. The history of these inves-

tigations would be worth noting if for no other reason than to see how persistent and critical mathematicians can be. It is necessary here to forgo the history and jump to the results. The truth that destroyed truth was seen clearly by the greatest of all 19th-century mathematicians, Karl Friedrich Gauss (1777–1855). His first point was somewhat technical but essential, namely, that the parallel axiom is independent of the other nine axioms; that is, it is logically possible to choose a contradictory axiom and use it in conjunction with the other nine Euclidean axioms to deduce theorems of a new geometry. Thus one might assume that given a line l and a point P not on l, there is an infinite number of lines through P and in the plane of P and l that do not meet l. Gauss adopted this very axiom and from it and the other nine axioms deduced a number of theorems. Gauss called his new geometry non-Euclidean geometry.

As might be expected, many theorems of the new geometry contradict theorems of Euclidean geometry. The sum of the angles of a triangle in this geometry is always less than 180 degrees. Moreover, the sum varies with the size of the triangle; the closer the area of the triangle is to zero, the closer the angle sum is to 180 degrees.

The existence of a logical alternative to Euclidean geometry was in itself a startling fact. Geometry up to this time had been essentially Euclidean geometry; analytic and differential geometry were merely alternative technical methodologies, and although projective geometry dealt with new concepts and new themes, they were entirely in accord with Euclidean geometry. Non-Euclidean geometry was in conflict with Euclidean geometry.

Gauss's second conclusion was even more disturbing. It was that non-Eu-

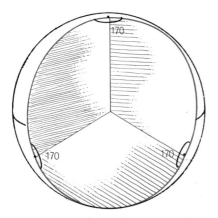

grees. Such triangles typify concepts of Bernhard Riemann's non-Euclidean geometry.

clidean geometry could be used to represent physical space just as well as Euclidean geometry does. This assertion seems at first to be downright nonsense. If the sum of the angles of a triangle is 180 degrees, how could it also be less than 180 degrees? The answer to this seeming impossibility is that the non-Euclidean geometry calls for an angle sum arbitrarily close to 180 degrees when the size of the triangle is small enough. The triangles man usually deals with are small; therefore the angle sums of these triangles might be so close to 180 degrees that measurement of the sum, in view of the inevitable errors of measurement, would not exclude either possibility.

The implications of non-Euclidean geometry are drastic. If both Euclidean and non-Euclidean geometry can represent physical space equally well, which is the truth about space and figures in space? One cannot say. In fact, the choice might not be limited to just these two. This doleful possibility was soon to be realized. The fact gradually forced on the mathematicians is that geometry is not the truth about physical space but the study of possible spaces. Several of these mathematically constructed spaces, differing sharply from one another, could fit physical space equally well as far as experience could decide.

The concept of geometry had then to be revised, but the same was true for the concept of mathematics itself. Since for more than 2,000 years mathematics had been the bastion of truth, non-Euclidean geometry, the triumph of reason, proved to be an intellectual disaster. This new geometry drove home the idea that mathematics, for all its usefulness in organizing thought and advancing the works of man, does not offer truths but is a man-made fable having the semblance of fact.

The new vista opening up in geom-

etry was widened immeasurably by the work of Georg Friedrich Bernhard Riemann (1826–1866). Riemann was one of Gauss's students and undoubtedly acquired from him an interest in the study of the physical world. Riemann's first observation in the field of geometry was that the mathematicians had been deceived into believing the Euclidean parallel axiom was necessarily true. Perhaps they were equally deceived in accepting one or more of the other axioms of Euclid. Riemann fastened at once on the axiom that a straight line is infinite. Experience, he pointed out, does not assure us of the infinitude of the physical straight line. Experience tells us only that in following a straight line we do not come to an end. But neither would one come to an end if one followed the Equator of the earth. In other words, experience tells us only that the straight line is endless or unbounded. If we change the relevant axiom of Euclid accordingly, and if we assume that there are *no* parallel lines, we have another set of axioms from which we can deduce still another non-Euclidean geometry.

In a paper of 1854 entitled "On the Hypotheses Which Underlie Geometry" Riemann launched an even deeper investigation of possible spaces, utilizing only the surest facts about physical space. He constructed a new branch of geometry, now known as Riemannian geometry, that opened up the variety of mathematical spaces a thousandfold [see "The Curvature of Space," by P.

Le Corbeiller, on page 128 of this volume].

To appreciate Riemannian geometry one must first perceive that what is chosen as the distance between two points determines the geometry that results. This can be readily seen. Consider three points on the surface of the earth. One can take as the distance between any two the length of the ordinary straight-line segment that joins them through the earth. In this case one obtains a triangle that has all the properties of a Euclidean triangle. In particular, the sum of the angles of this triangle is 180 degrees. One could, however, take as the distance between any two points the distance along the surface of the earth, meaning the distance along the great circle through these points. In this case the three points determine what is called a spherical triangle. Such triangles possess quite different properties. For example, the sum of the angles in them can be any number between 180 degrees and 540 degrees [*see illustration at the top of these two pages*]. This is a fact of spherical geometry.

What Riemann had in mind was a geometry for changing configurations. Suppose one were to try to design a geometry that would fit the surface of a mountainous region. In some places the surface might be flat, in others there might be conical hills and in still others hemispherical hills. The character of the surface changes from place to place,

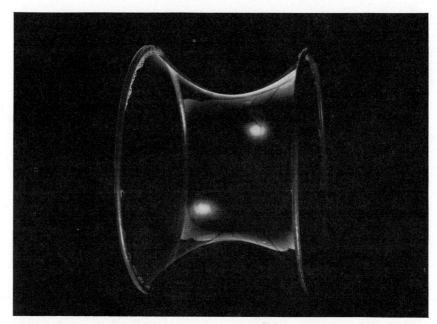

SOAP FILMS, which always assume a shape with the least possible area, illustrate a concern of differential geometry: surfaces of least area bounded by curves in space. Differential geometry is also applicable to problems of map making and curvature of surfaces.

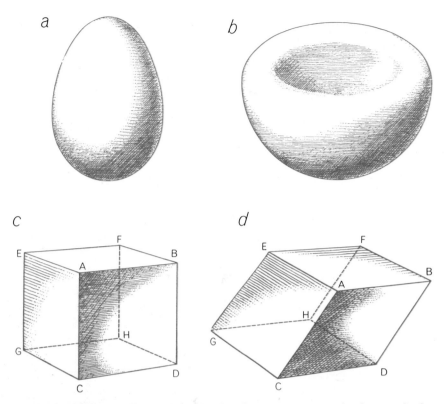

TOPOLOGICAL DEFORMATIONS of familiar shapes are portrayed. A sphere can be deformed into an egg shape (*a*), a squashed-ball shape (*b*), a cube (*c*) and a deformation of the cube (*d*). Each deformation is topologically equivalent to the others and to the sphere.

and so the distance formula that determines the geometry must change from place to place and possibly even from point to point. Riemann proposed, in other words, nonhomogeneous spaces—spaces whose characteristics vary from point to point or spaces with varying curvature.

Riemann died at the age of 40 and was therefore able to do little more than sketch the broad outline of his conception of space. The further development of Riemannian geometry became the task of many men and is still under way. Early in this century the Italian mathematicians Gregorio Ricci and Tullio Levi-Civita made significant contributions. Ricci introduced the tensor calculus, a formalism that enables one to express geometric relations independently of the coordinate system. Levi-Civita brought a concept of parallelism to Riemannian geometry: it provided a way of expressing the Euclidean notion of parallelism for more general spaces.

The creation of the general theory of relativity by Albert Einstein not only stimulated further work in Riemannian geometry but also suggested the problem of unifying gravitation and electromagnetism in one mathematical framework. Toward this end Hermann Weyl in 1918 introduced what he called

affinely connected spaces, a concept that uses Levi-Civita's notion of parallelism rather than the notion of distance to relate the points of a space to one another. An expression of distance even more generalized than Riemann's produced the spaces called Finsler spaces.

Riemann was also the founder of topology, another branch of geometry in which research is most active today. During the 1850's he was working with what are now called functions of a complex variable, and he introduced a class of surfaces, called Riemann surfaces, to represent such functions. The properties of the functions proved to be intimately connected with the geometric properties of the surfaces. For any given function, however, the precise shape of the surface was not critical, and so he found it desirable to classify surfaces in accordance with a new principle.

Given two similar figures, for example a large and a small triangle having the same shape, either can be regarded as a deformation, or transformation, of the other, the change being a uniform expansion of the smaller to obtain the larger, or a uniform contraction of the larger to obtain the smaller. Under projection and section the deformation of one figure into another is more radical. Yet even in these deformations a quad-

rilateral, say, remains a quadrilateral. It is possible to make still more radical deformations. For instance, a circle can be deformed by being bent into an ellipse or into an even more complicated shape, and a sphere can be stretched to assume the shape of an egg. For Riemann's purposes the circle could be replaced by the ellipse and the sphere by the egg shape. On the other hand, a circle, a figure eight and a trefoil were not interchangeable curves, and the sphere, the doughnut-shaped torus and the pretzel-shaped double torus were not interchangeable surfaces.

Hence Riemann was led to consider deformations that permit stretching, bending, contracting and even twisting. Figures that can be obtained from one another by such deformations are said to be homeomorphic, or topologically equivalent. If, however, one tears a figure or contracts it in such a way as to make points coalesce, the new figure is not topologically equivalent to the old one. Thus one can pinch a circle top and bottom and form a figure eight, but the latter is not topologically the same as the original. It is also possible to describe topologically equivalent figures by imagining them to be made of rubber. Then any figure that can be obtained by stretching, bending or contracting but not tearing the rubber would be topologically equivalent to the initial one.

The major problem of topology is to know when two figures are topologically equivalent. This may be difficult to see by looking at the figures, particularly since topology considers three-dimensional and even higher-dimensional figures. For this reason and others one seeks to characterize equivalent figures by some definitive properties so that if two figures possess these properties, they must be topologically equivalent, just as the congruence of two triangles is guaranteed if two sides and the included angle of one triangle are equal to the respective parts of the other. For example, if one draws any closed curve on the surface of a sphere or on an ellipsoid, the curve bounds a region on the surface. This is not true on the torus [*see illustration on opposite page*]. The sphere and the torus are therefore not topologically equivalent. It is possible to characterize closed surfaces in terms of curves that do or do not bound on the surface, but this criterion will not suffice for more complicated surfaces or for higher-dimensional figures.

Although many basic problems of topology remain unsolved, mathematicians make progress where they can, and in the past 10 years they have turned to the branch called differential topology. In this endeavor they combine the methods of topology and of differential geometry in the hope that two tools will be better than one.

Another enormously active field today is algebraic geometry. Two hundred years ago this subject was an extension of coordinate geometry and was devoted to the study of curves that are more complicated than the conic sections and are represented by equations of degree higher than the second. Since the latter part of the 19th century, however, the proper domain of algebraic geometry has been regarded as the study of the properties of curves, surfaces and higher-dimensional structures defined by algebraic equations and invariant under rational transformations. Such transformations distort a figure more than projective transformations and less than topological transformations do.

Mathematicians, yielding to their propensity to complicate and to algebraicize, have allowed the coordinates in the equations of algebraic geometry to take on complex values and even values in algebraic fields [see "Number," page 89, and "Algebra," page 102]. Consequently even the simple equation $x^2 + y^2 = 25$, which when x and y have real values represents the circle discussed previously, can represent a complicated Riemann surface or a structure so unconventional that it can hardly be imagined. The geometry suffers, but the algebra flourishes.

This discussion of geometry as the study of the properties of space and of figures in space may have exhibited the growth, variety and vitality of geometry and the interconnections of the branches with each other and with other divisions of mathematics, but it does not present the full nature of modern geometry. It is often said that algebra is a language. So is geometry.

Today mathematicians pursue the subject of abstract spaces, and one might infer from the term that the pursuit involves some highly idealized, esoteric spaces. This is true, but the major use of the theory of abstract spaces—indeed, historically the motivation for its study—is to expedite the use of classes of functions in analysis. The "points" of an abstract space are usually functions, and the distance between two points is some significant measure of a difference between two functions. Thus one might be interested in studying functions such as x^2, $3x^2$ and $x^3 - 2x$ and be interested in the values of these functions as x varies from 0 to 1. One could define the distance between any two of these functions as the largest numerical difference between the two for all values of x between 0 and 1. Such function spaces prove to be infinite-dimensional. The Hilbert spaces and Banach spaces about which one hears much today are function spaces. On the mathematical side these are important in the subject known as functional analysis, which is now the chief tool in quantum mechanics.

Why talk about spaces when one is really dealing with functions? It is because the geometrical mode of thinking is helpful and even suggestive of theorems about functions. What may be complicated and obscure when formulated analytically may in the geometrical interpretation be intuitively obvious. The study of abstract spaces is, surprisingly, part of topology because the properties of these structures that are important, whether the structures are regarded as actual spaces or as collections of functions, are preserved, or invariant, under topological transformations.

The subject of abstract spaces clearly exhibits the abstractness of modern mathematics. Geometry supplies models not only of physical space but also of any structure whose concepts and properties fit the geometric framework.

In still another vital respect geometry proves to be far more than the receptacle for matter. The present century is witnessing the realization of an assertion by Descartes that physics could be geometrized. In the theory of relativity, one of the two most notable scientific advances of this century (quantum theory is the other), the gravitational effect of gross matter has been reduced to geometry. Just as the geometry of a mountainous region requires a distance formula that varies from place to place to represent the varying shape of the land, so Einstein's geometry has a variable distance formula to represent the different masses in space. Matter determines the geometry, and the geometry as a result accounts for phenomena previously ascribed to gravitation.

Geometry has ingested part of reality and may have to ingest all of it. Today in quantum mechanics physicists are striving to resolve the seemingly contradictory wave and particle properties of subatomic matter, and they may have to generate both from quanta of space. Perhaps matter itself will also dissolve into pure space.

If one assesses today the competition between number and geometry, one must admit that insofar as methodology of proof is concerned, geometry has largely given way to algebra and analysis. The geometric treatment of complicated structures and of course of higher-dimensional spaces can, as Descartes complained of Euclidean geometry, "exercise the understanding only on condition of greatly fatiguing the imagination." Moreover, the quantitative needs of science can be met only by ultimate recourse to number.

Geometry, however, supplies sustenance and meaning to bare formulas. Geometry remains the major source of rich and fruitful intuitions, which in turn supply creative power to mathematics. Most mathematicians think in terms of geometric schemes, even though they leave no trace of that scaffolding when they present the complicated analytical structures. One can still believe Plato's statement that "geometry draws the soul toward truth."

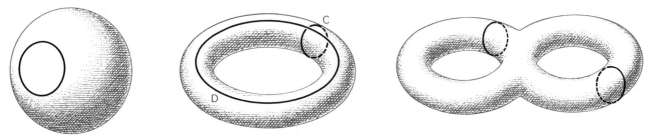

TOPOLOGICAL EQUIVALENCE of surfaces can be determined by drawing closed curves on the figures. If each curve bounds an area on a surface, the surface is topologically equivalent to a sphere. The type of curve drawn on the sphere at left does not bound an area on the torus at center or on the double torus at right; thus the latter figures are not topologically equivalent to a sphere.

17 PROJECTIVE GEOMETRY

MORRIS KLINE · January 1955

In the house of mathematics there are many mansions and of these the most elegant is projective geometry. The beauty of its concepts, the logical perfection of its structure and its fundamental role in geometry recommend the subject to every student of mathematics.

Projective geometry had its origins in the work of the Renaissance artists. Medieval painters had been content to express themselves in symbolic terms. They portrayed people and objects in a highly stylized manner, usually on a gold background, as if to emphasize that the subject of the painting, generally religious, had no connection with the real world. An excellent example, regarded by critics as the flower of medieval painting, is Simone Martini's "The Annunciation." With the Renaissance came not only a desire to paint realistically but

also a revival of the Greek doctrine that the essence of nature is mathematical law. Renaissance painters struggled for over a hundred years to find a mathematical scheme which would enable them to depict the three-dimensional real world on a two-dimensional canvas. Since many of the Renaissance painters were architects and engineers as well as artists, they eventually succeeded in their objective. To see how well they succeeded one need only compare Leonardo da Vinci's "Last Supper" with Martini's "Annunciation" [*see opposite page*].

The key to three-dimensional representation was found in what is known as the principle of projection and section. The Renaissance painter imagined that a ray of light proceeded from each point in the scene he was painting to one eye.

This collection of converging lines he called a projection. He then imagined that his canvas was a glass screen interposed between the scene and the eye. The collection of points where the lines of the projection intersected the glass screen was a "section." To achieve realism the painter had to reproduce on canvas the section that appeared on the glass screen.

Two woodcuts by the German painter Albrecht Dürer illustrate this principle of projection and section [*see below*]. In "The Designer of the Sitting Man" the artist is about to mark on a glass screen a point where one of the light rays from the scene to the artist's eye intersects the screen. The second woodcut, "The Designer of the Lute," shows the section marked out on the glass screen.

Of course the section depends not only

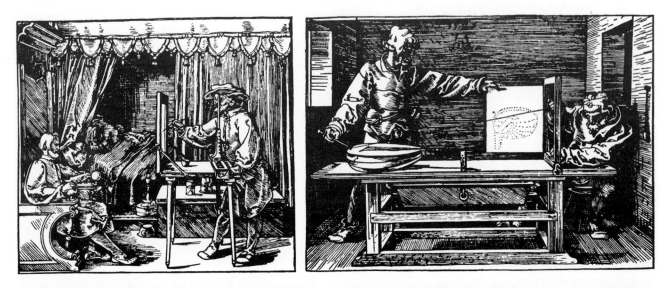

WOODCUTS by Albrecht Dürer illustrate the principle of projection and section. In the first woodcut the artist is about to mark the point at which a light ray from the scene to his eye intersects a glass screen. In the second a scene is marked out on the screen.

upon where the artist stands but also where the glass screen is placed between the eye and the scene. But this just means that there can be many different portrayals of the same scene. What matters is that, when he has chosen his scene, his position and the position of the glass screen, the painter's task is to put on canvas precisely what the section contains. Since the artist's canvas is not transparent and since the scenes he paints sometimes exist only in his imagination, the Renaissance artists had to derive theorems which would specify exactly how a scene would appear on the imaginary glass screen (the location, sizes and shapes of objects) so that it could be put on canvas.

The theorems they deduced raised questions which proved to be momentous for mathematics. Professional mathematicians took over the investigation of these questions and developed a geometry of great generality and power. Let us trace its development.

Suppose that a square is viewed from a point somewhat to the side [*Figure 1*]. On a glass screen interposed between the eye and the square, a section of its projection is not a square but some other quadrilateral. Thus square floor tiles, for instance, are not drawn square in a painting. A change in the position of the screen changes the shape of the section, but so long as the position of the viewer is kept fixed, the impression created by the section on the eye is the same. Likewise various sections of the projection of a circle viewed from a fixed position differ considerably—they may be more or less flattened ellipses—but the impression created by all these sections on the eye will still be that created by the original circle at that fixed position.

To the intellectually curious mathematicians this phenomenon raised a question: Should not the various sections presenting the same impression to the eye have some geometrical properties in common? For that matter, should not sections of an object viewed from different positions also have some properties in common, since they all derive from the same object? In other words, the mathematicians were stimulated to seek geometrical properties common to all sections of the same projection and to sections of two different projections of a given scene. This problem is essentially the one that has been the chief concern of projective geometers in their development of the subject.

It is evident that, just as the shape of a square or a circle varies in different

THE ANNUNCIATION by Simone Martini is an outstanding example of the flat, stylized painting of the medieval artists. The figures were symbolic and framed in a gold background.

THE LAST SUPPER by Leonardo da Vinci utilized projective geometry to create the illusion of three dimensions. Lines have been drawn on this reproduction to a point at infinity.

DRAWING by da Vinci, made as a study for his painting "The Adoration of the Magi," shows how he painstakingly projected the geometry of the entire scene before he actually painted it.

sections of the same projection or in different projections of the figure, so also will the length of a line segment, the size of an angle or the size of an area. More than that, lines which are parallel in a physical scene are not parallel in a painting of it but meet in one point; see, for example, the lines of the ceiling

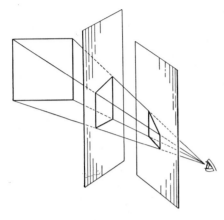

Figure 1 (see text)

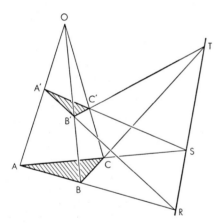

Figure 2

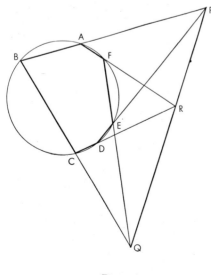

Figure 3

beams in da Vinci's "Last Supper." In other words, the study of properties common to the various sections of projections of an object does not seem to lie within the province of ordinary Euclidean geometry.

Yet some rather simple properties that do carry over from section to section can at once be discerned. For example, a straight line will remain a line (that is, it will not become a curve) in all sections of all projections of it; a triangle will remain a triangle; a quadrilateral will remain a quadrilateral. This is not only intuitively evident but easily proved by Euclidean geometry. However, the discovery of these few fixed properties hardly elates the finder or adds appreciably to the structure and power of mathematics. Much deeper insight was required to obtain significant properties common to different sections.

The first man to supply such insight was Gérard Desargues, the self-educated architect and engineer who worked during the first half of the 17th century. Desargues's motivation was to help the artists; his interest in art even extended to writing a book on how to teach children to sing well. He sought to combine the many theorems on perspective in a compact form, and he invented a special terminology which he thought would be more comprehensible than the usual language of mathematics.

His chief result, still known as Desargues's theorem and still fundamental in the subject of projective geometry, states a significant property common to two sections of the same projection of a triangle. Desargues considered the situation represented here by two different sections of the projection of a triangle from the point *O* [*Figure 2*]. The relationship of the two triangles is described by saying that they are perspective from the point *O*. Desargues then asserted that each pair of corresponding sides of these two triangles will meet in a point, and, most important, these three points will lie on one straight line. With reference to the figure, the assertion is that *AB* and *A'B'* meet in the point *R*; *AC* and *A'C'* meet in *S*; *BC* and *B'C'* meet in *T*; and that *R*, *S* and *T* lie on one straight line. While in the case stated here the two triangle sections are in different planes, Desargues's assertion holds even if triangles *ABC* and *A'B'C'* are in the same plane, *e.g.*, the plane of this paper, though the proof of the theorem is different in the latter case.

The reader may be troubled about the assertion in Desargues's theorem that each pair of corresponding sides of the

two triangles must meet in a point. He may ask: What about a case in which the sides happen to be parallel? Desargues disposed of such cases by invoking the mathematical convention that any set of parallel lines is to be regarded as having a point in common, which the student is often advised to think of as being at infinity—a bit of advice which essentially amounts to answering a question by not answering it. However, whether or not one can visualize this point at infinity is immaterial. It is logically possible to agree that parallel lines are to be regarded as having a point in common, which point is to be distinct from the usual, finitely located points of the lines considered in Euclidean geometry. In addition, it is agreed in projective geometry that all the intersection points of the different sets of parallel lines in a given plane lie on one line, sometimes called the line at infinity. Hence even if each of the three pairs of corresponding sides of the triangles involved in Desargues's theorem should consist of parallel lines, it would follow from our agreements that the three points of intersection lie on one line, the line at infinity.

These conventions or agreements not only are logically justifiable but also are recommended by the argument that projective geometry is concerned with problems which arise from the phenomenon of vision, and we never actually see parallel lines, as the familiar example of the apparently converging railroad tracks remind us. Indeed, the property of parallelism plays no role in projective geometry.

At the age of 16 the precocious French mathematician and philosopher Blaise Pascal, a contemporary of Desargues, formulated another major theorem in projective geometry. Pascal asserted that if the opposite sides of any hexagon inscribed in a circle are prolonged, the three points at which the extended pairs of lines meet will lie on a straight line [*Figure 3*].

As stated, Pascal's theorem seems to have no bearing on the subject of projection and section. However, let us visualize a projection of the figure involved in Pascal's theorem and then visualize a section of this projection [*Figure 4*]. The projection of the circle is a cone, and in general a section of this cone will not be a circle but an ellipse, a hyperbola, or a parabola—that is, one of the curves usually called a conic section. In any conic section the hexagon in the original circle will give rise to a corresponding hexagon. Now Pascal's theorem asserts that the pairs of opposite sides of the new hexagon will meet on one straight

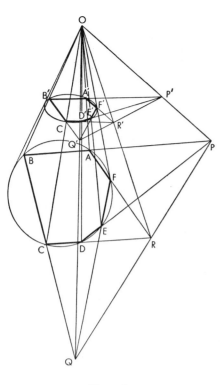

Figure 4

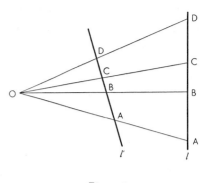

Figure 5

sargues's major work. In the meantime most of Desargues's and Pascal's discoveries had had to be remade independently by 19th-century geometers.

Projective geometry was revived through a series of accidents and events almost as striking as those that had originally given rise to the subject. Gaspard Monge, the inventor of descriptive geometry, which uses projection and section, gathered about him at the Ecole Polytechnique a host of bright pupils, among them Sadi Carnot and Jean Poncelet. These men were greatly impressed by Monge's geometry. Pure geometry had been eclipsed for almost 200 years by the algebraic or analytic geometry of Descartes. They set out to show that purely geometric methods could accomplish more than Descartes's.

It was Poncelet who revived projective geometry. As an officer in Napoleon's army during the invasion of Russia, he was captured and spent the year 1813-14 in a Russian prison. There Poncelet reconstructed, without the aid of any books, all that he had learned from Monge and Carnot, and he then proceeded to create new results in projective geometry. He was perhaps the first mathematician to appreciate fully that this subject was indeed a totally new branch of mathematics. After he had reopened the subject, a whole group of French and, later, German mathematicians went on to develop it intensively.

One of the foundations on which they built was a concept whose importance had not previously been appreciated. Consider a section of the projection of a line divided by four points [*Figure 5*]. Obviously the segments of the line in the section are not equal in length to those of the original line. One might venture that perhaps the ratio of two segments, say $A'C'/B'C'$, would equal the corresponding ratio AC/BC. This conjecture is incorrect. But the surprising fact is that the ratio of the ratios, namely $(A'C'/C'B')/(A'D'/D'B')$, will equal $(AC/CB)/(AD/DB)$. Thus this ratio of ratios, or cross ratio as it is called, is a projective invariant. It is necessary to note only that the lengths involved must be directed lengths; that is, if the direction from A to D is positive, then the length AD is positive but the length DB must be taken as negative.

The fact that any line intersecting the four lines OA, OB, OC and OD contains segments possessing the same cross ratio as the original segments suggests that we assign to the four projection lines meeting in the point O a particular cross ratio, namely the cross ratio of the segments on any section. Moreover, the

cross ratio of the four lines is a projective invariant, that is, if a projection of these four lines is formed and a section made of this projection, the section will contain four concurrent lines whose cross ratio is the same as that of the original four [*Figure 6*]. Here in the section $O'A'B'C'D'$, formed in the projection of the figure $OABCD$ from the point O'', the four lines $O'A'$, $O'B'$, $O'C'$ and $O'D'$ have the same cross ratio as OA, OB, OC and OD.

The projective invariance of cross ratio was put to extensive use by the 19th-century geometers. We noted earlier in connection with Pascal's theorem that under projection and section a circle may become an ellipse, a hyperbola or a parabola, that is, any one of the conic sections. The geometers sought some common property which would account for the fact that a conic section always gave rise to a conic section, and they found the answer in terms of cross ratio. Given the points O, A, B, C, D, and a sixth point P on a conic section containing the others [*Figure 7*], then a remarkable theorem of projective geometry states that the lines PA, PB, PC and PD have the same cross ratio as OA, OB, OC and OD. Conversely, if P is any point such that PA, PB, PC, and PD have the same

line which corresponds to the line derived from the original figure. Thus the theorem states a property of a circle which continues to hold in any section of any projection of that circle. It is indeed a theorem of projective geometry.

It would be pleasant to relate that the theorems of Desargues and Pascal were immediately appreciated by their fellow mathematicians and that the potentialities in their methods and ideas were eagerly seized upon and further developed. Actually this pleasure is denied us. Perhaps Desargues's novel terminology baffled mathematicians of his day, just as many people today are baffled and repelled by the language of mathematics. At any rate, all of Desargues's colleagues except René Descartes exhibited the usual reaction to radical ideas: they called Desargues crazy and dismissed projective geometry. Desargues himself became discouraged and returned to the practice of architecture and engineering. Every printed copy of Desargues's book, originally published in 1639, was lost. Pascal's work on conics and his other work on projective geometry, published in 1640, also were forgotten. Fortunately a pupil of Desargues, Philippe de la Hire, made a manuscript copy of Desargues's book. In the 19th century this copy was picked up by accident in a bookshop by the geometer Michel Chasles, and thereby the world learned the full extent of De-

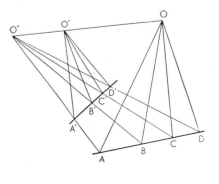

Figure 6

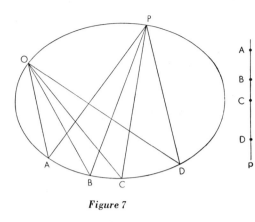

Figure 7

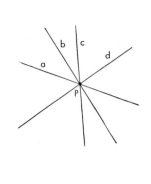

Figure 8

cross ratio as *OA*, *OB*, *OC* and *OD*, then *P* must lie on the conic through *O*, *A*, *B*, *C* and *D*. The essential point of this theorem and its converse is that a conic section is determined by the property of cross ratio. This new characterization of a conic was most welcome, not only because it utilized a projective property but also because it opened up a whole new line of investigation on the theory of conics.

The satisfying accomplishments of projective geometry were capped by the discovery of one of the most beautiful principles of all mathematics—the principle of duality. It is true in projective geometry, as in Euclidean geometry, that any two points determine one line, or as we prefer to put it, any two points lie on one line. But it is also true in projective geometry that any two lines determine, or lie on, one point. (The reader who has refused to accept the convention that parallel lines in Euclid's sense are also to be regarded as having a point in common will have to forego the next few paragraphs and pay for his stubbornness.) It will be noted that the second statement can be obtained from the first merely by interchanging the words point and line. We say in projective geometry that we have dualized the original statement. Thus we can speak not only of a

set of points on a line but also of a set of lines on a point [*Figure 8*]. Likewise the dual of the figure consisting of four points no three of which lie on the same line is a figure of four lines no three of which lie on the same point [*Figure 9*].

Let us attempt this rephrasing for a slightly more complicated figure. A triangle consists of three points not all on the same line and the lines joining these points. The dual statement would read: three lines not all on the same point and the points joining them (that is, the points in which the lines intersect). The figure we get by rephrasing the definition of a triangle is again a triangle, and so the triangle is called self-dual.

Now let us rephrase Desargues's theorem in dual terms, using the fact that the dual of a triangle is a triangle and assuming in this case that the two triangles and the point *O* lie in one plane. The theorem says:

"If we have two triangles such that lines joining corresponding vertices pass through one point *O*, then the pairs of corresponding sides of the two triangles join in three points lying on one straight line."

Its dual reads:

"If we have two triangles such that points which are the joins of corresponding sides lie on one line *O*, then the pairs

of corresponding vertices of the two triangles are joined by three lines lying on one point."

We see that the dual statement is really the converse of Desargues's theorem, that is, it is the result of interchanging his hypothesis with his conclusion. Hence by interchanging point and line we have discovered the statement of a new theorem. It would be too much to ask that the proof of the new theorem should be obtainable from the proof of the old one by interchanging point and line. But if it is too much to ask, the gods have been generous beyond our merits, for the new proof can be obtained in precisely this way.

Projective geometry also deals with curves. How should one dualize a statement involving curves? The clue lies in the fact that a curve is after all but a collection of points; we may think of a figure dual to a given curve as a collection of lines. And indeed a collection of lines which satisfies the condition dual to that satisfied by a conic section turns out to be the set of tangents to that curve [*Figure 10*]. If the conic section is a circle, the dual figure is the collection of tangents to the circle [*Figure 11*]. This collection of tangents suggests the circle as well as does the usual collection of points, and we shall call the collection of tangents the line circle.

Let us now dualize Pascal's theorem on the hexagon in a circle. His theorem goes:

"If we take six points, *A*, *B*, *C*, *D*, *E* and *F*, on the point circle, then the lines which join *A* and *B* and *D* and *E* join in a point *P*; the lines which join *B* and *C* and *E* and *F* join in a point *Q*; the lines which join *C* and *D* and *F* and *A* join in a point *R*. The three points *P*, *Q* and *R* lie on one line *l*."

Its dual reads:

"If we take six lines, *a*, *b*, *c*, *d*, *e* and *f*, on the line circle, then the points

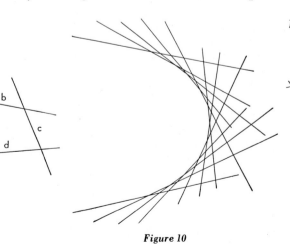

Figure 9

Figure 10

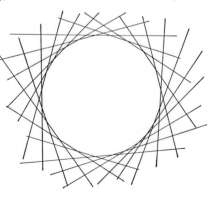

Figure 11

which join *a* and *b* and *d* and *e* are joined by the line *p*; the points which join *b* and *c* and *e* and *f* are joined by the line *q*; the points which join *c* and *d* and *f* and *a* are joined by the line *r*. The three lines *p*, *q* and *r* lie on one point *L*."

The geometric meaning of the dual statement amounts to this: Since the line circle is the collection of tangents to the point circle, the six lines on the line circle are any six tangents to the point circle, and these six tangents form a hexagon circumscribed about the point circle. Hence the dual statement tells us that if we circumscribe a hexagon about a point circle, the lines joining opposite vertices of the hexagon, lines *p*, *q* and *r* in the dual statement, meet in one point [*Figure 12*]. This dual statement is indeed a theorem of projective geometry. It is called Brianchon's theorem, after Monge's student Charles Brianchon, who discovered it by applying the principle of duality to Pascal's theorem pretty much as we have done.

It is possible to show by a single proof that every rephrasing of a theorem of projective geometry in accordance with the principle of duality must lead to a new theorem. This principle is a remarkable possession of projective geometry. It reveals the symmetry in the roles that point and line play in the structure of that geometry. The principle of duality also gives us insight into the process of creating mathematics. Whereas the discovery of this principle, as well as of theorems such as Desargues's and Pascal's, calls for imagination and genius, the discovery of new theorems by means of the principle is an almost mechanical procedure.

As one might suspect, projective geometry turns out to be more fundamental than Euclidean geometry. The clue to the relationship between the two geometries may be obtained by again considering projection and section. Consider the projection of a rectangle and a section in a plane parallel to the rectangle [*Figure 13*]. The section is a rectangle similar to the original one. If now the point *O* moves off indefinitely far to the left, the lines of the projection come closer and closer to parallelism with each other. When these lines become parallel and the center of the projection is the "point at infinity," the rectangles become not merely similar but congruent [*Figure 14*]. In other words, from the standpoint of projective geometry the relationships of congruence and similarity, which are so intensively studied in Euclidean geometry, can be studied through projection and section for special projections.

If projective geometry is indeed logically fundamental to Euclidean geometry, then all the concepts of the latter geometry should be defined in terms of projective concepts. However, in projective geometry as described so far there is a logical blemish: our definition of cross ratio, and hence concepts based on cross ratio, rely on the notion of length, which should play no role in projective geometry proper because length is not an invariant under arbitrary projection and section. The 19th-century geometer Felix Klein removed this blemish. He showed how to define length as well as the size of angles entirely in terms of projective concepts. Hence it became possible to affirm that projective geometry was indeed logically prior to Euclidean geometry and that the latter could be built up as a special case. Both Klein and Arthur Cayley even showed that the basic non-Euclidean geometries could be derived as special cases of projective geometry. No wonder that Cayley exclaimed: "Projective geometry is all geometry!"

It remained only to deduce the theorems of Euclidean and non-Euclidean geometry from axioms of projective geometry, and this geometers succeeded in doing in the late 19th and early 20th centuries. What Euclid did to organize the work of three hundred years preceding his time, the projective geometers did recently for the investigations which Desargues and Pascal initiated.

Research in projective geometry is now less active. Geometers are seeking to find simpler axioms and more elegant proofs. Some research is concerned with projective geometry in n-dimensional space. A vast new allied field is projective differential geometry, concerned with local or infinitesimal properties of curves and surfaces.

Projective geometry has had an important bearing on current mathematical research in several other fields. Projection and section amount to what is called in mathematics a transformation, and it seeks invariants under this transformation. Mathematicians asked: Are there other transformations more general than projection and section whose invariants might be studied? In recent times one new geometry has been developed by pursuing this line of thought, namely, topology. It would take us too far afield to consider topological transformations. It must suffice here to state that topology considers transformations more general than projection and section and that it is now clear that topology is logically prior to projective geometry. Cayley was too hasty in affirming that projective geometry is all geometry.

The work of the projective geometers has had an important influence on modern physical science. They prepared the way for the workers in the theory of relativity, who sought laws of the universe that were invariant under transformation from the coordinate system of one observer to that of another. It was the projective geometers and other mathematicians who invented the calculus of tensors, which proved to be the most convenient means for expressing invariant scientific laws.

It is of course true that the algebra of differential equations and some other branches of mathematics have contributed more to the advancement of science than has projective geometry. But no branch of mathematics competes with projective geometry in originality of ideas, coordination of intuition in discovery and rigor in proof, purity of thought, logical finish, elegance of proofs and comprehensiveness of concepts. The science born of art proved to be an art.

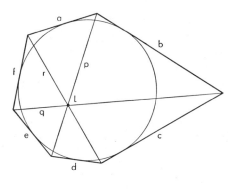

Figure 12

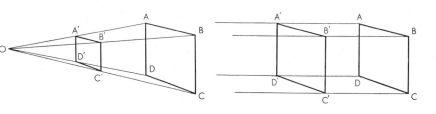

Figure 13   *Figure 14*

18 THE CURVATURE OF SPACE

P. LE CORBEILLER · November 1954

In the spring of 1854 a young German mathematician named Bernhard Riemann was greatly worried about his future and about a test he faced immediately. He was already 28, and still not earning—he was living meagerly on a few thalers sent each month by his father, a Protestant minister in a small Hanover town. He wrote modestly to his father and brother that the most famous university professors, in Berlin and in Göttingen, had unaccountably been extraordinarily kind to him. He had his doctor's degree; now, to obtain an appointment as a lecturer (without stipend), he had to give a satisfactory lecture before the whole Faculty of Philosophy at Göttingen. He had offered three subjects. "The two first ones I had well prepared," Bernhard wrote his brother, "but Gauss chose the third one, and now I'm in trouble."

Karl Friedrich Gauss was the dean of German mathematicians and the glory of his university. In Bernhard's picture of Heaven, Gauss's professorial armchair was not very far from the Lord's throne. (This is still the general view in Göttingen today.) The subject Gauss had chosen for young Riemann's lecture was "The Hypotheses That Are the Foundations of Geometry." Gauss had published nothing but a few cryptic remarks on this topic, but he selected it in preference to the two others proposed by Riemann because he was curious to find out what the young man would have to say on such a deep and novel subject—a subject to which Gauss himself had given much thought and had already made a great, though as yet not widely appreciated, contribution.

The day of Riemann's public lecture was Saturday, June 10, 1854. Most of his auditors were classicists, historians, philosophers—anyway, not mathematicians. Riemann had decided that he would discourse about the curvature of n-dimensional spaces without writing any equations. Was that a courteous gesture on his part, or a mildly Machiavellian scheme? We shall never know. What is sure is that without equations Gauss understood him very well, for walking home after the lecture he told his colleague Wilhelm Weber, with unwonted warmth, of his utmost admiration for the ideas presented by Riemann.

Gauss's enthusiasm was justified. The young man had reached into realms of thought so new that few scientists then could follow him. But his abstract ideas were to make contact with experimental reality half a century later through the work of Albert Einstein, who saw that Riemann's speculations were directly applicable to the problem of the interaction between light and gravitation, and made them the basis of his Generalized Relativity Theory, which today controls our view of the universe.

Let us then go back 100 years and acquaint ourselves with the thoughts which Riemann made public on that June day of 1854. Before reaching Riemann's ideas we first have to cover some rather elementary background.

Everybody is familiar with the elements of plane geometry. A straight line is the shortest way between two points; parallel lines never meet; the sum of the three angles of a triangle equals two right angles, or 180 degrees, and so on and so forth. Also familiar is the geometry of figures drawn on the surface of a sphere, which obey somewhat different rules. The shortest route between two points on a sphere is called a "great circle"; this is the curve made by a cut through the points and the center of the sphere, splitting the sphere into equal halves. Two great circles always meet in two points; for instance, any two meridians of the earth always meet at the North and South poles. When segments of three great circles (for instance, one quarter of the earth's equator and the northern halves of two meridians) intersect to form a "spherical triangle," the three angles of 90 degrees add up to 270 degrees, or three right angles. The difference between this triangle and one in a plane derives from the fact that the sides of the former are drawn on a curved surface instead of on a flat one.

Now how do we know that the surface of a table is flat and that of the earth is spherical? All early civilizations imagined the earth as a flat disk, with mountains heaped upon it like food on the king's table. Not being able to go to the moon to look at the earth, men could not see its true shape. How, then, did Greek astronomers come to the conclusion that the earth was round? By observing that the North Star was higher in the sky in Greece than in Egypt. Thus it is evident that we can recognize that a sphere is round either by observing it from a distance or, if we stand on it, by observing objects far away.

Man also could, and did, discover that the earth was round in two entirely different ways. One way was his circumnavigation of the earth. He found that while the surface of the earth had no "edge," no boundaries, its area was nevertheless limited. This is a most remarkable fact: the surface of the earth is boundless and yet it is finite. Obviously that situation rules out the possibility that the earth could be a plane. The surface of a plane is boundless and also infinite. (In common speech we consider these two words strictly synonymous—one of the many instances which prove that the sphericity of the world has not yet really taken hold of our consciousness.)

Thus mankind would have discovered that the earth is round even if it were constantly covered with a canopy of thick clouds. But suppose that he had somehow been prevented from exploring the whole planet. There is still another way in which he could have found out he was living on a globe, and that is by using the spherical geometry we have been talking about. If we look at a small triangle on the earth's surface, say one with sides about 30 feet long, it is indistinguishable from a flat triangle; the sum of its three angles exceeds 180 degrees by an amount so small that it cannot be measured. As we consider larger and larger triangles on the earth's spherical surface, however, their curvature will become more and more significant, and it will show up in the excess of the sum of their angles over 180 degrees. Thus by developing more and more precise methods of surveying and of making maps men eventually could prove the sphericity of the earth, and from their measurements they could find out the globe's radius. We shall return presently to this matter.

There are many types of surfaces besides those of a plane and a sphere. Consider an egg. It has a large end and a small end. A round piece of shell from the large end looks as if it were cut from a sphere; a round piece from the small end looks as if it belonged to a sphere with a smaller radius than the first. The piece from the small end looks more curved thàn that from the large end. Geometers define the curvature of a sphere as the inverse of its radius squared. So the smaller the radius, the larger the curvature, and *vice versa*.

If we were given a piece of shell from the middle zone of the egg, could we define its curvature? That is a little difficult, because such a piece cannot be identified with a portion of a simple sphere. The problem has been solved as follows. Suppose we lay the piece, which has the shape of a more or less elongated oval, on a table. It forms a rather flat dome. Any vertical cross section of that dome will be a curve concave downward. Every vertical cross section will look approximately like a portion of a circle, but not all will have the same radius. The section through the narrowest part of the base will have the smallest radius; the section through the elongated part, the largest. Let us call the first radius R_1 and the second R_2. Geometers then take a sort of average, and define the curvature of that small

portion of eggshell as the inverse of the product R_1R_2. You can see that if the eggshell were a perfect sphere, we would be brought back to the previous definition.

On the basis of these definitions one finds that the curvature of a small piece of an eggshell changes as we travel on the surface of the egg. It would make no sense to talk about the curvature of the whole egg; we can only talk about the curvature of a small piece.

Consider next the surface of a saddle. A crosswise vertical section cut through a saddle forms a curve which is concave downward, whereas a lengthwise vertical cut forms a curve concave upward. This makes even a small piece of the surface of a saddle something radically different from a small piece of an eggshell. Geometers say that the eggshell has everywhere positive curvature, and the saddle has everywhere negative curvature. The curvature of a small portion of a saddle-shaped surface can again be defined as the inverse of the product R_1R_2, but this time it must be given a negative sign.

And here is still something else. Consider a doughnut. If you compare the inner half of the surface (facing the center of the hole in the doughnut) with the outer half, you will recognize that any small portion of the outer half has positive curvature, while any small por-

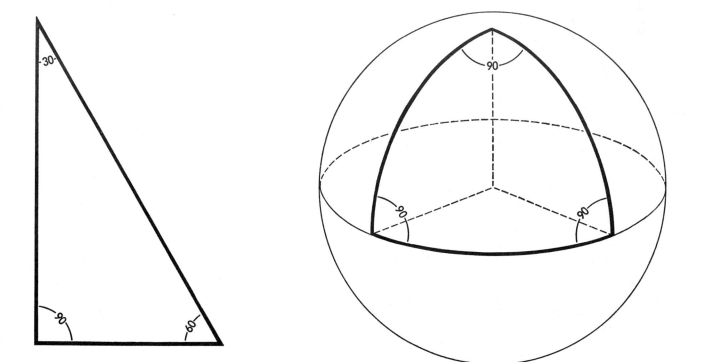

TRIANGLES drawn on a plane and on a sphere obey somewhat different rules. On a plane the sum of the angles of a triangle always is equal to 180 degrees. The intersection of three great circles on the surface of a sphere forms three angles adding up to 270 degrees.

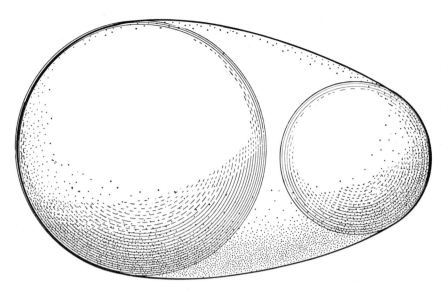

AN EGG has a curved surface which looks as if the surface of the large end belonged to one sphere and the surface of the small end to another. The middle has a different curvature.

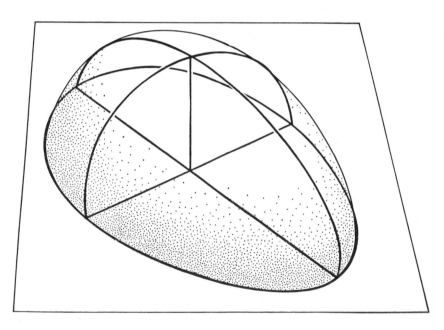

HALF AN EGG, laid on a table and cut into vertical cross sections, will yield sections with concave curves downward. These curves look like portions of circles of different radii.

tion of the inner half has negative curvature, as in the case of a saddle. Thus we must not think that the curvature need be positive or negative all over a given surface; as we travel from point to point on a surface the curvature not only can become greater or smaller, it can also change its sign.

Remember that we are engaged in taking a bird's-eye view of what was known about the curvature of surfaces before Riemann's time. What we have seen so far had been recognized in the 18th century by Leonhard Euler, a Swiss mathematician of considerable imagina-

tion and output, and had been developed by a group of French geometers at the newly founded Ecole Polytechnique. Then in 1827 Gauss, Riemann's senior examiner, added much generality and precision to the topic. He published a memoir on curved surfaces which is so jewel-perfect that one can still use it today in a college course.

Gauss started from the fact that geographers specify the location of a city on the globe by giving its longitude and latitude. They draw meridians of longitude (such as the one which unites all the points on the globe 85 degrees west of the north-and-south great circle

through Greenwich) and also parallels of latitude. We may speak of the "family" of meridians and the "family" of parallels. In order to specify the location of a point on any mathematically given surface, Gauss imagined that we draw on that surface two families of curves, called p-curves and q-curves. We take suitable precautions so that any point on the surface will be pinpointed if we specify its p-coordinate and its q-coordinate.

Gauss's great insight was this. On an absolutely flat surface, if we travel three miles in one direction, then turn left and travel four miles in the perpendicular direction, we know from Pythagoras' theorem that we are at a point five miles from home. But Gauss reasoned that on a curved surface, whether egg, or saddle or what have you, the distance will be different. To begin with, the p-curves and q-curves will not intersect everywhere at right angles, and this adds a third term to the sum of the two squares in the Pythagorean equation $a^2 + b^2 = c^2$. Moreover, if we visualize the two families of curves as a kind of fish net drawn tight all over the surface, the angles and sides of the small meshes will change slowly as we travel from one region of the surface to another where the curvature is different.

Gauss expressed his reasoning in a famous mathematical equation. One p-curve and one q-curve pass through a given point M on a curved surface. The "quasi longitude" p and the "quasi latitude" q of point M have specific numerical values. We wish to move from point M to a neighboring point P on the surface. We first increase the value of p by a small quantity, letting q remain the same. Gauss used dp as the symbol for an arbitrarily small increase of p. We thus get to a point N, of longitude $p+dp$ and latitude q. We next increase the value of q by a small quantity, dq, letting $p+dp$ remain the same. We thus reach a point P, of longitude $p+dp$ and latitude $q+dq$. We wish to know the distance from point M to point P. Since this distance is arbitrarily small, Gauss used for it the symbol ds. In Gauss's notation, the square of the distance ds will be expressed by the sum of three terms:

$$ds^2 = E\ dp^2 + 2F\ dp\ dq + G\ dq^2$$

This equation is one of the high points in the whole of mathematics and physics —a mountain-top where we should exclaim in awe, like Faust suddenly perceiving the symbol of the macrocosm: "Was he a god, whoever wrote these signs?" It needed only two steps, one taken by Riemann and the other by Einstein, to carry us from Gauss's equation into the land of general relativity.

At any point M on our arbitrary surface, this equation is not different from a Euclidean theorem about the square of the third side, ds, of any triangle, the first two being dp, dq. That is because in the immediate neighborhood of a point the surface is very nearly a plane. But here is the novelty: Gauss introduced the functions E, F and G, whose numerical values change continuously as we move from point to point on the surface. Gauss saw that each of the quantities E, F, G was a function of the two arbitrary quantities p and q, the quasi longitude and the quasi latitude of point M. On a plane we can draw p-lines and q-lines dividing the plane into small equal squares, as on a chessboard; we have then $ds^2 = dp^2 + dq^2$, so that E is constantly equal to 1, F to zero and G to 1 all over the plane. But on a curved surface E, F and G vary in a way which expresses, in an abstract but precise manner, just those variations in the curvature of a surface that make every point different from every other.

Gauss now proved this remarkable theorem: that the curvature of the surface at any point can be found as soon as one knows the values of E, F and G at the point, and how they vary in its immediate neighborhood. Why is this theorem so remarkable? Because if we return to our fictional humanity living on some beclouded globe, not a spherical one this time but of arbitrary shape, the surveyors of any particular nation on that globe, knowing the theorem, could obtain all the information about E, F and G without seeing the stars and without going to the moon. Thus from measurements taken on the surface itself they would be able to calculate the curvature of their globe at various points and to find out whether the surface of their country was curved like a portion of an egg, saddle or doughnut, as the case might be.

Now of all the ridiculous and useless puzzles scientists like to solve, this one, you may think, surely takes the prize. Why should mathematicians find it important to describe the behavior of imaginary people in a nonexistent world? For a very good reason: *These people are ourselves.* Only it takes some little explanation to make you realize I have been talking about you and me.

Let us imagine small bits of paper of various irregular shapes on a large, smooth sphere. These bits of paper are

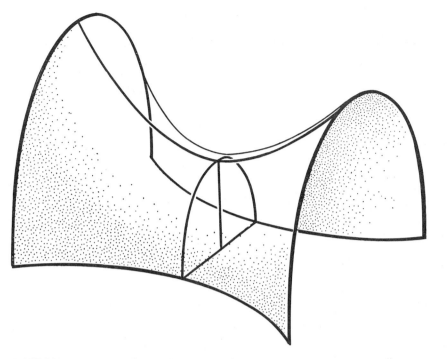

A SADDLE cut into lengthwise cross sections forms curves upward, while crosswise sections curve downward with shorter radii. A saddle is described as having negative curvature.

alive and moving: they are the people of that world, only their bodies are not volumes enclosed by surfaces but surfaces enclosed by curves. These people, having absolutely flat bodies without thickness, can form no conception of the space above or below them. They are themselves only portions of surfaces, two-dimensional beings. Their senses are adapted to give them information about the surroundings in their two-dimensional world. But they have no experience whatsoever of anything outside that world; so they cannot conceive of a third dimension.

However, they are intelligent; they have discovered mathematics and physics. Their geometry consists of two parts —line geometry and plane geometry. In physics they illustrate problems in one variable by diagrams on a line; problems in two variables, by surface diagrams. Problems in three, four or more variables they solve by algebra: "It's too bad," they say, "that for these we can't have the help of diagrams."

In the first half of the 19th century (*their* 19th century) an idea dawned upon several of them. "We cannot," they said, "imagine a third dimension, but we do handle physical problems in three variables, x, y, z. Why couldn't we *talk* about a space of three dimensions? Even if we cannot visualize it, it might be helpful to be able to talk about points, lines and areas located in that space. Maybe something might come of it; anyway, there's no harm in trying." And so they tried.

We need not carry this fable any farther; its meaning is clear enough. We are just like these people, only our bodies have three dimensions and are moving about in a three-dimensional world. Neither you nor I can visualize a fourth dimension; yet we handle problems about a particle moving in space, and this is a problem in four variables: x, y, z for space and t for time. We also handle problems about electromagnetic fields. Well, the electric field vector E at any point (x, y, z) has three projections, E_x, E_y, E_z, and it changes in space and time; that makes seven variables. Add three more for its twin brother, the magnetic field B, and we have 10. It looks as if the mathematical physicist could well use spaces of four or 10 or any number of dimensions.

Riemann in his dissertation assumed at the outset a space of an arbitrary number of dimensions. Now a lesser geometer would have found it very straightforward to define the distance of two neighboring points in that space. Don't we know from Pythagoras' theorem that in a plane the square of that distance, ds^2, is equal to the sum of two squares: $ds^2 = dx^2 + dy^2$? Well then obviously in an n-dimensional space ds^2 must be the sum of n squares, the sum of all the terms similar to dx^2 which we can find. A very convenient shorthand for the expression "the sum of all the terms similar to" is the Greek capital Σ. Thus a simple-minded geometer would have written $ds^2 = \Sigma\, dx^2$. But Riemann saw farther than that. He had given much thought to the 1827 memoir of his master Gauss. He reasoned that, if we assumed that $ds^2 = \Sigma\, dx^2$, we were beaten at the outset. For Pythagoras' theorem is valid only in a plane, divided into equal little squares like a chessboard. Actually what we need to generalize is Gauss's equation, which works for any curved surface whatsoever, including a plane as a very special case. Gauss had added two things to Pythagoras' formula: (1) to the squares of dp and dq he had added the product dp dq of these two quantities; (2) he had multiplied each of these three terms by a coefficient of its own, and assumed that these coefficients E, F, G varied from point to point over the surface.

Let us do the same thing, then, for a "supersurface" of three dimensions, whatever that may be. We shall stretch over this supersurface three families of surfaces p, q, r or, as they are more conveniently designated, x_1, x_2, x_3. The square of the distance between two neighboring points, ds^2, should be built not only from the squares of dx_1, dx_2, dx_3, but also from their products two by two, and there are three such products: dx_2dx_3, dx_3dx_1 and dx_1dx_2. This makes a total of six terms, and we must give them six coefficients. Let us represent these coefficients by the letter g, with suitable subscripts. We must then write:
$$ds^2 = g_{11}dx_1{}^2 + g_{22}dx_2{}^2 + g_{33}dx_3{}^2 + 2g_{23}dx_2dx_3 + 2g_{31}dx_3dx_1 + 2g_{12}dx_1dx_2.$$
(The factor 2 is not indispensable, but it is esthetically satisfying to the algebraist, and Gauss had taken a fit when a young Berlin professor, Dirichlet, had committed the *faux pas* of writing a memoir which dispensed with the factor 2.) This, then, is the correct form of the ds^2 for a supersurface of three dimensions, and the six coefficients will in general vary from point to point over the supersurface.

Riemann, as we have said, assumed at the outset that he had n variables to deal with, not a specific number such as three or four. He needed a name for the kind of geometrical objects he was thinking about. He noticed two things. First, a particle is free (in theory) to move smoothly and continuously from one point of a line or curve to another; it may also move continuously from one point to another on a surface or in space. Second, while studying plane geometry we think of nothing but figures drawn on a plane; that plane is for the time being our whole "universe of discourse," as logicians say. Yet the next year, as we study solid geometry, we imagine planes

of any orientation in space. Any one of these planes might well be *the* plane of plane geometry which was last year's universe of discourse. It makes no difference in the geometry of a plane whether this plane exists all by itself or whether it is "embedded," as we now say, in three-dimensional space.

Putting these remarks together, Riemann coined the name "continuum" for any geometrical object, of any number of dimensions, upon which a point can continuously roam about. A straight line, for instance, is a continuum in one dimension—and it makes no difference to the geometry of points and segments on that line whether this one-dimensional continuum exists all by itself or is embedded in a plane, in three-dimensional space or for that matter in a space of any number of dimensions. The surface of a sphere or of a saddle is, as we have seen, a two-dimensional continuum; again it makes no difference whether we consider it by itself or embedded in a space of any number of dimensions.

Now our space is a three-dimensional continuum. And we are bound to add that geometry in our space will be the same whether we consider that space by itself or assume it is embedded in a space of four, five or any number of dimensions. We cannot visualize what this means. Just the same, we might follow up this trail and see where logic leads us.

Such must have been young Riemann's thoughts about the year 1850. We must now try to say in a few words how far he progressed from there, and what, mainly, his dissertation of 1854 contained.

At a first reading, the outstanding result of Riemann's efforts seems to be that he succeeded in defining the curvature of a continuum of more than two dimensions. A two-dimensional continuum is a surface, and we have seen that its curvature is defined, for a small region surrounding any point of the sur-

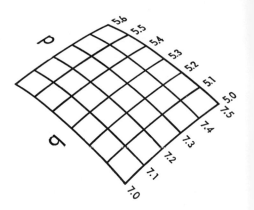

LOCATION of a point on any mathematically given surface may be specified by giving one coordinate from the family of p-curves and one from the intersecting family of q-curves. On any surface but a sphere these curves will not intersect at right angles.

face, by a single number—positive on an egg-shaped surface, negative on a saddle-shaped surface. If the curvature is zero at every point, the surface is a plane, and *vice versa*. Riemann showed that the concept of curvature can be generalized for the case of a continuum of n dimensions. Only it will not be a single number any more; a set of three numbers will be needed to define the curvature of a continuum of three dimensions, a set of six numbers for one of four dimensions, and so forth. Riemann only stated these results and made them seem mathematically plausible; their proof and elaboration would have filled a long memoir or occupied several weeks of lectures.

These considerations seem purely abstract—a completely vacuous game of mathematics running wild. However, Riemann's main object in his dissertation was to convince us that he was talking not about abstract mathematical concepts but about a question of physics which could be settled by the experimental method.

Let us return to those perfectly flat beings that live on a huge surface. Gauss's "remarkable theorem" proves that the two-dimensional inhabitants of this two-dimensional universe, provided they understood enough mathematics, could find the curvature of any small region of their universe. How could these people conceive of a curved surface, if they could not visualize a space of three dimensions? The answer is that such is precisely the power of mathematics. These people would be familiar with the concept of a curved road, contrasting with a "straight" road which would be the shortest route between two points. If then some Riemann among them had generalized this notion, *in a purely algebraic way*, into a theory of the curvature

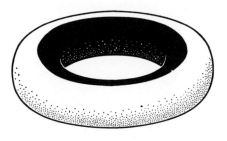

A DOUGHNUT'S SURFACE shows positive curvature in its outer half, while the inner half has negative curvature (*black*).

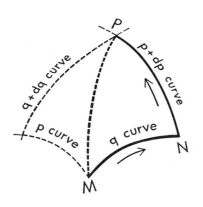

DISTANCE from one point *P* to a point *M* on a surface of any curvature cannot be determined by the Pythagorean rule. Gauss defined it as a function of the intersecting coordinates locating points and curvature varying on the surface from point to point.

of a continuum of *n* dimensions, their surveyors would be able to calculate from a formula given by Riemann a certain number which, they would find, would change slightly from country to country. Thus they would have measured the curvature of their two-dimensional universe without being able in any way to visualize what that could be.

Such, of course, is exactly our situation regarding the curvature of our own universe, and we must return to Riemann's work to form some idea of how he came to define it.

Riemann suggested that if all the numbers which defined the curvature of an n-dimensional space were zero, this space should be called flat, for that is what we call a surface whose curvature is zero. Now if we divide a three-dimensional space into equal little cubes, as a chessboard is divided into equal little squares, then ds^2 is simply the sum dx^2 + dy^2 + dz^2, with dx, dy, dz representing the three sides of each little cube. That space is a "flat" space, just as a plane is a flat surface. In other words, what our intuition tells us is that space is flat—in the sense given to that word by Riemann.

Is it really so? That the small portion of space in our neighborhood should appear flat is only to be expected. It may well be that space is actually flat, not only in our vicinity but away into the realm of the farthest nebulae. On the other hand, it is equally possible that space is ever so slightly curved. How could we ever find out? Riemann's answer was: *from experience.* That is the revolutionary message which, very quietly but very firmly, he brought to the scientific world.

Euclid and Kant had unconsciously accepted the intuitive notion of space as flat. Riemann declared that this proposition should not be asserted without proof, as self-evident; it was only a hypothesis, subject to test by experiment. To start with we could make three hypotheses about our space: that it had constant positive curvature, or constant negative curvature or no curvature at all (*i.e.*, that it was flat, or Euclidean, as we now say). Which of these hypotheses was correct was for astronomers and physicists to find out. Such was the meaning of Riemann's cryptic title, "On the Hypotheses That Are the Foundations of Geometry," which had, how very rightly, aroused the curiosity of Gauss.

There are many other important things in this dissertation of Riemann's, such as a very clear-sighted appreciation of the possibility that we may have to adopt eventually a quantum theory of space—something our physicists are just now rather gingerly trying out. But the point we have presented here—the appeal to experiment in order to find out a possible curvature of space—is, we believe, the most important one.

Riemann wisely made no attempt to suggest what specific experiments should be made. Looking back from the vantage point of our post-Einsteinian knowledge, we realize they were very difficult to discover. One might have expected them to lie in the domain of classical astronomy, of measurement of angles between stars, but that doesn't cut deep enough. Einstein showed that gravitation had a great deal to do with the matter and that Riemann's provisional hypothesis of a space of constant curvature had to be abandoned in favor of local variations (*e.g.*, the curvature in the neighborhood of the sun or of Sirius was greater than in empty interstellar space). He also showed that time had to be brought in; in other words, a four-dimensional space-time was what had to be investigated experimentally. And thus it came about that in the three experimental checks on Einstein's theory obtained in 1920, space, time and gravitation were seen to be indissolubly mixed.

Riemann's contention that the geometry of the universe was just a chapter of physics to be advanced like any other by the close cooperation of theory and experiment, was thereby fully justified. So also was Riemann's faith in his master, Gauss. The more we gaze upon Riemann's and Einstein's truly gigantic pyramids of thought, the more we admire how much was invisibly contained in the short, unassuming formula written by Gauss in 1827.

19 TOPOLOGY

ALBERT W. TUCKER AND HERBERT S. BAILEY, JR. • January 1950

He killed the noble Mudjokivis.
Of the skin he made him mittens,
Made them with the fur side inside
Made them with the skin side out-
side.
He, to get the warm side inside
Put the inside skin side outside;
He, to get the cold side outside
Put the warm side fur side inside.
That's why he put the fur side in-
side,
Why he put the skin side outside
Why he turned them inside outside.
—From *A Book of Humorous Verse,*
compiled by Carolyn Wells.

LO, the poor Indian was faced with a problem in topology, and by putting the skin side outside and the fur side inside he solved it admirably, both from the physiological and topological points of view. Although the connection between this problem and mathematics may not be obvious, actually it is an exercise in topological reasoning that enables one to predict that turning a pair of mittens inside out will convert the right-hand mitten into a left and the left into a right. Insideness and outsideness are basic concepts in topology, one of the most active branches of modern mathematics.

Topology is the branch of mathematics that deals with properties of position that are unaffected by changes in size or shape. Its subjects are surfaces, knots, networks and many other figures. Perhaps the easiest way to define topological properties is to say that they are geometric properties which stay the same in spite of stretching or bending. Topology is full of apparent paradoxes and impossibilities, and is probably more fun than any other branch of mathematics.

The problems used as examples in this article may strike many readers as being mere curiosities. While the novel properties studied by topologists make the subject interesting and at times weird, this article will have failed in its purpose if it leaves the reader with the impression that topology is nothing more than a collection of Chinese puzzles. Topology is one of the most fundamental branches of mathematics. It may be described as the mathematics of the possible. Its function is to settle questions for other branches of mathematics, *i.e.*, whether certain solutions do or do not exist, or whether certain conditions are possible or impossible. It does not usually tell how to find solutions. Thus topology has not yet had much application to everyday problems in science or technology; it has an important indirect influence on practical affairs, however, because it is a basic part of the structure supporting those branches of mathematics that are directly applied.

Here is a typical topological problem, similar to that of the Indian's mittens but of a higher order of subtlety: Can the inner tube of a tire be turned inside out? This is not an easy problem for a non-topologist. The answer to the question is Yes, and what might be labeled "instructions for turning an inner tube inside out" are illustrated in the series of drawings on the opposite page. We assume that the rubber may be stretched as much as one pleases and that there is a hole in the tube at the place where the customary valve stem is attached. The reader is not advised to try the process with a real inner tube; it would require prodigious stretching. One begins by putting a finger in the hole and spreading the hole wider and wider until the tube is stretched out to a shape like two long strips of paper, attached to each other and interlocked. Give each ring a half-twist; this in effect turns the surface inside out. Next stretch the strips of rubber back into the shape of an inner tube. Note that the direction of the grain, if one assumes that rubber has a grain, has been changed; whereas originally it ran lengthwise along the tube, it now runs around the thickness of the tube. You have turned the tube inside out. And topologically the figure remains the same through all its contortions, since nothing has intervened except stretching. Topologically, if not practically, the inner tube is still an inner tube at every stage.

Problems such as this make topology amusing, and there have been a number of popular illustrations of various aspects of it. The most famous of them are the Moebius band, the seven bridges of Koenigsberg and the four-color map problem.

THE Moebius band is a favorite plaything of topologists. In 1858 the German mathematician A. F. Moebius discovered that if one takes a long strip of paper, gives it a half-twist and connects the ends to make a ring, one creates a seeming impossibility—an object that has only one side. Turn or trace it any way you wish; you will always find that it has a single continuous surface. A child of four can paint an ordinary paper ring blue on one side and red on the other, but not even Picasso could do that to a Moebius band. Consider further what happens if you cut the band along a line running around the middle of it. Cut it all the way around until you return to your starting point. Although you have cut the band "in two," it still is in one piece (*see top drawings on page 136*). This is known as a "loop cut," and some of its fascinating variations will be considered presently.

Another one-sided form is the Klein bottle, invented in 1882 by the great German mathematician Felix Klein. The easiest way to visualize this object is to imagine that an inner tube is cut through and straightened out like a cylinder, with one end stretched out to make a base and the other end narrowed like the neck of a bottle; then the narrow end is twisted over and thrust through the valve-stem hole in the side of the tube and finally is flared out and joined with the open end at the base (*see middle drawings on page 136*). This may be called a "punctured" Klein bottle, the

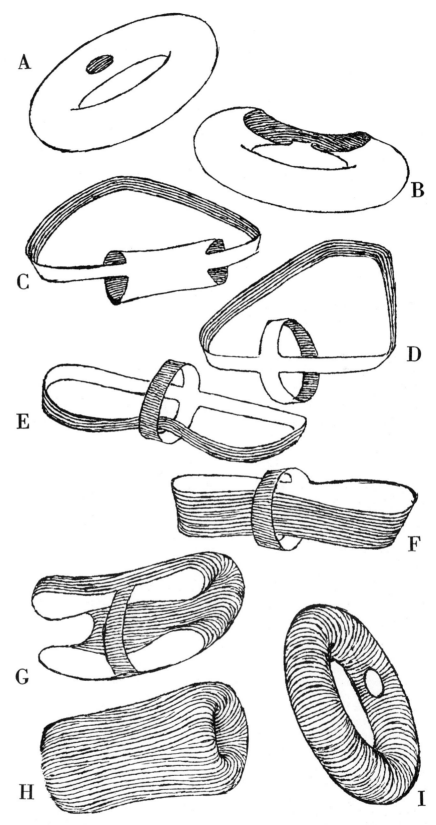

hole in the tube being the puncture in the bottle. For topological purposes one usually supposes that no hole actually exists, so that the continuous one-sided surface passes through itself. This of course is physically impossible, but topologists make free use of such ghostly properties. A Klein bottle may be thought of as a pair of Moebius bands with the edges glued together; the bottom drawings on page 136 show how a Klein bottle can be split in half and opened out to make two Moebius bands.

These properties of Moebius bands and Klein bottles have been summarized in a pair of limericks:

A mathematician confided
That a Moebius band is one-sided,
  And you'll get quite a laugh
  If you cut one in half,
For it stays in one piece when divided.

A mathematician named Klein
Thought the Moebius band was divine.
  Said he, "If you glue
  The edges of two,
You'll get a weird bottle like mine."

AN ordinary flat surface such as a sheet of paper can be considered as a punctured sphere that has been stretched and flattened out into a sheet or disk. Topologists customarily proceed from such simple figures to more complicated surfaces, and they generalize their findings in two and three dimensions to include figures in four, five, and on to n dimensions, but here we shall confine our attention to the simple surfaces.

Since it may be difficult to recognize inner tubes or Klein bottles when they are badly stretched out of shape, it is desirable to characterize each topological type of surface by simple invariant properties. One of the distinguishing invariant properties of a surface is the number of edges, and here we are considering only surfaces with one edge. Another distinguishing invariant is the number of sides: one or two. A Moebius band or a punctured Klein bottle is an example of a one-sided surface; a disk or an inner tube has two sides. A third distinguishing invariant, unfamiliar to laymen but mathematically important and not difficult to grasp, is the Betti number. It is the maximum number of cross cuts that can be made on a surface without dividing it into more than one piece. A cross cut may be thought of as a simple cut with scissors; it begins and ends on the edge. Any cross cut on a disk will divide it into two pieces, so the Betti number of a disk is zero. The Betti number of a Moebius band is one; for a Klein bottle or inner tube it is two.

Loop cuts provide another way of finding the Betti number of a surface. These cuts begin and end at a point in

AN INNER TUBE may be turned inside out if one assumes that it is made of a remarkable kind of rubber that may be enormously stretched and shrunk. At the upper left is an inner tube (A) with the hole for the valve stem somewhat enlarged for clarity. The hole is first greatly stretched until rubber is in two strips (B, C and D). Each of the two interconnected rings is then given a half-twist and the whole process is reversed (E, F, G, H and I). Notice that the grain of the rubber, assuming it has a grain, now runs around the thickness of the tube instead of lengthwise along it.

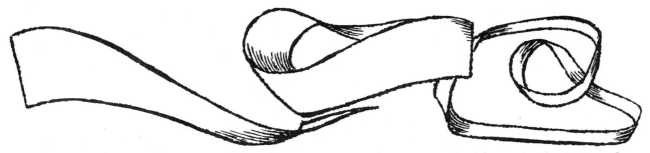

A MOEBIUS BAND may be constructed by taking an ordinary strip of paper (*left*), giving it a half-twist and pasting its ends together. The resulting figure (*center*) has only one side instead of two. If the fig- ure is then punctured with a pair of scissors and cut lengthwise down the middle, it will not, as one might expect, fall into two pieces. It will be changed into a band that has two sides and two full twists (*right*).

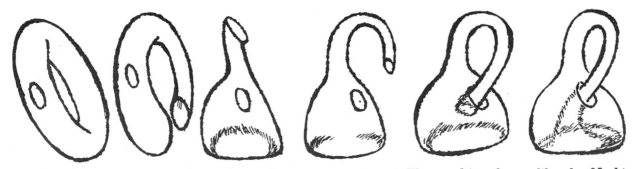

A KLEIN BOTTLE cannot be constructed as easily as a Moebius band, except in the imagination. There it can be made readily if one assumes that glass can be stretched and shrunk rather like the rubber of the inner tube on page 135. The resulting figure, like the Moebius band, has only one side. If it is assumed to have no hole, it has no edge. The punctured Klein bottle at the right, however, has a hole and one edge.

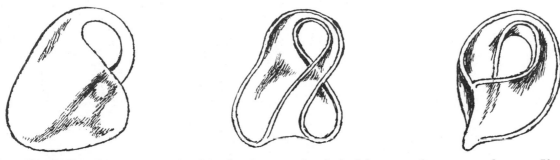

BAND AND BOTTLE have a close kinship that is revealed when the bottle is cut in half. The figure at the left is an intact Klein bottle. The figure in the center shows how one of its two halves would look if the bottle had been cut from top to bottom. If one again assumes glass that can be stretched and shrunk, half of a Klein bottle can be shaped into a Moebius band. The process has been nearly completed at the right.

the surface, avoiding the edge entirely. By counting the maximum number of loop cuts that can be made without dividing a one-edged surface into more than one piece (or a surface with m edges into more than m pieces) we again get the Betti number of the surface. Cross cuts and loop cuts were used by the German mathematician Bernhard Riemann in 1857 to define the connectivity of a surface. Riemann called a disk "simply connected," a band or halo "doubly connected," and so on, his connectivity number being always one greater than the Betti number.

By examining the drawings at the left on the opposite page, you will see that each loop cut intersects one and only one cross cut. This pairing illustrates a fundamental relation called duality. When generalized in n dimensions, it provides

the content of a "duality theorem," formulated by S. Lefschetz of Princeton University in 1927, that is one of the major achievements of modern topological research.

So the intrinsic topological invariants of a two-dimensional surface are: 1) the number of edges, 2) the number of sides, 3) the Betti number. These will always be the same no matter how the surfaces are stretched or reshaped in three-dimensional space, provided there is no tearing or welding. Keeping these intrinsic invariants in mind, consider a Moebius band formed by making three half-twists in a paper band before connecting the ends. Such a band has only one edge and one side, and since only one cross cut is possible the Betti number is one. Intrinsically it is the same as the ordinary Moebius band with only one

half-twist. But there is a difference in the way it is situated relative to three-dimensional space: the edge of the band traces out a knot, whereas the edge of an ordinary one half-twisted Moebius band is a simple unknotted curve (*see drawings at right on opposite page*).

Knots intrinsically are all the same; they are just loops or circles. The problem of classifying them by some reasonable system of invariants is as yet unsolved. But one-edged surfaces provide an excellent means of studying knots. For example, two distinct knots can be made by twisting a thrice half-twisted Moebius band to the right or to the left. One way produces a right-handed trefoil knot, the other a left-handed trefoil knot, and neither can be stretched or reshaped to make the other. Most of the known properties of any knot can be convenient-

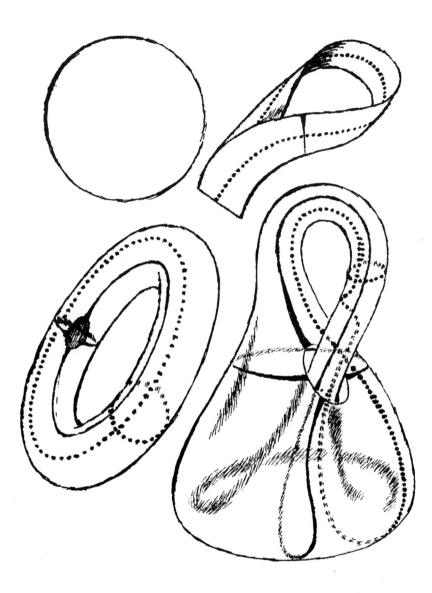

CROSS CUTS (*solid lines*) begin and end at the edge. Loop cuts (*dotted lines*) avoid edges. The Betti numbers are zero for a disk (two sides, one edge), one for a Moebius band (one side, one edge), two for an inner tube (two sides, one edge) and two for a punctured Klein bottle (one side, one edge).

TREFOIL KNOT (*bottom*) may be compared to a Moebius band that has three half-twists (*top*) by flattening a band and tracing path of its edge.

ly derived by associating it with the one-edged, two-sided surface of lowest Betti number whose edge can be arranged to form the knot—a method introduced in 1934 by Herbert Seifert of Heidelberg. If the problem of the classification of knots could be solved by a general principle covering all cases, the road would be clear for many advances in related topological fields.

Since topology allows any amount of stretching or reshaping of the forms it considers, the ordinary knots that one can tie in a rope do not interest topologists. Every such knot can be reshaped into a straight line. In topology the only true knots are those that are untyable and un-untyable, so a topologist may legitimately raise the question, "Is this knot a knot or not?" Topologists have been known to discuss varying degrees of

knottedness, knottiness and even beknottedness.

NETWORKS, unlike knots, do have intrinsic topological interest. The Koenigsberg bridge problem, one of the oldest of topology, has to do with an intrinsic property of a particular network formed from four points and seven lines. The German city of Koenigsberg, now part of the U.S.S.R., has its center on an island in the river Pregel. In the 17th century this island was joined to each bank of the Pregel by two bridges, and it was also linked by a bridge to a neighboring island, which in turn was joined to each bank by one bridge (*see top drawing on page 138*). The citizens of Koenigsberg liked to stroll on the bridges, and the question was proposed: "How could one stroll across all seven

bridges without crossing any one of them twice?" The reader may convince himself after several tries that the feat is impossible.

In 1736 the great Swiss mathematician Leonhard Euler settled the question for all time by working out the general principle that underlies all such network problems. Suppose we replace the land areas by points and represent the bridges as lines between the points. The points are called vertices. A point with an odd number of paths leading from it is called an odd vertex; one with an even number is an even vertex. The general principle is: The number of journeys necessary to traverse a connected network is equal to half the number of odd vertices. (It is impossible to construct a network with an odd number of odd vertices, for each line is required to begin at a vertex and

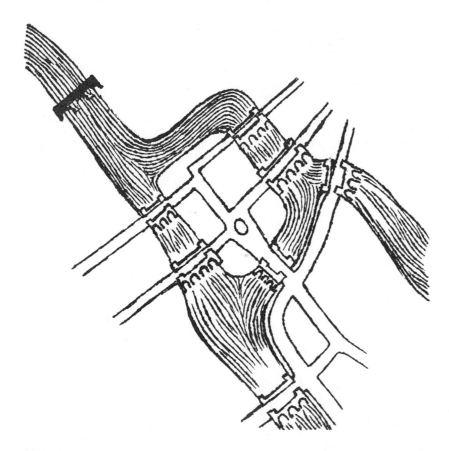

BRIDGES OF KOENIGSBERG are a classical problem of topology. The problem is to try to walk across all the seven bridges that interconnect two islands and the mainland without crossing any bridge twice. The problem could be solved only after an eighth bridge had been built (*upper left*).

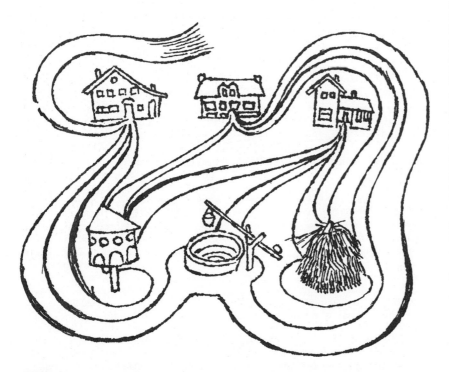

THREE COTTAGES make a problem rather similar to that of the Koenigsberg bridges. The problem here is to connect each cottage with a dovecote, a well and a haystack by paths that do not cross. As the unfinished path from the cottage at the upper left indicates, the problem cannot be solved.

end at one.) If the vertices are all even, or if there are not more than two odd vertices, it may be traversed in one journey. (In 1935 one of the authors—Tucker—actually walked the Koenigsberg bridges without crossing any bridge twice. An eighth bridge had been built.)

A connected network in which there are no cycles, or loops, is appropriately called a "tree." Such a network can always be built up from a single vertex by attaching lines and vertices alternately. Each time a new line is attached to any existing vertex a new vertex must be introduced as its terminus, else the line would terminate in an old vertex and create a cycle. So the number of vertices in a tree is one plus the number of lines. A connected network that is not a tree can always be reduced to a tree by removing a number of lines without removing any vertices. If the network has V vertices and L lines to start with, and B lines are removed to obtain the tree, then V=1+ (L−B) for the tree, and so B=1+L−V. This B is the Betti number of the network. It can be defined as the maximum number of lines that can be cut or removed from the network so as to leave all the vertices connected together in one piece by the remaining lines. For example, the Betti number of the Koenigsberg bridge network is four. The marked resemblance of the definition of the Betti number for a network to that for a surface is, of course, no accident.

The Betti number has a long and interesting history, although it was not so named until 1895. The German physicist G. R. Kirchhoff, in his paper of 1847 that introduced two famous laws for electric networks, used the concept of Betti number to characterize the number of independent loop equations involved in determining the distribution of current in a network. The concept was picked up by the British physicist James Clerk Maxwell, who called it "cyclomatic number" in his famous text *Electricity and Magnetism* published in 1873. Thus two physicists had used the idea of the Betti number a generation before Henri Poincaré, the French mathematician, established it firmly in mathematics in 1895. Poincaré, who is regarded as the father of modern topology, named the Betti number after Enrico Betti, an Italian mathematical physicist who in 1871 had generalized the connectivity numbers of Riemann.

WE now turn to networks drawn on some surface, it being required that the network lines meet only at the vertices. For a connected network drawn on the surface of a sphere there is a famous formula, V−L+A=2, named after the same great Euler who settled the Koenigsberg bridge problem. Again V and L are the numbers of vertices and lines in the network; A is the number of areas into which the surface is divided by the network. Euler confined his attention to the vertices, lines and areas (or faces) of a polyhedron with a convex surface, but, of course, the properties are the same as on the surface of a sphere, since a polyhedral surface can be stretched and rounded out into spherical shape.

A spherical network can be turned into a network on a plane surface by puncturing the spherical surface in the middle of one of the areas and flattening the punctured sphere out into a disk. For the planar network, $V-L+A=1$, since one area is lost through the puncture. By rewriting this as $A=1+L-V$ the reader may observe that the number of areas enmeshed in a connected network on a plane surface is the Betti number of the network.

But some networks cannot be drawn in a plane without having their lines cross and create new unwanted vertices. Consider the following problem, which is as old as its wording suggests: Can you connect each of three cottages to a dovecote, a well and a haystack by paths that do not cross? A few tries will probably convince you that the problem is insoluble (*see bottom drawing on opposite page*). The Polish mathematician Casimir Kuratowski proved in 1930 that six points cannot be so connected, nor can five points be completely interconnected; but any network can be drawn in a plane without crossings except when one of the foregoing situations arises. On a Moebius band, however, even six points can be completely interconnected, and on an inner tube seven points can be so connected. In the full freedom of three-dimensional space, of course, any network can be drawn without unwanted crossings.

We cannot leave the subject of networks without referring to the famous four-color problem. Although it seems so simple that almost anyone feels he could solve it easily, no one has ever solved it, nor has anyone proved that it is insoluble. The rules are that a map must be colored so that every country is colored differently from every other country that it borders (point contact is not counted as a border), and that the minimum number of colors must be used. The problem is to prove that four colors are sufficient to color any map on a sphere or in a plane, or else to construct a map that requires five colors. The Belgian mathematician S. M. de Backer showed in 1946 that four colors are sufficient to color any map containing 35 countries or less, and C. N. Reynolds of the University of West Virginia has informed us that he has recently pushed this number up to 83, but no one has established a principle to cover all possible cases. Many maps require only three colors. The map of the U. S. requires four colors in the states bordering on Kentucky

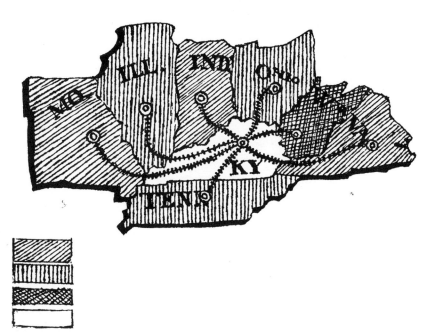

FOUR-COLOR MAP sets forth the four-color problem. The four colors are symbolized by four tones. The basis of the problem is that each state be colored differently from all those adjacent to it. The problem is to prove that four colors are sufficient, or to invent a map that requires five.

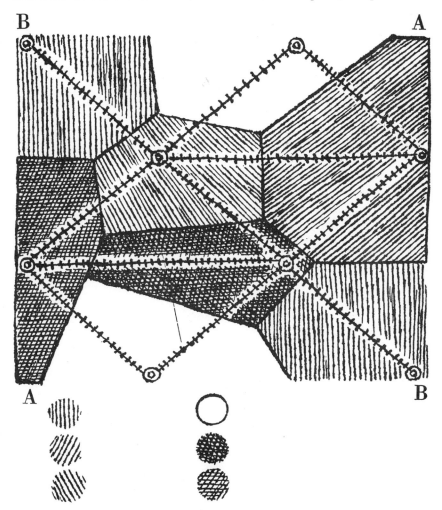

SIX-COLOR MAP can be made on a Moebius band. Upper and lower edges are joined so that A meets A and B meets B. The colors are assumed to have soaked through the paper. Capital at upper left is the same as that at lower right. Capital at upper right center is the same as that at lower left center.

(see top drawing on page 139). The four-color problem applies only to plane surfaces or spheres; other surfaces create different problems.

THERE are listed below a group of related theorems concerning topological properties of spherical surfaces. Each theorem seems to be merely a bit of curiosa, an odd fact stated only for its oddity. But the theorems are illustrations of an important body of mathematical knowledge, and though the discussion given here is extremely brief, it is hoped that they will give the reader some insight into still another aspect of topology.

1. The wind cannot be blowing everywhere on the earth at once. At every instant there must be at least one windless point on the earth's surface. But it is possible for the wind to be blowing everywhere except at one place, *e.g.*, the South Pole.

2. If the wind is blowing everywhere in the Northern Hemisphere at any given instant, then on the Equator it must blow in every direction of the compass. That is, for any given direction—say, northeast—there must be some place on the Equator where the wind has this given direction.

3. Also, under the same conditions, there must be on the Equator at least one pair of diametrically opposite places at which the wind blows in exactly opposite directions of the compass.

4. At any given instant there is at least one pair of antipodal points on the earth's surface that have equal temperatures and equal readings of humidity.

5. If three empires covered the entire surface of the earth, land and water, then at least one empire could boast that the sun never set on its territory. For at least one of the three empires would have to contain a pair of antipodal points within or on its borders.

Of course these are mathematical theorems rather than physical actualities. The wind that is mentioned is an ideal wind without discontinuities and restricted to its surface component, and temperature and humidity are assumed to be continuous variables.

Theorems 1 and 2 are simple consequences of a general "fixed-point" theorem formulated for *n* dimensions by the Dutch mathematician L. E. J. Brouwer in 1912. Theorems 3 and 4 are simple consequences of a general "antipodal-point" theorem formulated for *n* dimensions by Karol Borsuk and S. M. Ulam of Poland in 1933. Theorem 5 follows from a general *n*-dimensional theorem stated by L. Lusternick and L. Schnirelmann of the U.S.S.R. in 1930. None of these five theorems would be true on a hypothetical ring-shaped planet.

The five theorems concern such diverse properties of spheres that it is difficult to see how they are related to one another. Yet all except the first can be proved by means of the general solution of the following apparently simple problem: Is it possible to arrange playing cards in a square so that no two cards of the same color are adjacent to each other—vertically, horizontally, or diagonally—unless they are of the same suit, and so that on the outside rows each pair of opposite cards is of the same color but of different suits? The answer is, No. (Topologists have won bets by challenging non-topologists to solve it.) Why should such a simple "card trick,"

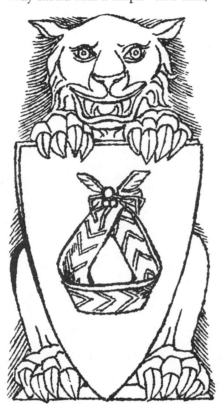

STONE LION beside a fireplace at Princeton University displays a Moebius strip on which a fly can crawl anywhere without crossing an edge.

one that cannot even be worked, be a revealing topological problem? Why should the generalized theorem which says that this cannot be solved be useful in solving so many other problems?

In order to understand this paradox you must notice that basically this problem is quite different from most of the other problems discussed here. The other problems dealt with whole bodies, areas or surfaces; this theorem deals with a pattern that can be made to approximate the points of the square as closely as you please. This playing-card problem, then, shows a fundamental interplay between microscopic and macroscopic characteristics of a square (or disk, or other simple area). The theorem has been extended to *n* dimensions, where it may be used to show whether certain analogous relations can exist. Thus this playing-card

problem has very deep topological significance.

MANY of the simpler topological concepts are used every day by people who have never heard of topology. The basic ideas of topology are so fundamental that we learn many of them as infants. The concepts of insideness and outsideness, of right-handedness and left-handedness, of linkedness and unlinkedness are forced on us at an early age.

During the last decade applied mathematicians and engineers have begun to realize the usefulness of topology in attacking certain types of problems, particularly those involving nonlinear differential equations. Most physical phenomena can be described mathematically by differential equations, *i.e.*, equations relating rates of change. In the past it was usually assumed that effects were linear, that is, directly proportional to causes; thus the vibrations of a spring were assumed to follow Hooke's law that stress is proportional to strain, and in calculating the gain of an amplifier the current in a vacuum tube was assumed to be proportional to the grid voltage. The assumption of linearity was made because calculation of nonlinear differential equations was extremely difficult if not impossible. But nature is rarely if ever "linear"; and for many modern applications, such as certain problems in electronics and supersonic aerodynamics, the assumption of linearity is downright misleading.

Topology is coming into use to show what types of solutions of certain nonlinear differential equations are possible. The answers are qualitative, not quantitative. Topology may tell an engineer what general type of circuit can satisfy his requirements, but it will not tell him the values of the circuit elements; these must be determined by other means. Nevertheless, the engineer might fail to hit on the desired general type of circuit without the aid of topology.

Topology is young as a branch of mathematics. Though the simpler ideas of topology are forced on every child by experience, its sophisticated development is only about a century old, and by far the most active development has been during the past 50 years, since Poincaré's contributions. Many of the theorems of topology are insufficiently related to other branches of mathematics. Many apparently simple problems still await solution. But topology is moving ahead rapidly, and most topologists are confident that progress in the next 50 years will be as significant as the developments of the first half of this century.

20 THE KOENIGSBERG BRIDGES

LEONHARD EULER · July 1953
Edited by JAMES R. NEWMAN

Leonhard Euler, the most eminent of Switzerland's scientists, was a gifted 18th-century mathematician who enriched mathematics in almost every department and whose energy was at least as remarkable as his genius. "Euler calculated without apparent effort, as men breathe, or as eagles sustain themselves in the wind," wrote François Arago, the French astronomer and physicist. It is said that Euler "dashed off memoirs in the half-hour between the first and second calls to dinner." According to the mathematical historian Eric Temple Bell he "would often compose his memoirs with a baby in his lap while the older children played all about him"—the number of Euler's children was 13. At the age of 28 he solved in three days a difficult astronomical problem which astronomers had agreed would take several months of labor; this prodigious feat so overtaxed his eyesight that he lost the sight of one eye and eventually became totally blind. But his handicap in no way diminished either the volume or the quality of his mathematical output. His writings will, it is estimated, fill 60 to 80 large quarto volumes when the edition of his collected works is completed.

The memoir published below is Euler's own account of one of his most famous achievements: his solution of the celebrated problem of the Koenigsberg bridges. The problem is a classic exercise in the branch of mathematics called topology (see "Topology," by Albert W. Tucker and Herbert S. Bailey, Jr., page 134 in this volume). Topology is the geometry of distortion; it deals with the properties of an object that survive stretching, twisting, bending or other changes of its size or shape. The Koenigsberg puzzle is a so-called network problem in topology.

In the town of Koenigsberg (where the philosopher Immanuel Kant was born) there were in the 18th century seven bridges which crossed the river Pregel. They connected two islands in the river with each other and with the opposite banks. The townsfolk had long amused themselves with this problem: Is it possible to cross the seven bridges in a continuous walk without recrossing any of them? When the puzzle came to Euler's attention, he recognized that an important scientific principle lay concealed in it. He applied himself to discovering this principle and shortly thereafter presented his simple and ingenious solution. He provided a mathematical demonstration, as some of the townsfolk had already proved to their own satisfaction by repeated trials, that the journey is impossible. He also found a rule which answered the question in general, whatever the number of bridges.

The Koenigsberg puzzle is related to the familiar exercise of trying to trace a given figure on paper without lifting the pencil or retracing a line. In graph form the Koenigsberg pattern is represented by the drawing on the left at the bottom of this page. Inspection shows that this pattern cannot be traced with a single stroke of the pencil. But if there are eight bridges, the pattern is the one at the right, and this one can be traced in a single stroke.

Euler's memoir gives a beautiful explanation of the principles involved and furnishes an admirable example of the deceptive simplicity of topology problems.—JAMES R. NEWMAN

* * *

THE BRANCH of geometry that deals with magnitudes has been zealously studied throughout the past, but there is another branch that has been almost unknown up to now; Leibnitz spoke of it first, calling it the "geometry of position" (*geometria situs*). This branch of geometry deals with relations dependent on position alone, and investigates the properties of position; it does not take magnitudes into consideration, nor does it involve calculation with quantities. But as yet no satisfactory definition has been given of the problems that belong to this geometry of position or of the method to be used in solving them. Recently there was announced a problem which, while it certainly seemed to belong to geometry, was nevertheless so designed that it did not call for the determination of a magnitude, nor could it be solved by quantitative calculation; consequently I did not hesitate to assign it to the geometry of position, especially since the solution required only the consideration of position, calculation being of no use. In this paper I shall give an account of the method that I discovered for solving this type of problem, which may serve as an example of the geometry of position.

The problem, which I understand is quite well known, is stated as follows: In the town of Koenigsberg in Prussia there is an island A, called Kneiphof, with the two branches of the river Pregel flowing around it. There are seven bridges—*a, b, c, d, e, f* and *g*—crossing the two branches [*see illustration at the top of page 143*]. The question is whether a person can plan a walk in such a way that he will cross each

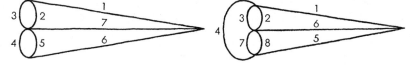

The figure at right can be drawn in one stroke; the one at left cannot

of these bridges once but not more than once. I was told that while some denied the possibility of doing this and others were in doubt, no one maintained that it was actually possible. On the basis of the above I formulated the following very general problem for myself: Given any configuration of the river and the branches into which it may divide, as well as any number of bridges, to determine whether or not it is possible to cross each bridge exactly once.

The particular problem of the seven bridges of Koenigsberg could be solved by carefully tabulating all possible paths, thereby ascertaining by inspection which of them, if any, met the requirement. This method of solution, however, is too tedious and too difficult because of the large number of possible combinations, and in other problems where many more bridges are involved it could not be used at all. . . . Hence I discarded it and searched for another more restricted in its scope; namely, a method which would show only whether a journey satisfying the prescribed condition could in the first instance be discovered; such an approach, I believed, would be simpler.

MY ENTIRE method rests on the appropriate and convenient way in which I denote the crossing of bridges, in that I use capital letters, A, B, C, D, to designate the various land areas that are separated from one another by the river. Thus when a person goes from area A to area B across bridge *a* or *b*, I denote this crossing by the letters AB, the first of which designates the area whence he came, the second the area where he arrives after crossing the bridge. If the traveler then crosses from B over bridge *f* into D, this crossing is denoted by the letters BD; the two crossings AB and BD performed in succession I denote simply by the three letters ABD, since the middle letter B designates the area into which the first crossing leads as well as the area out of which the second leads.

Similarly, if the traveler proceeds from D across bridge *g* into C, I designate the three successive crossings by the four letters ABDC. . . . The crossing of four bridges will be represented by five letters, and if the traveler crosses an arbitrary number of bridges his journey will be described by a number of letters which is one greater than the number of bridges. For example, eight letters are needed to denote the crossing of seven bridges.

With this method I pay no attention to which bridges are used; that is to say, if the crossing from one area to another can be made by way of several bridges it makes no difference which one is used, so long as it leads to the desired area. Thus if a route could be laid out over the seven Koenigsberg bridges so that each bridge were crossed once and only once, we would be able to describe this route

Leonhard Euler (pronounced oiler); born Basel 1707; died Petrograd 1783

by using eight letters, and in this series of letters the combination AB (or BA) would have to occur twice, since there are two bridges, *a* and *b*, connecting the regions A and B. Similarly the combination AC would occur twice, while the combinations AB, BD, and CD would each occur once.

Our question is now reduced to whether from the four letters A, B, C and D a series of eight letters can be formed in which all the combinations just mentioned occur the required number of times. Before making the effort, however, of trying to find such an arrangement we do well to consider whether its existence is even theoretically possible or

not. For if it could be shown that such an arrangement is in fact impossible, then the effort expended on finding it would be wasted. Therefore I have sought for a rule that would determine without difficulty, as regards this and all similar questions, whether the required arrangement of letters is feasible.

For the purpose of finding such a rule I take a single region A into which an arbitrary number of bridges, *a*, *b*, *c*, *d*, etc., lead [*middle illustration on the next page*]. Of these bridges I first consider only *a*. If the traveler crosses this bridge, he must either have been in A before crossing or have reached A after crossing, so that according to the above

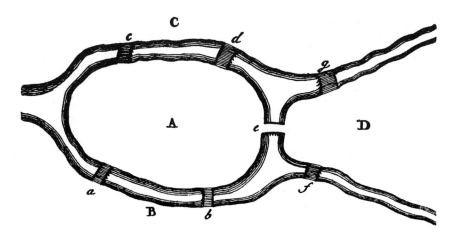

Seven bridges of Koenigsberg crossed the River Pregel

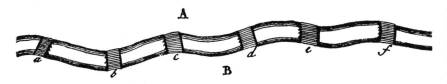

Euler used a simpler case to elucidate his principle

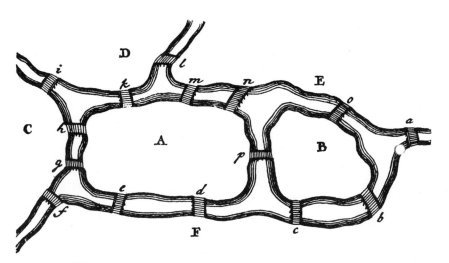

This trip is possible though the Koenigsberg one is not

which indicate how often each individual letter must occur. On the other hand, if this sum is greater than the number of bridges plus one, as it is in our example, then the desired route cannot be constructed. The rule that I gave for determining from the number of bridges that lead to A how often the letter A will occur in the route description is independent of whether these bridges all come from a single region B or from several regions, because I was considering only the region A, and attempting to determine how often the letter A must occur.

When the number of bridges leading to A is even, we must take into account whether the route begins in A or not. For example, if there are two bridges that lead to A and the route starts from A, then the letter A will occur twice—once to indicate the departure from A by one of the bridges and a second time to indicate the return to A by the other bridge. However, if the traveler starts his journey in another region, the letter A will occur only once, since by my method of description the single occurrence of A indicates an entrance into as well as a departure from A.

Suppose, as in our case, there are four bridges leading into the region A, and the route is to begin at A. The letter A will then occur three times in the expression for the whole route, while if the journey had started in another region, A would occur only twice. With six bridges leading to A, the letter A will occur four times if A is the starting point, otherwise only three times. In general, if the number of bridges is even, the number of occurrences of the letter A, when the starting region is not A, will be half the number of the bridges; when the route starts from A, one more than half.

Every route must, of course, start in some one region. Thus from the number of bridges that lead to each region I determine the number of times that the corresponding letter will occur in the expression for the entire route as follows: When the number of the bridges is odd, I increase it by one and divide by two; when the number is even, I simply divide it by two. Then if the sum of the resulting numbers is equal to the actual number of bridges plus one, the journey can be accomplished, though it must start in a region approached by an odd number of bridges. But if the sum is one less than the number of bridges plus one, the journey is feasible if its starting point is a region approached by an even number of bridges, for in that case the sum is again increased by one.

MY PROCEDURE for determining whether in any given system of rivers and bridges it is possible to cross each bridge exactly once is as follows: First I designate the individual regions separated from one another by the water as A, B, C, etc. Second, I take the total number of bridges, increase it by one,

method of denotation the letter A will appear exactly once. If there are three bridges leading to A and the traveler crosses all three, then the letter A will occur twice in the expression for his journey, whether it begins at A or not. And if there are five bridges leading to A, the expression for a route that crosses them all will contain the letter A three times. If the number of bridges is odd, increase it by one, and take half the sum; the quotient represents the number of times the letter A appears.

LET US now return to the Koenigsberg problem [*top illustration above*]. Since there are five bridges leading to (and from) island A, the letter A must occur three times in the expression de-

scribing the route. The letter B must occur twice, since three bridges lead to B; similarly D and C must each occur twice. That is to say, the series of . . . letters that represents the crossing of the seven bridges must contain A three times and B, C and D each twice. But this is quite impossible with a series of eight letters [for the sum of the required letters is nine]. Thus it is apparent that a crossing of the seven bridges of Koenigsberg in the manner required cannot be effected.

Using this method we are always able, whenever the number of bridges leading to a particular region is odd, to determine whether it is possible in a journey to cross each bridge exactly once. Such a route exists if the number of bridges plus one is equal to the sum of the numbers

and write the resulting number at the top of the paper. Third, under this number I write the letters A, B, C, etc., in a column, and opposite each letter I note the number of bridges that lead to that particular region. Fourth, I place an asterisk next to each letter that has an even number opposite it. Fifth, in a third column I write opposite each even number the half of that number, and opposite each odd number I write half of the sum formed by that number plus one. Sixth, I add up the last column of numbers. If the sum is one less than, or equal to, the number written at the top, I conclude that the required journey can be made. But it must be noted that when the sum is one less than the number at the top, the route must start from a region marked with an asterisk, and . . . when these two numbers are equal, it must start from a region that does not have an asterisk.

For the Koenigsberg problem I would set up the tabulation as follows:

Number of bridges 7,
giving 8 (=7+1)

A	5	3
B	3	2
C	3	2
D	3	2

The last column now adds up to more than 8, and hence the required journey cannot be made.

Let us take an example of two islands with four rivers forming the surrounding water [*bottom illustration on the preceding page*]. Fifteen bridges, marked *a, b, c, d*, etc., across the water around the islands and the adjoining rivers. The question is whether a journey can be arranged that will pass over all the bridges, but not over any of them more than once. I begin by marking the regions that are separated from one another by water with the letters A, B, C, D, E, F—there are six of them. Second, I take the number of bridges (15) add one and write this number (16) uppermost. Third, I write the letters A, B, C, etc., in a column and opposite each letter I write the number of bridges connecting with that region, *e.g.*, eight bridges for A, four for B, etc. Fourth, the letters that have even numbers opposite them I mark with an asterisk. Fifth, in a third column I write the half of each corresponding even number, or, if the number is odd, I

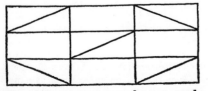

This figure requires only one stroke

add one to it, and put down half the sum. Sixth, I add the numbers in the third column and get 16 as the sum. Thus:

		16
A*	8	4
B*	4	2
C*	4	2
D	3	2
E	5	3
F*	6	3
		16

The sum of the third column is the same as the number 16 that appears above, and hence it follows that the journey can be effected if it begins in regions D or E, whose symbols have no asterisk. The following expression represents such a route:

EaFbBcFdAeFfCgAhCiDkAmEnAp-
BoElD.

Here I have indicated, by small letters between the capitals, which bridges are crossed.

BY THIS METHOD we can easily determine, even in cases of considerable complexity, whether a single crossing of each of the bridges in sequence is possible. But I should now like to give another and much simpler method, which follows quite easily from the preceding, after a few preliminary remarks. In the first place, I note that the sum of the numbers written down in the second column is necessarily double the actual number of bridges. The reason is that in the tabulation of the bridges leading to the various regions each bridge is counted twice, once for each of the two regions that it connects.

From this observation it follows that the sum of the numbers in the second column must be an even number, since half of it represents the actual number of bridges. Hence . . . if any of the numbers opposite the letters A, B, C, etc., are odd, an even number of them must be odd. In the Koenigsberg problem for instance, all four of the numbers opposite the letters A, B, C, D, were odd, while in the example just given only two of the numbers were odd, namely those opposite D and E.

Since the sum of the numbers opposite A, B, C, etc., is double the number of bridges, it is clear that if this sum is increased by two in the latter example and then divided by two, the result will be the number written at the top. When all the numbers in the second column are even, and the half of each is written down in the third column, the total of this column will be one less than the

This figure requires two strokes

number at the top. In that case it will always be possible to cross all the bridges. For in whatever region the journey begins, there will be an even number of bridges leading to it, which is the requirement. . . .

Further, when only two of the numbers opposite the letters are odd, and the others even, the required route is possible provided it begins in a region approached by an odd number of bridges. We take half of each even number, and likewise half of each odd number after adding one, as our procedure requires; the sum of these halves will then be one greater than the number of bridges, and hence equal to the number written at the top. But [when more than two, and an even number] of the numbers in the second column are odd, it is evident that the sum of the numbers in the third column will be greater than the top number, and hence the desired journey is impossible.

Thus for any configuration that may arise the easiest way of determining whether a single crossing of all the bridges is possible is to apply the following rules:

If there are more than two regions which are approached by an odd number of bridges, no route satisfying the required conditions can be found.

If, however, there are only two regions with an odd number of approach bridges the required journey can be completed provided it originates in one of these regions.

If, finally, there is no region with an odd number of approach bridges, the required journey can be effected, no matter where it begins.

These rules solve completely the problem initially proposed.

AFTER we have determined that a route actually exists we are left with the question how to find it. To this end the following rule will serve: Wherever possible we mentally eliminate any two bridges that connect the same two regions; this usually reduces the number of bridges considerably. Then—and this should not be difficult—we proceed to trace the required route across the remaining bridges. The pattern of this route, once we have found it, will not be substantially affected by the restoration of the bridges which were first eliminated from consideration—as a little thought will show. Therefore I do not think I need say more about finding the routes themselves.

21 FIXED-POINT THEOREMS

MARVIN SHINBROT · January 1966

If you mark a series of points on a rubber band and then stretch it, the order in which the points appear does not change. This is an intuitively acceptable conclusion of topology: the study of properties that persist when geometric figures are bent, stretched, twisted or otherwise continuously deformed. Other topological facts are not so clear; their validity seems intuitively unacceptable. In this intriguing category are the fixed-point theorems, a group of results concerning points that reappear exactly in their original positions after the surfaces on which they lie have been deformed.

An example will serve to introduce them. Suppose we stir a cup of coffee, in any way and for any length of time but gently enough so that the surface is never disrupted. (As they say in cookbooks, "Stir, do not whip.") According to one of the simplest fixed-point theorems, when we have finished stir-ring and the motion of the liquid has stopped, at least one point on the surface will be back where it started! Such a point is called a fixed point. A particle at the exact center of the surface would be the fixed point in the simplest case: when the liquid is swirled only in circles. Usually the motion of stirred coffee is more complicated, with any particle susceptible to being moved to any position on the surface. The relevant fixed-point theorem, first proved by

CONTINUOUS DEFORMATION of a geometric surface is represented by the gentle swirling of coffee in which the thin film of cream on top is never disrupted. Here the coffee is being swirled in such a way that the particle in the exact center does not move.

FIXED-POINT THEOREM states that no matter how the surface of the coffee is continuously deformed, there will always be a point on the surface in the position it occupied at the start. This theorem does not stipulate which point is fixed at any instant in time.

the Dutch mathematician L. E. J. Brouwer, does not specify which point remains fixed but only that one or more points must do so.

Consider another application of Brouwer's theorem. If this page of the book were to be torn out, crumpled, and folded in any way (but not torn) and then placed back on the book in such a way that no part of it extended beyond the edges of its original position, then at least one of the points on the crumpled page would lie directly above the spot it originally occupied. This fact, guaranteed by the Brouwer theorem, strikes many people as even more surprising than the certainty of a fixed point on the surface of the coffee. To the mathematician, however, it is more readily explained because the crumpling of a page is a simpler deformation than the swirling of coffee; the paper cannot be stretched, whereas the distance between two points on the surface of the coffee can easily change.

In order to understand how the proof of a fixed-point theorem might be constructed, it is simplest to look not at a two-dimensional surface such as the surface of the coffee or the sheet of paper but at a one-dimensional surface exemplified by a piece of string. Suppose we stretch a string to its full length so that it forms a straight line and then place it on a table. Next we fold the string any number of times and shift it around within the confines of the line made by the straight string. It can now be shown that a point on the string has returned to the exact spot it occupied before the manipulation and is therefore a fixed point. This is the one-dimensional version of the Brouwer theorem.

The theorem is proved by representing both the original string and the folded string as curves on a graph, comparing the curves and demonstrating that they intersect at some point [*see illustrations on these two pages*]. To begin, we measure the original straight string. We call the left end zero and specify each point on the string by its distance in inches from the left end. If the string is, say, eight inches long, we can speak of the point at the far right as "point eight." By the same token the position of each point on the folded string can be specified by its new distance from the left end of the string. If a point originally four inches from the left has been moved as a result of the deformation to three inches from the left, its new position is designated simply as "point three."

In this way we define a function, which can be denoted by $f(x)$. The value of this function at any point on the string is the number representing the position to which that point has been moved. Thus if point four is moved to point three, the value of f at four is three; in symbols $f(4) = 3$. To say that some point has not been moved—that is, to say that some point is a fixed point— is just a geometrically appealing way of saying that the equation $f(x) = x$ has a solution.

Now we construct a familiar Cartesian plane and graph the function $f(x)$. In this plane the horizontal axis designates the distance of each point from the left when the string was in its original position, and the vertical axis designates the distance of each point from the left after the string has been folded. On such a graph the point shifted from four to three can be plotted as a point with the coordinates four (on the horizontal axis) and three (on the vertical axis). When all the points on the folded string are plotted in this way, the curve connecting them is a mathematical representa-

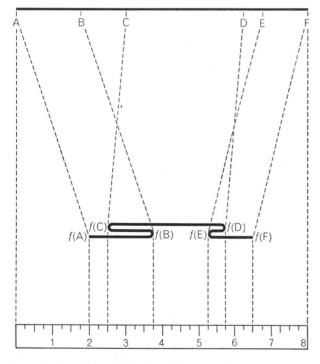

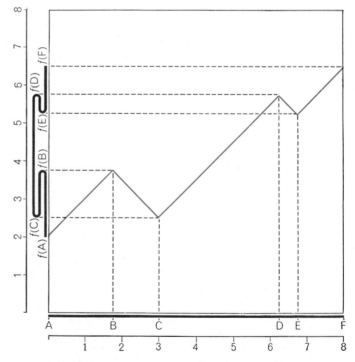

FOLDING OF A STRING is a continuous deformation of a one-dimensional surface. Points on an eight-inch string (*top*) assume new positions when the string is folded (*middle*), with point *A*, for example, moving to point designated $f(A)$. A fixed-point theorem states that some point $f(P)$ on the folded string must be as far from the left of the ruler (*bottom*) as point *P* was on the straight string.

DESCRIPTION OF FOLDED STRING in illustration at left is provided by the jagged curve on this graph. Horizontal axis designates the distance of a point, in inches, from the left end of the original string. Vertical axis designates distance of a point on the folded string from same point on the original. Thus point *C* has the coordinates three (horizontal axis) and 2.5 (vertical axis).

tion of the physical folding of the string. This curve may be extremely complicated, but it has two nice and particularly significant properties. It lies entirely within one quadrant of the Cartesian plane; indeed, it lies within the square having zero to eight on the horizontal axis as its base. This is ensured by the fact that the deformed string was never moved off the original eight-inch segment; therefore the function $f(x)$ describing the deformation can be neither negative nor greater than eight. Moreover, the curve is continuous; since the string was not broken in the process of deformation, there are no breaks in the curve describing that deformation. These two properties of the curve suffice, as we shall show, to guarantee that the string has a fixed point.

We know how to represent the folded string as a curve on a graph; we now have to demonstrate that if the original, undeformed string were also represented as a curve, the two curves *must* intersect. This is not difficult to show. Assume that we have picked up the straight string and returned it, still straight, to its original position. Even though it has not changed shape, we can consider that it has undergone a deformation and we can plot the function corresponding to this deformation. If we plot the "new" distances from the left end against the old, we get points that are equidistant from the two axes—points with coordinates one and one, two and two and so forth. When we connect these points, we have in fact drawn the diagonal of the square built on the base of zero to eight on the horizontal axis.

Now, recall the curve that represents the folded string. It must by definition begin at zero (the left side of our square) and end at eight (the right side). It also must lie between zero and eight on the vertical axis and can have no breaks. To get from one side of the square to the other it is necessary that this curve cross, or at least touch, the diagonal. The only way for the curve representing the folded string not to cross the diagonal is for it to begin at the lower left corner of the square or end at the upper right corner. The first case, however, merely implies that point zero is a fixed point, and the second that point eight is fixed. Therefore in all cases there is some point of intersection between the two curves and thus a fixed point on the deformed string. This would hold true, incidentally, even if, instead of the string, we had used an elastic material such as rubber, provided only that the deformed piece was not broken and was replaced so as not to lie outside the position occupied by the undeformed piece. The only difference that the use of rubber would make is that the curve representing the stretched piece need not consist of line segments—as the representation of the folded string must—but may have a curved shape.

The form of the Brouwer theorem that applies to two-dimensional surfaces would also hold if, instead of the surface of coffee in a cup, we were considering an infinitely elastic circular piece of rubber. We can transform such a rubber disk by stretching and folding it in various ways, making sure only that the disk is not torn and that it is replaced within the original circumference. The proof of the two-dimensional version of the Brouwer theorem is most elegant. We first consider a disk and assume that, contrary to the theorem, no point on it remains fixed after a deformation; it is then possible to show that this assumption is untenable. The steps of the proof (which holds not only for a disk but also for a

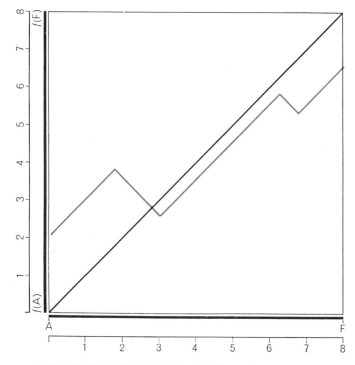

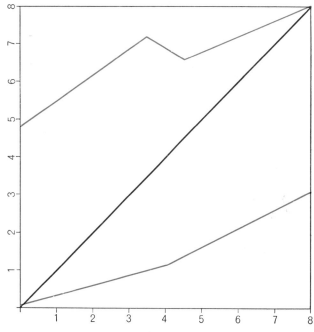

DESCRIPTION OF STRAIGHT STRING eight inches long is, by the same mathematical convention, the diagonal connecting the bottom left and top right corners of a square built on zero to eight on the horizontal axis (because the original and the "new" position of each point are the same). The intersection of the diagonal and the curve describing the folded string specifies a fixed point.

PROOF OF FIXED-POINT THEOREM depends on fact that every curve describing a folded string that is replaced uncut on top of a straight one must cross the diagonal describing the straight string. Two special cases are the curves of string with fixed point at right (*top*) and string with fixed point at left end (*bottom*). The theorem was set forth by the Dutch mathematician L. E. J. Brouwer.

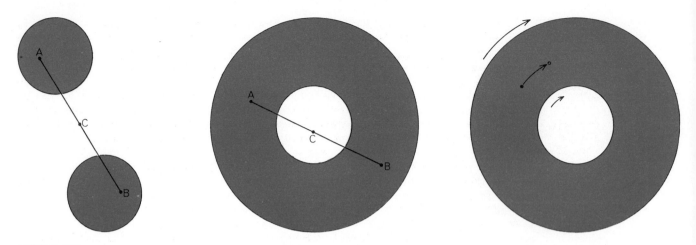

CONVEXITY is one of two conditions a surface must satisfy if fixed-point theorems are to hold true on it (the other is boundedness). An area is convex if it contains every point on the line connecting any two of its points. The two circles at left do not form a convex surface; if one switches their position, the surface is transformed so that no fixed point remains. The ring (*second from left*)

rectangle such as our sheet of paper) are outlined in the illustration on the opposite page.

The Brouwer theorem does not apply to any area regardless of shape. An infinite domain, for example, need have no fixed point, even in one dimension. An infinitely long string can be moved in such a way that no point remains fixed. We need only to shift every point of the string one inch to the right. Since every point of the string has been moved an inch away from its original position, there is no fixed point. Hence we see that for an area always to have a fixed point when it is transformed, it must be bounded. It must also satisfy some other condition of shape, one that mathematicians call convexity. An area is defined as convex if it is possible to draw the line connecting any two points in the area so that no point of the line lies outside the area [*see illustration at top of these two pages*].

The Brouwer fixed-point theorem we have described as being applicable to one-dimensional and two-dimensional surfaces is in fact applicable to surfaces with any finite number of dimensions. The theorem does not hold, however, if the surface is infinite-dimensional. Fortunately there are fixed-point theorems that do apply in infinite-dimensional situations. We say "fortunately" because, surprising as it may seem, the greatest interest in fixed-point theorems is in the infinite-dimensional case. To understand why, let us consider Newton's famous second law of motion, which states that force is the product of mass and acceleration ($F = ma$). In most instances when the law is used, the force is a given function of the position of an object, and this position

can always be found, given the acceleration of the object, by the techniques of calculus known as integration. Thus Newton's formula can be considered an equation for the position with the general form $f(x) = x$, where x denotes the position of the object and the known function, f, is determined by the forces, the masses and the initial positions and velocities. Fixed-point theorems are of great usefulness in helping us to understand equations of this type; indeed, a fixed-point theorem is usually cited in the proof that such equations have solutions.

Now consider the following question: Is it possible to put a satellite into a figure-eight orbit around both the earth and the moon? An affirmative answer amounts to saying that an equation $f(x) = x$ has a solution describing an orbit of the desired type. Any solution to such a problem is, of course, a function of time. It follows that we are trying to find if there is a function of time that satisfies the equation. The function $f(x)$ can be considered a transformation of functions of time into new functions of time in the same way that stirring coffee can be looked on as a transformation of points on a disk into new points. Accordingly the question becomes: Does the transformation represented by the function $f(x)$ have a fixed point? Such a function, since it is dependent on time, must be regarded as a "point" in an infinite-dimensional space. It is in trying to ascertain if such equations—equations involving unknown functions—have solutions of a given type that we require fixed-point theorems holding true even for infinite-dimensional surfaces.

Such questions of orbits can also be attacked by other methods; in fact,

other methods, not involving fixed-point theorems directly, would normally be used to answer them. The most powerful methods of which we are aware, however, are those that appeal directly to fixed-point theorems in infinite-dimensional surfaces. It should come as no surprise, then, that there are many physical problems for which the only known method of solution involves fixed-point theorems. Problems of fluid flow are often of this type. Consider a stream bed with a bottom that rises and falls periodically like a sine curve [*see middle illustration on page 150*]. Is it possible for water to flow over this bottom in such a way that the surface of the water exhibits the same general periodicity as the bottom, or is every kind of flow necessarily nonperiodic? The answer is found to be that the surface can be periodic. This suggests a further question: Can the high points and low points of the surface occur directly above the high points and low points of the bottom, or must they be shifted slightly, either upstream or downstream? It has recently been demonstrated that there can be a flow with the high points of its surface lying directly over the high points of the bottom. There is no known way to show this without relying on high-powered fixed-point theorems, which cannot easily be visualized for cases involving simple surfaces such as a plane.

There is, however, one fixed-point theorem that can be readily described for finite-dimensional spaces and that remains valid in the infinite-dimensional case. Let us describe the theorem as it applies to a plane, which is of course a two-dimensional surface. Let P and Q represent points on the plane. If

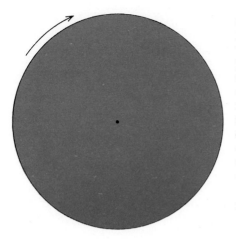

is not convex either, since rotation of the ring would cause every point on it to move. The circular disk at far right *is* convex.

the plane is transformed by stretching, twisting or folding part or all of it, the two points P and Q are transformed into new points that are determined by the deformation process and are therefore functions of P and Q. We denote this function by f, so that P is trans-

formed into the point $f(P)$ and Q into $f(Q)$. If, following a certain transformation, the distance between the two points $f(P)$ and $f(Q)$ is always strictly smaller than the distance between the original points P and Q, then the transformation is called a contraction. There is a fixed-point theorem stating that every contraction has a fixed point; in other words, there must be a point in the same position before and after any contraction.

The proof of this theorem is not difficult to visualize [*see bottom illustration on next page*]. When a contraction takes place, any point P_1 on the original plane assumes a new position P_2. The point we have just designated P_2 occupies the spot originally occupied by a point that we say has moved to P_3. This point in turn now occupies the spot originally occupied by a point that we say has moved to P_4; and so on. Since we know that the transformation under consideration is a contraction, the distance between P_2 and P_3 must be smaller than the distance between P_2 and P_1. Similarly, the distance between P_4 and P_3 is

smaller than the distance between P_3 and P_2, and so on. We obtain a sequence of points, $P_1, P_2, P_3 \ldots$, that get closer and closer together. This implies that the sequence must have a limit, which means only that all these points get closer and closer to some one point on the plane. This limiting point is a fixed point for the transformation.

The theorem for contractions has been stated and the idea of its proof has been outlined for transformations of a plane. In the preceding argument, however, the concept of dimension is never used. It follows that the theorem remains valid even in infinite-dimensional spaces whose "points" consist of functions of time.

Not only does every contraction have a fixed point; it has only one fixed point. The proof of this is straightforward. Suppose P and Q were two different fixed points of the contraction $f(P)$. If this were the case, we should have $P = f(P)$ and $Q = f(Q)$. Now consider the distance between P and Q. Since these are fixed points, the dis-

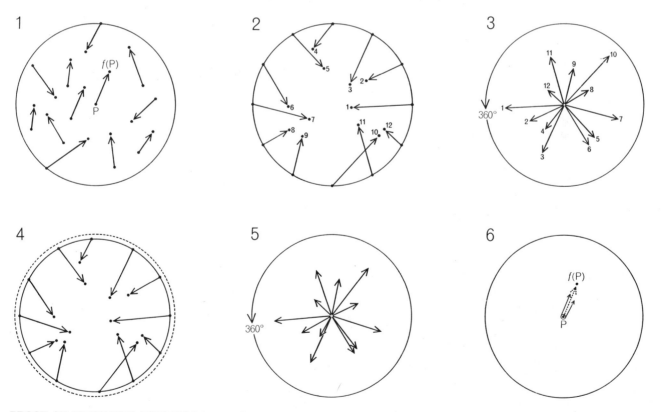

PROOF OF BROUWER'S THEOREM for two-dimensional surface such as a circular disk begins with the assumption, contrary to the theorem, that after deformation no point remains fixed. An arrow is drawn from each point to the position to which it is moved (*1*). Since no point is moved outside the disk all arrows from points on the boundary must head into the circle (*2*). These arrows are drawn again as if they emanated from a point within the circle (*3*). Considered thus, the arrows (called transformation vectors) make one complete rotation of 360 degrees around the circle. If we

next trace the movement of points on the boundary of a concentric circle only slightly smaller than the original one (*4*), the number of rotations made by the arrows must, by the nature of continuous deformation, remain one (*5*). This must be true for all concentric circles because the rotation of the transformation vectors represents a continuous function. But when we consider a very small circle, all the arrows on its boundary head in roughly the same direction (*6*) and the net number of rotations is not one but zero. This contradiction shows that the assumption of no fixed point is untenable.

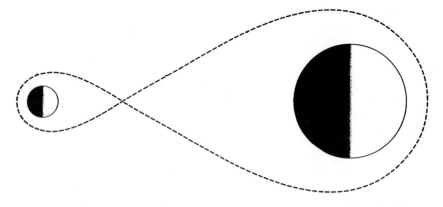

FEASIBILITY OF AN ORBIT by which a satellite would revolve around earth and moon is the type of question to which mathematicians apply fixed-point theorems for infinite-dimensional surfaces. The element of time in any equation for the orbit makes the problem infinite-dimensional, rendering such simple theorems as Brouwer's theorem inapplicable.

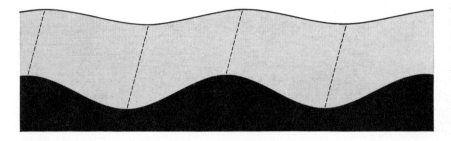

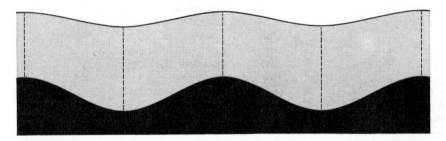

FEASIBILITY OF WATER FLOW of a certain type over a periodically rising and falling bottom can only be demonstrated by use of fixed-point theorems. Until recently it was not known if the surface of the water could rise and fall according to the same general period as the bottom. Now it has been demonstrated that such a flow is possible and that the high and low points of the surface can lie directly above the high and low points of the bottom.

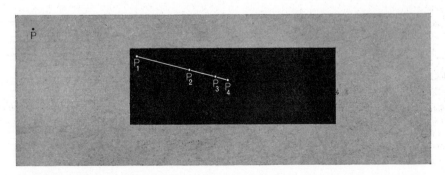

CONTRACTION of a surface must result in one point remaining in the position it occupied before the contraction. The larger rectangle represents the original surface, a sheet of rubber stretched taut; the darker, smaller rectangle represents the sheet after it has sprung back to its relaxed position. We consider the point, P, near the corner at top left on the original rectangle. After the contraction it assumes a position we designate P_1. The point that was at P_1 originally has moved inward to a new position, P_2. The point originally at P_2 has moved to P_3, and so on. The interval between P_2 and P_3 is smaller than the interval between P_1 and P_2. In fact $P_1, P_2, P_3 \ldots$ form a series approaching a limit: the fixed point.

tance between them should be the same as the distance between $f(P)$ and $f(Q)$. But the distance between $f(P)$ and $f(Q)$ must, by the definition of a contraction, be strictly less than the distance between P and Q. This contradiction, calling for the distance between P and Q to be less than itself, shows that the original assumption that P and Q are two different fixed points is untenable and thus proves that there can be only one fixed point.

The fact that every contraction has a fixed point is customarily used to prove that differential equations (of which Newton's second law of motion, $F = ma$, is an example) have solutions. And, as we have seen, such equations can have only one solution. This suggests one highly practical consequence of the fixed-point theorems on contractions: in any mechanical system, whether it is the moon and the earth or a swinging pendulum, the motions of the system are completely determined by its initial displacements and velocities.

Much was made of this fact by the great French mathematician and astronomer Pierre Simon de Laplace. In his *Essai Philosophique sur les Probabilités* Laplace used it as the basis for commenting: "Given for one instant an intelligence which could comprehend all the forces by which nature is animated and the respective situation of the beings who compose it—an intelligence sufficiently vast to submit these data to analysis—it would embrace in the same formula the movements of the greatest bodies of the universe and those of the lightest atom; for it, nothing would be uncertain and the future, as the past, would be present to its eyes." There has probably never been a more definite statement of the doctrine of predestination. It stood, seemingly irrefutable, for more than a century, until the theories of thermodynamics and quantum mechanics enabled it to be contradicted.

This discussion of fixed-point theorems serves to illustrate a phenomenon characteristic of mathematics. A purely geometric idea—the concept of a fixed point of a transformation of a plane or a line—has been generalized by analogy to apply to problems in mechanics and hydrodynamics and ultimately to the philosophical problem of predestination. Although it would be hard to maintain that all keys to philosophy lie in mathematics, it is true that modern mathematics, concerned with such interactions of geometric, algebraic and analytic ideas as we have described, does lend itself to philosophical applications.

22 CHANCE

A. J. AYER · October 1965

The word "chance" is commonly used in several different senses. One of the things I hope to accomplish in this article is to disentangle them. In some of these senses, although not in all, "chance" is a synonym for "probability." Thus such statements as that the chance of throwing double-six with a pair of true dice is one in 36, that there is a slightly better than even chance that any given unborn infant will be a boy, and that there is now very little chance that Britain will join the Common Market can all be regarded as expressing judgments of probability.

It is to be noted, however, that each of these examples illustrates a different kind of judgment of probability. The first is an example of what is often called a judgment of a priori probability: it relates to the mathematical calculus of chances. The second is an example of a statistical judgment: it estimates the actual frequency with which some property is distributed among the members of a given class. The third is an example of what, for want of a better expression, I describe as a judgment of credibility: it evaluates the degree of confidence we are entitled to have in the truth of some proposition or in the occurrence of some particular event.

Although any of these judgments of probability can correctly be expressed as an estimate of chances, it is with judgments of the first type that the concept of chance is most closely associated. Thus it is characteristic of what are known as games of chance that their results are substantially in accordance with the a priori probabilities. Our first problem, then, is to try to make clear exactly what this implies.

The Calculus of Chances

In dealing with this problem, the most important point to bear in mind is that the calculus of chances is a branch of pure mathematics. Hence the propositions it sets forth are necessarily true. This point tends to be obscured by the fact that statements such as "The chance of throwing heads with an unbiased penny is a half" are open to more than one interpretation. An unbiased penny (or a true die) could be defined in physical terms as one that was constructed of such and such materials and had its center of gravity in such and such a place. In that case these statements would be statistical; their truth

would depend on the actual frequency with which the results in question were obtained with coins or dice that met these physical stipulations.

More commonly, however, what is understood by a true die or an unbiased penny is simply one that yields results matching the a priori probabilities. When our examples are interpreted in this way, they turn into statements of elementary arithmetic. It being presupposed that a penny has two faces, and that when it is tossed it will come down with one or the other of them uppermost, to say that if it is an unbiased penny there is an even chance of its coming up heads is to say no more than that one is the half of two.

Not all our computations of chances are as simple as this, but the principle remains the same. For instance, when it is said that the odds against throwing heads with an unbiased penny three times in succession are seven to one, what is meant is that of all the possible ordered triplets of the numbers 1 and 2—such as 121, 211, 212 and so forth—the sequence 111 is just one out of eight. If we generalize this and say that the odds against throwing heads n times in succession are $2^n - 1$ to 1,

There are no laws of chance in the sense that the laws dictate the pattern of events

what we are saying is that of all the possible ordered n-tuplets of the numbers 1 and 2, the sequence of n 1's is one out of a total of 2^n possibilities.

Now, clearly the value of $1 : 2^n$ diminishes as n increases, and this is what is meant by saying that a long run of consecutive heads or tails or a long run of either red or black at roulette is highly improbable. Whatever the initial fraction representing the chance of a given result for any given turn, the chance of obtaining this result n times in succession will be represented by this fraction raised to the power of n, always provided that the successive turns are independent of each other. This is again a proposition of simple arithmetic. The only empirical assumption being made is that a game like roulette is in fact a game of chance—in other words, that it is possible to construct and operate an object such as a roulette wheel in such a way that the calculus of chances is approximately satisfied by the results.

In applying the calculus to gambling games of this kind the assumption that the turns are independent must be given particular attention. Otherwise one might find oneself committing the celebrated Monte Carlo fallacy, which in this instance can be described as the tendency to think that a run of heads in coin-flipping or of red in roulette increases the likelihood that tails or black will come up on the next turn. As we have just seen, the chances of throwing n successive heads with an unbiased coin or of having a run of n red numbers at roulette are very small if n is at all large; for example, the odds against a series of as few as 10 heads are more than 1,000 to one. Gamblers are tempted to infer from this fact that if n is a large number by these standards and heads have come up $n - 1$ times in succession, the odds against its coming up again the nth time must also be large. Hence a roulette player who has watched red come up nine times in succession will bet heavily on black.

The reasoning, however, is fallacious. The very calculation that makes a long run of red improbable is based on the premise that each spin of the wheel is independent of every other, so that the probability of red—or in the case of the coin the probability of heads —is the same in each instance, no matter what the results of the preceding spins or tosses have been. Even if a million tosses of an unbiased coin had yielded heads on every occasion, the odds against which are astronomical, the

chance that it would come up tails on the next toss is still no better than a half.

Many people find this conclusion difficult to accept, because they do not realize that these estimates of chances are no more than the enumeration of abstract possibilities. To say that the odds against a million successive heads are astronomical is merely to say that if we were to list all the possible million-term sequences of heads and tails, the sequence consisting of heads a million times over is just one out of an astronomically large number of alternatives. To say that the odds against heads coming up on the million-and-first occasion are still no more than $1 : 2$ is to say, quite correctly, that one is no less than the half of two.

It will be objected that if we put ourselves in the position of a gambler who has to place his bets, it is not really so clear that the Monte Carlo fallacy is fallacious. If the coin he is tossing is unbiased, it follows by definition that it comes up tails as often as it comes up heads. So if at some stage in the series of tosses a long run of either face of the coin disturbs the balance, the other face will come up more often in order to restore it. Surely, then, the rational course for the gambler to pursue would be to note the relative frequencies with which the two faces have appeared and to support whichever of them has any leeway to make up.

The answer to this assertion is that it would indeed be the right policy if the gambler were justified in making the assumption that there was some finite number of tosses, some number that he could in principle specify, within which equality would be reached. That proposition, however, cannot be derived from the calculus of chances or even from the assumption that the coin is unbiased. If the gambler could know that the coin was unbiased, in the sense here in question, then he would know that any imbalance in the relative frequency of heads and tails would be corrected if the series of tosses were sufficiently continued. As long as no limit is set to the number of further tosses allowed for this end to be reached, however, he can draw no conclusion about the way he ought to bet. All he can say is that if the existing ratio of heads to tails is $m : n$, then the result of the next toss will be to change it either to $m + 1 : n + 1$ or to $m : n + 1$. No matter what numbers m and n may be, and however much one exceeds the other, only these two abstract possibilities exist.

The odds are based on imaginary coins

As far as the calculus of chances goes, there is nothing to choose between them.

An example that may bring this point out more clearly is that of drawing cards from an ordinary pack. Since the number of red and the number of black cards are equal and finite, it is obvious that the greater the preponderance of red cards that have been drawn, the greater is the chance that the next card will be black, provided that when a card is drawn it is not replaced. If, on the other hand, it is replaced, then it is as if the game started afresh with each drawing, so that no matter how large the preponderance of red cards has been, the chance that the next card to be drawn will be black remains even. The Monte Carlo fallacy may then be said to consist in treating the game in which the cards are replaced after being drawn as though it were on a level with the game in which they are not replaced.

It must be remembered, however, that to talk about chance in this way is not in itself to say anything about what is actually likely to happen; it is not to make a judgment of credibility. In actual practice the roulette player who observed that red numbers came up very much more often than black might well conclude that the wheel was biased or that the croupier had discovered some means of spinning it unfairly. Then it would be rational for him to regard the odds on each occasion as being in favor of red.

Whatever view he takes, he has to rely on some empirical assumption, because to suppose that the wheel is true (in the sense that its operations satisfy the calculus of chances) is as much an empirical assumption as to suppose that it is biased. These assumptions are empirical because they are concerned with the way in which some physical object actually behaves. The question is

Deviations from probability may change

whether or not some particular roulette wheel, coin, die pack of cards or whatever it may be is constructed and manipulated in such a way that any one of a number of equally possible alternatives is realized about as often as any other. In the cases where the results have shown themselves to be unequal—in the sense that one side of the coin, one face of the die, some group of numbers or some distribution of the cards has been particularly favored—it is a matter of predicting whether this bias will continue or whether it will be corrected. This is a question not of abstract mathematics but of fact.

It is true that if there is no limit in theory to the duration of the game, the hypothesis that it is fair can never be strictly refuted. No matter how large the deviations have been found to be, it remains conceivable that they will subsequently be corrected—or at least that they would be corrected if the game were sufficiently continued. Although there is never any logical inconsistency in holding to this assumption, there may come a point at which it ceases to be credible.

Applications of the Calculus

It should be clear by now that no conclusions about any matter of fact can be derived solely from the calculus of chances. There are no such things as the laws of chance in the sense in which a law dictates some pattern of events. In themselves the propositions of the calculus are mathematical truisms. What we can learn from them is that if we assume that certain ratios hold with respect to the distribution of some property, then we are committed to the conclusion that certain other ratios hold as well. If each of a pair of dice has six faces, and in each case the faces are respectively numbered one to six, and in each case when the die is thrown any one face comes uppermost as often as any other, then the sum of the numbers that come up when both dice are thrown will be eight on five occasions out of 36. In other words, the chances of making a point of eight with a single throw of two dice are a little worse than seven to one against.

These other words, however, are misleading, because the proposition in question is merely a proposition about numbers. The references to dice, coins, packs of cards or roulette wheels that occur in expositions of the theory of probability are entirely adventitious. These objects are dummies whose only function is to adorn the mathematical theory with concrete illustrations. The proof that they are dummies is that they exercise no control over the propositions they serve to illustrate. The question is whether they measure up to the theory, not whether the theory measures up to them.

Suppose that someone has brought himself to doubt that the odds against making a point of eight with a pair of dice are more than seven to one, and has decided to test the question by experiment. Suppose further that after recording the results of many thousands of throws he finds that the proportion of times in which his pair of dice has yielded a total of eight is as high as one in five. What has he proved? Perhaps no more than that his dice are biased; at most that tossing dice is not an affair of chance in the way that it has been taken to be, but certainly nothing that has any bearing on the theory of probability.

The fact that the propositions of the calculus of chances are not empirically testable does not, of course, entail that they have no factual application. What we require in order to be able to apply them successfully is to discover a set of possible states of affairs that satisfy the following conditions: (1) that they be finite in number, (2) that they be mutually exclusive, (3) that they be logically equal, in a sense that I shall explain, and (4) that they occur with at least approximately equal frequency. When all these conditions are satisfied, the respective states of affairs may be said to be equally probable.

What I mean by saying that the states of affairs in question must be logically equal is that each state has to be treated as a unity on a level with each of the others. This treatment does not preclude their being complex, in the sense of embracing a number of alternatives. If any member of the set is represented as a disjunction of such alternatives, however, we must not allow these disjuncts themselves to rank as members of the set. Otherwise we shall find ourselves falling into contradiction.

For example, it has been held by some writers that in a case where we have no evidence either for or against a given proposition, we are entitled to assume that it is equally likely to be true or false. Suppose, then, that I am playing a game of drawing marbles from a bag and that, relying on this principle, I take it to be an even chance that the first one to be drawn will be blue. This would be a foolish assumption to bet on, but it would not be contradictory as long as I treat not-blue as a single color on a level with blue. If, however, I follow the natural course of breaking down not-blue into a disjunction of other colors—and if, by parity of reasoning, I also take it to be an even chance that the first marble to be drawn will be black, an even chance that it will be red, an even chance that it will be green and so forth—then I am involved in contradiction. If there are more than two possibilities, it is impossible that each of them should have an even chance of being realized. This is again a question of simple arithmetic. One is not the half of any number higher than two.

To avoid contradictions of this sort, we have to decide at the outset what possibilities we are going to regard as logically equal and then adhere consistently to our decision. As Rudolf Carnap of the University of California at Los Angeles has shown in his *Logical Foundations of Probability*, such decisions can be taken on purely semantic grounds. We can construct a language with a limited number of primitive predicates and the power to refer to some finite number of individuals; we can then decide, in a more or less arbitrary fashion, that certain states of affairs, which are describable by these means, are to be counted as equally probable, and we can select our logical operators in such a way that the probability of any possible state of affairs within the selected universe of discourse can be calculated on this basis. This procedure, however, has an unduly narrow application; moreover, there is no reason to suppose that our judgments of equal probability will conform to anything that actually happens.

On the other hand, if we follow a more liberal course by relying on *ad hoc* estimates of what it seems fair to regard as equal possibilities, we shall come on situations in which what appear to be equally reasonable decisions will lead to incompatible results. I borrow a simple example from an article by J. L. Watling of University College London. Suppose "we are following a man along a road and reach a place where the road divides into three, two paths climbing the hillside, one lying in the valley." Knowing nothing but that the man, now out of sight, will take one of the three paths, how are we to estimate the probability that he will take the path lying in the valley? If we follow the classical procedure of assigning equal probability to equal possibilities, and if we regard it as equally possible that the man will take any one of the three paths, we shall have to conclude that the chance of his taking the valley path is one in three. But we might just as well regard it as equally possible that he will go into the valley or into the hills, and in that case it would follow that the chance of his taking the valley path was one in two. These conclusions are mutually incompatible, but in default of further information there is nothing to choose between them.

Watling takes this situation as a proof that "the classical interpretation" of probability is inconsistent. I should prefer to say in cases of this kind that it was inoperative. The calculus of chances is not inconsistent in itself. As long as we have a consistent rule for deciding what states of affairs are to count as equally possible, the calculus can be consistently applied. If its application is to be of any use to us, however—in the way of helping us to win our bets on what will actually happen—we cannot allow the assignment of initial probabilities simply to depend on an arbitrary decision. In the example chosen, if we really knew nothing more than that the man would take one of the three paths, we should have no right to assume either that it was equally likely that he would take any one of the three or that it was equally likely that he would go into the valley or into the hills. Before we could make any such assumptions, we should have to have something further to go on than the mere arithmetical fact that one is the half of two or the third part of three. We should need some factual information such as the man's habits in order to supply the calculus of chances with a foothold in reality. In general, we can-

not assume that any two states of affairs are equally probable unless we have reason to believe that they occur with equal frequency. But pure mathematics cannot tell us anything about actual frequencies, and neither can semantics. We must rely on empirical evidence.

The upshot of this argument is that when we come to apply the calculus of chances, our judgments of probability undergo a change of character: they become statistical judgments. To say that there is one chance in eight that a true coin will come up heads on each of three successive tosses may, as we have seen, be just a colorful way of expressing an arithmetical truism, but to say the same applies to the penny that I have in my hand is to make the empirical statement that if it were tossed on a fairly large number of occasions and the results were set out in groups of three, the sequence heads-heads-heads would be found to occur on the average once in eight times. This is, indeed, a consequence of the more general assumption that in a sufficiently long series of tosses with this penny each of the possible sequences of a given length would occur on the average as often as any other.

Here, however, we are faced with the difficulty that unless some limit is set to the length of the sequence within which this equality is to be realized,

the empirical evidence in favor of such an assumption is bound to be incomplete. Even if a limit were to be set, so that we could in principle run through all the members of the series to which our judgment of probability refers, it is only as long as we have not done this that a judgment of this kind is of any interest to us. When we already know that a given event has occurred or that it has failed to occur, we do not speculate about its chances. The point of collecting statistics is to extrapolate them.

Samples and Classes

In other words, we normally examine only a sample of the total class of events in which we are interested; if we find that the property about which we are inquiring is distributed in a certain proportion among the members of this sample, we infer that it would be distributed in much the same proportion among the members of a further sample or throughout the class as a whole. Admittedly if we were to toss our penny 50 times, say, and found that heads came up in the ratio of three to two, we should not feel ourselves bound to regard this as a typical sample. In default of physical evidence that the penny was biased, we might rather expect that if the series of tosses were continued, the balance would be re-

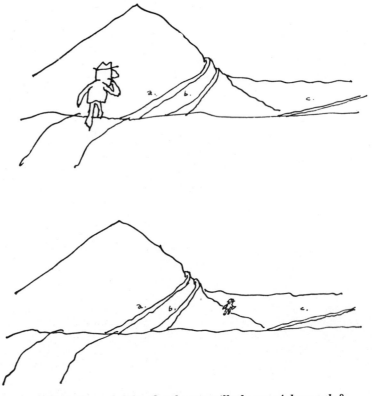

What is the probability that the man will take one of three paths?

Confidence that one has beaten the odds may be misplaced

dressed. But the reason for this expectation would be that we were influenced by our knowledge that pennies physically similar to this one had been found to come up heads about as often as they came up tails. In so thinking we should be drawing on a wider range of statistics, but we should still be going beyond our evidence. We should in fact be making a deduction from a general hypothesis about the distribution of heads and tails—a hypothesis that had been derived from our knowledge of their distribution in a reasonably large sample.

The question is how such a procedure can be justified. The usual answer is that inferences from the character of a sample to the character of the total class or population from which the sample is drawn are logically justified (provided that the sample is large enough) by the law of large numbers. I shall not go into the mathematical formulation and proof of this law, which is to be found in the standard textbooks. What it comes to is that if a proportion $m : n$ of the members of some class possess the property P and we select from this class all possible samples of a given size, it must be true of the majority of these samples that the proportion in which P is distributed among their members also lies in the neighborhood of $m : n$. Moreover, as the size of the samples increases, so does the extent of the con-

centration around $m : n$, with the result that if the samples are made large enough, the frequency with which P occurs in practically all of them will differ only negligibly from the frequency with which it occurs in the parent class.

A common way of expressing this fact is to say that it is very highly probable that the distribution of a property throughout a given class is almost exactly reflected in any large sample drawn from that class; and since if A matches B it must also be true that B matches A, it will follow that if a property is distributed in such and such a proportion among the members of a large sample (A), there is a very high probability that it is distributed in approximately the same proportion among the members of the class (B) from which the sample has been drawn. It is in this way that the law of large numbers is thought to justify this familiar type of inference.

There is, however, a point to be made here that is rather too often overlooked. When one speaks in this context of its being highly probable that what is true of a large sample is also true of the parent class, this judgment of probability belongs to the first of my three types. It is not a judgment of credibility but a judgment that relates merely to the distribution of logical possibilities.

What one is saying in fact is that among all possible samples of the size in question the number of those that roughly match the parent class is very much greater than the number of those that do not. It follows that if our sample is seriously deceptive with respect to the incidence of some property in the class from which it is drawn, it is highly untypical. This is all that follows. Even to say that the sample is untypical does not mean that it deviates from most of the samples that are actually drawn but only that it deviates from the vast majority of possible samples. This is the most that can be extracted from the law of large numbers.

But is it really likely that our sampling of nature should be untypical? The trouble with this question is that it smuggles in a judgment of credibility, for which no basis has yet been assigned. If we make suitable assumptions about the constitution of the universe, we can supply ourselves with premises from which to deduce that our sampling is fair. The premises will themselves need to be justified, however, and I do not see how this can be done except by an appeal to our experience. Then, as David Hume saw, we are landed in a circle, because this appeal to our experience makes use of the very assumptions we are attempting to justify. I am strongly inclined to think that this circle is unavoidable, but to develop this argument would lead me into the heart of the problem of induction, which I shall not attempt to penetrate here.

A Valid Application

I have tried to show that although there is nothing wrong with the law of large numbers in itself, the support it gives to arguments from inverse probability—the reasoning that a large sample is unlikely to deviate in character from its parent class—is much more precarious than has commonly been supposed. There is, however, one set of cases in which an argument of this type can be applied with complete safety. These are the cases in which the class that concerns us is finite and the unexamined portion of it is relatively very small. Suppose we know the total number of births within a given area throughout a given period but our statistics on their sex distribution are not quite complete. Then let the fraction of the class for which this information is lacking be comparatively small, say less than 3 percent. In that case, whatever the proportion of male births in our sample may be, we can be sure that the proportion in the whole class does not differ from it much, just because there are not enough unexamined instances to make any substantial difference. By supposing all of the births in the unexamined instances to be male or all of them female, we can establish the fairly narrow limits within which the correct answer for the whole class must lie.

We now find, however, that the very security of this conclusion robs it of any interest. It tells us no more than we know already. The prospective father who wants to know whether his child is more likely to be a boy or a girl learns nothing at all to his purpose from the information that the available statistics are such that the proportion of boys among the children born or about to be born within the relevant period is bound to be more than 50 percent. All he learns is that the figures have now reached a stage where it is not going to make any appreciable difference to the final percentage which his child is. Not only can he deduce nothing about the sex of his own child—since judgments of probability, in the sense of frequency, refer to classes and not to individuals—but also he can deduce nothing about the frequency of male births in the subclass of so-far-unexamined cases to which his child belongs.

In fact, the ratio of male to female births has been found to be fairly constant, so that if the statistics had shown that slightly more female children had been born so far in the course of the year, the prospective father, knowing that there was normally a slight preponderance of males, might be encouraged to expect that his child would be a boy as the result of a belief in what is popularly known as the law of averages. If he did argue in this way, he could easily be disappointed. What is not generally realized is that the law of averages only works deductively. If we already know, with respect to the incidence of some property in a limited series of events, what the

final percentage is going to be, and if we also know what the percentage is in the part of the series that has already been traversed, we can calculate what the percentage will be in the instances still to come.

This situation, however, carries the consequence that the law of averages can only be applied with any safety when it is backed by statistical laws that are very well established. We might perhaps rely on the Mendelian laws of heredity for the assurance that if a recessive character had already appeared in a given generation among the members of a certain family of plants or animals, the character of the kind in question that would be displayed in the same generation by the remaining members of the family would be dominant. On the other hand, it would be a foolish man who argued that because the total number of automobile accidents in the current year had already risen to the average of previous years, he could drive as recklessly as he pleased, since the law of averages would keep him safe. The reason he would be foolish is not only that the incidence of automobile accidents is not known to fall under any very constant statistical laws but also that for the most part these accidents, although they may be in some measure due to common causes, are causally independent of one another. The fact that a number of accidents have occurred recently in your neighborhood does not make it any less likely that another one will occur there today—unless, perhaps, the knowledge that the accidents have occurred makes people more careful. Certainly the occurrence of another accident is not made any less likely by the law of averages.

The same reasoning applies to our example of the prospective father, in spite of the greater constancy of the birth statistics. Whatever factors may determine the sex of his child, there is no reason to believe that the sex of other children who are not his kindred but merely happen also to be born in

the current year has anything to do with it. Consequently, if there has been an unusual preponderance of female births, the inference he should draw is not that there is any greater likelihood that his child will be a boy but rather that this is a year in which, for a multiplicity of reasons, the usual balance of the sexes has been altered.

Questions about Chance

We have seen that what is required for the application of the calculus of chances is a finite set of logically equal possibilities, which are fulfilled in the long run with equal frequency. It is because we suppose these conditions to be at least roughly satisfied in games played with coins, dice, cards or roulette wheels that we characterize them as games of chance. Conversely, if we play one of these games and find in a particular instance that the different possibilities are not fulfilled with anything like equal frequency, we may decide that the results are not to be ascribed to chance. Then we look for some other explanation.

It is not only in gambling games that this procedure operates. Very often, when a statistical result is said to be significant, what is meant is that it deviates from chance in the sense that it fails to accord with the a priori probabilities. A good illustration of this is to be found in the experiments that are supposed to prove the existence of extrasensory perception. A typical experiment might be conducted with a set of cards numbered one to five and another set of five cards respectively symbolizing a lion, an elephant, a pelican, a zebra and a giraffe. Both packs are shuffled; the experimenter draws a card from the numbered pack, and then he draws from the animal pack the card that corresponds in order to the number he has drawn. This procedure is repeated 100 times, the cards being replaced and the packs reshuffled after each drawing. The subject is required to say on each occasion which animal

A rise in the number of accidents does not imply that there will be a drop to maintain the statistical average

is represented by the card drawn from the animal pack.

It is assumed that if it were merely a matter of guesswork he would be right, on the average, 20 times out of 100. Sometimes, however, a subject fairly consistently gets as many as 28 right. This result is sufficiently improbable to be counted as statistically significant. It is therefore inferred that the subject's achievement cannot be put down to chance, and he is credited with extrasensory perception. (Admittedly, to talk of extrasensory perception is not to give any explanation of the subject's performance but merely to stake the claim that an explanation is called for, but this does not matter for our present purposes. Our only concern is with the meaning and implications of the statement that such things do not occur by chance.)

Let us look into this case a little more closely. Why is it assumed that if the subject had no special power of divination he would pick the right card about 20 times out of 100? The answer is that if we take every possible sequence of 100 drawings from this set of cards and every possible sequence of 100 guesses, then the proportion of cases in which the two selections match is 20 in 100. To say that it is rather improbable that as many as 28 guesses should be right is just to say that out of the total number of possible parallel sequences of 100 drawings and guesses, the proportion in which the two coincide in as many as 28 places is rather small.

It is to be noted that both these calculations are a priori. They relate to the distribution of logical possibilities and are in no way derived from the study of anything that actually happens. Why, then, should we regard it as a matter of no interest—as something only to be expected—that the series of guesses should match the series of drawings in the same proportion as the total of possible matches stands to the total of possible combinations, but think it quite extraordinary that a subject should achieve a number of matchings 8 percent higher than the a priori average? Why should it be more remarkable that the proportion of actual coincidences should deviate from the proportion of possible coincidences than that they should be in conformity with one another? What we must be assuming is that the natural thing in a card-guessing game of this kind is for every possible combination of the members of the two series to appear with equal frequency. What reason could we have for making

Apparent extrasensory perception in drawing cards may involve other factors

such an assumption antecedently to any experience? As far as I can see, none whatsoever.

If I am right about this, we are not entitled to assume that it is only a deviation from the a priori frequencies that calls for explanation. Conformity with them may equally have to be accounted for. In fact, there are many cases in which this necessity seems to be recognized. If a coin, a die or a roulette wheel yields "improbable" results, if it favors one side or area at the expense of the others, we do indeed assume that some physical bias is at work: the coin is weighted; its center of gravity has been displaced. Yet equally we think that there is a physical explanation in the case where such objects run true. It is quite an art to make dice and roulette wheels operate in such a way that each number comes up in a reasonably long run about as often as any other. There are physical reasons for this just as much as there are for the fact that one number or set of numbers comes up much more often than the others. In the sense in which chance is contrasted with design, or a chance event is one to which we do not assign a cause, it is not by chance that these operations obey the laws of chance.

Antecedently to experience, then, we have no more reason to expect that the results of tossing coins or throwing dice will conform to the a priori probabilities than that they will deviate from them. The reason we think that results that are highly improbable in this sense call for a special explanation is that they are empirically abnormal. What is significant is not the deviation from the a priori frequencies but the deviation from frequencies that have been empirically established. The special interest we take in the case where a die turns out to be biased stems from the fact that we have found by experience that most dice run true.

I believe that the same applies to the other cases in which we conclude, on purely statistical grounds, that such and such an occurrence cannot be ascribed to chance. Suppose that wherever I go in the course of a day I keep running across the same stranger. I may well conclude that this cannot be a matter of chance: the man must be following me. But my reason for this conclusion is not that our meeting so often is improbable a priori. Of course, I could argue in that way. Starting with the assumption that we are both moving within a certain limited area, I could think of this area as divided

into a finite number of equal squares, like a chessboard, and then make the assumption that each of us is as likely at any moment of the day to be in any one of these squares as in any other. My reason for concluding that we were not meeting by chance would then be that out of the total number of possible paths we could severally follow, the number of those that intersected at several places was only a tiny fraction. But not only is this line of argument not necessary for me to arrive at my conclusion; in addition it rests on a premise that is entirely open to question. If the assumption that each of us is as likely to be in any one square as in any other at any given time is merely a way of stating that the squares are equal, then it is true *ex hypothesi* but is not to the purpose. If it implies that over a certain period of time we are actually to be found in any one square as often as in any other, then, in default of empirical evidence, there can be no reason for accepting it. If I nevertheless conclude that these meetings do not occur by chance, my reason will be that experience has shown me that when two people are living independently in a large city with many different venues for business and for recreation, the occasions on which their separate pursuit of their affairs leads them to be in the same place at the same time are relatively few. Here again, what needs to be particularly explained is the deviation not from an a priori frequency but from an empirically established one.

This is also, in my view, the way we should interpret the card-guessing experiments. Antecedently to experience, there is no reason to believe that the degree to which any series of guesses matches any series of drawings will or will not reflect the distribution of the logical possibilities. What is known a priori is that any card drawn will be one of five possibilities, and that any guess will also be one of five possibilities, but from this nothing at all follows about the number of matchings that will actually occur. We have to discover by experiment that certain methods of shuffling and selecting the cards do have the result that any one of them comes up about as often as any other. We have also to discover by experiment that the guesses people make are evenly distributed; or if this is not true, as for psychological reasons it may well not be in many instances, that their tendency to favor certain choices does not result in a number of matchings that is higher than the aver-

age. From these empirical premises the standard conclusions about the results that would occur by chance do follow mathematically.

But then if the results show a significant deviation, what is put in doubt is the truth of one or other of the empirical premises. The only thing that is remarkable about the subject who is credited with extrasensory perception is that he is consistently rather better at guessing cards than the ordinary run of people have shown themselves to be. The fact that he also does "better than chance" proves nothing in itself.

The same confusion is commonly found in discussions of the question whether or not the universe exists by chance. It is not, indeed, immediately clear what meaning this question could be given in terms of the a priori calculus of chances. If, however, one can make the assumptions that there is a finite number of ultimate particles in the universe and that the space in which they operate is also finite, then I suppose it could be said that the actual state of the universe is highly improbable, in the sense that the actual distribution of the particles is only one of a fantastically large number of possible distributions. In this sense, of course, any other distribution of the particles would be equally improbable, but it might be argued that their actual distribution was more improbable than some others would be, on the ground that it exhibited a greater deviation from the a priori average.

Alternatively, if we were able by what would have to be a rather arbitrary procedure to draw up a finite list of the simple properties that it was logically possible for anything to have, we might say that the actual state of the universe was improbable in the sense that the number of ways in which these properties were actually found to be com-

Misconceptions of chance are persistent

bined was only a tiny fraction of the total number of possible combinations. In neither case, however, would anything of interest follow unless we had reason to believe that some different constitution of the universe from the one that actually obtains was antecedently more likely. But what reason could there possibly be for such a belief? What meaning can be attached even to this notion of antecedent likelihood?

The most that we can say is that given the number of fundamental particles and the finitude of space, or given the number of primary properties and the range of their possible combinations, the number of possible universes in which the particles are more evenly distributed or the combinations of properties are more various is larger than the number of those in which the particles are not more evenly distributed or the combinations of properties are not more various than they are in our actual universe. But should it be supposed that a more probable universe, in this special sense, is more to be expected than the one in which we actually find ourselves? The answer is that there can be no reason at all for any supposition of this kind. The concept of a priori probability relates only to the counting of logical possibilities. How probable it is that these logical possibilities are realized in a balanced or unbalanced way can be estimated only in the light of our experience. But we can have no experience of a universe other than our own.

It is perhaps worth adding that the fact that our universe can be said to be improbable, in the senses I have just defined, does nothing at all for the traditional argument for a universe arising from design. In order to give any force to this argument, it would have to be shown that we have good reason to believe first that the universe is a teleological, or purposive, system. Secondly, it would have to be shown that it is the kind of teleological system that has been demonstrated by our experience to be usually the result of conscious planning. I take it to be sufficiently obvious that neither of these conditions is actually satisfied.

Chance, Design and Cause

We are now in a position to distinguish with some precision the various senses in which we speak of things as happening by chance. Chief among them are these five:

1. A chance event may be one that is a member of some series that conforms, in the manner we have shown to be required, with the a priori calculus of chances. (It is to be noted that this does not imply that the event is not caused, or even that it is not designed. The results of individual tosses of a coin or throws of a die are commonly not designed, but it is often the fruit of design that the series as a whole conforms to the a priori calculus.) A corollary of this usage is that when the frequency with which a certain type of event has been found to occur conforms to the a priori calculus and we meet with a significant deviation, as in the case of the card-guessing experiments, our inclination is to say that this deviation cannot be attributed to chance.

2. On the other hand, there are cases in which our reason, or one of our reasons, for saying that an event occurs by chance is just that it is a deviation from an established frequency. This is the sense, for example, in which we talk of chance mutations in biology. A similar usage occurs in historical instances where we look on the cause as incommensurate with the effect. "For want of a nail the shoe was lost, for want of a shoe the horse was lost, for want of a horse the rider was lost, for want of the rider the battle was lost, for want of the battle the kingdom was lost, and all for the want of a horseshoe nail." We say it was a mischance that the kingdom was lost because we do not ordinarily expect something so trivial as the loss of a horseshoe nail to have such far-reaching consequences. There is also the point that the loss of a nail at such and such a moment is not easily predictable, although again this is not to say that it lacked a cause.

3. When we are speaking of events brought about by human beings, or by other animals insofar as they can be regarded as purposive agents, to say that an event occurs by chance often means no more than that it was not intended by the agent or, in some cases, by anybody else. This is the sense in which "by chance" is contrasted with "by design." Again there is no implication that such events are not caused, but rather the implication that they are.

4. We talk of chance collocations of events when their concurrence is not designed and when, although we may be able to account for them severally, we have failed to establish any lawlike proposition that binds them together. The ascription of such concurrences to chance is most often made in cases where something of particular interest follows from them or in cases where the concurrence would normally be the fruit of design. Thus if I go away on holiday and in the course of my journey keep running into friends whom I had not arranged to meet, I am struck by the coincidence, although in fact it is no more of a coincidence than my meeting anybody else. As we have seen, however, if such encounters become excessively frequent, I may begin to suspect that they are not occurring by chance. In general, to speak of events as coming together by chance does not imply that they are not connected in a lawlike way or that no law connecting them will ever be discovered, but only that no such laws figure in our accepted system of beliefs.

5. In the case of statistical generalizations it can be said to be a matter of chance which of the individuals that fall under the generalization display the property in question and which do not. Thus in the case of a law of genetics we can be confident that just one out of n individuals in the third generation will display some recessive characteristic, but we regard it as a matter of chance which one of them it will be. In microscopic physics one may accept the generalization that m out of n electrons will move from one orbit to another within a given period but regard it as a matter of chance which individuals move and which remain. This usage of chance is the only one in which it is implied that the individual events themselves, as distinct from their concurrences, have not been found capable of being brought under causal laws.

Actually, might not such events be the outcome of chance in an even stronger sense? Might it not be the case not only that we had been unable to subsume them under causal laws but also that there really were no causal laws that governed them? This is not an easy question to answer, partly because it is not clear what would count as an instance of such a chance event. One difficulty is that if no limit is set to the complexity of our hypotheses, then as long as we are dealing with a closed set of events we shall always be able to find some generalizations the hypotheses satisfy. It might be stipulated, however, that such generalizations were not to be counted as laws unless they applied to events outside the set they were already known to cover, and it might in fact turn out in certain domains that we never succeeded in making any such extrapolations. If this led us to conclude that the phenomena in question were such that attempts of this kind never would succeed, we could reasonably express the conclusion by saying that the phenomena contained an irreducible element of chance.

There are, indeed, those who maintain that this stage has already been reached in quantum physics, but this is still a matter for dispute. The ground for saying that determinism has broken down in this domain is that the determinism that was postulated in classical physics required that it be possible, at least in principle, to ascertain the position and momentum at any given instant of all the particles in the universe. This is a condition that microscopic particles do not satisfy. It can still be argued, however, that this reasoning does not logically preclude their falling into some deterministic pattern. Even so, the fact remains that such a pattern has not yet been found. Until

it is found, the view that the fundamental laws of physics are not causal but only statistical would appear to hold the field.

I think there is another important sense in which chance can be held to intrude into the world. Even in a field in which causal laws are well established, there is often a certain looseness in the way they fit the facts. The phenomena that are taken as verifying the laws cover a certain range. If the phenomena are quantitative, the values actually recorded may be scattered around the values the law prescribes. These slight deviations are not held to be significant; they are ascribed to errors of observation.

"Errors of observation," however, is here a term of art. Apart from the existence of the deviations there is usually no reason to suppose that any errors have occurred. Now, I think it possible

that this looseness of fit cannot be wholly eliminated; in other words, that there are limits to the precision with which the course of nature can be prospectively charted. If this were so, it might be said that anything that fell outside these limits remained in the hands of chance.

Of course this cannot be proved. Whatever limit is set, there can be no a priori reason for assuming that it will never be overstepped. The person who believes in chance, in this absolute sense, can properly do no more than issue a challenge. He points to certain features of the world and defies anyone to show that they fall entirely in every detail within the grasp of causal laws. But however long he triumphs, there remains, in yet another of the manifold senses of "chance," the chance that his challenge will eventually be met.

23 PROBABILITY

WARREN WEAVER · October 1950

Probability is the very guide of life.
                    —Cicero, *De Natura*

OVER three centuries ago some gamblers asked the great Italian scientist Galileo why a throw of three dice turns up a sum of 10 more often than a sum of nine. In 1654 the Chevalier de Mere—another gambler—asked the French mathematician and philosopher Pascal why it was unprofitable to bet even money that at least one double six would come up in 24 throws of two dice. This problem of de Mere really started off the mathematical theory of probability, and the end is not yet in sight.

Probability theory has now outgrown its disreputable origin in the gaming rooms, but its basic notions can still be most easily stated in terms of some familiar game.

When you toss a die—one carefully made, so that it is reasonable to believe that it is as likely to land on one of its six faces as on any other—a gambler would say that the odds against any specified number are five to one. A mathematician defines the probability to be one-sixth. Suppose we ask now: What is the probability of getting a three and a four in one roll of two dice? For convenience we make one die white and one red. Since any one of six results on the white die can be paired with any one of six results on the red die, there is now a total of 36 ways in which the two can land—all equally likely. The difference in color makes it clear that a red three and a white four is a different throw from a white three and a red four. The probability of throwing a three and a four is the ratio of 2—the number of favorable cases—to 36, the total number of equally likely cases; that is, the probability is 2/36, or 1/18.

What is the probability of throwing a sum of seven with two dice? An experienced crapshooter knows that seven is a "six-way point," which is his way of saying that there are six favorable cases (six and one, one and six, three and four, four and three, five and two, two and five). So the probability of throwing a ·sum of seven with two dice is 6/36, or 1/6.

In general, the probability of any event is defined to be the fraction obtained by dividing the number of cases favorable to the event by the total number of equally likely cases. The probability of an impossible event (no favorable cases) obviously is 0, and the probability of an inevitable or certain event (all cases favorable) is 1. In all other cases the probability will be a number somewhere between 0 and 1.

Logically cautious readers may have noticed a disturbing aspect of this definition of probability. Since it speaks of "equally likely," *i.e.*, equally probable, events, the definition sits on its own tail, so to speak, defining probability in terms of probability. This difficulty, which has caused a vast amount of technical discussion, is handled in one of two ways. · · ·

WHEN one deals with purely *mathematical probability*, "equally likely cases" is an admittedly undefined concept, similar to the theoretical "points" and "lines" of geometry. And there are cases, such as birth statistics for males and females, where the ordinary concept of "equally likely cases" is artificial, so that the notion must be generalized. But a logically consistent theory can be erected on the undefined concept of equally likely cases, just as Euclidean geometry is developed from theoretical points and lines. Only through experience can one decide whether any actual events conform to the theory. The answer of experience is, of course, that the theory does in fact have useful application.

The other way of avoiding the dilemma is illustrated by defining the probability of throwing a four with a particular die as the actual fraction of fours obtained in a long series of throws under essentially uniform conditions. This, the "frequency definition," leads to what is called a *statistical probability*.

On the basis of the mathematical definition of probability, a large and fascinating body of theory has been developed. We can only hint here at the range and interest of the problems that can be solved. Two rival candidates in an election are eventually going to receive m and n votes respectively, with m greater than n. They are sitting by their radios listening to the count of the returns. What is the probability that as the votes come in the eventual winner is always ahead? The answer is $m-n/m+n$. A storekeeper sells, on the average, 10 of a certain item per week. How many should he stock·each Monday to reduce to one in 20 the chance that he will disappoint a customer by being sold out? The answer is 15. Throw a toothpick onto a floor whose narrow boards are just as wide as the toothpick is long. In what fraction of the cases will the toothpick land so as to cross a crack? The answer is $2/\pi$, where π is the familiar constant we all met when we studied high-school geometry. A tavern is 10 blocks east and seven blocks north of a customer's home. If he is so drunk that at each corner it is a matter of pure chance whether he continues straight or turns right or left, what is the probability that he will eventually arrive home? This is a trivial case of a very general "random walk" problem which has serious applications in physics; it applies, for example, to the so-called Brownian movement of very small particles suspended in a liquid, caused by accidental bumps from the liquid's moving molecules. This latter problem, incidentally, was first solved by Einstein when he was 26 years old.

THERE are laws of chance. We must avoid the philosophically intriguing question as to why chance, which seems to be the antithesis of all order and regularity, can be described at all in terms of laws. Let us consider the Law of Large Numbers, which plays a central role in the whole theory of probability.

The Law of Large Numbers has been established with great rigor and for very general circumstances. The essence of the matter can be illustrated with a simple case. Suppose someone makes a great many tosses of a symmetrical coin, and records the number of times heads and tails appear. One aspect—the more familiar aspect—of the Law of Large Numbers states that by throwing enough times we can make it as probable as desired that the ratio of heads to total throws differ by as little as one pleases from the predicted value 1/2. If you want the ratio to differ from 1/2 by as little as 1/100,000, for example, and if you want to be 99 per cent sure (*i.e.*, the probability = .99) of accomplishing this purpose, then there is a perfectly definite but admittedly large number of throws which will meet your demand. Note that there is no number of throws, however large, that will really *guarantee* that the fraction of heads be within 1/100,000 of 1/2. The law simply states, in a very precise way, that as the number of experiments gets larger and larger, there is a stronger and stronger tendency for the results to conform, *in a ratio sense,* to the probability prediction.

This is the part of probability theory that is vaguely but not always properly understood by those who talk of the "law of averages," and who say that the probabilities "work out" in the long run. There are two points which such persons sometimes misunderstand.

The first of these relates to the less familiar aspect of the Law of Large Numbers. For the same law that tells us that the *ratio* of successes tends to match the probability of success better and better as the trials increase also tells us that as we increase the number of trials the *absolute number* of successes tends to deviate more and more from the expected number. Suppose, for example, that in 100 throws of a coin 40 heads are obtained, and that as one goes on further and throws 1,000 times, 450 heads are obtained. The *ratio* of heads to total throws has changed from 40 per cent to 45 per cent, and has therefore come closer to the probability expectation of 50 per cent, or 1/2. But in 100 throws the absolute number of heads (40) differs by only 10 from 50, the theoretically expected number, whereas in 1,000 throws, the absolute number of heads (450) differs by 50, or five times as much as before, from the expected number (500). Thus the ratio has improved, but the absolute number has deteriorated.

The second point which is often misunderstood has to do with the independence of any throw relative to the results obtained on previous throws. If heads have come up several times in a row, many persons are inclined to think that the "law of averages" makes a toss of tails now rather more likely than heads. Granting a fair, symmetrical coin, this is simply and positively not so. Even after a very long uninterrupted run of heads, a fair coin is, on the next throw, precisely as likely to come up heads as tails. Actually the less familiar aspect of the Law of Large Numbers already mentioned makes it likely that longer and longer

uninterrupted sequences of either heads or tails will occur as we go on throwing, although the familiar aspect of the same law assures us that, in spite of these large absolute deviations, the ratio of heads to tails is likely to come closer and closer to one.

ALL of these remarks, of course, apply to a series of *independent* trials. Probability theory has also been most fruitfully applied to series of dependent trials—that is, to cases, such as arise in medicine, genetics, and so on, where past events do influence present probabilities. This study is called the probability of causes.

Suppose we have a covered box about which we know only that it contains a large number of small colored balls. Suppose that without looking into the box we scoop out a handful and find that one third of the balls we have taken are white and two thirds red. What proba-

ROULETTE WHEEL makes possible bets against several probabilities. At Monte Carlo red once came up 32 times in a row. This probability is: $1/(2)^{32}$, or about one in 4 billion.

bility statements can we make about the mixture in the box?

This schematic problem, which sounds so formal and trivial, is closely related to the very essence of the procedure of obtaining knowledge about nature through experimentation. Nature is, so to speak, a large closed box whose contents are initially unknown. We take samples out of the box—*i.e.*, we do experiments. What conclusions can be drawn, how are they to be drawn and how secure are they?

This is a subject which has caused considerable controversy in probability, and in the related field of statistics as well. The problem of the balls as stated above is, as a matter of fact, not a proper problem. The theorem of probability theory which applies here (it is known as Bayes' theorem, and it was first developed by a clergyman) makes clear just how the experimental evidence of the sample justifies one in changing a

previously held opinion about the contents of the box; but the application of the theorem requires you to have an opinion prior to the experiment. You cannot construct a conclusion concerning the probability of various mixtures out of the experiment alone. If many repeated experiments continue to give the same indication of one third white and two thirds red, then of course the evidence becomes more and more able to outweigh a previously held contrary opinion, whatever its nature.

Recently there have been developed powerful new methods of dealing with situations of this general sort, in which one wishes to draw all the justified inferences out of experimental evidence. Although Bayes' theorem cannot be applied unless one possesses or assumes prior opinions, it has been found that other procedures, associated with statistical theory rather than pure probability, are capable of drawing most useful conclusions.

WHAT does a probability mean? What does it mean, for instance, to tell a patient: "If you decide to submit to this surgical operation, the probability that you will survive and be cured is .72"? Obviously this patient is going to make only one experiment, and it will either succeed or fail. What useful sense does the number .72 have for him?

The answer to this—and essentially to any question whatsoever that involves the interpretation of a probability—is: "If a large number of individuals just like you and just in your present circumstances were to submit to this operation, about 72 out of every 100 of them would survive and get well. The larger the number of individuals, the more likely it is that the ratio would be very close to 72 in each 100."

This answer may at first seem a little artificial and disappointing. It admittedly involves some entirely unrealizable conditions. A complicated intuitive process is required to translate the statement into a useful aid to the making of decisions. But experience does nevertheless show that it is a useful aid.

A theory may be called right or wrong according as it is or is not confirmed by actual experience. In this sense, can probability theory ever be proved right or wrong?

In a strict sense the answer is no. If you toss a coin you expect to get about half heads. But if you toss 100 times and get 75 heads instead of the expected 50, you have not disproved probability: probability theory can easily reckon the chance of getting 75 heads in 100 tosses. If that probability be written as 1/N, you would then expect that if you tossed 100 coins N times, in about one of those N times you would actually get 75 heads. So suppose you now toss 100 coins N times, and suppose that you get 75 heads

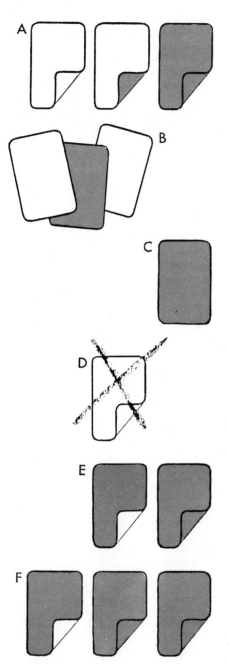

THREE-CARD GAME, classically known as The Problem of Three Chests, illustrates deceptiveness of probability. One card is white on both sides; the second is white on one side and red on the other; the third is red on both sides (A). The dealer shuffles the cards in a hat (B), takes one out and places it flat on the table. The side showing is red (C). The dealer now says: "Obviously this is not the white-white card (D). It must be either red-white or red-red (E). I will bet even money that the other side is red." It is a poor bet for anyone else. Actually there are three possible cases (F). One is that the other side is white. The other two are that it is one or the other side of the red-red card. Thus the chance that the underside is red is 2 to 1.

not just one or two times, as you expect, but say 25 times! Is probability now disproved?

Again no. For the event that has now occurred, although amazingly rare, is still an event whose probability can be calculated, and while its probability is exceedingly small, it is not zero. Thus one goes on, again making a new experiment which consists of many repetitions of the previous experiment. And even if miracles persist in occurring, these would be, from the point of view of probability, not impossible miracles.

Thus in a strict sense probability cannot be proved either right or wrong. But this is, as a matter of fact, a purely illusory difficulty. Although probability cannot be strictly proved either right or wrong, it can be proved useful. The facts of experience show that it works.

THERE are two different—or at least apparently different—types of problems to which probability theory applies. For the first type of problem probability theory is used not so much because we are convinced that we have to use it but because it is so very convenient. For the second type, probability theory seems to be even theoretically unavoidable. We shall see, however, that the distinction between the two cases, while of practical value, is really something of an illusion.

The first type has to do with situations which may be considered deterministic but which are so complex that the outcome is for all practical purposes unpredictable. In this kind of situation we realize that the final result has depended, often in a very sensitive way, on the interaction of a large number of causes. Many of these causes may be somewhat obscure in character, or otherwise impractical of detailed study, but it is at least thinkable that science could, if it were worth-while, analyze every cause in turn and thus arrive at a theory which could predict and explain what happens. When, in such circumstances, we say that the main final result "depends upon chance," we merely mean that, conveniently for us, the very complexity that makes a detailed analysis practically impossible assures an over-all behavior which is describable through the laws of probability.

Perhaps tossing a coin is again the simplest and most familiar illustration of this kind of case. There seems to be no essential mystery about why a coin lands heads or tails. The exact position of the coin above the table, the velocities of movement and spin given by the fingers, the resistance of the air, and so on—one can state what he needs to know in order to compute, by well-known dynamical laws, whether the coin will land heads or tails. But such a study would be very complicated, and would require very precise and extensive quantitative information.

There are many situations of this sort in serious everyday life, where we use probability theory not because it is clear that "chance" plays some obscure and mysterious role but primarily because the situation is so complicated, so intricately affected by so many small causes, that it is prohibitively inconvenient to attempt a detailed analysis. The experience of insurance companies, the occurrence of telephone calls and the resulting demands on telephone traffic and switching equipment, the sampling techniques used when one wishes to estimate the quality of many objects or the opinions of many individuals, the ordinary theory of errors of measurement, problems in epidemiology, the kinetic theory of gases—all these are practical instances in which the causes are too numerous, too complicated, and/or too poorly understood to permit a complete deterministic theory. We therefore deal with these subjects through probability. But in all these cases we would say, with Poincaré, that chance "is only the measure of our ignorance."

THE second type of probability problem at first sight seems very different. Most scientists now believe that some of the most elementary occurrences in nature are essentially and inescapably probabilistic. Thus in modern quantum theory, which forms the basis of our working knowledge of the atom, it seems to be not only impossible but essentially meaningless to attempt to compute just where a certain electron will be at a certain instant. All that one can do is reckon, as through the Schrödinger wave equation, the values of a probability position function. One cannot predict where the electron will be—one can only compute the probability that it will or will not be at a given place or places. And any attempt to frame an experiment that would resolve this probability vagueness, by showing just where the electron is, turns out to be a self-defeating experiment which destroys the conditions under which the original question can be asked.

It is only fair to remark that there remain scientists who do not accept the inevitable role of probability in atomic phenomena. The great example, of course, is Einstein, who has remarked in a characteristically appealing way that "I shall never believe that God plays dice with the world." But it is also fair to remark that Einstein, for all his great genius, is in a small minority on this point.

The problems that involve probability in this inescapable way are of the most fundamental kind. Quantum theory and statistical mechanics, which combine to furnish a large part of the basic theory of the physical universe, are essentially built upon probability. The gene-shuffling which controls inheritance in the living world is subject to probability laws. The inner character of the process of communication, which plays so great and so obvious a role in human life, has recently been found to be probabilistic in nature. The concept of the ever forward flow of time has been shown to depend upon entropy change, and thus to rest upon probability ideas. The whole theory of inference and evidence, and in fact of knowledge in general, goes back to probability.

We are now in a position to see that the two types of probability problems are, if we wish to be logically precise, not so different as we first supposed. Is it correct to think of the fall of a coin as being complicated but determinate, and the position of an electron as being essentially indeterminate? Obviously not. From a large-scale and practical point of view, one could doubtless deal quite successfully with coin-tossing on the basis of very careful actual measurements, plus all the analytical resources of dynamical theory. It remains true, however, that the coin is made of elementary particles whose positions and motions can be known, as science now views the matter, only in a probability sense. Thus we refine our original distinction between the two types of cases by saying that the second type, whatever the scale involved, is essentially indeterminate, whereas the first type involves large-scale phenomena which may usefully be considered determinate, even though these large-scale phenomena depend ultimately on small-scale phenomena which are probabilistic.

SCIENCE deals (as in mathematics) with statements about theory which are logically accurate, but to which the concept of "truth" does not apply; it also deals (as in physics) with statements about nature which can never in a rigorous sense be known to be true, but can at best only be known to be highly probable. It is rather surprisingly the case that the only time man is ever really sure is not when he is dealing with science, but when he is dealing with matters of faith.

There is, moreover, some justification for saying that in science probability almost plays the role that faith does in other fields of human activity. For in a vast range of cases in which it is entirely impossible for science to answer the question "Is this statement true?" probability theory does furnish the basis for judgment as to how likely it is that the statement is true. It is probability which, in an important fraction of cases, enables man to resolve the paradoxical dilemma pointed out by Samuel Butler: "Life is the art of drawing sufficient conclusions from insufficient premises."

24 PROBABILITY

MARK KAC · September 1964

A secretary has typed 10 letters and addressed 10 envelopes. If she now puts the letters in the envelopes entirely at random (without looking at the addresses), what is the probability that not a single letter will wind up in its correct envelope? It may surprise the reader to learn that the probability is better than one chance in three: more specifically, it is almost $1/2.71828\ldots$ (This famous number $2.71828\ldots$, or e, the base of the natural logarithms, turns out to be an important one in the theory of probability and comes up again and again, as we shall see.)

The method used to solve the problem is called combinatorial analysis. An older and more familiar example of problems in combinatorial analysis is: What is the probability of drawing a flush in a single deal of five cards from a deck of 52? Combinatorial analysis has more profound and more practical applications, of course, than estimating the chances of poker hands or answering amusing questions about the hypothetical behavior of absentminded secretaries. It has become an extremely useful branch of mathematics. But its principles are best illustrated by simple examples. Let us work out the poker problem in detail so that we can perceive some of its probabilistic implications.

Pierre Simon de Laplace (1749–1827) based an entire theory of probability on combinatorial analysis by defining probability as $p = n/N$. This expression states that the probability of an event is the ratio of the number of ways in which the event can be realized (n) to the total number of possible events (N), provided that all the possible events are equally likely—an important proviso. The probability of a poker flush therefore is the ratio of the number of possible flushes to the total number of possible poker hands. The problem of combinatorial analysis is to calculate both numbers.

Let us start with a simpler case involving more manageable numbers. Given a set of four objects, *A, B, C, D*, how many subsets, or combinations, of two objects can be made from them? It is easy to answer by simple pairing and counting: there are six possible combinations of size 2, *AB, AC, AD, BC, BD, CD*. As we go on to larger numbers of objects, however, this process soon becomes all but impossible. We must find shortcuts—ways to make the calculations without actually counting. (Combinatorial analysis is sometimes called "counting without counting.")

Suppose we add a fifth object and consider how many pairs can be formed from the five. It is apparent that the new object, *E*, adds just four to the total of possible pairs, because it can combine with each of the other four. So the total is $6 + 4$, or 10, possible pairs. To put it in the conventional symbols of combinatorial analysis, we have $C(5,2) = C(4,2) + C(4,1)$. *C* represents the number of combinations, and the numbers in parentheses stand respectively for the total number of objects and the number in each subset: for instance, $C(5,2)$ means the combinations of five objects taken two at a time. To calculate on the same principle the number of combinations of four objects that could be made out of a total of 10 objects, we could write $C(10,4) = C(9,4) + C(9,3)$ and then continue the reduction to smaller and smaller numbers until we finally computed the answer by simple addition of all the numbers. In practice what we actually do in such a case is to build the *C*'s from the ground up (the bookkeeping is easier).

The whole scheme is conveniently summarized in a handy table known as Pascal's triangle after Blaise Pascal (1623–1662), one of the founders of the theory of probability. The triangle is made up of the coefficients of the binomial expansion, each successive row representing the next higher power [*see top illustration on page 167*]. Each number in the table is the sum of the two numbers to the right and the left of it in the row above. The number of combinations for any set of objects can be read from left to right across a row. For example, the fourth row describes the possible combinations when the total number of objects is four: reading from the left, we have first the number 1, for the "empty set" (containing no objects); then 4, the number of subsets containing one object; then 6, the number of possible combinations of two objects; then 4, the number of three-object combinations, and finally 1 for the "full set" of four objects. With this table, to find the number of quadruplets that can be formed from a total of 10 objects one goes to the 10th row, reads across five steps to the right and finds the answer: 210.

Even the Pascal triangle becomes inconvenient when it has to be extended to large numbers such as are involved in our poker problem. Fortunately the pioneers of the theory of probability were able to work out and prove a simple general formula. This now familiar formula, in which (n,r) means n objects taken r at a time and "!" is the symbol meaning "factorial," is

$$C(n,r) = \frac{n!}{r!(n-r)!} \, .$$

In the case of $C(10,4)$ the formula—simplified by dividing both numerator

```
                              1              1
                        1          2          1
                  1          3          3          1
            1          4          6          4          1
      1          5         10         10          5          1
1          6         15         20         15          6          1
   1      7         21         35         35         21          7          1
1      8         28         56         70         56         28          8         1
1      9         36         84        126        126         84         36          9        1
1     10         45        120        210        252        210        120         45        10        1
```

PASCAL'S TRIANGLE, an aid to calculating probabilities, is made up of the coefficients of the binomial expansion. Each number is the sum of the two numbers immediately above it. Some of its characteristics and applications are discussed in the text.

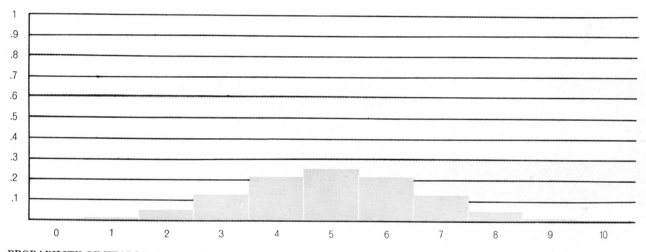

PROBABILITY OF HEADS in 10 tosses of a coin produces a histogram that is reminiscent of the normal distribution. As the 10th row of Pascal's triangle shows, there are 210 possible sequences containing exactly four heads out of a total of 1,024 possible sequences of heads in 10 tosses. Thus the chance of four heads is about 21 percent. Roughly the chances of zero, one, two, three, four and five heads in 10 tosses (*horizontal scale*) are respectively .001, .01, .045, .12, .21 and .25 (*vertical scale*). The probabilities and the bars representing them occur in descending order for six through 10 heads in 10 tosses. On the same scale a nistogram for 10,000 tosses would be much wider and lower, and would have to be rescaled to bring out its relation to the normal curve.

and denominator by $(n - r)!$—becomes

$$C(10,4) = \frac{10 \cdot 9 \cdot 8 \cdot 7}{1 \cdot 2 \cdot 3 \cdot 4} = 210.$$

Now it is not difficult to compute the probability of a poker flush. There are $C(13,5)$ possible flushes in each suit, a total of $4C(13,5)$ in the four suits. The total number of possible poker hands is $C(52,5)$. Hence the probability of getting a flush out of all the hands that might be dealt is

$$\frac{4C(13,5)}{C(52,5)} = \frac{4 \dfrac{13 \cdot 12 \cdot 11 \cdot 10 \cdot 9}{1 \cdot 2 \cdot 3 \cdot 4 \cdot 5}}{\dfrac{52 \cdot 51 \cdot 50 \cdot 49 \cdot 48}{1 \cdot 2 \cdot 3 \cdot 4 \cdot 5}} = \frac{33}{16,600}.$$

This comes out to about two chances in 1,000 of drawing a flush of any kind in a five-card deal from a full deck.

Let us proceed to investigate probability further by the classic device of coin-tossing. Suppose I toss a coin 10 times; what is the probability that in the 10 throws I shall get exactly four

PROBABILITY DEMONSTRATOR shown on the opposite page mechanically produces an approximation to the bell-shaped "normal," or Gaussian distribution. The little red balls rolling from the reservoir at the top pass an array of hexagonal obstacles and collect in receptacles at the bottom. At each obstacle the probability ought in theory to be one-half that a ball will go to the right and one-half that it will go to the left. Thus the balls tend to distribute themselves according to the proportions of Pascal's triangle, shown in the top illustration above. In the photograph the balls falling through the array of obstacles are blurred because of their motion. The balls have not produced the full distribution curve because some are still moving through the channels. The apparatus is known as a Galton Board after Sir Francis Galton, who constructed the first one. The version shown here is based on a design by the Science Materials Center, patented under the name "Hexstat."

heads? Looking at the 10th row of the Pascal triangle, we see that the possible sequences of heads and/or tails for 10 tosses add up to a total of 1,024. In this total there are 210 sequences containing exactly four heads. Therefore, if the coin-tossing is "honest," in the sense that all the 1,024 possible outcomes are equally likely, the probability of just four heads in 10 throws is 210/1,024, or roughly 21 percent.

The sum of all the entries in any given row (numbered n) of the Pascal triangle is equal to 2 to the nth power (for example, $1,024 = 2^{10}$). Thus in general the probability of tossing exactly k heads in a sequence of n throws is $C(n,k)/2^n$. Suppose we plot the various probabilities of tossing exactly 0, 1, 2, 3 and so on up to 10 heads in 10 throws in the form of a series of rectangles, with the height of each rectangle representing the probability [*see bottom illustration on preceding page*]. The graph peaks at the center (a probability of 252/1,024 for five heads) and tapers off gradually to both sides (down to probabilities of 1/1,024 for no heads and for 10 heads). If we plot the same kind of graph for 10,000 tosses, it becomes much wider and lower: the high point (for 5,000 heads) is not in the neighborhood of 25 percent but only $1/100\sqrt{\pi}$, or approximately .56 percent. (It may seem odd that in increasing the number of tosses we greatly reduce the chances of heads coming up exactly half the time, but the oddity disappears as soon as one realizes that a strict 50–50 division between heads and tails is still only one of the possible outcomes, and with each toss we have increased the total number of possible results.)

Drawn on the basis I have just described, the probability graph for a large number of tosses is so flat that it is hardly distinguishable from a straight line. But by increasing the heights of all the rectangles by a certain factor ($\sqrt{n/2}$) and shrinking the width of the base by the same factor, one can see that the tops of the rectangles trace out a symmetrical curve with the peak in the middle. The larger the number of tosses, the closer this profile comes to a smooth, continuous curve, which is described by the equation

$$y = \frac{1}{\sqrt{2\pi}}\, e^{-x^2/2}.$$

The e is our celebrated number 2.71828..., the base of the natural logarithms. (If a bank were foolish enough to offer interest at the annual rate of 100 percent and were to compound this interest continuously—not just daily, hourly or even every second but every instant—one dollar would grow to \$2.71828... at the end of a year.)

The close approach of the probability diagram to a continuous curve with many tosses of a coin illustrates what is called a law of large numbers. If an "honest" coin is tossed hundreds of thousands or millions of times, the distribution of heads in the series of trials, when properly centered and scaled on a graph, will follow almost exactly the curve whose formula I have just given. This curve has become one of the most celebrated in science. Known as the "normal" or "Gaussian" curve, it has been used (with varying degrees of justification) to describe the distribution of heights of men and of women, the sizes of peas, the weights of newborn babies, the velocities of particles in a gas and numerous other properties of the physical and biological worlds.

The remarkable connection between coin-tossing and the normal curve was both gratifying and suggestive. It provided one of the main stimuli for the further development of probability theory. It also formed the basis for the "random walk" model of tracing the paths of particles. This in turn solved the mystery of Brownian motion, thus establishing the foundations of modern atomic theory.

Probability today is a cornerstone of all the sciences, and its daughter, the science of statistics, enters into all human activities. How prophetic, in retrospect, are the words of Laplace in his pioneering work *Théorie analytique des probabilités*, published in 1812: "It is remarkable that a science which began with the consideration of games of chance should have become the most important object of human knowledge. ... The most important questions of life are, for the most part, really only problems of probability."

It seems to be a characteristic of "the most important objects of human knowledge" that they generally take a long time to become established as such. After Laplace interest in probability theory declined, and through the rest of the 19th century and the first two decades of the 20th it all but disappeared as a mathematical discipline. Only a few mathematicians went on with the work; among these were the brilliant and original Russian mathematicians P. L. Chebyshëv and his pupil A. A. Markov (which accounts for the strong development of probability theory in the U.S.S.R. today). There were spectacular applications of probability theory to physics, not only by Albert Einstein and Marian Smoluchowski in their solution of the problem of Brownian motion but also by James Clerk Maxwell, Ludwig Boltzmann and Josiah Willard Gibbs in the kinetic theory of gases. At the turn of the century Henri Poincaré and David Hilbert,

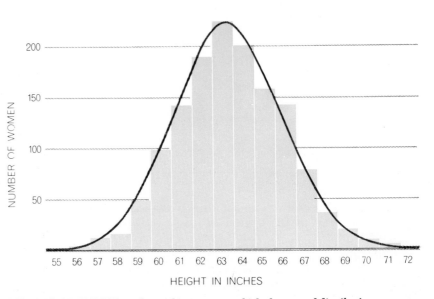

HEIGHTS OF WOMEN produce a histogram to which the normal-distribution curve can be fitted. There were 1,375 women in this sample population. The bell-shaped curve conforms to many other empirical distributions found in the physical and biological worlds.

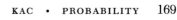

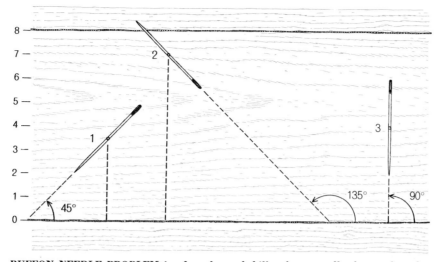

BUFFON NEEDLE PROBLEM involves the probability that a needle shorter than the width of a plank will fall across the crack between two planks. Here each needle is half as long as the plank is wide. The eight units used to measure the plank represent inches.

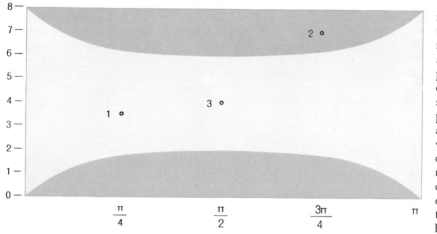

ABSTRACT DIAGRAM also shows positions of the three needles. The horizontal scale represents the angle of each needle with respect to the bottom edge of the plank. The angle is given in terms of π, which is defined as 180 degrees. The vertical scale is the width of the plank in inches. The three dots are the center points of the needles. Called the "sample space," the rectangle represents all the possible positions in which a needle can fall. The dark colored areas cover all the positions in which a needle lies across a crack.

the two greatest mathematicians of the day, tried to revive interest in probability theory, but in spite of their original and provocative contributions there was remarkably little response.

Why this apathy toward the subject among professional mathematicians? There were various reasons. The main one was the feeling that the entire theory seemed to be built on loose and nonrigorous foundations. Laplace's definition of probability, for instance, is based on the assumption that all the possible outcomes in question are equally likely; since this notion itself is a statement of probability, the definition appears to be a circular one. And that

was not the worst objection. The field was plagued with apparent paradoxes and other difficulties. The rising standards of rigor in all branches of mathematics made probability seem an unprofitable subject to cultivate.

In the 1930's, however, it was restored to high standing among mathematicians by a significant clarification of its basic concepts and by its relation to measure theory, a branch of mathematics that goes back to Euclid and that early in this century was greatly extended and generalized by the French mathematicians Émile Borel and Henri Lebesgue. To understand and appre-

ciate this development let us start with a celebrated problem in geometrical probability known as the Buffon needle problem. If a needle of a certain length (say four inches) is thrown at random on a floor made of planks wider than that length (say eight inches wide), what is the probability that the needle will fall across a crack between two planks? We can define the position of the needle at each throw by noting the location of the midpoint of the needle on a plank and the angle between the needle and a given crack [*see upper illustration at left*]. Now, we can also show the various possible positions of the needle by means of an abstract diagram in the form of a rectangle [*see lower illustration at left*], in which the height represents the width of the plank and the base represents the angle (in terms of π, with π equal to 180 degrees, $\pi/2$ equal to 90 degrees and so on).

This rectangle as a whole, whose area is πd, represents all the possible positions in which the needle can fall. Technically it is called the "sample space," a general term used to denote all the possible outcomes in any probability experiment. (In tossing 10 coins the sample space is the set of all the 1,024 possible 10-item sequences of heads and/or tails.) In the needle experiment what part of the area of the rectangle corresponds to those positions of the needle in which it crosses a crack? This can be calculated by simple trigonometry, and it is represented by two sections within the rectangle with curved boundaries. Their combined area, which can be calculated by elementary calculus, turns out to be 2 times l, the length of the needle.

Now, if all the possible positions of the needle are equally likely, then the probability of the needle falling on a crack is the ratio of the dark colored areas in the illustration to the total area of the rectangle, or $2l/\pi d$. This is where the theory stumbles over its own arbitrary assumption. There is really no compelling reason to treat all the points in this abstract rectangle as equally likely, but the assumption is so natural as to appear inevitable. The degree of arbitrariness was dramatized by the French mathematician J. L. F. Bertrand, who devised examples (known as Bertrand paradoxes) in which, from assumptions that seemed equally natural, he could obtain quite different answers to a probability problem.

This was an unhappy situation, and a deeper understanding of the role and of the nature of probabilistic assumptions

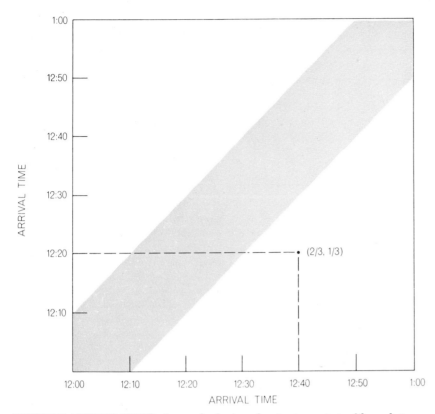

POSSIBLE ARRIVAL TIMES of two suburbanites planning to meet at a library between 12:00 noon and 1:00 P.M. can be plotted. Arrival times for one person are on the vertical scale, for the other on the horizontal scale. Colored area covers region corresponding to a meeting. In order to meet they must arrive at library within 10 minutes of each other. As can be seen, if one arrives at 12:20 (a third of the way up) and the other at 12:40 (two-thirds of the way across), they will not meet. The (1/3, 2/3) point falls outside the shaded region.

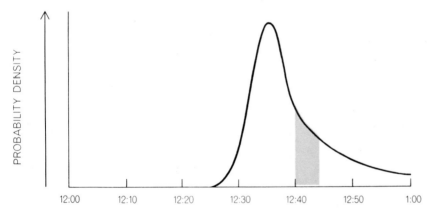

PROBABILITY-DENSITY CURVE illustrates degree of unpredictability of arrival time if there is only one train, coming in at 12:20. Most likely meeting time at library is 12:35. Area of shaded portion represents probability of arrival between 12:40 and 12:44 P.M.

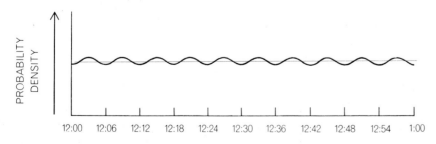

TRAINS ARRIVING EVERY SIX MINUTES give density curve shown by black line. The colored straight line is the "curve" in case all the arrival times are equally likely.

was called for. I can best explain the modern view of these matters by means of another example.

Suppose two friends living in different suburbs of New York City want to meet in front of the Forty-second Street Public Library at noontime. Railroad schedules (and performance) being what they are, the friends can only count on arriving sometime between 12:00 noon and 1:00 P.M. They agree to show up at the library somewhere in that interval, with the stipulation that, in order not to waste too much time waiting, each will wait only 10 minutes after arriving and then leave if the other has not shown up. What is the probability of their actually meeting?

I should mention that, although this case is admittedly artificial, it is by no means a trivial problem. Extended to many members instead of just two, it is analogous to (but far simpler than) an important unsolved problem in statistical mechanics whose solution would shed much light on the theory of changes of states of matter—for instance, from solid to liquid.

If we assume that each of the two friends may arrive anytime between 12:00 and 1:00, we can plot a geometrical "sample space" as in the Buffon needle problem. One person's possible times of arrival are denoted on the x axis, the other's on the y axis [*see top illustration on this page*]. We can then designate every possible pair of arrival times by a point in the square graph. Those points that lie within the part of the square that represents arrival times no more than 10 minutes apart will signify a meeting; all the other points will mean "no meeting." Taking the ratio of the two areas as the probability, as in the needle problem, we can calculate that the probability of the two friends meeting is 11/36—not quite one chance in three.

This case makes clear that we have made two different assumptions. Let us analyze them in a more general context.

In very general terms probability theory, as a mathematical discipline, is concerned with the problem of calculating the probabilities of complex events consisting of collections of "elementary" events whose probabilities are known or postulated. For example, in rolling two dice the appearance of a 10 is a "complex" event that consists of three elementary events: (1) the first die shows a 4 and the second a 6, (2) the first die shows a 5 and the second a 5 and

(3) the first die shows a 6 and the second a 4. The meeting of our two friends is also a complex event; an example of an elementary event would be the arrival of one of the friends in the interval between 12:20 and 12:25.

In our calculation of the probability of the two friends meeting, the first assumption we made was that each of the two individuals may arrive anytime between 12:00 and 1:00, all times of arrival being "equally likely." (The corresponding assumption about the dice is that any one of the six faces of each die may come up with equal probability.) But if each person is limited to only one train scheduled to arrive at Grand Central during the hour (say at 12:20 or later), this assumption is completely unrealistic: he will certainly not arrive in the early part of the hour. The situation corresponds to the two dice being load-

ed. On the other hand, if there are six scheduled trains, due to arrive at 10-minute intervals from 12:00 on, and if they tend to be haphazardly off schedule, the assumption becomes more reasonable, although it may still not be strictly correct to say that all the times of arrival are equally probable.

The second assumption we made was that the arrival times of the two friends are completely independent of each other. This assumption, like the first, is of crucial importance. In mathematical terms it is reflected in the rule of the multiplication of probabilities. This rule states that when individual events are independent of each other, the probability of the complex event that *all* of them will occur is the product of individual probabilities. (Actually from a strictly logical point of view the rule of the multiplication of probabilities constitutes a *definition* of independence.) Independence is assumed in the throw of two dice (which presumably are not linked in any way) as well as in the case of the two suburbanites coming into New York (provided that they have not "coupled" their arrival times by an understanding about the selection of particular trains).

It should be noted that there is an important difference between the dice-throwing and suburbanite-meeting problems. In the first case the number of possible outcomes is finite (just 36), whereas in the second it is infinite, in the sense that the arrival times may occur at any instant within the hour; that is to say, the sample space is a continuum with an infinite number of "points."

To enable one to go on with calculations of probabilities two very general rules, or axioms, are introduced. The first concerns mutually exclusive events: events such that the occurrence of one precludes the occurrence of any other. For such events the probability that at least one will occur is the *sum* of individual probabilities (the axiom of additivity). The second concerns pairs of events such that one *implies* the other. In this case the probability that one will occur but not the other is obtained by subtracting the smaller probability from the larger.

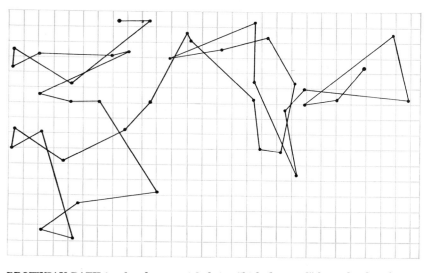

BROWNIAN PATH is taken by a particle being "kicked around" by molecules of a surrounding liquid or gas. A stochastic process (it varies continuously with time), Brownian motion can be analyzed and modeled (*illustration below*) by probabilistic techniques.

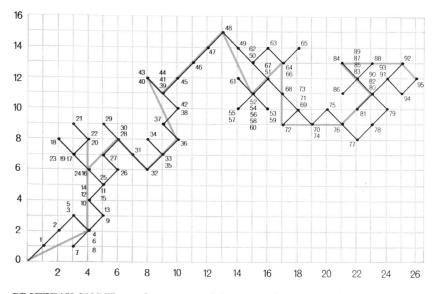

BROWNIAN MODEL can be constructed from records of coin tosses. Two series of 90-odd tosses of a coin were used, one plotted on the horizontal scale, the other on the vertical scale. The cumulative total of tails at each toss was subtracted from the cumulative total of heads. The first three tosses in both series were heads and the fourth toss in the horizontal series was heads, but the fourth toss in the vertical series was tails. Numbers on the dots are the toss numbers. Colored line traces "position" at every fourth toss, just as the track of a Brownian particle recorded by a camera shows only a small fraction of the staggering number of "kicks" such a particle receives from molecules around it.

Now, these rules for calculating probabilities of complex events are identical with those used for calculating areas and volumes in geometry. We can substitute the word "set" for "event" and "area" or "volume" for "probability." The problem then is to assign appropriate areas to sets, and this is the province of measure theory, which has been given that name because the word "measure" is now used to refer to areas of very complex sets.

If we go back to the problem of the two suburbanite friends, we note that the set that corresponds to their meeting is quite simple. Its area, or probability, is well within Euclid's framework, and its calculation can be based on the manipulation of only a finite number of nonoverlapping rectangles. In the Buffon needle problem, since the region of interest is bounded by curves, one must allow an infinite number of rectangles, but the calculation of the area is still relatively simple and requires nothing more than elementary calculus. What was surprising and exciting about measure theory as it was de-

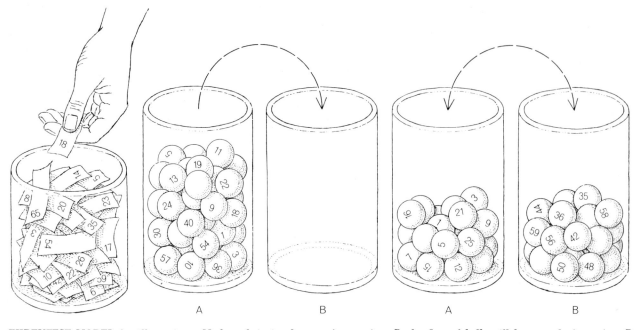

EHRENFEST MODEL for illustrating a Markov chain involves a game in which balls are moved from one container to another according to numbers drawn at random from a third container (*left*). As long as there are many more balls in container *A* than in container *B*, the flow of balls will be strongly from *A* to *B*. The probability of finding in *A* the ball with the drawn number changes in a way that depends on past drawings. This form of dependence of probability on past events is called a Markov chain.

PLAYED ON A COMPUTER, an Ehrenfest game with 16,384 hypothetical balls and 200,000 drawings took just two minutes. Starting with all the balls in container *A*, the number of balls in *A* was recorded with a dot every 1,000 drawings. It declined exponentially until equilibrium was reached with 8,192 balls (half of them) in each container. After that fluctuations were not great.

veloped by Borel and Lebesgue was that, by merely postulating that the measure of an *infinite* collection of unconnected sets should be the *sum* of the measures of the individual ones (corresponding to requiring that the probability that at least one out of *infinitely many* mutually exclusive events will occur should be the sum of individual probabilities), it was possible to assign measures to extremely complex sets.

Because of this, measure theory opened the way to the posing and solving of problems in probability that would have been unthinkable in Laplace's time. Here, for instance, is one of the problems that received much attention in the 1920's and 1930's and contributed greatly to bringing probability theory into the mainstream of mathematics.

Consider the infinite series

$$\frac{1}{1} + \frac{1}{2} + \frac{1}{3} + \frac{1}{4} + \frac{1}{5} + \frac{1}{6} + \frac{1}{7} + \frac{1}{8} + \cdots$$

This is known as a diverging series; that is, by adding more and more terms one could exceed any given number.

Suppose the signs between the terms, instead of being all pluses, were made plus or minus at random by means of independent tosses of an honest coin. What is the probability that the resulting series would converge? That is to say, what is the probability that by extending the series to more and more terms one would come closer and closer to some terminating number?

To answer the question one must consider all the possible infinite sequences of heads and tails as the sample space. One sequence might begin: *H H T T T H T H*.... If we let *H* represent plus and *T* represent minus, the number series above becomes

$$+\frac{1}{1} + \frac{1}{2} - \frac{1}{3} - \frac{1}{4} - \frac{1}{5} + \frac{1}{6} - \frac{1}{7} + \frac{1}{8} \cdots$$

With each such sequence we can associate a real number, t, between 0 and 1, and each t can be represented by a binary number in which the digit 1 denotes H and the digit 0 stands for T. The sequence cited above is then written as $t = .11000101\ldots$. The binary digits form a model of independent tosses of a coin. Now those t's that will yield convergent series form a set, and the probability that t falls into this set is the "measure" of the set. It turns out that the set of hypothetical t's that do *not* yield convergent series is so sparse that its measure, or probability, is zero

(although the set has a very complex structure and is far from being empty). Hence the answer to the problem is that, when the series above is given random signs, the probability that it will converge is 1.

The foregoing is an example of problems in "denumerable probabilities," that is, those involving events described in discrete terms. During the past two decades mathematicians have pursued an even more productive investigation of the theory of "stochastic processes": the probabilistic analysis of phenomena that vary continuously in time. Stochastic processes arise in physics, astronomy, economics, genetics, ecology and many other fields of science. The simplest and most celebrated example of a stochastic process is the Brownian motion of a particle.

The late Norbert Wiener conceived the idea of basing the theory of Brownian motion on a theory of measure in a set of all continuous paths. This idea proved enormously fruitful for probability theory. It breathed new life into old problems such as that of determining the electrostatic potential of a conductor of "arbitrary" shape, a problem that occupied the minds of illustrious mathematicians for more than a century. More than that, it opened up entire new areas of research and led to fascinating connections between probability theory and other branches of mathematics.

A single article can only touch on a few of the main developments and sample problems in probability theory. The subject today embraces vast new fields such as information theory, the theory of queues, diffusion theory and mathematical statistics. One can sum up the position of probability in general by observing that it has become both an indispensable tool of the engineer and a thriving branch of pure mathematics now raised to a high level of formalism and rigor.

I want to close with a brief comment on the philosophical aspect of probability theory (in itself a vast subject on which many volumes have been written). The philosophical implications can be best illustrated by a specific case, and the one I shall discuss has to do with a conflict between the thermodynamic and the mechanical views of the behavior of matter.

Consider two containers, one containing gas, the other a vacuum. If the two containers are connected by a tube

and a valve in the tube is suddenly opened, what happens? According to the second law of thermodynamics, gas rushes from container A into container B at an exponential rate until the pressure in the two containers is the same. This is an expression of the law of increasing entropy, which in its most pessimistic form predicts that ultimately all matter and energy in the universe will even out and settle down to what Rudolf Clausius, one of the fathers of the second law, called *Wärmetod* (heat death).

Now, the mechanical, or kinetic, view of matter pictures the situation in an entirely different way. True, the molecules of gas will tend to move from the region of higher pressure into the one of lower pressure, but the movement is not merely one-way. Bouncing against the walls and against one another, the molecules will take off in random directions, and those that travel into container B will be as likely to wander back to container A as to remain where they are. As a matter of fact, Poincaré showed in a mathematical theorem that a dynamical system such as this one would eventually return arbitrarily close to its original state, with all or virtually all the gas molecules back in container A.

In 1907 Paul and Tatiana Ehrenfest illustrated this idea with a simple and beautiful probabilistic model. Consider two containers, A and B, with a large number of numbered balls in A and none in B. From a container filled with numbered slips of paper pick a numeral at random (say 6) and then transfer the ball marked with that number from container A to container B. Put the slip of paper back and go on playing the game this way, each time drawing at random a number between 1 and N (the total number of balls originally in container A) and moving the ball of that number from the container where it happens to be to the other container [*see upper illustration on page 172*].

It is intuitively clear that as long as there are many more balls in A than there are in B the probability of drawing a number that corresponds to a ball in A will be considerably higher than vice versa. Thus the flow of balls at first will certainly be strongly from A to B. As the drawings continue, the probability of finding the drawn number in A will change in a way that depends on the past drawings. This form of dependence of probability on past events is called a Markov chain, and in the game we are considering, all pertinent facts can be explicitly and rigorously deduced. It turns out that, on an averaging basis, the number of balls in container A will indeed decrease at an exponential rate, as the thermodynamic theory predicts, until about half of the balls are in container B. But the calculation also shows that if the game is played long enough, then, with probability equal to 1, all the balls will eventually wind up back in container A, as Poincaré's theorem says!

How long, on the average, would it take to return to the initial state? The answer is 2^N drawings, which is a staggeringly large number even if the total number of balls (N) is as small as 100. This explains why behavior in nature, as we observe it, moves only in one direction instead of oscillating back and forth. The entire history of man is piti-

fully short compared with the time it would take for nature to reverse itself.

To test the theoretical calculations experimentally, the Ehrenfest game was played on a high-speed computer. It began with 16,384 "balls" in container A, and each run consisted of 200,000 drawings (which took less than two minutes on the computer). A curve was drawn showing the number of balls in A on the basis of the number recorded after every 1,000 drawings [*see lower illustration on page 172*]. As was to be expected, the curve of decline in the number of balls in A was almost perfectly exponential. After the number nearly reached the equilibrium level (that is, 8,192, or half the original number) the curve became wiggly, moving randomly up and down around that number. The wiggles were somewhat exaggerated by the vagaries of the ma-

chine itself, but they represented actual fluctuations that were bound to occur in the number of balls in A.

Those small, capricious fluctuations are models of the variability in nature and are all that stands between us and the heat death to which we are seemingly condemned by the second law of thermodynamics! Probability theory has reconciled the apparent conflict between the thermodynamic and the kinetic views of nature by showing that there is no real contradiction between them if the second law is interpreted flexibly. In fact, the development of the theory of probability in the 20th century has changed our attitudes to such an extent that we no longer expect the laws of nature to be construed rigidly or dogmatically.

25 STATISTICS

WARREN WEAVER · January 1952

Statistical thinking will one day be as necessary for efficient citizenship as the ability to read and write.
—H. G. Wells

THERE are two main forms of logical thinking—deduction and induction. For the former we are chiefly indebted to the Greeks, who first saw clearly revealed the great power of announcing general axioms or assumptions and deducing from these a useful array of implied propositions Inductive thinking, which has been called "the second great stage of intellectual liberation," did not begin to become a systematic tool of man until late in the 18th century. Induction proceeds in the opposite direction from deduction. Starting from the facts of experience, it leads us to infer general conclusions.

Deductive reasoning is definite and absolute. Its specific inferences follow inescapably from the general assumptions. Inductive reasoning, on the other hand, is uncertain inference. The concrete and special facts of experience, from which inductive reasoning begins, generally do not lead inexorably to categorical general conclusions. Rather they lead to judgments concerning the plausibility of various general conclusions.

Francis Bacon was the first properly to emphasize inductive methods as the basis of scientific procedure, but it was not until 1763 that the English clergyman Thomas Bayes gave the first mathematical basis to this branch of logic. To get an idea of what Bayes did, let us look at an admittedly artificial example. Suppose you have a closed box containing a large number of black and white balls. You do not know the proportion of black to white but have reason to think that the odds are two to one that there are about equal numbers of black and white balls. You reach into this box, take out a sample of balls and find that three fourths of the sample are black. Now before taking this sample you tended strongly to think that the unknown mixture was half white, half black. After taking the sample you clearly should

change your thinking and begin to lean toward the view that black balls outnumber the white in the box. Bayes worked out a theorem which indicates exactly how opinions held before the experiment should be modified by the evidence of the sample. Though the usefulness of this theorem itself has proved to be very limited, it was the beginning of the whole modern theory of statistics, and thus of a mathematical theory of inductive reasoning.

WHAT'S this, you will say; is statistics something as general and profound as all that? Isn't statistics merely the name for the numerical information with which propagandists try to convince and sometimes even to confuse us?

The word statistics has two somewhat different meanings. In familiar usage, to be sure, statistics does mean simply numerical information, usually arranged in tables or graphs. It is in this sense that we say *The World Almanac* contains a great deal of useful statistics. But more broadly, and more technically, statistics is the name for that science and art which deals with uncertain inference—which uses numbers to find out something about nature and experience.

The importance of inductive reasoning depends on the basic fact that, apart from trivial exceptions, the events and phenomena of nature are too multiform, too numerous, too extensive or too inaccessible to permit complete observation. As the author of *Ecclesiastes* remarked, "No man can find out the work that God maketh from the beginning to the end." We can't measure cosmic rays everywhere and all the time. We can't try a new drug on everybody. We can't test every shell or bomb we manufacture—for one thing, there would then be none to use. So we have to content ourselves with samples. The measurements involved in every scientific experiment constitute a sample of that unlimited set of measurements which would result if one performed the same experiment over and over indefinitely. This total set of potential measurements is referred to as

the population. Almost always one is interested in the sample only insofar as it is capable of revealing something about the population from which it came.

The four principal questions to be asked about samples are these: 1) How can one describe the sample usefully and clearly? 2) From the evidence of this sample how does one best infer conclusions concerning the total population? 3) How reliable are these conclusions? 4) How should samples be taken in order that they may be as illuminating and dependable as possible?

Question 1 pretty well covers the subject matter of elementary statistics. Tables, graphs, bar and pie diagrams and the schematic pictorial representations which can be so useful (and sometimes so deceptive) are all ways of summarizing the evidence of a sample. Averages and other related quantities—arithmetical means, medians, modes, geometric means, harmonic means, quartiles, deciles, and so on—are useful for similar purposes; and these also must be used with discretion if they are to be really illuminating. The arithmetical mean income of a certain Princeton class five years after graduation, for example, is not a very useful figure if the class happens to include one man who has an income of half a million dollars.

Descriptive statistics of this sort is concerned with broad and vague questions like "What's going on here?"; and the answers returned are a not unworthy example of "doing one's damndest with one's mind, no holds barred," to use Percy W. Bridgman's phrase. It is only when we pass to Questions 2, 3 and 4, however, that we get to the heart of modern mathematical statistics.

THESE three questions have to do with different aspects of one common problem: namely, how much can one learn, and how reliably, about a population by taking and analyzing a sample from that population? First of all, what sort of knowledge about a population is possible?

Remember that a population, as one

uses the word in statistics, is a collection —usually a large or even infinite collection—of numbers which are measurements of something. It is not possible in the case of an infinite collection, and usually not feasible in other cases, to describe one at a time all the individual measurements that make up the population. So what one does is to lump similar or nearly similar measurements together, describing the population by telling what fraction of all measurements are of this approximate size, what fraction of that size, and so on. This is done by stating in a table, a graph or a formula just what fraction of the whole population of values fall within any stated interval of values. When this is done graphically, the result is a frequency curve, which describes the distribution of measurements in the population in question. The most widely useful population distribution is the so-called normal or Gaussian probability distribution, which takes the form of the familiar bell-shaped curve. A frequency curve can, of course, be described by stating its mathematical equation.

It is frequently useful to give a condensed description of a distribution. If circumstances make it necessary to be content with only two items of information, then one would usually choose the average (which the statistician calls the arithmetical mean) and the variance. The variance is defined as the average of the squares of the differences between all measurements of the population and the mean of the population. It is a very useful measure of the degree of scatter of the measurements, being relatively small when the distribution clusters closely about the mean and relatively large when the distribution is a widely spread-out one. The square root of the variance is called the standard deviation. A small variance always means, of course, a small standard deviation, and *vice versa*.

The statistician's shorthand usually denotes the arithmetical mean by the Greek letter mu, the variance by sigma squared and the standard deviation by sigma. In the special case of normal distributions, a knowledge of the mean, mu, and of the standard deviation, sigma, is sufficient to pick out of all possible normal distributions the specific one in question. Thus the mathematical formula for the normal distribution curve need involve, in addition to the variable, just the two quantities mu and sigma. More complicated distributions may depend upon more than two.

Using the notions just introduced, we can now restate our last three questions:

2) Using the evidence of a sample, what can one say about the population distribution?

3) How can one characterize the reliability of these estimates?

4) How can one select the sample so as to produce the most reliable estimates?

BEFORE going on to indicate the kind of answer modern statistical theory can give to these three questions, it would be well to stop a moment to consider once more, and somewhat more accurately now, the relation between the descriptive statistician who deals only with our original Question 1, and the mathematical statistician who deals with Questions 2, 3 and 4.

In seeking to summarize and describe a sample, the descriptive statistician is in fact trying to shed some light, however dim and indirect, on the nature of the population. Thus he is often trying to give some sort of informal and loose answer to Question 2; and he frequently succeeds in a really useful way. He differs from the mathematical statistician in that he uses only elementary mathematical tools and is therefore unable to give any really precise answers to Question 2 or any answers at all to Questions 3 and 4.

The problem of drawing inferences concerning a population from a sample is a problem in probability. There is an obvious analogy between this procedure and the artificial case of sampling the box of colored balls. It is important to remember that when you take a sample of colored balls out of an unknown mixture, you cannot make simple probability statements about the mixture unless you start out by having some idea about what is in the box. In technical terms, this means that you have to have knowledge, before the drawing of the sample, of the *a priori* probabilities of all possible mixtures that might be in the box. As we have mentioned earlier, Bayes' theorem furnishes a basis for modifying this prior opinion, but it is powerless to originate an opinion.

Bayes' theorem furnishes a sound and simple procedure. But unfortunately it is very seldom applicable to really serious problems of statistical theory, for the good reason that in such situations one seldom has any positive knowledge of the *a priori* probabilities. Consequently it is necessary for statistics to take recourse to more complicated and more subtle theorems.

It is evident that the statistician can never say for certain what the parent population is merely by sampling it, because the samples will vary. If, for example, you draw from a mixture containing 60 per cent white balls and 40 per cent black, you will by no means get this 60-40 ratio of white to black in every sample you take. However, for a given kind of parent population and with suitable methods of sampling it is possible to work out theoretically the pattern of variation for samples. This knowledge of the pattern of sample variability gives the statistician a toe hold. It permits him

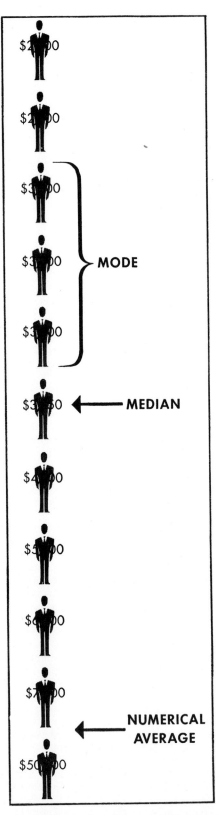

ELEVEN SALARIES illustrate how a single number may be used to characterize a set of numbers. The numerical average of the salaries ($8,159) is heavily influenced by one very large salary ($50,000). Hence the average is not as representative of this set of numbers as the median (the salary in the middle) or the mode (the salary that occurs most often).

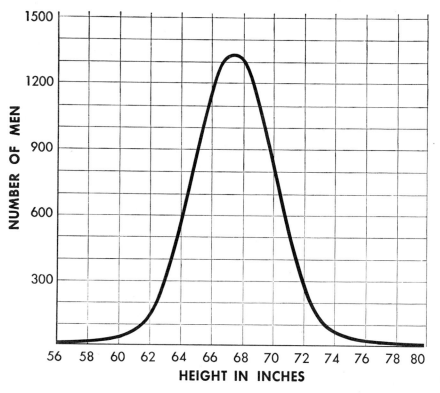

FREQUENCY DISTRIBUTION OF HEIGHT for 8,585 men is expressed as a normal distribution curve. The actual points from which the curve was derived are not shown, but only a theoretical approximation of them.

to look at samples and draw inferences about the parent population.

The pattern of variation depends not only on the population being sampled; it also depends sensitively upon the method of sampling. If you were interested in family sizes in the U. S. and took your evidence solely from houses with eight rooms or more, obviously the sample pattern would be atypical. When samples are deliberately selected in an atypical way, we call that rigging the evidence. But often samples have quite innocently been taken in an atypical way, as Mr. George Gallup will remember.

It turns out that in general the only good method of sampling is a random method. In a random method the sample is picked in accordance with purely probabilistic criteria, personal choice or prejudice being completely excluded. Suppose television tubes are passing an inspector on a moving belt and it is desired to test on the average one of every six tubes in a random way. The inspector could throw two dice each time a tube passed him and take off the tube for test only when he threw a double number. This, of course, would happen on the average once in six throws of the dice. The tubes thus selected would be a random sample of the whole population of tubes.

NOW we must note an important fact about the pattern of variation of random samples. Suppose you have a parent population which is normally distributed, with a certain mean value and a certain standard deviation. Suppose you take from this population random samples consisting of a certain number of items, n. Compute the mean for each sample. You will find that this new population of means is normally distributed, just as the parent population was. Because an averaging process has entered in, it is more tightly clustered than was the original population. In fact, its standard deviation is found by dividing the standard deviation of the parent population by the square root of n, the number of items in each sample. Thus if the samples each contain 64 items, the standard deviation of the means of these samples will be one eighth of the standard deviation of the parent population.

The fact that samples from a normal population have means which are themselves normally distributed tells us that normally distributed populations have a kind of reproductive character. Their offspring (samples) inherit their most important character (normality). And it is comforting to know further that if large samples are taken from almost any kind of population, their means also have almost normal distributions.

The importance of sample pattern can easily be illustrated by a concrete example in manufacturing. A manufacturer makes large numbers of a part which in one dimension should measure one inch with high accuracy. Random samples of the product are measured. If the sam-

ples consistently average more than one inch, he knows there is some systematic error in his manufacturing procedure. But if the mean of the samples is just an inch, and the variations from the mean fall into the pattern of distribution which is theoretically to be expected when the parent population itself is normally distributed about an average of one inch, the manufacturer can conclude that systematic errors have been eliminated, and that his manufacturing process is "under control."

Sampling is not merely convenient; it is often the only possible way to deal with a problem. In the social sciences particularly it opens up fields of inquiry which would otherwise be quite inaccessible. The British Ministry of Labor was able to carry out a most useful study of working-family budgets for the entire nation from detailed figures on the expenditures of only 9,000 families over a period of four weeks. Without sampling such studies would be wholly impracticable.

TO return to our main argument. We are now better prepared to deal with Questions 2 and 3. (We shall omit Question 4, on the design of experiments, because it is a large subject that would make this article far too long.)

Suppose that the mean lifetime of a certain type of electronic tube is known to be 10,000 hours and the standard deviation 800 hours. The engineers now develop a new design of tube. A sample of 64 of the new-type tubes is tested, and the mean life of the 64 tubes in the sample is found to be 10,200 hours—200 hours longer than the mean life of the old population.

Now the new design may actually be no longer-lived than the old. In that case the sample of 64 just happened to be a somewhat better than average sample. Clearly what the engineers want to know is whether the apparent improvement of 200 hours is real or merely due to a chance variation.

The amount of variation one expects from chance can be estimated by comparing the actual deviation with the standard deviation. Since the standard deviation of the means of samples of 64 items is one eighth the standard deviation of the parent population, in this case the standard deviation in the means of such samples would be one eighth of 800, or 100 hours. Hence the apparent improvement of 200 hours in our sample of new-type tubes is twice the standard deviation in the means of such samples.

Probability theory tells the statistician that the odds are 19 to 1 against a difference of this size between the sample and population means occurring merely by chance. He therefore reports: "It seems sensible to conclude that this mildly rare event has not occurred, that on the contrary the sample of 64 in fact came from a new population with a higher mean life. In other words, I conclude that the new design is probably an improvement."

This is one of the common ways of dealing with such a situation. There are various rather complicated and subtle weaknesses in the argument just given, but we need not go into them here. A more satisfactory way of dealing with the same problem would be to apply the modern theory of statistical estimation, which involves the use of so-called confidence intervals and confidence coefficients. Here the statistician proceeds as follows: He says that the sample of 64 tubes comes from a new population which, while assumed normal, has an unknown mean and variance; and he very much wants to know something about the mean of this population, for that information will help him to conclude whether the new design is an improvement.

Now we must remember that statistics deals with uncertain inference. We must not expect the statistician to come to an absolutely firm conclusion. We must expect him always to give a two-part answer to our question. One part of this reply goes: "My best estimate is. . . ." The inescapable other part of his reply is: "The degree of confidence which you are justified in placing in my estimate is. . . ."

Thus we are not surprised that the statistician starts out by choosing a number which he calls a confidence coefficient. He might, for example, choose the confidence coefficient .95. This means that he is about to adopt a course of action which will be right 95 per cent of the time on the average. We therefore know how much confidence we are justified in placing in his results. Having decided on this figure, statistical theory now furnishes him with the width of a

so-called confidence interval whose midpoint is the mean of the sample. In our example this interval turns out to be 10,200 plus or minus 195 hours, or from 10,005 to 10,395 hours. The statistician then answers Questions 2 and 3 as follows: "I estimate that the mean of the population of lifetimes of new-design tubes is greater than 10,005 hours and less than 10,395 hours. I can't guarantee that I am correct; but in a long series of such statements I will be right 95 per cent of the time. Since this range is above the mean life of the old tubes, I conclude that the new design is probably an improvement."

If the statistician had originally decided to adopt a procedure that would be correct 99 per cent of the time, his confidence interval would have turned out wider. He could make a less precise statement but make it with greater confidence. Conversely, he could arrange to make a more precise statement with somewhat less confidence.

Finally, let us examine this same question in the still more sophisticated manner that goes under the name "testing of statistical hypotheses." Here one starts by making some sort of guess about the situation, and then goes through a statistical argument to find out whether it is sensible, and how sensible, to discard this guess or retain it.

Thus the statistician might tentatively assume that the new design is equivalent to the old in average tube life. Of course he hopes that this is not true. Although it sounds a little perverse, it is in fact customary to start with a hypothesis that one hopes to disprove.

Here, just as in the previous case, the statistician first picks out a number which is going to tell what confidence we dare have in his statements. Actually he uses something which might be called an "unconfidence coefficient," for it

measures the per cent of the time he expects to be wrong, rather than the per cent he expects to be right.

This unconfidence coefficient is technically called the significance level. Let us say that the statistician chooses a significance level of .05, which is exactly equivalent to .95 as a confidence coefficient. Then he calculates the confidence interval for this confidence coefficient. Since we have the same confidence coefficient as before, we already know that this particular confidence interval reaches from 10,005 hours to 10,395 hours. The statistician then reports: "The mean life of the old population (10,000 hours) does not fall within my confidence interval. Therefore theory tells me to discard the assumed hypothesis that the new tube has the same average lifetime as the old. The assumed hypothesis may of course actually be true. But theory further tells me that in cases in which the hypothesis is true, and in which I proceed as I just have done, I will turn out to make mistakes only 5 per cent of the time."

This report, if one thinks it over carefully, is rather incomplete. It says something about the probability of one sort of error—the error of discarding the hypothesis when it is in fact true. But it says nothing about another sort of error—accepting the hypothesis when it is in fact false. In certain situations one of these two mistakes might be very dangerous and costly and the other relatively innocuous. There are available still more refined statistical procedures (called the Neyman-Pearson methods and the theory of decision functions) in which one designs the test so as to make a desirable compromise with respect to the probabilities of the two types of error.

IV

THE
FOUNDATIONS
OF
MATHEMATICS

THE FOUNDATIONS OF MATHEMATICS

INTRODUCTION

At almost every stage in the history of mathematics mathematicians faced crises. These arose from the manner in which mathematics was built.

The structure of present day mathematics may be likened roughly to that of a skyscraper. However when mathematicians first began the structure, they did not excavate and sink a deep foundation. Rather they built directly on the surface of the earth. It was reasonable to do this because no one at that time envisioned a tall structure and the earth itself seemed to offer a secure base. Moreover the material with which they commenced construction—facts about numbers and geometrical figures—seemed to be solidly grounded in simple earthly experiences. This historical origin of mathematics is still manifest in our continuing use of the word geometry, which means to measure land.

But as the structure began to rise above the ground it became obvious that it was shaky and that further additions to it might imperil the building. It was the Greeks of the classical period (the period from 600 to 300 B.C.) who not only saw the danger but supplied the necessary strengthening. They suggested two measures. The first was to select firm strips of ground along which one could run the walls. These strips were the self-evident truths of nature. The second was to put steel into the framework. The steel was deductive proof of each addition to the structure.

Insofar as mathematics was developed in Greek times, the structure, consisting mainly of Euclidean geometry, proved to be stable. One fault did show up, namely, that certain line segments such as the diagonal of an isosceles right triangle whose arms are 1 unit long would have to have a length of $\sqrt{2}$ units. Because the only numbers that the Greeks knew were the ordinary whole numbers, they would not accept as numbers such entities as $\sqrt{2}$. They resolved the dilemma by ostracizing these irrational "numbers" and abandoned the idea of assigning lengths to line segments.

However the events of history forced a reconsideration of this decision. First of all, about the year 600 A.D. the Hindus introduced negative numbers. Then the Arabs, less fastidious than the Greeks, not only accepted irrational numbers but even developed rules for operating with them. The Renaissance Europeans, who had adopted the mathematics of the Greeks, Hindus, and Arabs, balked at accepting both of these foreign elements. But at this time in the history of Europe, science began to flourish and the Europeans found, as had the Greeks, that mathematics was vital in the scientific enterprise. Moreover the new science was applied to technology and for such applications quantitative results were indispensable. Reluctantly the Europeans began to apply negative numbers and irrational numbers and, as they accomplished more and more with them, they overcame their logical scruples and used these numbers freely. However, as they added this extension of arithmetic and algebra to the mathematical structure, they used intuitive and physical beams where the Greeks had used steel in the lower floors. Nevertheless the enlarged structure housed the ideas firmly, and the opposition to negative and irrational numbers collapsed.

Heady with success, the mathematicians rushed into the calculus, differential equations, differential geometry, the calculus of variations, and other branches of analysis while constantly using intuitive and physical arguments to support these additions. The doubts that were expressed about the soundness of the construction were silenced by exhortations, such as d'Alembert's "Persist and faith will come to you." But intuition proved unequal to the burden placed upon it and cracks began to show in the walls. The nature of these faults is described in Hahn's article. Fortunately, through the work of Bernhard Bolzano, Augustin Louis Cauchy, and Karl Weierstrass, the superstructure was rebuilt. This work is referred to in the history of mathematics as the rigorization of analysis.

While the superstructure was being strengthened, the ground under the walls—the axioms chosen by the Greeks—caved in. The creation of non-Euclidean geometry revealed that the axioms of Euclidean geometry were not solid ground but only seemed to be so on superficial inspection. Nor were the axioms of the non-Euclidean geometries any more solidly grounded. What the mathematicians thought to be the reality of nature, believing that their minds gave unfailing support for this cognition, proved to be unreliable sense data.

To add to their troubles, William R. Hamilton (see Whittaker's article in Section II), seeking an algebra to represent vectors in space, created a new kind of number, quaternions. Prior to this creation every mathematician would have sworn that for any kinds of numbers a and b, $a \cdot b$ must equal $b \cdot a$, but this did not prove to be true for quaternions. Nor was it true for matrices, which were created about fifteen years later. Now the mathematicians began to worry about whether they had been too naive in accepting the properties of ordinary numbers. To their dismay they recalled that when they added negative and irrational numbers to mathematics they had relied upon physical and intuitive arguments. Thus the entire structure of mathematics—geometry and arithmetic with its extensions to algebra and analysis—was in grave peril. The now lofty building was in danger of sinking into a quagmire.

To maintain the house of mathematics called for strong measures, and the mathematicians rose to the occasion. It was clear that there was no solid earth on which to base mathematics, because the seemingly firm ground of truth had proved to be deceptive. But perhaps the structure could be made stable by digging down into the earth and erecting a solid foundation of another kind. This foundation would consist of complete sharply worded axioms and definitions and explicit proof of all results, no matter how obvious they might seem to the intuition. Moreover, in place of truth there was to be logical compatibility, or what the mathematicians called consistency. The theorems were to be tied into and woven into each other so that the entire structure would be solidly knit together. No matter how it rested in relation to the earth it would hold together much as a modern skyscraper rocks with the wind but remains firm from base to tip. The strength of mathematics, then, would lie in its consistency rather than in its truth. The reconstruction which the mathematicians thereupon undertook is known as the axiomatization of mathematics and it is further explained in Quine's article, "The Foundations of Mathematics."

When the reconstruction was completed the mathematicians were immensely cheered up. At an International Congress of Mathematicians, which was held in Paris in 1900, Henri Poincaré, the leading mathematician of his time, proudly proclaimed that perfect rigor had been attained. So the most dire crisis thus far in the history of mathematics was resolved and though mathematics lost some face it had saved its life.

Poincaré was wrong. In the reconstruction of the foundations the mathematicians employed symbolic logic, the nature of which is explained in Pfeiffer's article, to insure precision of language and reasoning. No difficulties arose from this usage. But they also used set theory or the theory of classes, which had been created in the 1880's by Georg Cantor. This theory seemed to provide the clearest and securest starting point for the axiomatic development but it harbored unsuspected defects. At about the very time that Poincaré was pointing with pride to the newly achieved perfection of mathematical rigor, contradictions or logical inconsistencies were discovered in the very theory of sets that had seemed to provide the excellent foundation. Unable to face the harsh reality, the mathematicians euphemistically called these contradictions paradoxes. Just what these paradoxes are can be found in Quine's article "Paradox" and in the latter part of his article on the foundations.

Of course the mathematicians were not going to sit by and see centuries of effort crumble into ruins. Many groups undertook new approaches to the foundations of mathematics, with the resolution of the paradoxes as the central difficulty to be overcome. Since the axiomatization of many branches of mathematics had proved to be a source of strength, it is not surprising to find that the first move was to replace Cantor's rather intuitive construction of set theory by an axiomatic approach to set theory. This movement, begun by E. Zermelo, sought not only to eliminate the paradoxes but to resolve other open questions of set theory, one of these being what is called the continuum hypothesis. However, Zermelo used what is often called the principle of choice, or axiom of choice, and this axiom did not appeal to some mathematicians.

Two questions then assumed considerable importance. The first was whether the refinement of set theory achieved by the axiomatization would be adequate to prove or disprove the continuum hypothesis. The second was whether the axiom of choice was essential to the axiomatization of set theory. The story of what was learned about these two questions is presented in the article by Cohen and Hersh. One of the great results explained in the article was obtained by Cohen himself.

These results in set theory, vital as they are and offering one avenue to the resolution of the paradoxes, did not remove the major concern that was plaguing the mathematicians, namely, "Is mathematics consistent?" The removal of known contradictions did not guarantee that others would not show up. The establishment of the consistency of the several major branches of mathematics became the overriding problem in the foundations of mathematics.

Critical examination of these foundations produced new bones of contention. The legitimacy of infinite sets as entities in themselves, the application of the law of exluded middle to infinite sets, the role of logic in the foundation of mathematics, and, indeed, the whole question of what is the proper foundation of all of mathematics became subjects of dispute. In attempting to resolve these matters, mathematicians adopted strikingly different approaches.

For a time it seemed that the most promising approach led by the greatest of twentieth-century mathematicians, David Hilbert, would resolve all the issues. But this approach was shattered by an astonishing theorem of the logician Kurt Gödel. Just what the theorem states and how it is proved are discussed in detail in the article by Nagel and Newman. Here it may be sufficient to state the key result: a consistent body of mathematics cannot be entirely contained in one axiomatic framework.

It is heart-rending to describe the current state of mathematical rigor and we do not have the courage to do so. The mathematicians have found some slight consolation in the remark of E. H. Moore, "Sufficient unto the day is the rigor thereof." But to avoid despair they have turned to humor, and one hears such quips as, "Logic is the art of going wrong with confidence," and "We can no longer hope to be logical; the best we can hope for is not to be illogical."

Now that logic has defeated logic, like a dog chasing its tail, mathematicians are desperately employing logic to grasp the logic of mathematics. The crises of the past were resolved, though, only by abandoning the truth of mathematics. Perhaps the confutation of the present impasse will be accomplished without sacrificing another cherished feature of the subject. Or perhaps the thought expressed by the precocious Évariste Galois at the age of 19 expresses the position that mathematicians will have to adopt: "Mathematics is the work of the human spirit which is as much destined to study as to know, to seek as to find the truth."

26 GEOMETRY AND INTUITION

HANS HAHN · April 1954

We have grown so accustomed to the revolutionary nature of modern science that any theory which affronts common sense is apt to be regarded today as half proved by that very fact. In the language of science and philosophy the word for common sense is intuition—it relates to that which is directly sensed or apprehended. Twentieth-century discoveries have dealt harshly with our intuitive beliefs about the physical world. The one area that is commonly supposed to remain a stronghold of intuition is mathematics. The Pythagorean theorem is still in pretty good shape; the self-evident truths of mathematics are in the main still true. Yet the fact is that even in mathematics intuition has been taking a beating. Cornered by paradoxes—logical contradictions—arising from old intuitive concepts, modern mathematicians have been forced to reform their thinking and to step out on the uncertain footing of radically new premises.

Some years ago the brilliant Austrian mathematician Hans Hahn surveyed the situation in a Vienna Circle lecture which he titled "The Crisis in Intuition." His analysis is still fresh and timely, and it is published here, in part, for the first time in English. Hahn began with Immanuel Kant, the foremost exponent of the importance of intuition, and showed how the foundations of Kant's ideas about knowledge "have been shaken" by modern science. The intuitive conceptions of space and time were jolted by Einstein's theory of relativity and by advances in physics which proved that the location of an event in space and time cannot be determined with unlimited precision. Hahn went on to consider the demolition of Kant's ideas about mathematics, and he illustrated his theme with the case of geometry, where "intuition was gradually brought into disrepute and finally was completely banished." This section of his lecture, somewhat condensed, follows.

*　　　*　　　*

One of the outstanding events in [the banishment of intuition from geometry] was the discovery that, in apparent contradiction to what had previously been accepted as intuitively certain, there are curves that possess no tangent at any point, or—what amounts to the same thing—that it is possible to imagine a point moving in such a manner that at no instant does it have a definite velocity. The questions involved here directly affect the foundations of the differential calculus as developed by Newton and Leibnitz.

Newton calculated the velocity of a moving point at the instant t as the limiting value approached by the average velocity between t and an instant close to it, t', as t' approaches t without limit. Leibnitz similarly declared that the slope of a curve at a point p is the limiting value approached by the average slope between p and a nearby point p' as p' approaches p without limit.

Now one asks: Is this true for every curve? It is indeed for all the old familiar ones—circles, ellipses, hyperbolas, parabolas, cycloids, etc. But it is not true,

for example, of a wave curve such as is shown here [*Figure 1*]. In the neighborhood of the point p the curve has infinitely many waves. The wavelength and the amplitude of the waves decrease without limit as they approach p. If we take successive points closer and closer to p, the average slope between p and p' (the moving point) drops from plus 1 through 0 to minus 1 and then rises from minus 1 to plus 1. That is, as p' approaches p without limit through infinitely many waves, the average slope between p and p' keeps oscillating between the values 1 and -1. Thus there can be no question of a limit or of a definite slope of the curve at the point p. In other words, the curve we are considering has no tangent at p.

This relatively simple illustration demonstrates that a curve does not have to have a tangent at every point. Nevertheless it used to be thought, intuitively, that such a deficiency could occur only at exceptional points of a curve. It was therefore a great surprise when the great Berlin mathematician Karl Weierstrass announced in 1861 a curve that lacked a precise slope or tangent at *any* point.

Weierstrass invented the curve by an intricate and arduous calculation, which I shall not attempt to reproduce. But his result can today be achieved in a much simpler way, and this I shall attempt to explain, at least in outline.

We start with a simple figure which consists of an ascending and a descending line [*Figure 2*]. We then replace the ascending line with a broken line in six parts, first rising to half the height of the

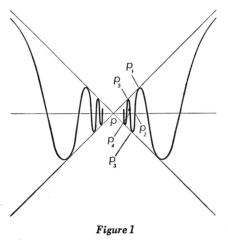

Figure 1

original line, then dropping all the way down, then again rising to half the height, continuing to full height, dropping back again to half height and finally rising once more to full height [*Figure 3*]. We replace the descending line also with a broken line of six similar parts. From this figure of 12 line segments we evolve, again by replacing each segment with a broken line of six parts, a figure of 72 line segments [*Figure 4*]. It is easy to see that repetition of this procedure will lead to more and more complicated figures. It can be demonstrated that the geometric objects constructed according to this rule approach without limit a definite curve possessing the desired property; namely, at no point will it have a precise slope, and hence at no point a tangent. The character of this curve of course entirely eludes intuition; indeed, after a few repetitions of the segmenting process the evolving figure has grown so intricate that intuition can scarcely follow. The fact is that only logical analysis can pursue this strange object to its final form.

Lest it be supposed that intuition fails only in the more complex branches of mathematics, I propose now to examine a failure in the elementary branches. At the very threshold of geometry lies the concept of the curve; everyone believes that he has an intuitively clear notion of what a curve is. Since ancient times it has been held that this idea could be expressed by the following definition: Curves are geometric figures generated by the motion of a point. But attend! In the year 1890 the Italian mathematician Giuseppe Peano (who is also renowned for his investigations in logic) proved that the geometric figures that can be generated by a moving point also include *entire plane surfaces*. For instance, it is possible to imagine a point moving in such a way that in a finite time

it will pass through all the points of a square—and yet no one would consider the entire area of a square as simply a curve. With the aid of a few diagrams I shall attempt to give at least a general idea of how this space-filling motion is generated.

Divide a square into four small squares of equal size and join the center points of these squares by a continuous curve composed of straight-line segments [*Figure 5*]. Now imagine a point moving at uniform velocity so that it will traverse the continuous curve made of these line segments in a certain unit of time. Next divide each of the four squares again into four equal squares so that there are 16 squares, and connect their center points [*Figure 6*]. Imagine the point moving so that in the same time as before it will traverse this second curve at uniform velocity. Repeat the procedure, each time imagining the point to move so that in the same unit of time it will traverse the new system of lines at a uniform velocity. Figure 7 shows one of the later stages, when the original square has been divided into 4,096 small squares. It is now possible to give a rigorous proof that the successive motions considered here approach without limit a curve that takes the moving point through all the points of the large square in the given time. This motion cannot possibly be grasped by intuition; it can only be understood by logical analysis.

While a geometric object such as a square, which no one regards as a curve, can be generated by the motion of a point, other objects which one would not hesitate to classify as curves cannot be so generated. Observe, for instance, the wave curve shown here [*Figure 8*]. In the neighborhood of the line segment *ab* the curve consists of infinitely many waves whose lengths decrease without limit but whose amplitudes do not de-

crease. It is not difficult to prove that this figure, in spite of its linear character, cannot be generated by the motion of a point, for no motion of a point is conceivable that would carry it through all the points of this wave curve in a finite time.

Two important questions now suggest themselves. (1) Since the time-honored definition of a curve fails to cover the fundamental concept, what serviceable definition can be substituted for it? (2) Since the class of geometric objects that can be produced by the motion of a point does not coincide with the class of all curves, how shall the former class be defined? Today both questions are satisfactorily answered; I shall defer for a moment the answer to the first question and speak briefly about the second. This was solved with the aid of a new geometric concept—"connectivity in the small." Consider a line, a circle or a square. In each of these cases, we can move from one point on the figure to another very close to it along a path which does not leave the confines of the figure, and we remain always in close proximity to both points. This is the property called "connectivity in the small." Now the wave curve we have just considered does not have this property. Take for example the neighboring points *p* and *q* [*Figure 9*]. In order to move from *p* to *q* without leaving the curve it is necessary to traverse the infinitely many waves lying between them. The points on this path are not all in close proximity to *p* and *q*, for the waves all have the same amplitude.

It is important to realize that "connectivity in the small" is the basic characteristic of figures that can be generated by the motion of a point. A line, a circle and a square can be generated by the motion of a point because they are connected in the small; the wave figure shown cannot be generated by the mo-

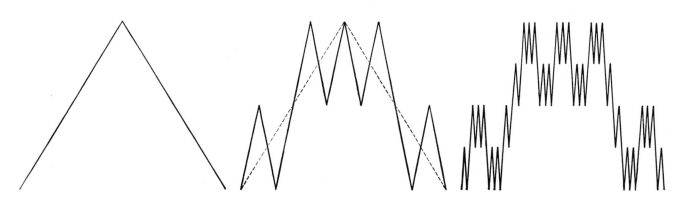

Figure 2   Figure 3   Figure 4

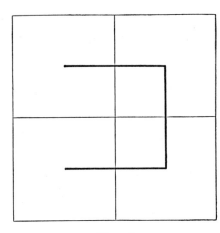

Figure 5

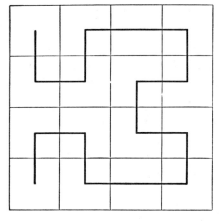

Figure 6

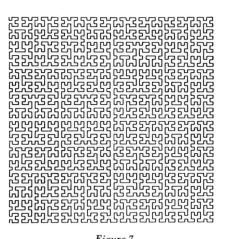

Figure 7

tion of a point because it is not connected in the small.

We can convince ourselves of the undependability of intuition, even as regards such elementary geometrical questions, with a second example. Think of a map of three adjoining countries [*Figure 9*]. There are certain points at which all three countries come together—so-called "three-country corners" (points *a* and *b*). Intuition seems to indicate that such corners can occur only at isolated points, and that at the great majority of boundary points on the map only two countries will be in contact. Yet the Dutch mathematician L. E. J. Brouwer showed in 1910 how a map can be divided into three countries in such a way that all three countries will touch one another at every boundary point!

Start with a map of three countries—one hatched (A), one dotted (B) and one solid (C)—and an adjoining unoccupied area [*Figure 10*]. Country A, seeking to bring this land into its sphere of influence, decides to push out a corridor which approaches within one mile of every point of the unoccupied territory but—to avoid trouble—does not impinge upon either of the two other countries

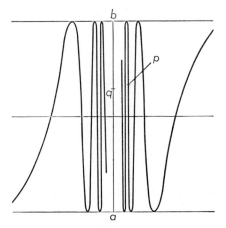

Figure 8

[*Figure 11*]. After this has been done, country B decides that it must do the same and proceeds to drive into the remaining unoccupied territory a corridor that comes within one-half mile of all the unoccupied points but does not touch either of the other two countries [*Figure 12*]. Thereupon country C decides that it cannot lag behind, and it also extends a corridor into the territory as yet unoccupied, which comes to within a third of a mile of every point of this territory but does not touch the other countries [*Figure 13*]. Country A now proceeds to push a second corridor into the remaining unoccupied territory, which comes within a quarter of a mile of all points of this territory but does not touch the other two countries. The process continues: Country B extends a corridor that comes within a fifth of a mile of every unoccupied point; country C, one that comes within a sixth of a mile of every unoccupied point; country A starts over again, and so on and on. And since we are giving imagination free rein, let us assume further that country A required a year for the construction of its first corridor, country B, the following half-year for its first corridor, country C, the next quarter year for its first corridor; country A, the next eighth of a year for its second, and so on, each succeeding extension being completed in half the time of its predecessor. It can be seen that after two years none of the originally unoccupied territory will remain unclaimed; moreover the entire area will then be divided among the three countries in such a fashion that all three countries will meet at every boundary point. Intuition cannot comprehend this pattern, but logical analysis requires us to accept it.

Because intuition turned out to be deceptive in so many instances, and because propositions that had been ac-

counted true by intuition were repeatedly proved false by logic, mathematicians became more and more skeptical of the validity of intuition. The conviction grew that it was unsafe to accept any mathematical proposition, much less to base any mathematical discipline on intuitive convictions. Thus a demand arose for the expulsion of intuition from mathematical reasoning and for the complete formalization of mathematics. That is to say, every new mathematical concept was to be introduced through a purely logical definition; every mathematical proof was to be carried through by strictly logical means. The pioneers of this program (to mention only the most famous) were Augustin Cauchy (1789-1857), Bernhard Bolzano (1781-1848), Karl Weierstrass (1815-1897), Georg Cantor (1845-1918) and Julius Wilhelm Richard Dedekind (1831-1916).

The task of completely formalizing or logicizing mathematics was arduous and difficult; it meant nothing less than a root-and-branch reform. Propositions that had been accepted as intuitively evident had to be painstakingly proved. As the prototype of an *a priori* synthetic judgment based on pure intuition Kant expressly cited the proposition that space is three-dimensional. But by present-day

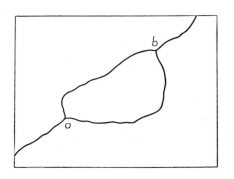

Figure 9

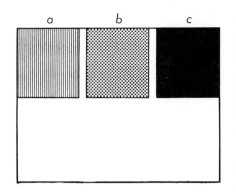

Figure 10

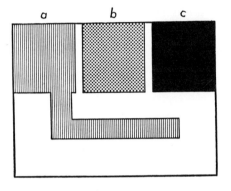

Figure 11

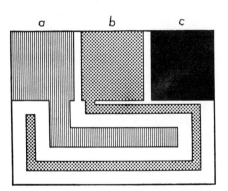

Figure 12

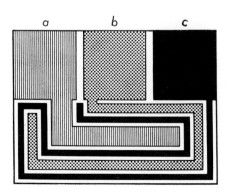

Figure 13

standards even this statement calls for searching logical analysis. First it is necessary to define purely logically what is meant by the "dimensionality" of a geometric figure, and then it must be proved logically that the space of ordinary geometry—which is also the space of Newtonian physics—as embraced in this definition is in fact three-dimensional. This proof was not achieved until 1922, and then simultaneously by the Vienna mathematician K. Menger and the Russian mathematician Pavel Uryson (who later succumbed to a tragic accident at the height of his creative powers). I wish to explain briefly how the dimensionality of a figure is defined.

A geometric figure is called a "point set." It is said to be null-dimensional if for each of its points there exists an arbitrarily small neighborhood whose boundary contains no point of the set. For example, every set consisting of a finite number of points is null-dimensional, but there are also many complicated null-dimensional points which consist of infinitely many points [*Figure 14*]. A point set that is not null-dimensional is called one-dimensional if for each of its points there is an arbitrarily small neighborhood whose boundary has only a null-dimensional set in common with the point set [*Figure 15*]. Every straight line, every figure composed of a finite number of straight lines, every circle, every ellipse—in short, all geometrical constructs that we ordinarily designate as curves—are one-dimensional in this sense. A point set that is neither null-dimensional nor one-dimensional is called two-dimensional if for each of its points there is an arbitrarily small neighborhood whose boundary has at the most a one-dimensional set in common with the point set. Every plane, every polygonic or circular area, every spherical surface—in short, every geometric construct ordinarily classified as a surface—is two-dimensional in this sense. A point set that is neither null-dimensional, one-dimensional nor two-dimensional is called three-dimensional if for each of its points there is an arbitrarily small neighborhood whose boundary has at most a two-dimensional set in common with the point set. It can be proved—not at all simply, however—that the space of ordinary geometry is a three-dimensional point set.

This theory provides what we have been seeking—a fully satisfactory definition of the concept of a curve. The essential characteristic of a curve turns out to be its one-dimensionality. But be-

yond that the theory also makes possible an unusually precise and subtle analysis of the structure of curves, about which I should like to comment briefly.

A point on a curve is called an end point if there are arbitrarily small neighborhoods surrounding it, each of whose boundaries has only a single point in common with the curve [*points* a *and* b *in Figure 16*]. A point on the curve that is not an end point is called an ordinary point if it has arbitrarily small neighborhoods each of whose boundaries has exactly two points in common with the curve [*point* c *in Figure 16*]. A point on a curve is called a branch point if the boundary of any of its arbitrarily small neighborhoods has more than two points in common with the curve [*point* d *in Figure 16*]. Intuition seems to indicate that it is impossible for a curve to be made up of nothing but end points or branch points. As far as end points are concerned, this intuitive conviction has been confirmed by logical analysis, but as regards branch points it has been refuted. The Polish mathematician W. Sierpinski proved in 1915 that there are curves *all of whose points are branch points*. Let us attempt to visualize how this comes about.

Suppose that an equilateral triangle has been inscribed within another equilateral triangle and the interior of the inscribed triangle erased [*Figure 17*]. In each of the three remaining triangles [*the unhatched areas*] inscribe an equilateral triangle and again erase its interior; there are now nine equilateral triangles together with their sides [*Figure 18*]. Imagine this process continued indefinitely. (Figure 19 shows the fifth step, where 243 triangles remain.) The points of the original equilateral triangle that survive the infinitely numerous erasures can be shown to form a curve all of whose points, with the exception of the vertex points *a*, *b* and *c* of the original triangle, are branch points. From this it is easy to obtain a curve with all its points branch points; for instance, by distorting the entire figure so that the three vertices of the original triangle are brought together in a single point.

But enough of examples—let us now summarize what has been said. Repeatedly we have found that in geometric questions, even in very simple and elementary ones, intuition is a wholly unreliable guide. And it is of course impossible to adopt this discredited aid as the basis of a mathematical discipline. The way is then open for other logical constructs in the form

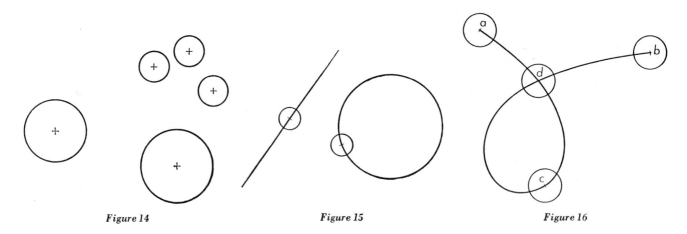

Figure 14   *Figure 15*   *Figure 16*

of spaces differing from the space of ordinary geometry; spaces, for instance, in which the so-called Euclidean parallel postulate is replaced by a contrary postulate (non-Euclidean spaces), spaces whose dimensionality is greater than three, non-Archimedean spaces (in which there are lengths that are greater than any multiple of a given length).

What, then, are we to say to the often-heard objection that the multidimensional, non-Euclidean, non-Archimedean geometries, though consistent as logical constructs, are useless in arranging our experience because they do not satisfy intuition? My first comment is that ordinary geometry itself is by no means a supreme example of the intuitive process. The fact is that *every* geometry —three-dimensional as well as multidimensional, Euclidean as well as non-Euclidean, Archimedean as well as non-Archimedean—is a logical construct. For several centuries, almost up to the present day, ordinary geometry admirably served the purpose of ordering our experience; thus we grew used to operating with it. This explains why we regard it as intuitive, and every departure from it contrary to intuition—intuitively impossible. But as we have seen, such "intuitional impossibilities" occur even in

ordinary geometry. They appear as soon as we reflect upon objects that we had not thought about before.

Modern physics now makes it appear appropriate to avail ourselves of the logical constructs of multidimensional and non-Euclidean geometries for the ordering of our experience. (Although we have as yet no indication that the inclusion of non-Archimedean geometry might prove useful, this possibility is by no means excluded.) But, because these advances in physics are very recent, we are not yet accustomed to the manipulation of these logical constructs; hence they are still considered an affront to intuition.

The same reaction occurred when the theory that the earth is a sphere was advanced. The hypothesis was widely rejected on the grounds that the existence of the antipodes was contrary to intuition; however, we have got used to the conception and today it no longer occurs to anyone to pronounce it impossible because it conflicts with intuition.

Physical concepts are also logical constructs, and here too we can see clearly how concepts whose application is familiar to us acquire an intuitive status which is denied to those whose application is unfamiliar. The concept "weight"

is so much a part of common experience that almost everyone regards it as intuitive. The concept "moment of inertia," however, does not enter into most people's activities and is therefore not regarded by them as intuitive; yet among many experimental physicists and engineers, who constantly work with it, moment of inertia possesses an intuitive status equal to that generally accorded the concept of weight. Similarly the concept "potential difference" is intuitive for the electrical technician, but not for most people.

If the use of multidimensional and non-Euclidean geometries for the ordering of our experience continues to prove itself so that we become more and more accustomed to dealing with these logical constructs; if they penetrate into the curriculum of the schools; if we, so to speak, learn them at our mother's knee as we now learn three-dimensional Euclidean geometry—then it will no longer occur to anyone to say that these geometries are contrary to intuition. They will be considered as deserving of intuitive status as three-dimensional Euclidean geometry is today. For it is not true, as Kant urged, that intuition is a pure *a priori* means of knowledge. Rather it is force of habit rooted in psychological inertia.

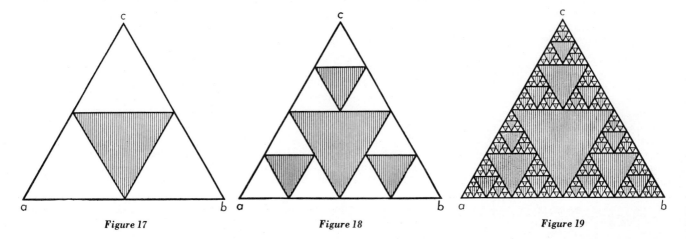

Figure 17   *Figure 18*   *Figure 19*

27 THE FOUNDATIONS OF MATHEMATICS

W. V. QUINE · September 1964

Irrefragability, thy name is mathematics. Let natural scientists accept evidence; the mathematician demands proof. Scientific standards have turned austere, it would seem, if anyone is to fuss about foundations for mathematics. Where might he find foundations half so firm as what he wants to found?

Concern for the foundations of mathematics has most often been expressed in emergency situations, when basic ideas begin to seem shaky and mathematicians are forced to examine them. Such an examination was accorded the idea of the infinitesimal long after Isaac Newton and Gottfried Wilhelm von Leibniz developed the differential calculus. This concept of a fractional quantity infinitely close to zero, yet different from zero, provided a foundation for the study of rates, the business of the differential calculus.

Consider a car accelerating from a standstill to a speed of 90 miles an hour. At the instant its speedometer needle points to 60 it is going a mile a minute; at earlier instants its speed is less, at later ones more. The instantaneous speed of a mile a minute does not consist in going a mile in one minute because it is not maintained for a

minute. It is not maintained for any time at all by the accelerating car. The distance covered at each instant is zero, and the characterization—no miles an instant—eliminates the distinction between one speed and another. So the founding fathers of the calculus assumed the existence of infinitesimal numbers, just barely distinct from zero and from one another. (We are familiar with smaller and smaller fractions—1/8, 1/16 and so on—but these are not infinitesimals; an infinitesimal is supposed to go into 1 not just 16 times but infinitely many times.)

Going a mile a minute, then, means going one of those infinitesimal distances in some infinitesimal time. Going half a mile a minute means going half that infinitesimal distance in that infinitesimal time. The absurdity of this approach was obvious, but the resulting calculus had made it possible to reason mathematically about rates. So a problem arose that is characteristic of problems in the foundations of mathematics: how to get rid of the infinitesimal and make do with clearer ideas while still saving the useful superstructure.

Augustin Cauchy and his followers in the 19th century solved the problem. Consider shorter and shorter intervals of time, each of them straddling our given instant. If over each interval we write the distance the car traveled therein, every distance-to-time ratio will be close to a mile a minute if the time interval is short. Whatever degree of accuracy we care to stipulate, there is a time interval such that for all intervals inside it our distance-to-time ratios will approximate a mile a minute with the stipulated accuracy. A sequence of such distance-to-time ratios, taken over increasingly narrow intervals, approach-

es a limit (which can be determined by the technique known as differentiation). The notion of limits concerns short but not infinitesimal distances. It can be used to define what it means to be going a mile a minute at a given instant.

The infinitesimal is not the only mathematical concept that had to be legitimized or eliminated. Take the 16th-century idea, still very much with us, of imaginary numbers: square roots of negative numbers. Square any real number, negative or positive, and the result is positive. What then are the square roots of negative numbers? Whatever they are, they have become so central to applied mathematics that if you so much as divide a time by a distance you end up, according to relativity physics, with an imaginary number. As in the differential calculus, an examination of the foundation must be made with an eye toward preserving the superstructure.

The square root of −1 is the imaginary unit called i. The rest of the imaginary numbers are the multiples of i by real numbers [see "Number," page 89]. Corresponding to the real number 3 there is the imaginary number $3i$; corresponding to the real number 1/2 there is the imaginary $\frac{1}{2}i$; corresponding to the real number π there is the imaginary πi. The imaginary numbers, thus constituted, then combine with the real numbers by addition; we get $3 + i$, $\pi + 2i$ and the like, known as complex numbers, and these impart a utility to the imaginary numbers. Any complex number is a convenient coding or packaging of two real numbers x and y, each of which can be uniquely recovered on demand. This correspondence can be represented on a plane defined by a real x axis and an imaginary y axis [see

THE NUMBER 4 is represented on the opposite page as a class containing all 4-member classes. The outer frame is not closed at right because membership in this class is not restricted to the examples shown here. A proper title for the whole design would be "4." To say that a class of tetrahedrons, cones, spheres or cylinders has 4 members implies that it belongs within "4." This view of number is one of several proposed by students of the foundations of mathematics.

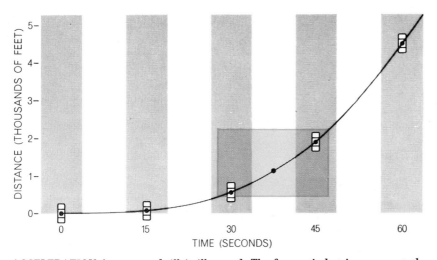

ACCELERATION from a standstill is illustrated. The five vertical strips represent the same one-mile stretch of road viewed at 15-second intervals. In the first 15 seconds the car (*colored object*) advances about 70 feet. In its fourth 15 seconds it moves 32 times farther.

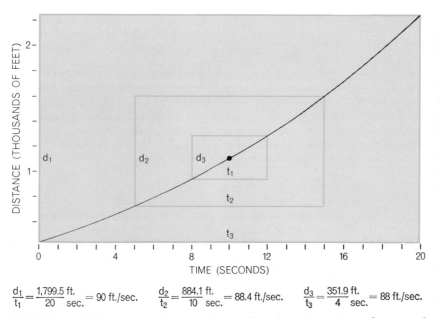

$$\frac{d_1}{t_1} = \frac{1,799.5 \text{ ft.}}{20 \text{ sec.}} = 90 \text{ ft./sec.} \qquad \frac{d_2}{t_2} = \frac{884.1 \text{ ft.}}{10 \text{ sec.}} = 88.4 \text{ ft./sec.} \qquad \frac{d_3}{t_3} = \frac{351.9 \text{ ft.}}{4 \text{ sec.}} = 88 \text{ ft./sec.}$$

INSTANT at which the car reaches a speed of a mile a minute is a point on the curve of acceleration, a section of which is transposed here. The distance-to-time ratios of ever narrowing intervals will form a sequence that approaches a finite and determinable limit.

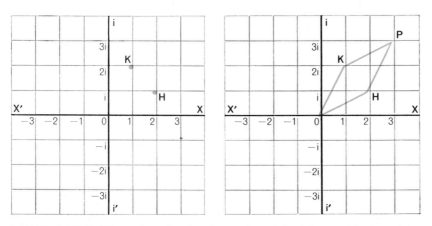

COMPLEX NUMBER $x + yi$ can be plotted on a plane defined by a real horizontal axis and an imaginary vertical axis, as the points $K(1 + 2i)$ and $H(2 + i)$ are plotted at left. If the two points and the origin are vertices of a parallelogram, the fourth vertex (P) is their sum.

bottom illustration on this page]. In retrospect it seems that the mystery of imaginary numbers could have been avoided and the role of complex numbers fulfilled by speaking of "ordered pairs" of real numbers.

The idea of an ordered pair is helpful at many other junctures in mathematics. Its use is always the same: it is a way of handling two things as one while losing track of neither. Commonly the ordered pair x and y, whether these be numbers or other things, such as fathers and sons, is denoted (x,y). I have not said what things such pairs are, and traditionally the question is skipped; what is important is what they do. Their one property that matters is that if (x,y) is (z,w), then x is z and y is w.

I have said that in principle the myth of imaginary roots could be bypassed. Still, it has value. It greatly simplifies the laws of algebra, an advantage that can be retained while the imaginary and complex numbers are explained away. This is done by a maneuver that is common in foundational studies: *defining the complex numbers as mere ordered pairs of real numbers* and then redefining the usual algebraic operations of plus, times and power so as to make sense of these operations when they are applied to the ordered pairs. The definitions can be so devised that they provide us with an algebra of ordered pairs that is formally indistinguishable from the algebra of complex numbers. One tends to say that the complex numbers have been explained as ordered pairs, but we could just as well say that they have been eliminated in favor of ordered pairs.

Instead of merely saying what the ordered pairs do, we might go on and try to settle what they are. This question lacks the urgency of the questions about infinitesimals and imaginary numbers, and savors more of casual philosophy. Any answer, however artificial, will serve as long as it upholds the law of pairs: if (x,y) is (z,w), then x is z and y is w. The usual version adopted nowadays comes from Norbert Wiener and Casimir Kuratowski. It does not identify the ordered pair (x,y) simply with the class whose members are x and y; that would confuse (x,y) with (y,x). It identifies (x,y) with a class of two classes. One of the two is the class whose sole member is x; the other is the class whose members are x and y. Here we can say that we have explained ordered pairs as certain two-member classes of classes, or that we have eliminated or-

SQUARE-ROOT FUNCTION can be represented by an outer frame unbounded on the bottom, containing ordered pairs (a,b) in which the relation "b is a times as big as a" holds. Each ordered pair is identified as a two-member class. One member class is shown at the left in each frame. *Its* sole member is the first element of the pair. The other member class is shown at the right containing the two elements of the pair. In this convention the bottom pair $(3,9)$ cannot be confused with $(9,3)$, the pair that represents the square function. Credit for this version of pair, which is widely used in modern mathematics, goes to Norbert Wiener and Casimir Kuratowski.

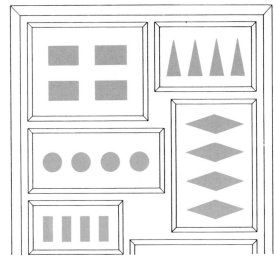

NATURAL NUMBER 4 is shown here as the class of all 4-member classes; thus the outer frame is bottomless. According to this version of number, first suggested by Gottlob Frege, 1 can be explained as the class of those classes that belong to 0 when deprived of a member.

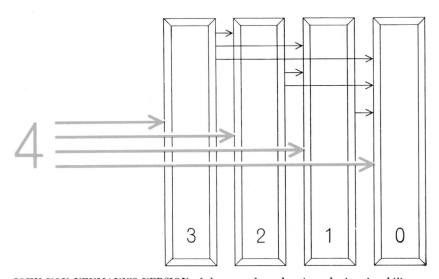

JOHN VON NEUMANN'S VERSION of the natural number 4 emphasizes its ability to pair off in one-to-one correspondence (*indicated by arrows*) with a class of 4 members. Three elements of this class are defined by correspondence. The other is the empty class.

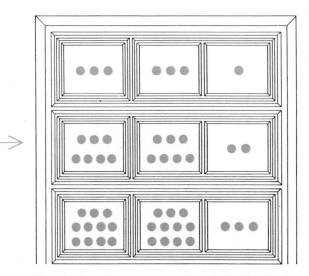

REAL NUMBER 4 is represented as the bottomless class (*outer frame*) of ordered pairs (*a,b*) in which *a* is "less than 4 times as big as" *b*. This is the relation that 3 bears to 1, 7 bears to 2 and 11 bears to 3. The convention applies to fractional and negative numbers.

dered pairs in favor of these two-member classes of classes. The difference is verbal, but the first description has the advantage of preserving the notation "(x,y)" and the word "pair."

Philosophical questions seem to lie somewhere between the indignant demands of offended common sense—What is an infinitesimal? What is the square root of a negative number?—and the compulsive questions of a bored child on a rainy Saturday. One philosophical question, deeper than the one about ordered pairs, is: What is number? Let us train this question first on the natural numbers, that is, the positive integers and zero.

Numerals name numbers. The symbol "12" names 12. To rephrase our question: What do the numerals name? What is 12? It is how many Apostles there were, how many months in a year, how many eggs in a carton. But 12 is not merely a property of a dozen eggs, months and Apostles, it is the property common to the class of a dozen eggs, the class of a dozen months and the class of a dozen Apostles.

One of the sources of clarity in mathematics is the tendency to talk of classes rather than properties. Whatever is accomplished by referring to a property can generally be accomplished at least as well by referring to the class of all things that have that property. Clarity is gained because for classes we have a clear idea of sameness and difference; it is a question simply of their having or not having the same members.

In particular, then, we do best to explain 12 not as the property of being a dozen but as the class of all dozens, the class of all 12-member classes. Each natural number *n* becomes the class of all *n*-member classes. The circularity of using *n* thus to define *n* can be avoided by defining each number in terms of its predecessor. Once we have got to 5, for instance, we can explain 6 as the class of those classes that, when deprived of a member, come to belong to 5. Starting at the beginning, we can explain 0 as the class whose sole member is the empty class; then 1 as the class of those classes that, when deprived of a member, come to belong to 0; then 2 as the class of those classes that, when deprived of a member, come to belong to 1, and so on up.

Just as any version of ordered pairs serves its purpose if it fulfills the law of pairs, so any version of natural number will serve if it fulfills this law: There is a first number and a successor operator that yields something new every time. The above version of number, presented by Gottlob Frege in 1884, meets the test [*see top illustration on page 194*]. Others do too. A version set forth by John von Neumann identifies each number with the class of all the preceding numbers [*see middle illustration on page 194*]. In this system 0 is itself the empty class; 1 is the class whose sole member is 0; 2 is the class of 0 and 1. Where Frege would say a class of *n* members belongs to *n*, von Neumann would say that a class of *n* members is one whose members can be paired off in one-to-one correspondence with the members of *n*.

Whether we consider numbers in either of these ways or in some other, a next step is to define the arithmetical operations. The idea behind addition is evident: $m + n$ is how many members a class has if part of it has m members and the rest has n. As for the product $m \times n$, this is how many mem-

STATEMENT ABOUT *n*	TERMS TO EXPAND	DEFINITION OF TERMS
n is a prime number.	prime number	*n* is a natural number and, for all natural numbers *h* and *k*, if *n* is $h \cdot k$, then *h* or *k* is 1.
n is a natural number and, for all natural numbers *h* and *k*, if *n* is $h \cdot k$, then *h* or *k* is 1.	*n* is $h \cdot k$	A class of *n* members falls into *h* parts having *k* members each.
n is a natural number and, for all natural numbers *h* and *k*, if a class of *n* members falls into *h* parts having *k* members each, then *h* or *k* is 1.	*x* falls into *h* parts having *h* members each	There is a class *y* of *h* members such that each member of *y* has *k* members and no members of *y* share members and all and only the members of *y* are members of *x*.
n is a natural number and, for all natural numbers *h* and *k*, if for every member *x* of *n* there is a member of *y* of *h* such that all members of *y* are members of *k* and no members of *y* share members and all and only the members of the members of *y* are members of *x*, then *h* or *k* is 1.	*n* is a natural number	*n* is a member of every class *z* such that 0 is a member of *z* and all successors of members of *z* are members of *z*.
	0	0 is the class whose sole member is the class without members.
	successor	The successor of any *m* is the class of all the classes that, when deprived of a member, come to belong to *m*.
	1	1 is the class of all the classes that, when deprived of a member, come to be the class without members.
n is a member of every class *z* such that the class whose sole member is the class without members is a member of *z* and, for every member *m* of *z* the class of all the classes that, when deprived of a member, come to belong to *m*, is a member of *z* and, for all *h* and *k* that are members of every class *z* such that the class whose sole member is the class without members, is a member of *z* and, for every member *m* of *z* the class of all the classes that, when deprived of a member, come to belong to *m*, is a member of *z*, if for every member *x* of *n* there is a member *y* of *h* such that all members of *y* are members of *k* and no members of *y* share members and all and only the members of the members of *y* are members of *x*, then *h* or *k* is the class of all the classes that, when deprived of a member, come to be the class without members.		

SIMPLIFIED SENTENCE appears at bottom left in this chart. Defining the statement "*n* is a prime number" creates a vocabulary of terms (*middle column*) that must be expanded (*as shown in column at right*). The final sentence deals only with class membership. It could be rewritten using only the locutions "and," "not," "is a member of," and the idiom of universal quantification, "everything *x* is such that...*x*...," if brevity were no object. The version of number used in the expansion of terms was developed by Frege.

bers a class has if it falls into m parts having n members each.

There are the negative numbers still to account for, and the fractional ones, and all the irrational numbers such as $\sqrt{2}$ and π; in short, all the real numbers except the natural numbers. Here again any version will serve that meets certain requirements. One overall version, with more unity than most, construes each real number as being a certain relation between natural numbers; in fact, a certain relation of comparative size. Take in particular the real number $1/2$. It is identified as the relation that 1 bears to each integer from 3 on, and that 2 bears to each from 5 on, and so forth. Similarly, each positive real number x is identified with the relation "less than x times as big as." The

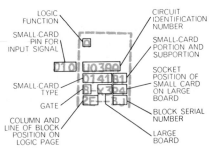

real number $1/\pi$, for instance, comes out as a relation that 1 bears to each integer from 4 on, and 2 bears to each from 7 on, and 3 to each from 10 on, and so forth. As for the negative real numbers, these are taken as the converse relations; since $1/2$ is the relation "less than half as big as," $-1/2$ comes out as the relation "more than twice as big as."

At the risk of sounding increasingly like the child on a rainy Saturday we may interject: But what is a relation? As suggested in our discussion of ordered pairs, a relation can be identified with the class of all the ordered pairs (a,b) such that a bears the relation to b. In this way the real numbers are ultimately identified with classes, as were the natural numbers. The number $1/2$ becomes the class of all ordered pairs (a,b) such that a is less than half as big as b. Whereas the class of ordered pairs identified with $1/2$ cannot contain a pair $(2,4)$ without violating the "less than" relation—a would be exactly x times as big as b—it could contain the ordered pair $(20,41)$ or any ordered pair where a is within any desired proximity of x times as big as b.

Each real number then corresponds to a distinct class of ordered pairs. This distinctness can be proved by the existence of a rational number between

any two points on a line of real numbers. That is, if x and y are different real numbers (say x is less than y), then there is a rational number a/b (a and b are integers) such that a/b is less than y but greater than x. Then the ordered pair (a,b) will fall into the class corresponding to y but not into the class corresponding to x, thus distinguishing the two.

The description of the positive real number x as the relation "less than x times as big as" falls into the same circularity we noticed in describing n as the class of all n-member classes. But now as then the description helps us to see what objects the numbers are to be. The reason it serves is that the circular reuse of "n" or "x" inside the description has a commonsense context. Actually the circularity can be eliminated in both cases by means of careful and complex definition.

We had to adopt a version of the natural numbers before construing the real numbers in general because we took these as being relations of natural numbers. The natural numbers must therefore be seen as distinct, however uselessly, from the corresponding whole real numbers. The real number 5, for example, comes out as the class of ordered pairs (a,b) of natural numbers

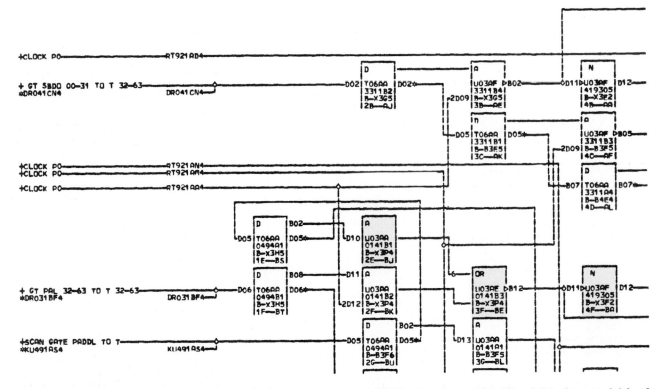

LOGIC DIAGRAM shows the design of a computer system in terms of connected elements known as "and/or blocks." The information associated with a block is given in the detail of an "and" block at top left. The logic functions A, OR and N in the upper left-hand corners of the colored blocks denote the logical locations "and," "or" and "not." The diagram is based on the IBM 360 system.

such that a is less than 5 times as big as b.

In mathematics, talk of functions is no less plentiful than talk of number. But the philosophical question—What are functions?—is more quickly settled than that of number. A function can be identified with the relation of its values to its arguments. The function "square root of" can be explained as the relation of root to square: the relation that 0 bears to 0, that 1 bears to 1, that 2 bears to 4, that 2/3 bears to 4/9 and so on. Thus the square-root function becomes the class of all the pairs $(0,0)$, $(1,1)$, $(2,4)$, $(2/3,4/9)$, in general (x,x^2).

The illustration on page 193 represents this function as a class.

Our sample studies in the foundations of mathematics started with troubleshooting and have leveled out into a general tidying up. It is a process, we see, of reducing some notions to others and thereby diminishing the inventory of basic mathematical concepts. Let us apply this technique in reducing a familiar notion, the definition of a prime number, into elemental class terms. To keep track of our presuppositions we must render our successive definitions in explicit detail and take note of all the logical and mathematical devices that are used in them. Each definition must explain how to eliminate some locution by paraphrasing it, or the sentences in which it appears, into a residual vocabulary that eventually narrows to rudimentary terms. We begin by changing

n *is a prime number*

to

n *is a natural number and for all natural numbers* h *and* k, *if* n *is* h × k, *then* n *or* k *is 1.*

Our first step eliminated the troublesome "prime number" from the residual vocabulary but left in its place "n is a natural number," the notation for multiplying h by k and the notation for 1. We know how to eliminate the multiplicative notation by expanding the clause $n = h \times k$ to read

a class of n *members falls into* h *parts having* k *members each.*

To replace the notion of "parts" of a class with the simpler concept of membership, this clause can be changed to

for every class x *with* n *members there is a class* y *of* h *members such that each member of* y *has* k *members and no members of* y *share members and all and only the members of the members of* y *are members of* x.

Cumbersomeness is increasing apace, but the vocabulary is being reduced to terms of class membership. We can now eliminate "x has n members" and kindred clauses. If we use Frege's version of the natural numbers, this becomes "x is a member of n." Our original phrase has now been analyzed to mean

n *is a natural number and, for all natural numbers* h *and* k, *if for every member* x *of* n *there is a member* y *of* h *such that all members of* y *are members of* k *and no members of* y *share members and all and only the members of the members of* y *are members of* x, *then* h *or* k *is 1.*

The dwindling of perspicuity is less noteworthy than the reduction of vocabulary. Where perspicuity is to our purposes the eliminated locutions can be restored, after all, as defined abbreviations.

The term that next calls for elimina-

NUMBER	STEP	SOURCE
1	$x = x - (y - y),$	AXIOM
2	$x - (y - z) = z - (y - x)$	AXIOM

(From these we derive theorems by substituting any one term for all occurrences of any variable or, given an equation, substituting its one side for its other side anywhere.)

3	$z = z - (y - y)$	Step 1
4	$z = z - (x - x)$	Step 3
5	$y - y = (y - y) - (x - x)$	Step 4
6	$x - (x - z) = z - (x - x)$	Step 2
7	$x - (x - (y - y)) = (y - y) - (x - x)$	Step 6
8	$x - x = (y - y) - (x - x)$	Steps 1, 7
9	$x - x = y - y$	Steps 5, 8

(The expression "$x + y$" can be defined as short for "$x - ((y - y) - y)$." The laws of addition then come through as mere abbreviations of laws of subtraction. Thus the law "$x + y = y + x$" is proved as follows.)

10	$x - ((x - x) - y) = y - ((x - x) - x)$	Step 2
11	$x - ((y - y) - y) = y - ((x - x) - x)$	Steps 9, 10
12	$x + y = y + x$	Step 11, definition

PROOF PROCEDURE for arithmetical addition and subtraction begins with equations (*Steps 1 and 2*) taken as axioms. Then the steps for deriving theorems by substitution are defined. Steps 3 through 9 follow from previous steps listed in the column at right. Addition is defined in terms of subtraction before its elementary law is proved (*Steps 10–12*).

tion is "is a natural number" (said of *n*, *h* and *k*). To say that *n* is a natural number is to say that *n* is 0 or successor of 0 or successor of that or so on. Frege showed how to dodge the "so on" idea by defining "a natural number" as

a member of every class z such that 0 is a member of z and all successors of members of z are members of z.

Frege explained "0" as the class whose sole member is the class without members, and the "successor" of any *m* as the class of all the classes that, when deprived of a member, come to belong to *m*. If we eliminate "0" and "successor" in rewriting the above version of

"is a natural number" and then use the result as a clause in rewriting our original phrase, we end up with a long story in a short vocabulary [*see illustration on page 195*]. The number "1" at the end of our intermediate definition is resolved too, because 1 is successor of 0. The vocabulary that remains refers to class membership and little else. There is an assortment of elementary logical particles: "is," "and," "or," "if-then," "every," "all" and the like.

By further steps, all of these can be reduced to several basic locutions. One is "and" as a connective of sentences. Another is "not." A third is the idiom of universal quantification, "everything is such that ... it ...," or, more flexibly, "everything *x* is such that ... *x* ...," with

variable letters. The prefix "everything *x* is such that" is compactly symbolized as "(x)." Fourth, there is the transitive verb "ϵ" meaning "is a member of." Perhaps the list should also include, fifth, the parentheses used to group clauses. The following, then, is an illustrative, brief sentence in our frugal notation:

$$(x) \ not \ (y) \ not \ (x \ \epsilon \ y \ and \ not \ y \ \epsilon \ x).$$

It amounts in effect to the words "Everything is a member of something not a member of it."

Every sentence expressible in the notation of pure classical mathematics, whether in arithmetic or the calculus or elsewhere, can be paraphrased into this thumbnail vocabulary, if not with comparable brevity. What "*n* is a prime number" was seen to stretch to is terse compared with what it would be if fully paraphrased in our five basic idioms. The five are not to be recommended as a *lingua franca* of mathematics, nor as a practical medium of computation. But it is of theoretical interest that so much in the way of mathematical ideas can be generated from so meager a basis, and from this basis in particular.

Four of the five basic locutions belong to logic. One, "ϵ," is peculiar to set theory, or the mathematics of classes. Or we might say that all five are in set theory; the logical locutions are a proper adjunct of every science, after all, and so of set theory.

It would appear, then, that all mathematics can be paraphrased in a set-theory vocabulary. Therefore all mathematical truth can be seen as truth of set theory. Every mathematical problem can be transformed into a problem of set theory. Either this augurs well for the outstanding problems of mathematics or else set theory has problems as deep as those of classical mathematics.

The latter is the case. And the worst aspect of set theory is not just that sentences can be written whose truth or falsity is hard to prove, but that sentences can be written whose simultaneous truth and falsity seem all too easy to prove. One such is the sentence

$$not \ (y) \ not \ (x) \ [not \ (x \ \epsilon \ y \ and \\ x \ \epsilon \ x) \ and \ not \ (not \ x \ \epsilon \ y \ and \ not \\ x \ \epsilon \ x)].$$

Partially transcribed with an eye to mortal communication, it says:

There is something y such that (x)

FIVE-COLOR MAP is uneconomical and can be redrawn using only four colors so that no two countries of like color share a border. No mathematical proof of this statement has been found for the general case, yet no one has drawn a map that will require five colors.

(x ε y *if and only if not* x ε x).

It seems to be true; just take *y* as the class of all the things *x* such that *x* is not a member of itself. Yet it must be false; if *y* were as averred, we could take *x* in particular as *y* and conclude, in self-contradiction, that *y* ε *y* if and only if not *y* ε *y*.

This paradox, turned up by Bertrand Russell in 1901, is the simplest of many in set theory. The moral of them all is that giving a necessary and sufficient condition for membership in a class does not guarantee that there is such a class. Russell's paradox shows in particular that there is no class of exactly the things that are not members of themselves. Consequently the great task of set theory comes to be that of deciding what classes there are. No natural and tenable answer is known; what seemed the natural answer, that there is a class for every membership condition, is untenable.

Since 1901 there has been a proliferation of set theories, no one of them clearly best. Even the question of freedom from self-contradiction is moot in such a framework, since we no longer can trust common sense for the plausibility of the propositions. Common sense in set theory is discredited by the paradoxes. As a foundation for mathematics, set theory is far less firm than what we have founded on it.

Clearly we must not look to the set-theoretical foundation of mathematics as a way of allaying misgivings regarding the soundness of classical mathematics. What we are looking for, as we evaluate various plans for a workable set theory, is a scheme that will reproduce in the eventual superstructure the

arithmetic, neglecting multiplication as well as the logical operators. If notations were added for these further purposes, then no proof procedure could cover all the expressible truths and avoid the falsehoods. This is the case even if we limit the values of the variables to natural numbers.

Such is the notation of what is called elementary number theory. A typical truth in this notation is

(x) (y) *not* (z) [*not* (x = y + z) *and not* (y = x + z)].

This amounts to saying of all natural numbers *x* and *y* that either *x = y + z* or *y = x + z* for some natural number *z*. Gödel showed that given a proof procedure we can construct a sentence in this meager notation that is false if it admits of proof under that procedure, and true if it does not. Therefore, Gödel accepted laws of classical mathematics. We find ourselves regarding set theory as a conveniently restricted vocabulary in which to formulate a general axiom system for classical mathematics—let the sets fall where they may.

Such a program of axiomatization can never be completed. There is no hope of a proof procedure strong enough to cover all the truths of classical mathematics, or even of arithmetic, while excluding all the falsehoods. This remarkable fact was proved by Kurt Gödel in 1931.

The proof procedure for addition and subtraction shown in the illustration on page 197 is *complete;* every truth that can be expressed in the notation can be proved by the procedure. This notation, however, covers only a few aspects of

concluded, our given procedure is either unsound, since it affords proof of a falsehood, or else incomplete, since it fails to afford proof of a truth of elementary number theory.

Gödel's discovery was a shock to preconceptions. The very nature of mathematical truth, one supposed, was its demonstrability. But not so. Surely each sentence constructible in this limited and lucid notation of elementary number theory is significant, each is true or false, each or its own negation is true; yet its truth does not assure demonstrability. The difference between truth in mathematics and truth in natural science is perhaps less abrupt than we thought.

Work in the foundations of mathematics can be concerned with concepts and it can be concerned with laws. Work with concepts—the reduction of concepts by defining some in terms of others—occupied us throughout much of this article. But it is to the study of laws and their encapsulation in axioms or proof procedures that Gödel's discovery relates. This type of work was not curtailed by the realization that we cannot get complete systems for substantial branches of mathematics; we *can* get incomplete ones that are illuminating in various ways.

The fact is that Gödel's result has greatly stimulated work in the branch of foundation studies devoted to laws. The remarkable techniques that went into Gödel's proof have brought about an imposing and thriving branch of mathematics: proof theory. Here is an instance where the foundation did give rise to the superstructure.

28 PARADOX

W. V. QUINE · April 1962

Frederic, the young protagonist of *The Pirates of Penzance*, has reached the age of 21 after passing only five birthdays. Several circumstances conspire to make this possible. Age is reckoned in elapsed time, whereas a birthday has to match the date of birth; and February 29 comes less frequently than once a year.

Granted that Frederic's situation is possible, wherein is it paradoxical? Merely in its initial air of absurdity. The likelihood that a man will be more than n years old on his nth birthday is as little as one to 1,460, or slightly better if we allow for seasonal trends; and this likelihood is so slight that we easily forget its existence.

May we say in general, then, that a paradox is just any conclusion that at first sounds absurd but that has an argument to sustain it? In the end I think this account stands up pretty well. But it leaves much unsaid. The argument that sustains a paradox may expose the absurdity of a buried premise or of some preconception previously reckoned as central to physical theory, to mathematics or to the thinking process. Catastrophe may lurk, therefore, in the most innocent-seeming paradox. More than once in history the discovery of paradox has been the occasion for major reconstruction at the foundations of thought. For some decades, indeed, studies of the foundation of mathematics have been confounded and greatly stimulated by confrontation with two paradoxes, one propounded by Bertrand Russell in 1901 and the other by Kurt Gödel in 1931.

As a first step onto this dangerous ground, let us consider another paradox: that of the village barber. This is not Russell's great paradox of 1901, to which we shall come, but a lesser one that Russell attributed to an unnamed source

in 1918. In a certain village there is a man, so the paradox runs, who is a barber; this barber shaves all and only those men in the village who do not shave themselves. Query: Does the barber shave himself?

Any man in this village is shaved by the barber if and only if he is not shaved by himself. Therefore in particular the barber shaves himself if and only if he does not. We are in trouble if we say the barber shaves himself and we are in trouble if we say he does not.

Now compare the two paradoxes. Frederic's situation seemed absurd at first, but a simple argument sufficed to make us acquiesce in it for good. In the case of the barber, on the other hand, the conclusion is too absurd to acquiesce in at any time.

What are we to say to the argument that goes to prove this unacceptable conclusion? Happily it rests on assumptions. We are asked to swallow a story about a village and a man in it who shaves all and only those men in the village who do not shave themselves. This is the source of our trouble; grant this and we end up saying, absurdly, that the barber shaves himself if and only if he does not. The proper conclusion to draw is just that there is no such barber. We are confronted with nothing more mysterious than what logicians have been referring to for a couple of thousand years as a *reductio ad absurdum*. We disprove the barber by assuming him and deducing the absurdity that he shaves himself if and only if he does not. The paradox is simply a proof that no village can contain a man who shaves all and only those men in it who do not shave themselves. This sweeping denial at first sounds absurd; why should there not be such a man in a village? But the argument shows why not, and so we ac-

quiesce in the sweeping denial just as we acquiesced in the possibility, absurd on first exposure, of Frederic's being so much more than five years old on his fifth birthday.

Both paradoxes are alike, after all, in sustaining prima facie absurdities by conclusive argument. What is strange but true in the one paradox is that one can be $4n$ years old on one's nth birthday; what is strange but true in the other paradox is that no village can contain a man who shaves all and only those men in the village who do not shave themselves.

Still, I would not limit the word "paradox" to cases where what is purportedly established is true. I shall call these, more particularly, veridical, or truth-telling, paradoxes. For the name of paradox is suited equally to falsidical ones. (This word is not so barbarous as it sounds; *falsidicus* occurs twice in Plautus and twice in earlier writers.)

The Frederic paradox is a veridical one if we take its proposition not as something about Frederic but as the abstract truth that a man can be $4n$ years old on his nth birthday. Similarly, the barber paradox is a veridical one if we take its proposition as being that no village contains such a barber. A falsidical paradox, on the other hand, is one whose proposition not only seems at first absurd but also is false, there being a fallacy in the purported proof. Typical falsidical paradoxes are the comic misproofs that $2 = 1$. Most of us have heard one or another such. Here is the version offered by the 19th-century English mathematician Augustus De Morgan: Let $x = 1$. Then $x^2 = x$. So $x^2 - 1 = x - 1$. Dividing both sides by $x - 1$, we conclude that $x + 1 = 1$; that is, since $x = 1$, $2 = 1$. The fallacy comes in the division by $x - 1$, which is 0.

Instead of "falsidical paradox" could I say simply "fallacy"? Not quite. Fallacies can lead to true conclusions as well as false ones, and to unsurprising conclusions as well as surprising ones. In a falsidical paradox there is always a fallacy in the argument, but the proposition purportedly established has furthermore to seem absurd and to be indeed false.

Some of the ancient paradoxes of Zeno belong under the head of falsidical paradoxes. Take the one about Achilles and the tortoise. Generalized beyond these two fictitious characters, what the paradox purports· to establish is the absurd proposition that so long as a runner keeps running, however slowly, another runner can never overtake him. The argument is that each time the pursuer reaches a spot where the pursued has been, the pursued has moved a bit beyond. When we try to make this argument more explicit, the fallacy that emerges is the mistaken notion that any infinite succession of intervals of time has to add up to all eternity. Actually when an infinite succession of intervals of time is so chosen that the succeeding intervals become shorter and shorter, the whole succession may take either a finite or an infinite time. It is a question of a convergent series.

Grelling's Paradox

The realm of paradox is not clearly exhausted even by the veridical and falsidical paradoxes together. The most startling of all paradoxes are not clearly assignable to either of these domains. Consider the paradox, devised by the German mathematician Kurt Grelling in 1908, concerning the heterological, or nonself-descriptive, adjectives.

To explain this paradox requires first a definition of the autological, or self-descriptive, adjective. The adjective "short" is short; the adjective "English" is English; the adjective "adjectival" is adjectival; the adjective "polysyllabic" is polysyllabic. Each of these adjectives is, in Grelling's terminology, autological: each is true of itself. Other adjectives are heterological; thus "long," which is not a long adjective; "German," which is not a German adjective; "monosyllabic," which is not a monosyllabic one.

Grelling's paradox arises from the query: Is the adjective "heterological" an autological or a heterological one? We are as badly off here as we were with the barber. If we decide that "heterological" is autological, then the adjective is true of itself. But that makes it heterological rather than autological, since whatever the adjective "heterological" is true of is heterological. If we therefore decide that the adjective "heterological" is heterological, then it is true of itself, and that makes it autological.

Our recourse in a comparable quandary over the village barber was to declare a *reductio ad absurdum* and conclude that there was no such barber. Here, however, there is no interim premise to disavow. We merely defined the adjective "heterological" and asked if it was heterological. In fact, we can get the paradox just as well without the adjective and its definition. "Heterological" was defined as meaning "not true of self"; we can therefore ask if the adjectival phrase "not true of self" is true of itself. We find that it is if and only if it is not, hence that it is and it is not; and so we have our paradox.

Thus viewed, Grelling's paradox seems unequivocally falsidical. Its proposition is a self-contradictory compound proposition to the effect that our adjective is and is not true of itself. But this paradox contrasts strangely with the falsidical paradoxes of Zeno, or of $2 = 1$, in that we are at a loss to spot the fallacy in the argument. It may for this reason be best seen as representing a third class of paradoxes, separate from the veridical and falsidical ones.

Antinomies

The paradoxes of this class are called antinomies, and it is they that bring on the crises in thought. An antinomy produces a self-contradiction by accepted ways of reasoning. It establishes that some tacit and trusted pattern of reasoning must be made explicit and henceforward be avoided or revised.

Take Grelling's paradox, in the form in which it shows the adjective phrase

"MOST INGENIOUS PARADOX" of *The Pirates of Penzance* involves Frederic, who was born on a February 29. He is 21, but going by birthdays "only five and a little bit over."

"not true of self" to be both true and false of itself. What tacit principles of reasoning does the argument depend on? Notably this one: the adjective "red" is true of a thing if and only if the thing is red; the adjective "big" is true of a thing if and only if the thing is big; the adjective "not true of self" is true of a thing if and only if the thing is not true of itself; and so on. This last case of the principle is the case that issues directly in the paradox.

There is no denying that this principle is constantly used, tacitly, when we speak of adjectives as true of things: the adjective "red" is true of a thing if and only if the thing is red, and correspondingly for all adjectives. This principle simply reflects what we mean in saying that adjectives are true of things. It is a hard principle to distrust, and yet it is obviously the principle that is to blame for our antinomy. The antinomy is directly a case of this principle. Take the adjective in the principle as the adjectival phrase "not true of self" instead of the adjective "red," and take the "thing" in the principle, of which the adjective is to be true, as that adjective over again; thereupon the principle says outright that "not true of self" is true of itself if and only if it is not true of itself. So the principle must be abandoned or at least somehow restricted.

Yet so faithfully does the principle reflect what we mean in calling adjectives true of things that we cannot abandon it without abjuring the very expression "true of" as pernicious nonsense. We could still go on using the adjectives themselves that had been said to be true of things; we could go on attributing them to things as usual; what we would be cutting out in "true of" is merely a special locution for talking about the attribution of the adjectives to the things.

This special locution, however, has its conveniences, and it would be missed. In fact, we do not have to do without it altogether. After all, to speak of adjectives as true or not true of things makes trouble only in a special case, involving one special adjective, namely the phrase "not true of self," in attribution to one special thing, namely that same phrase over again. If we forswear the use of the locution "true of" in connection with this particular phrase in relation to itself as object, we thereby silence our antinomy and may go on blithely using the locution "true of" in other cases as always, pending the discovery of further antinomies.

Actually related antinomies are still forthcoming. To inactivate the lot we have to cut a little deeper than our one case; we have to forswear the use of "true of" not only in connection with "not true of self" but also in connection with various other phrases relating to truth; and in such connections we have to forswear the use not only of "true of" but also of various other truth locutions. First let us look at some of the antinomies that would otherwise threaten.

The Paradox of Epimenides

There is the ancient paradox of Epimenides the Cretan, who said that all Cretans were liars. If he spoke the truth, he was a liar. It seems that this paradox may have reached the ears of St. Paul and that he missed the point of it. He warned, in his epistle to Titus: "One of themselves, even a prophet of their own, said, The Cretans are always liars."

Actually the paradox of Epimenides is untidy; there are loopholes. Perhaps some Cretans were liars, notably Epimenides, and others were not; perhaps Epimenides was a liar who occasionally told the truth; either way it turns out that the contradiction vanishes. Something of paradox can be salvaged with a little tinkering; but we do better to switch to a different and simpler rendering, also ancient, of the same idea. This is the *pseudomenon*, which runs simply: "I am lying." We can even drop the indirectness of a personal reference and speak directly of the sentence: "This sentence

BARBER PARADOX assumes that in a certain village there is a barber who shaves all and only those men who do not shave themselves. The question is whether this barber shaves himself. The paradox is that he does shave himself only if he does not.

is false." Here we seem to have the irreducible essence of antinomy: a sentence that is true if and only if it is false.

In an effort to clear up this antinomy it has been protested that the phrase "This sentence," so used, refers to nothing. This is claimed on the ground that you cannot get rid of the phrase by supplying a sentence that is referred to. For what sentence does the phrase refer to? The sentence "This sentence is false." If, accordingly, we supplant the phrase "This sentence" by a quotation of the sentence referred to, we get: " 'This sentence is false' is false." But the whole outside sentence here attributes falsity no longer to itself but merely to something other than itself, thereby engendering no paradox.

If, however, in our perversity we are still bent on constructing a sentence that does attribute falsity unequivocally to itself, we can do so thus: " 'Yields a falsehood when appended to its own quotation' yields a falsehood when appended to its own quotation." This sentence specifies a string of nine words and says of this string that if you put it down twice, with quotation marks around the first of the two occurrences, the result is false. But that result is the very sentence that is doing the telling. The sentence is true if and only if it is false, and we have our antinomy.

This is a genuine antinomy, on a par with the one about "heterological," or "false of self," or "not true of self," being true of itself. But whereas that earlier one turned on "true of," through the construct "not true of self," this new one turns merely on "true," through the construct "falsehood," or "statement not true." We can avoid both antinomies, and others related to them, by ceasing to use "true of" and "true" and their equivalents and derivatives, or at any rate ceasing to apply such truth locutions to adjectives or sentences that themselves contain such truth locutions.

This restriction can be relaxed somewhat by admitting a hierarchy of truth locutions, as suggested by the work of Bertrand Russell and the Polish mathematician Alfred Tarski, who is now at the University of California. The expressions "true," "true of," "false" and related ones can be used with numerical subscripts "0," "1," "2," and so on always attached or imagined; thus "$true_0$," "$true_1$," "$true_2$," "$false_0$" and so on. Then we can avoid the antinomies by taking care, when a truth locution (T) is applied to a sentence or other expression (S), that the subscript on T is higher than any subscript inside S. Violations of this restriction would be treated as

meaningless, or ungrammatical, rather than as true or false sentences. For instance, we could meaningfully ask whether the adjectives "long" and "short" are $true_0$ of themselves; the answers are respectively no and yes. But we could not meaningfully speak of the phrase "not $true_0$ of self" as $true_0$ or $false_0$ of itself; we would have to ask whether it is $true_1$ or $false_1$ of itself, and this is a question that leads to no antinomy. Either way the question can be answered with a simple and unpenalized negative.

This point deserves to be restated: Whereas "long" and "short" are adjectives that can meaningfully be applied to themselves, falsely in the one case and truly in the other, on the other hand "$true_0$ of self" and "not $true_0$ of self" are adjectival phrases that cannot be applied to themselves meaningfully at all, truly or falsely. Therefore to the question "Is '$true_0$ of self' $true_1$ of itself?" the answer is no; the adjectival phrase "$true_0$ of itself" is meaningless of itself rather than $true_1$ of itself.

Next let us consider, in terms of subscripts, the most perverse version of the *pseudomenon*. We have now, for meaningfulness, to insert subscripts on the two occurrences of the word "falsehood," and in ascending order, thus: " 'Yields a $falsehood_0$ when appended to its own quotation' yields a $falsehood_1$ when appended to its own quotation." Thereupon paradox vanishes. This sentence is unequivocally false. What it tells us is

that a certain described form of words is $false_1$, namely the form of words: " 'Yields a $falsehood_0$ when appended to its own quotation' yields a $falsehood_0$ when appended to its own quotation." But in fact this form of words is not $false_1$; it is meaningless. So the preceding sentence, which said that this form of words was $false_1$, is false. It is $false_2$.

This may seem an extravagant way of eliminating antinomies. But it would be much more costly to drop the word "true," and related locutions, once and for all. At an intermediate cost one could merely leave off applying such locutions to expressions containing such locutions. Either method is less economical than this method of subscripts. The subscripts do enable us to apply truth locutions to expressions containing such locutions, although in a manner disconcertingly at variance with custom. Each resort is desperate; each is an artificial departure from natural and established usage. Such is the way of antinomies.

A veridical paradox packs a surprise, but the surprise quickly dissipates itself as we ponder the proof. A falsidical paradox packs a surprise, but it is seen as a false alarm when we solve the underlying fallacy. An antinomy, however, packs a surprise that can be accommodated by nothing less than a repudiation of part of our conceptual heritage.

Revision of a conceptual scheme is not unprecedented. It happens in a small way with each advance in science, and it

EPIMENIDES THE CRETAN made the statement that all Cretans were liars. Such a statement can be simplified to "I am lying" or "This sentence is false." One can seemingly prove of such paradoxes, called antinomies, that they are true if and only if they are false.

ZENO'S PARADOX of Achilles and the tortoise proposes an absurdity: that so long as the tortoise continues to move, however slowly, the fleet Achilles can never overtake him. The paradox is called falsidical, there being a fallacy in its purported proof.

happens in a big way with the big advances, such as the Copernican revolution and the shift from Newtonian mechanics to Einstein's theory of relativity. We can hope in time even to get used to the biggest such changes and to find the new schemes natural. There was a time when the doctrine that the earth revolves around the sun was called the Copernican paradox, even by the men who accepted it. And perhaps a time will come when truth locutions without implicit subscripts, or like safeguards, will really sound as nonsensical as the antinomies show them to be.

Conversely, the falsidical paradoxes of Zeno must have been, in his day, genuine antinomies. We in our latter-day smugness point to a fallacy: the notion that an infinite succession of intervals must add up to an infinite interval. But surely this was part and parcel of the conceptual scheme of Zeno's day. Our recognition of convergent series, in which an infinite number of segments add up to a finite segment, is from Zeno's vantage point an artificiality comparable to our new subscripts on truth locutions. Perhaps these subscripts will seem as natural to our descendants of A.D. 4000, granted the tenuous hypothesis of there being any, as the convergent series does to us. One man's antinomy is another man's falsidical paradox, give or take a couple of thousand years.

I have not, by the way, exhausted the store of latter-day antinomies. Another good one is attributed by Russell to a librarian named Berry. Here the theme is numbers and syllables. Ten has a one-syllable name. Seventy-seven has a five-syllable name. The seventh power of seven hundred seventy-seven has a name that, if we were to work it out, might run to 100 syllables or so; but this number can also be specified more briefly in other terms. I have just specified it in 15 syllables. We can be sure, however, that there are no end of numbers that resist all specification, by name or description, under 19 syllables. There is only a finite stock of syllables altogether, and hence only a finite number of names or phrases of less than 19 syllables, whereas there are an infinite number of positive integers. Very well, then; of those numbers not specifiable in less than 19 syllables, there must be a least. And here is our antinomy: the least number not specifiable in less than nineteen syllables is specifiable in 18 syllables. I have just so specified it.

This antinomy belongs to the same family as the antinomies that have gone before. For the key word of this antinomy, "specifiable," is interdefinable with "true of." It is one more of the truth locutions that would take on subscripts under the Russell-Tarski plan. The least number not $specifiable_0$ in less than nineteen syllables is indeed $specifiable_1$ in 18 syllables, but it is not $specifiable_0$

in less than 19 syllables; for all I know it is not $specifiable_0$ in less than 23. This resolution of Berry's antinomy is the one that would come through automatically if we paraphrase "specifiable" in terms of "true of" and then subject "true of" to the subscript treatment.

Russell's Antinomy

Not all antinomies belong to this family. The most celebrated of all antinomies, discovered by Russell in 1901, belongs outside this family. It has to do with self-membership of classes. Some classes are members of themselves; some are not. For example, the class of all classes that have more than five members clearly has more than five classes as members; therefore the class is a member of itself. On the other hand, the class of all men is not a member of itself, not being a man. What of the class of all classes that are not members of themselves? Since its members are the nonself-members, it qualifies as a member of itself if and only if it is not. It is and it is not: antinomy's by now familiar face.

Russell's antinomy bears a conspicuous analogy to Grelling's antinomy of "not true of self," which it long antedates. But Russell's antinomy does not belong to the same family as the Epimenides antinomy and those of Berry and Grelling. By this I mean that Russell's antinomy cannot be blamed on any of the truth locutions, nor is it resolved by subjecting those locutions to subscripts. The crucial words in Russell's antinomy are "class" and "member," and neither of these is definable in terms of "true," "true of" or the like.

I said earlier that an antinomy estab-lishes that some tacit and trusted pattern of reasoning must be made explicit and be henceforward avoided or revised. In the case of Russell's antinomy, the tacit and trusted pattern of reasoning that is found wanting is this: for any condition you can formulate, there is a class whose members are the things meeting the condition.

This principle is not easily given up. The almost invariable way of specifying a class is by stating a necessary and sufficient condition for belonging to it. When we have stated such a condition, we feel

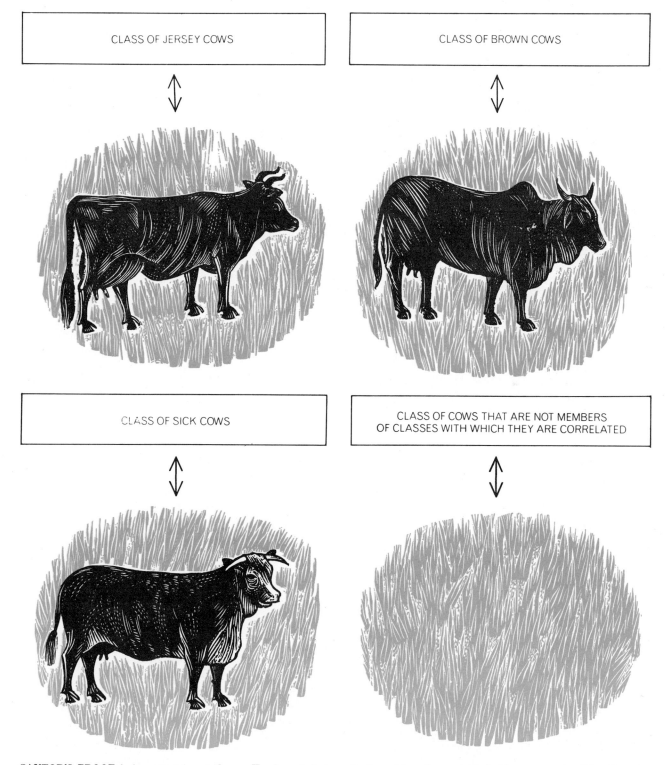

CLASS OF JERSEY COWS

CLASS OF BROWN COWS

CLASS OF SICK COWS

CLASS OF COWS THAT ARE NOT MEMBERS OF CLASSES WITH WHICH THEY ARE CORRELATED

CANTOR'S PROOF is important in set theory. He showed that there are always more classes of things of a kind than there are things of that kind. Take cows, for example, and classes of cows (*indicated here by rectangles*). If every cow is arbitrarily correlated with a class (of which it may or may not be a member), there will remain a class that is not correlated with any cow.

that we have "given" the class and can scarcely make sense of there not being such a class. The class may be empty, yes; but how could there not be such a class at all? What substance can be asked for it that the membership condition does not provide? Yet such exhortations avail us nothing in the face of the antinomy, which simply proves the principle untenable. It is a simple point of logic, once we look at it, that there is no class, empty or otherwise, that has as members precisely the classes that are not members of themselves. It would have to have itself as member if and only if it did not.

Russell's antinomy came as a shock to Gottlob Frege, the German mathematician who founded mathematical logic. In his *Grundgesetze der Arithmetik* Frege thought that he had secured the foundations of mathematics in the self-consistent laws of logic. He received a letter from Russell as the second volume of this work was on its way to press. "Arithmetic totters," Frege is said to have written in answer. An appendix that he added to the volume opens with the words: "A scientist can hardly encounter anything more undesirable than to have the foundation collapse just as the work is finished. I was put in this position by a letter from Bertrand Russell . . ."

In Russell's antinomy there is more than a hint of the paradox of the barber. The parallel is, in truth, exact. It was a simple point of logic that there was in no village a man who shaved all and only those men in the village who did not shave themselves; he would shave himself if and only if he did not. The barber paradox was a veridical paradox showing that there is no such barber. Why is Russell's antinomy then not a veridical paradox showing that there is no class whose members are all and only the nonself-members? Why does it count as an antinomy and the barber paradox not? The reason is that there has been in our habits of thought an overwhelming presumption of there being such a class but no presumption of there being such a barber. The barber paradox barely qualifies as paradox in that we are mildly surprised at being able to exclude the barber on purely logical grounds by reducing him to absurdity. Even this surprise ebbs as we review the argument; and anyway we had never positively believed in such a barber. Russell's paradox is a genuine antinomy because of the fundamental nature of the principle of class existence that it compels us to give up. When in a future century the absurdity of that principle has become a commonplace, and some substitute principle

has enjoyed long enough tenure to take on somewhat the air of common sense, perhaps we can begin to see Russell's paradox as no more than a veridical paradox, showing that there is no such class as that of the nonself-members. One man's antinomy can be another man's veridical paradox, and one man's veridical paradox can be another man's platitude.

Russell's antinomy made for a more serious crisis still than did Grelling's and Berry's and the one about Epimenides. For these strike at the semantics of truth and denotation, but Russell's strikes at the mathematics of classes. Classes are appealed to in an auxiliary way in most branches of mathematics, and increasingly so as passages of mathematical reasoning are made more explicit. The basic principle of classes that is tacitly used, at virtually every turn where classes are involved at all, is precisely the class-existence principle that is discredited by Russell's antinomy.

I spoke of Grelling's antinomy and Berry's and the Epimenides as all in a family, to which Russell's antinomy does not belong. For its part, Russell's antinomy has family connections of its own. In fact, it is the first of an infinite series of antinomies, as follows. Russell's antinomy shows that there is no class whose members are precisely the classes that are not members of themselves. Now there is a parallel antinomy that shows there is no class whose members are precisely the classes that are not members of members of themselves. Further, there is an antinomy that shows there is no class whose members are precisely the classes that are not members of members of members of themselves. And so on ad infinitum.

All these antinomies, and other related ones, can be inactivated by limiting the guilty principle of class existence in a very simple way. The principle is that for any membership condition you can formulate there is a class whose members are solely the things meeting the condition. We get Russell's antinomy and all the others of its series by taking the condition as nonmembership in self, or nonmembership in members of self, or the like. Each time the trouble comes of taking a membership condition that itself talks in turn of membership and nonmembership. If we withhold our principle of class existence from cases where the membership condition mentions membership, Russell's antinomy and related ones are no longer forthcoming. This restriction on class existence is parallel to a restriction on the truth locutions that we contemplated for a while,

before bringing in the subscripts; namely, not to apply the truth locutions to expressions containing any of the truth locutions.

Happily we can indeed withhold the principle of class existence from cases where the membership condition mentions membership, without unsettling those branches of mathematics that make only incidental use of classes. This is why it has been possible for most branches of mathematics to go on blithely using classes as auxiliary apparatus in spite of Russell's and related antinomies.

The Mathematics of Classes

There is a particular branch of mathematics in which the central concern is with classes: general set theory. In this domain one deals expressly with classes of classes, classes of classes of classes, and so on, in ways that would be paralyzed by the restriction just now contemplated: withholding the principle of class existence from cases where the membership condition mentions membership. So one tries in general set theory to manage with milder restrictions.

General set theory is rich in paradox. Even the endless series of antinomies that I mentioned above, of which Russell's was the first, by no means exhausts this vein of paradox. General set theory is primarily occupied with infinity—infinite classes, infinite numbers—and so is involved in paradoxes of the infinite. A rather tame old paradox under this head is that you can exhaust the members of a whole class by correlating them with the members of a mere part of the class. For instance, you can correlate all the positive integers with the multiples of 10, thus: 1 with 10, 2 with 20, 3 with 30 and so on. Every positive integer gets disposed of; there are as many multiples of 10 as integers altogether. This is no antinomy but a veridical paradox. Among adepts in the field it even loses the air of paradox altogether, as is indeed the way of veridical paradox.

Georg Cantor, the 19th-century pioneer in general set theory and infinite arithmetic, proved that there are always more classes of things of a given kind than there are things of that kind; more classes of cows than cows. A distinct air of paradox suffuses his proof of this.

First note the definition of "more." What it means when one says there are more things of one kind than another is that every correlation of things of the one kind to things of the other fails to exhaust the things of the one kind. So what **Cantor is proving is that no correlation of cow classes to cows accommodates all** the cow classes. The proof is as follows. Suppose a correlation of cow classes to cows. It can be any arbitrary correlation; a cow may or may not belong to the class correlated with it. Now consider the cows, if any, that do not belong to the classes correlated with them. These cows themselves form a cow class, empty or not. And it is a cow class that is not correlated with any cow. If the class were so correlated, that cow would have to belong to the class if and only if it did not.

This argument is typical of the arguments in general set theory that would be sacrificed if we were to withhold the principle of class existence from cases where the membership condition mentions membership. The recalcitrant cow class that clinched the proof was specified by a membership condition that mentioned membership. The condition was nonmembership in the correlated cow class.

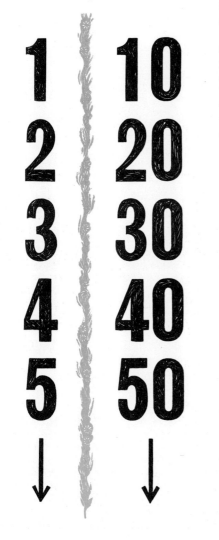

POSITIVE INTEGERS can all be correlated with multiples of 10 even though the latter are only part of the class of integers.

But what I am more concerned to bring out, regarding the cow-class argument, is its air of paradox. The argument makes its negative point in much the same way that the veridical barber paradox showed there to be no such barber, and in much the same way that Russell's antinomy showed there to be no class of nonself-members. So in Cantor's theorem —a theorem not only about cows and their classes but also about things of any sort and their classes—we see paradox, or something like it, seriously at work in the advancement of theory. His theorem establishes that for every class, even every infinite class, there is a larger class: the class of its subclasses.

So far, no antinomy. But now it is a short step to one. If for every class there is a larger class, what of the class of everything? Such is Cantor's antinomy. If you review the proof of Cantor's theorem in application directly to this disastrous example—speaking therefore not of cows but of everything—you will quickly see that Cantor's antinomy boils down, after all, to Russell's.

So the central problem in laying the foundations of general set theory is to inactivate Russell's antinomy and its suite. If such theorems as Cantor's are to be kept, the antinomies must be inactivated by milder restrictions than the total withholding of the principle of class existence from cases where the membership condition mentions membership. One tempting line is a scheme of subscripts analogous to the scheme used in avoiding the antinomies of truth and denotation. Something like this line was taken by Russell himself in 1908, under the name of the theory of logical types. A very different line was proposed in the same year by the German mathematician Ernst Zermelo, and further variations have been advanced in subsequent years.

All such foundations for general set theory have as their point of departure the counsel of the antinomies; namely, that a given condition, advanced as a necessary and sufficient condition of membership in some class, may or may not really have a class corresponding to it. So the various alternative foundations for general set theory differ from one another with respect to the membership conditions to which they do and do not guarantee corresponding classes. Nonself-membership is of course a condition to which none of the theories accord corresponding classes. The same holds true for the condition of not being a member of any own member; and for the conditions that give all the further antinomies of the series that began with Russell's;

and for any membership condition that would give rise to any other antinomy, if we can spot it.

But we cannot simply withhold each antinomy-producing membership condition and assume classes corresponding to the rest. The trouble is that there are membership conditions corresponding to each of which, by itself, we can innocuously assume a class, and yet these classes together can yield a contradiction. We are driven to seeking optimum consistent combinations of existence assumptions, and consequently there is a great variety of proposals for the foundations of general set theory. Each proposed scheme is unnatural, because the natural scheme is the unrestricted one that the antinomies discredit; and each has advantages, in power or simplicity or in attractive consequences in special directions, that each of its rivals lacks.

I remarked earlier that the discovery of antinomy is a crisis in the evolution of thought. In general set theory the crisis began 60 years ago and is not yet over.

Gödel's Proof

Up to now the heroes or villains of this piece have been the antinomies. Other paradoxes have paled in comparison. Other paradoxes have been less startling to us, anyway, and more readily adjusted to. Other paradoxes have not precipitated 60-year crises, at least not in our time. When any of them did in the past precipitate crises that durable (and surely the falsidical paradoxes of Zeno did), they themselves qualified as antinomies.

Let me, in closing, touch on a latter-day paradox that is by no means an antinomy but is strictly a veridical paradox, and yet is comparable to the antinomies in the pattern of its proof, in the surprisingness of the result and even in its capacity to precipitate a crisis. This is Gödel's proof of the incompletability of number theory.

What Kurt Gödel proved, in that great paper of 1931, was that no deductive system, with axioms however arbitrary, is capable of embracing among its theorems all the truths of the elementary arithmetic of positive integers unless it discredits itself by letting slip some of the falsehoods too [see "Gödel's Proof," by Ernest Nagel and James R. Newman; beginning on page 221 in this book]. Gödel showed how, for any given deductive system, he could construct a sentence of elementary number theory that would be true if and only if not provable in that system. Every such system is therefore either incomplete, in that it misses a relevant truth, or else bankrupt, in that it proves a falsehood.

Gödel's proof may conveniently be related to the Epimenides paradox or the *pseudomenon* in the "yields a falsehood" version. For "falsehood" read "nontheorem," thus: " 'Yields a nontheorem when appended to its own quotation' yields a nontheorem when appended to its own quotation."

This statement no longer presents an antinomy, because it no longer says of itself that it is false. What it does say of itself is that it is not a theorem (of some deductive theory that I have not yet specified). If it is true, here is one truth that that deductive theory, whatever it is, fails to include as a theorem. If the statement is false, it is a theorem, in which event that deductive theory has a false theorem and so is discredited.

What Gödel proceeds to do, in getting his proof of the incompletability of number theory, is the following. He shows how the sort of talk that occurs in the above statement—talk of nontheoremhood and of appending things to quotations—can be mirrored systematically in arithmetical talk of integers. In this way, with much ingenuity, he gets a sentence purely in the arithmetical vocabulary of number theory that inherits that crucial property of being true if and only if not a theorem of number theory. And Gödel's trick works for any deductive system we may choose as defining "theorem of number theory."

Gödel's discovery is not an antinomy but a veridical paradox. That there can be no sound and complete deductive systematization of elementary number theory, much less of pure mathematics generally, is true. It is decidedly para-doxical, in the sense that it upsets crucial preconceptions. We used to think that mathematical truth consisted in provability.

Like any veridical paradox, this is one we can get used to, thereby gradually sapping its quality of paradox. But this one takes some sapping. And mathematical logicians are at it, most assiduously. Gödel's result started a trend of research that has grown in 30 years to the proportions of a big and busy branch of mathematics sometimes called proof theory, having to do with recursive functions and related matters, and embracing indeed a general abstract theory of machine computation. Of all the ways of paradoxes, perhaps the quaintest is their capacity on occasion to turn out to be so very much less frivolous than they look.

29 SYMBOLIC LOGIC

JOHN E. PFEIFFER · December 1950

WHAT NUMBER added to one fifth of itself equals 21? This problem was too difficult for most of the scholars of ancient Egypt. According to papyrus records, many arithmeticians struggled with it in vain before a patient Egyptian finally arrived at the correct answer about 1600 B.C. Today a ninth-grade algebra student can find the answer in a moment: $x+x/5=21$; therefore $x=17\frac{1}{2}$. What made the problem hard for the Egyptians was that they lacked our handy symbols, i.e., digits for numbers and x for the unknown. Since they had to use words to represent numbers, their operations in arithmetic and algebra were cumbersome and slow.

The substitution of symbols for words is one of the things that has been largely responsible for man's progress in science. Yet in the process of logic—the basic tool with which we must test all ideas and also solve most of our everyday problems—we are still laboring under the Egyptians' handicap. We are at the mercy of the inadequacies and clumsiness of words.

Consider this simple exercise in logic, taken from a textbook on the subject by Lewis Carroll, mathematician and author of *Alice's Adventures in Wonderland*:

No kitten that loves fish is unteachable.

No kitten without a tail will play with a gorilla.

Kittens with whiskers always love fish.

No teachable kitten has green eyes.

No kittens have tails unless they have whiskers.

One, and only one, deduction can be drawn from this set of statements. After considerable trial and error you may find the answer by rewording and rearranging the statements:

Green-eyed kittens cannot be taught.

Kittens that cannot be taught do not love fish.

Kittens that do not love fish have no whiskers.

Kittens that have no whiskers have no tails.

Kittens that have no tails will not play with a gorilla.

The one valid deduction, then, is that green-eyed kittens will not play with a gorilla.

But now take a problem that is somewhat more complicated. The following is adapted from an examination in logic prepared recently by the mathematician Walter Pitts of the Massachusetts Institute of Technology:

If a mathematician does not have to wait 20 minutes for a bus, then he either likes Mozart in the morning or whisky at night, but not both.

If a man likes whisky at night, then he either likes Mozart in the morning and does not have to wait 20 minutes for a bus or he does not like Mozart in the morning and has to wait 20 minutes for a bus or else he is no mathematician.

If a man likes Mozart in the morning and does not have to wait 20 minutes for a bus, then he likes whisky at night.

If a mathematician likes Mozart in the morning, he either likes whisky at night or has to wait 20 minutes for a bus; conversely, if he likes whisky at night and has to wait 20 minutes for a bus, he is a mathematician—if he likes Mozart in the morning.

When must a mathematician wait 20 minutes for a bus?

The reader is not advised to try to work out the solution, for this problem is practically impossible to handle verbally.

ALTHOUGH these particular brain-teasers are artificial and trivial, in form they are quite typical of problems that arise every day in modern engineering and business operations. Many of the problems are so complex that they cannot be solved by the conventional processes of verbal logic. The necessary facts may all be known, but their interrelationships are so complex that no expert can organize them logically. In other words, the bigness of modern machines, business and government is creating more and more problems in reasoning which are too intricate for the human brain to analyze with words alone.

As a result a number of corporations and technicians have recently begun to take an active interest in the discipline known as symbolic logic. This invention, devised by mathematicians, is simply an attempt to use symbols to represent ideas and methods of handling them, just as symbols are employed to solve problems in mathematics. With the shorthand of symbolic logic it becomes possible to deal with such complex problems as the Pitts conundrum about the mathematician waiting for the bus.

Formal logic, as every schoolboy knows, began with the syllogisms of Aristotle, the most famous of which is: "All men are mortal; all heroes are men; therefore all heroes are mortal." The Greek philosopher set forth 14 such syllogisms and believed that they summed up most of the operations of reasoning. Medieval theologians added 5 syllogisms to Aristotle's 14. For hundreds of years these 19 syllogisms were the foundation of the teaching of logic.

Not until the 19th century did anyone successfully apply symbols and algebra to logic, in place of the verbalisms of Aristotle and his followers. In 1847 an English schoolteacher and mathematician named George Boole published a pamphlet called *The Mathematical Analysis of Logic—Being an Essay Towards a Calculus of Deductive Reasoning*. In it he stated a set of axioms from which more complex statements could be deduced. The statements were in algebraic terms, with symbols such as x and y representing classes of objects or ideas, and the deductions were arrived at by algebraic operations. Thus Boole became the inventor of symbolic logic. His work was followed up by mathematicians in many countries. Their chief aim was to use symbolic logic to solve logical paradoxes and other fundamental problems of mathematical thinking. By 1913 Alfred North Whitehead and Bertrand Russell, using a system of symbols invented by the Italian mathematician Giuseppe Peano, had developed a formal "mathematical logic," which they presented in their *Principia Mathematica* (see "Mathematics," by Sir Edmund Whittaker; SCIENTIFIC AMERICAN, September, 1950).

Today symbolic logic is an important

branch of mathematics, occupying the full time of about 200 mathematicians in the U. S. alone. But the main subject of this article is its practical applications in engineering and business.

LET US first take a few simple illustrations to indicate some of the basic symbols and operations employed in symbolic logic. Any single proposition, however simple or complex, is represented by a letter of the alphabet. For example, the letter a can stand for the statement "The sun is shining," or for something more involved, like "The three-power commission has been directed to look into the question of whether or not a West German federal police force should be created." Then certain special symbols are used to show relations between propositions. A dot, for example, stands for the word "and." Thus the two-proposition statement "The sun is shining and it is Thursday" can be represented by the expression $a \cdot b$.

The symbol $\supset$ stands for the logical relationship "if . . . then." Thus the assertion "If you love cats, then you are a true American" can be written $a \supset b$. Now by the use of other symbols and by operations similar to those in ordinary algebra, this statement can be transformed into a fully equivalent expression in another form. For example, using the symbol v, which stands for the word "or," and a superposed bar, representing the negative, the expression becomes $\bar{a}\ v\ b$, meaning "You do not love cats or you are a true American." The statement can also be transformed into one containing the symbol for "and." Thus $\overline{\bar{a} \cdot b}$ means "It is not the case both that you do not love cats and that you are a true American," or in ordinary English: "You cannot be indifferent or hostile to cats and also be a true American."

It is important to bear in mind that the symbols have nothing to do with the truth or falsity of the propositions themselves, just as algebra is not concerned with whether its symbols stand for ap-

ples or hours. The operations of symbolic logic can only show that, given certain premises, certain conclusions are valid and others are invalid. In this case, assuming that only cat-lovers are true Americans, if you are not a cat-lover the only logically valid conclusion is that you are not a true American, however debatable the proposition may be as a moral principle. The establishment of factually accurate premises is outside the province of logic; its concern is with the validity of the conclusions drawn from a given set of facts or assumptions.

By means of simple signs such as those here illustrated, symbolic logic reduces complex logical problems to manageable proportions. The symbols, like the schoolboy's algebra signs, do much of the logician's thinking for him. Large numbers of propositions can be related to one another in easy algebraic terms; equations can be arranged and rearranged, simplified and expanded, and the results, upon retranslation into English, can reveal new forms of statements that are equivalent to the original or can disclose inconsistencies.

THE FIRST application of symbolic logic to a business problem was made in 1936 by the mathematician Edmund C. Berkeley, who is also the designer of the small mechanical brain known as Simple Simon (SCIENTIFIC AMERICAN, November, 1950). Berkeley, then with the Prudential Life Insurance Company, applied symbolic logic to a difficult problem having to do with the rearrangement of premium payments by policyholders. Every year hundreds of thousands of persons request changes in the schedule of payments on their policies, and there is a bewildering array of factors that must be taken into account in making such changes. The company had devised two sets of rules, intended to take care of all possible cases. Were the two rules equivalent? Berkeley suspected that they were not; that there might be cases in which one rule would call for one method of rearranging the

payments and the other for a different method.

His problem was to prove that such cases existed. It was hopeless to try to analyze the possibilities by ordinary verbal logic. One part of one of the rules, for example, stipulated that if a policyholder was making premium payments several times a year, with one of the payments falling due on the policy anniversary, and if he requested that the schedule be changed to one annual payment on the policy anniversary, and if he was paid up to a date which was not an anniversary, and if he made this request more than two months after the issue date, and if his request also came within two months after a policy anniversary—then a certain action should be taken. These five ifs alone can occur in 32 combinations, and there were many other factors involved.

Berkeley decided to reduce the many clauses and possible combinations and actions to the algebraic shorthand of symbolic logic. The stipulation detailed above, for example, could be written $a \cdot b \cdot \bar{c} \cdot d \cdot e \supset C$, meaning that if the conditions a, b, $\bar{c}$, d and e existed, then the action C was called for. By an algebraic analysis Berkeley was able to show that there were four types of cases in which the two rules would indeed conflict, and an examination of the company's files revealed that such cases actually existed. The upshot of Berkeley's work was that the two rules were combined into one simpler and consistent rule.

Symbolic logic has since been used in many other insurance problems. Mathematicians at Equitable, Metropolitan, Aetna and other companies have applied it to the analysis of war clauses and employee eligibility under group contracts. And other corporations have found symbolic logic very helpful in analyzing their contracts. Contracts between large corporations may run into many pages of fine print packed with stipulations, contingencies and a maze of ifs, ands and buts. Are the clauses worded as simply as they might be? Are there loop-

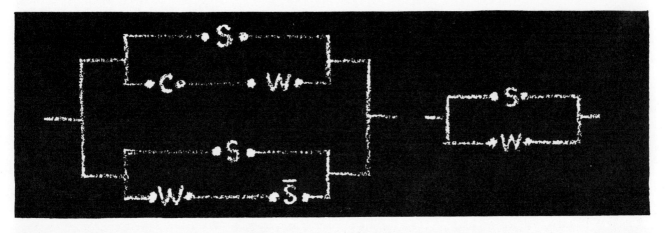

SWITCHING CIRCUITS may be analyzed and simplified by symbolic logic (*see text*). The switches are rep-resented by symbols. Each of these two circuits has the same functions. The one at the left is "redundant."

holes or inconsistencies? A symbolic analysis can readily answer such questions, and lawyers have begun to call on mathematicians to go over their contracts.

Another interesting use of the technique is in checking the accuracy of censuses and of polling reports. If a public opinion poll-taker reports that he has interviewed 100 persons, of whom 70 were white, 10 were women and 5 were Negro men, it is easy enough to see that something is wrong with his figures. But take an actual case such as this: A census of 1,000 cotton-mill employees listed 525 Negroes, 312 males, 470 married persons, 42 Negro males, 147 married Negroes, 86 married males, 25 married Negro males. Are these numbers consistent? Symbolic logic can give the answer quickly.

IN ENGINEERING symbolic logic is particularly useful for the analysis of electric circuits. A circuit can be likened to a contract—it has alternatives, contingencies and possible loopholes, the chief difference being that it uses patterns of switches instead of words and clauses.

More than a dozen years ago Claude E. Shannon, then still a student at the Massachusetts Institute of Technology, began to explore the application of symbolic logic to such problems. At the Bell Telephone Laboratories he has recently completed an elaborate analysis of switching circuits by "engineering logic."

Suppose, to take a simple example, the problem is to simplify the six-switch circuit schematized in the left-hand drawing on the preceding page. The switches are given various symbols. The one labeled C is independent of all the others. The two W switches are connected so that they open and close together. The two S switches also operate together. The sixth switch is designated $\bar{S}$ (not-S, or the opposite of S), because it is open when the S switches are closed and *vice versa*.

There are four possible paths across this circuit. Current will flow across it when the upper S switch is closed, when the C and the upper W switches are closed, when the lower S switch is closed and when the lower W and $\bar{S}$ switches are closed. In the language of symbolic logic this sentence becomes $S \, v \, W \cdot C \, v \, S \, v \, \bar{S} \, W$, with the symbol v, as we have seen, meaning "or." It is at once evident that we can drop one S, since S is equivalent to the expression $S \, v \, S$. The statement now becomes $W \cdot C \, v \, S \, v \, \bar{S} \cdot W$. Next, we can simplify further by dropping the $\bar{S}$, for $S \, v \, W$ is the logical equivalent of $S \, v \, \bar{S} \cdot W$—just as the statement "Williams struck out or Williams did not strike out and walked" is the same as "Williams struck out or walked." This reduces the circuit to $S \, v \, W \, v \, W \cdot C$. A further analysis shows that $W \, v \, W \cdot C$ is equivalent to W. Logically speaking, the statement

"Williams walked or Williams walked and was left at first base" provides only one unequivocal piece of information, namely that Williams walked. So the entire circuit boils down to $S \, v \, W$. It can be redesigned in a simple form, illustrated in the right-hand drawing on the preceding page, which eliminates four "redundant" switches and is fully equivalent to the original.

To use symbolic logic on a problem as simple as this would be like killing a mouse with an elephant gun. But in designing more complex circuits the method may save considerable time and money. At the Bell Laboratories, for example, a group of engineers some time ago undertook to design a special coding instrument. Applying conventional methods of analysis, they produced a 65-contact circuit for the job after several days of work. Then an engineer trained in symbolic logic, starting from scratch without seeing their design, designed an equally successful circuit, with 18 fewer contacts, in only three hours. Today more than 50 Bell engineers use symbolic logic in their work. The method has been applied successfully to a wide variety of problems, but it is not the final answer to all circuit difficulties. Its use is limited mainly to telephone equipment with about nine two-contact relays, which may be in 512 possible positions. In its present infant state even this powerful method of analysis cannot handle the breath-taking complexity of large central exchange stations where a single telephone call may cause the opening and closing of 10,000 contacts.

Perhaps the chief use of symbolic logic is in the design of large-scale electronic calculating machines. Eniac, the first of these machines, contains about 20,000 tubes and 500,000 soldered connections. One of the most important problems in the attempts to build more efficient and more elaborate computers is to reduce the number of tubes, and symbolic logic has been helpful in simplifying the circuits. For example, in building the Mark III all-electronic computer at the Naval Proving Ground in Dahlgren, Va., the engineers decided that a nine-tube circuit was about the minimum that would serve for its adding units. But Theodore Kalin and William Burkhart of the Harvard Computation Laboratory, applying symbolic logic, reduced it to six tubes.

THESE applications merely suggest the fruitful future that lies ahead for symbolic logic, not only in business and engineering but in science. Wherever complex problems in logical analysis arise, the new shorthand may help to find solutions. One such field is biology, which is beset with a host of complex logical problems. Already Walter Pitts and Warren McCulloch of the University of Illinois Medical School have begun to employ the symbolic logic of the

Principia Mathematica in an effort to analyze some of the relationships among the 10 billion nerve cells in the human brain. Norbert Wiener of M.I.T. emphasizes that the new study of cybernetics, which analyzes similarities between the brain and computing machines, leans heavily on modern logic.

Although its applications are steadily widening, the major part of the work being done in symbolic logic is still in the field of mathematics. In mathematics this new tool has had so powerful an influence during the past four decades that today some consider mathematics to be only a branch of logic. Mathematicians are applying symbolic logic to examine some of the basic assumptions upon which mathematical theories have been built—assumptions that have long been taken for granted as "obvious" but have never been subjected to rigorous analysis. They are using it to try to resolve verbal paradoxes, which have always baffled logicians: *e.g.*, "All rules have exceptions," a rule which denies itself, since by its own assertion this statement must also have exceptions and therefore cannot be true. Many other basic problems in logic and mathematics are being explored by the new analysis.

Indeed, modern logicians, assisted by the powerful new technique, have punched the classical Aristotelian system of logic full of holes. Of the 19 syllogisms stated by Aristotle and his medieval followers, four are now rejected, and the rest can be reduced to five theorems. Modern logic has abandoned one of Aristotle's most basic principles: the law of the excluded middle, meaning that a statement must be either true or false. In the new system a statement may have three values: true, false· or indeterminate. A close analogy to this system in the legal field is the Scottish trial law, which allows three verdicts—guilty, not guilty or "not proven."

BECAUSE the use of symbols sometimes makes it possible to determine by purely routine operations whether or not a particular statement follows from given assumptions, symbolic logicians have experimented in designing logical machines. Kalin and Burkhart have, for example, built one that can check Aristotelian syllogisms or solve certain insurance problems, and workers at the University of Manchester in England are developing a more elaborate machine.

Not even symbolic logic will ever produce a machine that can do all man's thinking for him. But some logicians believe that symbolic logic may lead to the construction of synthetic languages that will help to free scientific thinking from the murky tyranny of words.

NON-CANTORIAN SET THEORY

30

PAUL J. COHEN AND REUBEN HERSH · December 1967

The abstract theory of sets is currently in a state of change that in several ways is analogous to the 19th-century revolution in geometry. As in any revolution, political or scientific, it is difficult for those participating in the revolution or witnessing it to foretell its ultimate consequences, except perhaps that they will be profound. One thing that can be done is to try to use the past as a guide to the future. It is an unreliable guide, to be sure, but better than none.

We propose in this article to use the oft-told tale of non-Euclidean geometry to illuminate the now unfolding story of nonstandard set theory.

A set, of course, is one of the simplest and most primitive ideas in mathematics, so simple that today it is part of the kindergarten curriculum. No doubt for this very reason its role as the most fundamental concept of mathematics was not made explicit until the 1880's. Only then did Georg Cantor make the first nontrivial discovery in the theory of sets.

To describe his discovery we must first explain what we mean by an infinite set. An infinite set is merely a set with an infinite number of distinct elements; for example, the set of all "natural" numbers (1, 2, 3 and so on) is infinite. So too is the set of all the points on a given line segment.

Cantor pointed out that even for infinite sets it makes sense to talk about the number of elements in the set, or at least to state that two different sets have the same number of elements. Just as with finite sets, we can say that two sets have the same number of elements —the same "cardinality"—if we can match up the elements in the two sets one for one. If this can be done, we call the two sets equivalent.

The set of all natural numbers can be matched up with the set of all even numbers, and also with the set of all fractions [see illustration below]. These two examples illustrate a paradoxical property of infinite sets: an infinite set can be equivalent to one of its subsets. In fact, it is easily proved that a set is infinite if, and only if, it is equivalent to some proper subset of itself.

All of this is engaging, but it was not new with Cantor. The notion of the cardinality of infinite sets would be interesting only if it could be shown that not all infinite sets have the same cardinality. It was this that was Cantor's first great discovery in set theory. By his famous diagonal proof he showed that the set of natural numbers is *not* equivalent to the set of points on a line segment [see illustration on opposite page].

Thus there are at least two different kinds of infinity. The first, the infinity of the natural numbers (and of any equivalent infinite sets), is called aleph nought ($\aleph_0$). Sets with cardinality $\aleph_0$ are called countable. The second kind of infinity is the one represented by a line segment. Its cardinality is designated by a lower-case German c ($\mathfrak{c}$), for "continuum." *Any* line segment, of arbitrary length, has cardinality $\mathfrak{c}$ [see illustration on page 214]. So does any rectangle in the plane, any cube in space, or for that matter all of unbounded n-dimensional space, whether n is 1, 2, 3 or 1,000!

Once a single step up the chain of infinities has been taken, the next follows naturally. We encounter the notion of the set of all subsets of a given set [see illustration on page 215]. If the

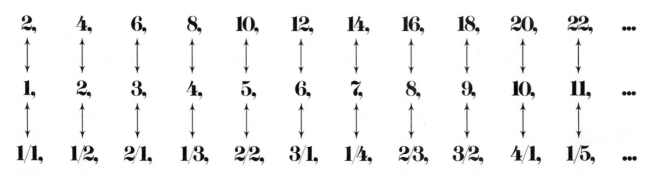

SET IS TERMED COUNTABLE if it can be matched one for one with the natural numbers (*middle row*). Thus the set of all even numbers (*top row*) is countable. The set of all fractions (*bottom row*) is also countable. The fractions shown here are the ones used by the German mathematician Georg Cantor (1845–1918); they are not in their natural order but in order according to the sum of the numerator and the denominator. Both examples show that an infinite set, unlike a finite set, can be equivalent to one of its subsets.

original set is called *A*, this new set is called the power set of *A* and is written 2^A. And just as we obtain the power set 2^A from *A*, we can next obtain $2^{(2^A)}$ from 2^A, and so on as long as we please.

Cantor proved that whether *A* is finite or infinite, 2^A is never equivalent to *A*. Therefore the procedure of forming the set of all subsets generates an endless chain of increasing, nonequivalent infinite sets. In particular, if *A* is the set of natural numbers, then it is easy to prove that 2^A (the set of all sets of natural numbers) is equivalent to the continuum (the set of all points on a line segment). In brief,

$$2^{\aleph_0} = \mathfrak{c}.$$

At this point a question may occur to the reader. Is there an infinite set with cardinality *between* $\aleph_0$ and $\mathfrak{c}$? That is, is there on a line segment an infinite set of points that is not equivalent to the whole segment, and also not equivalent to the set of natural numbers?

This question occurred to Cantor, but he was unable to find any such set. He concluded—or rather conjectured—that no such thing exists. This guess of Cantor's acquired the name "the continuum hypothesis." Its proof or disproof was first on the celebrated list of unsolved mathematical problems drawn up by David Hilbert in 1900. Only in 1963 was it finally settled. It was settled, however, in a sense utterly different from what Hilbert had in mind.

To tackle this problem one could no longer rely on Cantor's definition of a set as "any collection into a whole of definite and separate objects of our intuition or our thought." In fact, this definition, seemingly so transparent, turned out to conceal some treacherous pitfalls. An instance is the sad experience suffered by Gottlob Frege in 1902. Frege was about to publish a monumental work in which arithmetic was reconstructed on the foundation of set theory, that is, on the foundation of "intuitive" set theory as it was then known on the basis of Cantor's work. At this point Frege received a letter from the young Bertrand Russell, which he acknowledged by adding this postscript to his treatise: "A scientist can hardly meet with anything more undesirable than to have the foundation give way just as the work is finished. In this position I was put by a letter from Mr. Bertrand Russell as the work was nearly through the press."

Russell's blow consisted in pointing out a simple conundrum. There are two kinds of sets. First there are those, such as "the set of all objects describable in

1. .18347984639001...
2. .36948570110924...
3. .50472200173996...
4. .99801230109487...
5. .00102305497610...
6. .51546798371238...
7. .55119871350426...
⋮

SET OF REAL NUMBERS IS UNCOUNTABLE, as Cantor showed in his famous diagonal proof. Here a sample of the set is listed in decimal form and at random. If one takes the first digit of the first number, the second digit of the second and so on (*color*), one obtains a real number whose infinite decimal expansion is .1640277.... If one randomly changed every digit in the expansion, one might get .2751388.... A moment's thought will show that the new number is different in at least one place from every number on the list. Hence the number was not present on the list, and it has been proved that the list was incomplete.

exactly 11 English words," having the peculiar property that they themselves satisfy their defining property; in other words, sets that contain themselves as elements. We call them *R* sets, the *R* standing for Russell. Then there are all other sets—sets that do not belong to themselves. Call them the non-*R* sets. Now, said Russell, consider the collection of all non-*R* sets. (The word "collection" is introduced here simply as a convenient synonym for "set.") Call this set *M*. Then *M* is either an *R* set or a non-*R* set. But if *M* is a non-*R* set, then it belongs to *M*, by definition of *M*, so that it is an *R* set, by definition of *R* sets. This is a contradiction. On the other hand, if *M* is an *R* set, then by definition of *M* it does not belong to *M*. It does not belong to itself, that is, it is not an *R* set, which is again a contradiction.

The moral is this: The free use of Cantor's intuitive notion of a set can lead to contradictions. Set theory can serve as a secure foundation for mathematics only if a more sophisticated approach is employed to steer clear of antinomies, as contradictions of the type proposed by Russell later came to be known.

It has happened before that unwelcome paradoxes have intruded into a seemingly clear mathematical theory. There are the paradoxes of Zeno, which revealed to the Greeks unsuspected complexities in intuitive concepts of lines and points. We can draw an analogy: As Russell found a contradiction in the unrestricted use of the intuitive concept of set, so Zeno had found contradictions in the unrestricted use of the intuitive concepts of "line" and "point."

In its beginning with Thales in the sixth century B.C. Greek geometry had relied on an unspecified intuitive concept of "line" and "point." Some 300 years later, however, Euclid had given these concepts an axiomatic treatment. For Euclid geometric objects were still intuitively known real entities, but insofar as they were the subject of geometrical reasoning they were specified by certain unproved assertions ("axioms" and "postulates"), on the basis of which all their other properties were supposed to be proved as "theorems." We do not know if, and to what extent, this development was a response to paradoxes such as Zeno's. There is no doubt, however, that to the Greeks geometry was made much more secure by virtue of depending (at least so they believed and intended) only on logical inference from a small number of clearly stated assumptions.

The analogous development for set theory took not 300 years but only 35. If

Cantor played the role of Thales—the founder of the subject, who was able to rely on intuitive reasoning alone—then the role of Euclid was played by Ernst Zermelo, who in 1908 founded axiomatic set theory. Of course, Euclid was really only one of a long succession of Greek geometers who created "Euclidean geometry"; so also Zermelo was only the first of half a dozen great names in the creation of axiomatic set theory.

Just as Euclid had listed certain properties of points and lines and had regarded as proved only those theorems in geometry that could be obtained from these axioms (and not from any possibly intuitive arguments), so in axiomatic set theory a set is regarded simply as an undefined object satisfying a given list of axioms. Of course, we still want to study sets (or lines, as the case may be), and so the axioms are chosen not arbitrarily but in accord with our intuitive notion of a set or a line. Intuition is nonetheless barred from any further formal role; only those propositions are accepted that follow from the axioms. The fact that objects described by these axioms actually may exist in the real world is irrelevant to the process of formal deduction (although it is essential to discovery).

We agree to act as if the symbols for "line," "point" and "angle" in geometry, or the symbols for "set," "is a subset of" and so on in set theory, are mere marks on paper, which may be rearranged only according to a given list of rules (axioms and rules of inference). Accepted as theorems are only those statements that are obtained according to such manipulations of symbols. (In actual practice only those statements are accepted that clearly *could* be obtained in this manner if one took enough time and trouble.)

Now, in the history of geometry one postulate played a special role. This was the parallel postulate, which says that through a given point there can be drawn precisely one line parallel to a given line. The difficulty with this statement as an axiom is that it does not have the self-evident character one prefers in the foundation stones of a mathematical theory. In fact, parallel lines are defined as lines that never meet, even if they are extended indefinitely ("to infinity"). Since any lines we draw on paper or on a blackboard have finite length, this is an axiom that by its nature cannot be verified by direct observation of the senses. Nonetheless, it plays an indispensable role in Euclidean geometry. For many centuries a leading problem in geometry was to *prove* the parallel postulate, to show that it could be obtained as a theorem from the more self-evident Euclidean axioms.

In abstract set theory, it so happens, there also was a particular axiom that some mathematicians found hard to swallow. This was the axiom of choice, which says the following: If α is any collection of sets $\{A, B, \ldots\}$, and none of the sets in α is empty, then there exists a set Z consisting of precisely one element each from A, from B and so on through all the sets in α. For instance, if α consists of two sets, the set of all triangles and the set of all squares, then α clearly satisfies the axiom of choice. We merely choose some particular triangle and some particular square and then let these two elements constitute Z.

Most people find the axiom of choice, like the parallel postulate, intuitively very plausible. The difficulty with it is in the latitude we allow α: "any" collection of sets. As we have seen, there are endless chains of ever bigger infinite sets. For such an inconceivably huge collection of sets there is no way of actually choosing one by one from all its member sets. If we accept the axiom of choice, our acceptance is simply an act of faith that such a choice is possible, just as our acceptance of the parallel postulate is an act of faith about how lines would act if they were extended to infinity. It turns out that from the innocent-seeming axiom of choice some unexpected and extremely powerful conclusions follow. For example, we are able to use inductive reasoning to prove statements about the elements in *any* set, in much the same way that mathematical induction can be used to prove theorems about the natural numbers 1, 2, 3 and so on.

The axiom of choice played a special role in set theory. Many mathematicians thought its use should be avoided whenever possible. Such a form of axiomatic set theory, in which the axiom of choice is *not* assumed to be either true or false, would be one on which almost all mathematicians would be prepared to rely. In what follows we use the term "restricted set theory" for such an axiom system. We use the term "standard set theory" for the theory based on the full set of axioms put forward by Zermelo and Abraham Fraenkel: restricted set theory *plus* the axiom of choice.

In 1938 this subject was profoundly illuminated by Kurt Gödel. Gödel is best known for his great "incompleteness" theorems of 1930–1931 [see "Gödel's Proof," by Ernest Nagel and James R. Newman, beginning on page 221 in this book]. Here we refer to later work by Gödel that is not well known to nonmathematicians. In 1938 Gödel proved the following fundamental result: If restricted set theory is consistent, then so is standard set theory. In other words, the axiom of choice is no more dangerous than the other axioms; if a contradiction can be found in standard set theory, then there must already be a contradiction hidden within restricted set theory.

But that was not all Gödel proved. We remind the reader of Cantor's "continuum hypothesis," namely that no in-

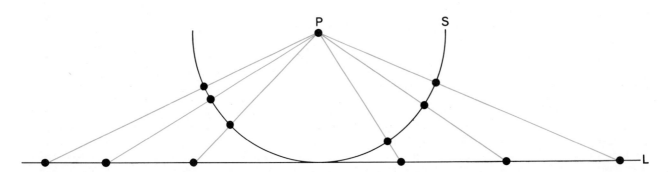

INFINITE LINE AND FINITE LINE SEGMENT can also be shown to have a one-to-one correspondence. Here P is the center of a semicircle S that is tangent to an infinite line L. A ray from P cuts S at only one point. In this way rays from P give a one-to-one match between points on S and points on L. As the ray changes direction from left to right no point is omitted from either S or L. Thus a one-to-one correspondence exists between the points on an infinite line and the points on a finite segment of arbitrary length.

finite cardinal exists that is greater than $\aleph_0$ and smaller than $\mathfrak{c}$. Gödel also showed that we can safely take the continuum hypothesis as an additional axiom in set theory; that is, if the continuum hypothesis plus restricted set theory implies a contradiction, then again there must already be a contradiction hidden within restricted set theory. This was a half-solution of Cantor's problem; it was not a *proof* of the continuum hypothesis but only a proof that it cannot be disproved.

To understand how Gödel achieved his results we need to understand what is meant by a model for an axiom system. Let us return for a moment to the axioms of plane geometry. If we take these axioms, including the parallel postulate, we have the axioms of Euclidean geometry; if instead we keep all the other axioms as before but replace the parallel postulate by its negation, we have the axioms of a non-Euclidean geometry. For both axiom systems—Euclidean and non-Euclidean—we ask: Can these axioms lead to a contradiction?

To ask the question of the Euclidean system may seem unreasonable. How could there be anything wrong with our familiar, 2,000-year-old high school geometry? On the other hand, to the non-mathematician there certainly is something suspicious about the second axiom system, with its denial of the intuitively plausible parallel postulate. Nonetheless, from the viewpoint of 20th-century mathematics the two kinds of geometry stand more or less on an equal footing. Both are sometimes applicable to the physical world and both are consistent, in a relative sense we shall now explain.

First we show that non-Euclidean geometry is consistent. In order to do this we merely replace the word "line" everywhere by the phrase "great circle," a line formed on the surface of a sphere by a plane passing through the center of the sphere. We now regard the axioms as statements about points and great circles on a given sphere. Moreover, we agree to identify each pair of diametrically opposite points on the sphere as a single point. If the reader prefers, he can imagine the axioms of non-Euclidean geometry rewritten, with the word "line" everywhere replaced by "great circle," the word "point" everywhere replaced by "point pair." Then it is evident that all the axioms are true, at least insofar as our ordinary notions about the surface of a sphere are true. In fact, from the axioms of Euclidean solid geometry one can easily prove as theorems that the surface of a sphere is a non-Euclidean

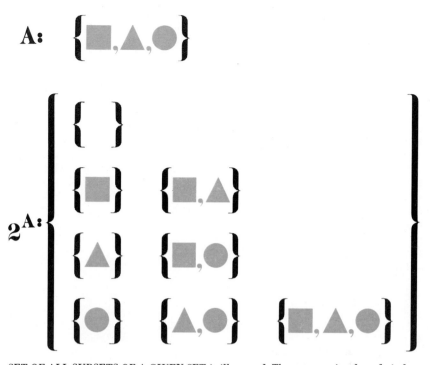

SET OF ALL SUBSETS OF A GIVEN SET is illustrated. The square, triangle and circle at top form the three-element set A. This set has 2^3, or 8, subsets (provided that the whole set and the empty set are somewhat improperly included). This new set consisting of eight elements is called the power set of A, and it is denoted 2^A. If A has n elements, the power set of A has 2^n elements. If A is infinite, 2^A is also infinite, and it is not equivalent to A.

surface in the sense we have just described. In other words, we now see that if the axioms of non-Euclidean geometry led to a contradiction, then so would the ordinary Euclidean geometry of spheres lead to a contradiction. Thus we have a *relative* proof of consistency; if Euclidean three-dimensional geometry is consistent, then so is non-Euclidean two-dimensional geometry. We say that the surface of the Euclidean sphere is a model for the axioms of non-Euclidean geometry. (In the particular model we have used the parallel postulate fails because there are no parallel lines. It is also possible to construct a surface, the "pseudosphere," for which the parallel postulate is false because there is more than one line through a point parallel to a given line.)

The invention of non-Euclidean geometry, and the recognition that its consistency is implied by the consistency of Euclidean geometry, was the work of many great 19th-century mathematicians; we mention the name of Bernhard Riemann in particular. Only in the 20th century was the question raised of whether or not Euclidean geometry itself is consistent.

This question was asked and answered by David Hilbert. Hilbert's solution was a simple application of the idea of a coordinate system. As many college freshmen learn, to each point in the plane we can associate a pair of numbers: its x and y coordinates. Then with each line or circle we can associate an equation: a relation between the x and y coordinates that is true only for the points on that line or circle. In this way we set up a correspondence between geometry and elementary algebra. For every statement in one subject there is a corresponding statement in the other. It follows that the axioms of Euclidean geometry can lead to a contradiction only if the rules of elementary algebra—the properties of the ordinary real numbers—can lead to a contradiction. Here again we have a relative proof of consistency. Non-Euclidean geometry was consistent if Euclidean geometry was consistent; now Euclidean geometry is consistent if elementary algebra is consistent. The Euclidean sphere was a model for the non-Euclidean plane; the set of pairs of coordinates is in turn a model for the Euclidean plane.

With these examples before us we can say that Gödel's proof of the relative consistency of the axiom of choice and of the continuum hypothesis is analogous to Hilbert's proof of the relative consistency of Euclidean geometry. In both instances the standard theory was justified in terms of a more elementary one. Of course, no one ever seriously doubted the reliability of Euclidean geometry, whereas such outstanding mathematicians as L. E. J. Brouwer, Hermann Weyl and Henri Poincaré had grave doubts about the axiom of choice. In this sense Gödel's result had a much greater impact and significance.

The analogous development with respect to non-Euclidean geometry—what we might call non-Cantorian set theory—has taken place only since 1963, in the work of one of the authors of this article (Cohen). What is meant by "non-Cantorian set theory"? Just as Euclidean and non-Euclidean geometry use the same axioms, with the one exception of the parallel postulate, so standard ("Cantorian") and nonstandard ("non-Cantorian") set theory differ only in one axiom. Non-Cantorian set theory takes the axioms of restricted set theory and adds not the axiom of choice but rather one or another form of the negation of the axiom of choice. In particular we can take as an axiom the negation of the continuum hypothesis. Thus, as we shall explain, there now exists a complete solution of the continuum problem. To Gödel's discovery that the continuum hypothesis is not disprovable is added the fact that it is also not provable.

Both Gödel's result and the new discoveries require the construction of a model, just as the consistency proofs for geometry that we have described required a model. In both cases we want to prove that if restricted set theory is consistent, then so is standard set theory (or nonstandard theory).

Gödel's idea was to construct a model for restricted set theory, and to prove that in this model the axiom of choice and the continuum hypothesis were theorems. He proceeded in the following way. Using only the axioms of restricted set theory [see illustration on page 217], we are guaranteed first the existence of at least one set (the empty set) by Axiom 2; then by Axiom 3 and Axiom 4 we are guaranteed the existence of an infinite sequence of ever larger finite sets; then by Axiom 5, the existence of an infinite set; then by Axiom 7, of an endless sequence of ever larger (nonequivalent) infinite sets, and so on. In essentially this way Gödel specified a class of sets by the manner in which they could actually be constructed in successive steps from simpler sets. These sets he called the "constructible sets"; their existence was guaranteed by the axioms of restricted set theory. Then he showed that within the realm of the constructible sets the axiom of choice and the continuum hypothesis can both be proved. That is to say, first, from any constructible collection α of constructible sets $(A, B, \ldots)$ one can choose a constructible set Z consisting of at least one element each from A, B and so on. This is the axiom of choice, which here might more properly be called the theorem of choice. Second, if A is any infinite constructible set, then there is no constructible set "between" A and 2^A (bigger than A, smaller than the power set of A and equivalent to neither). If A is taken as the first infinite cardinal, this last statement is the continuum hypothesis.

Hence a "generalized continuum hypothesis" was proved in the case of constructible set theory. Gödel's work would therefore dispose of these two questions completely if we were prepared to adopt the axiom that only constructible sets exist. Why not do so? Because one feels it is unreasonable to insist that a set must be constructed according to any prescribed formula in order to be recognized as a genuine set. Thus in ordinary (not necessarily constructible) set theory neither the axiom of choice nor the continuum hypothesis had been proved. At least this much was

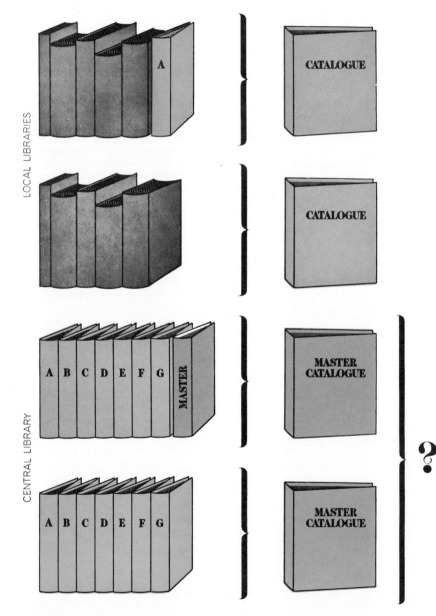

LOCAL LIBRARIES

CENTRAL LIBRARY

A

CATALOGUE

CATALOGUE

A B C D E F G   MASTER

MASTER CATALOGUE

A B C D E F G

MASTER CATALOGUE

?

RUSSELL'S PARADOX is illustrated by supposing that in a certain country it is the custom of librarians to list their books not in a card catalogue but in a looseleaf catalogue; that is, the catalogue itself is a book. Some librarians list the catalogue itself in the catalogue (top); some do not (second from top). The first kind of catalogue is called an R-set, after Bertrand Russell; R-sets are sets that include themselves. What happens, however, if the head librarian of the country decides to make a master catalogue of all the catalogues that do not list themselves? Does his own catalogue belong in the master catalogue or not?

∀ FOR ALL	↔ IF AND ONLY IF	∈ IS A MEMBER (ELEMENT) OF
∃ THERE EXISTS	V OR	= EQUALS
∃! THERE EXISTS UNIQUELY	& AND	≠ DOES NOT EQUAL
∪ UNION	~ NOT	φ THE EMPTY SET
→ IMPLIES	⊆ IS A SUBSET OF	

1. AXIOM OF EXTENSIONALITY

$$\forall x, y \, (\forall z \, (z \in x \to z \in y) \to x = y).$$

Two sets are equal if and only if they have the same members.

2. AXIOM OF THE NULL SET

$$\exists x \, \forall y \, (\sim y \in x).$$

There exists a set with no members (the empty set).

3. AXIOM OF UNORDERED PAIRS

$$\forall x, y \, \exists z \, \forall w \, (w \in z \leftrightarrow w = x \lor w = y).$$

If x and y are sets, then the (unordered) pair $\{x,y\}$ is a set.

4. AXIOM OF THE SUM SET OR UNION

$$\forall x \, \exists y \, \forall z \, (z \in y \leftrightarrow \exists t \, (z \in t \, \& \, t \in x) \,).$$

If x is a set of sets, the union of all its members is a set. (For example, if $x = \left\{ \begin{matrix} \{a,b,c\} \\ \{a,c,d,e\} \end{matrix} \right\}$, then the union of the (two) elements of x is the set $\{a,b,c,d,e\}$.)

5. AXIOM OF INFINITY

$$\exists x \, (\phi \in x \, \& \, \forall y \, (y \in x \to y \cup \{y\} \in x).$$

There exists a set x that contains the empty set. and that is such that if y belongs to x, then the union of y and $\{y\}$ is also in x. The distinction between the element y and the singleton set $\{y\}$ is basic. This axiom guarantees the existence of infinite sets.

6_n. AXIOM OF REPLACEMENT

$$\forall t_1,...,t_k \, (\forall x \, \exists! \, y \, A_n(x,y;t_1,...,t_k) \to \forall u \, \exists v \, B(u,v) \,) \quad \text{where} \quad B(u,v) \, \Xi \, \forall r \, (r \in v \leftrightarrow \exists s \, (s \in u \, \& \, A_n(s,r;t_1,...,t_k) \,) \,).$$

This axiom is difficult to restate in English. It is called 6_n rather than 6 because it is really a whole family of axioms. We suppose that all the formulas expressible in our system have been enumerated; the nth is called A_n. Then the axiom of replacement says that if for fixed $t_1,...,t_k$, $A_n(x,y;t_i)$ defines y uniquely as a function of x, say $y = \varphi(x)$, then for each u the range of φ on u is a set. This means, roughly, that any ("reasonable") property that can be stated in the formal language of the theory can be used to define a set (the set of things having the stated property).

7. AXIOM OF THE POWER SET

$$\forall x \, \exists y \, \forall z \, (z \in y \leftrightarrow z \subseteq x).$$

This axiom says that there exists for each x the set y of all subsets of x. Although y is thus defined by a property, it is not covered by the replacement axiom because it is not given as the range of any function. Indeed, the cardinality of y will be greater than that of x, so that this axiom allows us to construct higher cardinals.

8. AXIOM OF CHOICE

If $a \to A_a \neq \phi$ is a function defined for all $a \in x$, then there exists another function $f(a)$ for $a \in x$, and $f(a) \in A_a$.

This is the well-known axiom of choice, which allows us to do an infinite amount of "choosing" even though we have no property that would define the choice function and thus enable us to use 6_n instead.

9. AXIOM OF REGULARITY

$$\forall x \, \exists y \, (x = \phi \lor (y \in x \, \& \, \forall z \, (z \in x \to \sim z \in y) \,) \,).$$

This axiom explicitly prohibits $x \in x$, for example.

ZERMELO-FRAENKEL AXIOMS FOR SET THEORY are listed. In order to state these theorems it is necessary to use the symbols of set theory, a glossary of which is given at top. This axiom system was put forward by Ernst Zermelo and Abraham Fraenkel.

"COMMON NOTIONS"

1. Things that are equal to the same thing are also equal to one another.

2. If equals are added to equals, the wholes are equal.

3. If equals are subtracted from equals, the remainders are equal.

4. Things that coincide with one another are equal to one another.

5. The whole is greater than the part.

"POSTULATES"

1. (It is possible) to draw (exactly one) straight line from any point to any point.

2. (It is possible) to extend a finite straight line continuously in a straight line.

3. (It is possible) to describe a circle with any center and distance.

4. All right angles are equal to one another.

5. If a straight line falling on two straight lines makes the interior angles on the same side less than two right angles, the two straight lines, if produced indefinitely, meet on that side on which are the angles less than the two right angles.

EUCLID'S AXIOMS were of two kinds: "common notions" and "postulates." The Scottish physicist and mathematician John Playfair (1748–1819) is identified with an axiom that may be shown to be equivalent to Euclid's Postulate 5: Through a given point A not on a given line m there passes one line that does not intersect m. A non-Euclidean geometry is obtained by replacing "one" with either "none" or "more than one." It should be said that Euclid's axioms are not clear or complete by modern standards.

certain: either of them could be assumed without causing any contradiction unless the "safe" axioms of restricted set theory already are self-contradictory. Any contradiction they cause must already be present in constructible set theory, which is a model for ordinary set theory. In other words, it was known that neither could be disproved from the other axioms but not whether they could be proved. Here the analogy with the parallel postulate in Euclidean geometry becomes particularly apt. That Euclid's axioms are consistent was taken for granted until quite recently. The ques-

tion that interested geometers was whether or not they are independent, that is, whether the parallel postulate could be proved on the basis of the others. A whole series of geometers tried to prove the parallel postulate by showing that its negation led to absurdities. It seems that Carl Friedrich Gauss was the first to see that these "absurdities" were simply the theorems of a new, non-Euclidean geometry. But what Gauss had the courage to think he did not have the courage to publish. It was left for János Bolyai, Nikolai Ivanovich Lobachevsky and Riemann to carry out the logical consequences of denying the parallel postulate. These consequences were the discovery of "fantastic" geometries that had as much logical consistency as the Euclidean geometry of "the real world." Only after this had happened was it recognized that two-dimensional non-Euclidean geometry was just the ordinary Euclidean geometry of certain curved surfaces (spheres and pseudospheres).

The analogous step in set theory would be to deny the axiom of choice or the continuum hypothesis. By this we mean, of course, that the step would be to prove that such a negation is consistent with restricted set theory, in the same sense in which Gödel had proved that the affirmation was consistent. It is this proof that has been accomplished in the past few years, giving rise to a surge of activity in mathematical logic whose final outcome cannot be guessed.

Since it is a question of proving the relative consistency of an axiom system, we naturally think of constructing a model. As we have seen, the relative consistency of non-Euclidean geometry was established when surfaces in Euclidean three-space were shown to be models of two-dimensional non-Euclidean geometry. In a comparable way, in order to prove the legitimacy of a non-Cantorian set theory in which the axiom of choice or the continuum hypothesis is false we must use the axioms of restricted set theory to construct a model in which the negation of the axiom of choice or the negation of the continuum hypothesis can be proved as theorems.

It must be confessed that construction of this model is a complex and delicate affair. This is perhaps to be expected. In Gödel's constructible sets, his model of Cantorian set theory, the task was to create something essentially the same as our intuitive notion of sets but more tractable. In our present task we have to create a model of something unintuitive and strange, using the familiar building stones of restricted set theory.

Rather than throw up our hands and say it is impossible to describe this model in a nontechnical article, we shall attempt at least to give a descriptive account of one or two of the leading ideas that are involved. Our starting point is ordinary set theory (without the axiom of choice). We hope only to prove the consistency of non-Cantorian set theory in a relative sense. Just as the models of non-Euclidean geometry prove that non-Euclidean geometry is consistent if Euclidean geometry is consistent, so we shall prove that if restricted set theory is consistent, it remains so if we add the statement "The axiom of choice is false" or the statement "The continuum hypothesis is false." We may now assume that we have available as a starting point a model for restricted set theory. Call this model M; it can be regarded as Gödel's class of constructible sets.

We know from Gödel's work that in order for the axiom of choice or the continuum hypothesis to fail we must add to M at least one nonconstructible set. How to do this? We introduce the letter a to stand for an object to be added to M; it remains to determine what kind of thing a should be. Once we add a we must also add everything that can be formed from a by the permitted operations of restricted set theory: uniting two or more sets to form a new set, forming the power set and so on. The new collection of sets generated in this way by $M + a$ will be called N. The problem is how to choose a in such a way that (1) N is a model for restricted set theory, as M was by assumption, and (2) a is not constructible in N. Only if this is possible is there any hope of denying the axiom of choice or the continuum hypothesis.

We can get a vague feeling of what has to be done by asking how a geometer of 1850 who was trying to discover the pseudosphere might have proceeded. In a very rough sense, it is as if he had started with a curve M in the Euclidean plane, thought of a point a not in that plane, and then connected that point a to all the points in M. Since a is chosen not to lie in the plane of M, the resulting surface N will surely not be the same as the Euclidean plane. Thus it is reasonable to think that with enough ingenuity and technical skill one could show that it is really a model for a non-Euclidean geometry.

The analogous thing in non-Cantorian set theory is to choose the new set a as a nonconstructible set, then to generate a new model N consisting of all sets obtained by the operations of restricted set theory applied to a and to the sets in M. If this can be done, it will have been

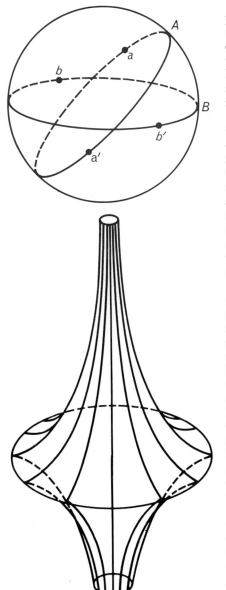

ON SURFACE OF A SPHERE "straight line" is interpreted to mean "great circle" (*A* and *B* at top). Through any pair of diametrically opposite points (*aa'* and *bb'*) there pass many great circles. If we interpret "point" to mean "point pair," then Euclid's first postulate is true. The second postulate is true if one allows the extended "straight line" to have a finite total length, or to retrace itself many times as it goes around the sphere. The third postulate is also true if one understands distance to be measured along great circles that can be retraced several times; here a "circle" means merely the set of points on the sphere at a given great-circle distance from a given point. The fourth postulate is likewise true. Playfair's postulate is false, because any two great circles intersect. Thus the sphere is a model of non-Euclidean geometry. So is the pseudosphere (*bottom*), if straight lines are interpreted as being the shortest curves connecting any two points on the surface. On the surface of the pseudosphere there are many "straight lines" that pass through a given point and do not cross a given straight line.

proved that one is safely able to negate the axiom of constructibility. Since Gödel showed that constructibility implies the axiom of choice and the continuum hypothesis, this is the necessary first step in negating either of these two statements.

In order to carry out this first step two things must be shown: that *a* can be chosen so that it remains nonconstructible, not only in *M* but also in *N*, and that *N*, like *M*, is a model for restricted set theory. To specify *a* we take a roundabout procedure. We imagine that we are going to make a list of all possible statements about *a*, as a set in *N*. Then *a* will be specified if we give a rule by which we can determine whether or not any such statement is true.

The crucial idea turns out to be to choose *a* to be a "generic" element, that is, to choose *a* so that only those statements are true for *a* that are true for almost all sets in *M*. This is a paradoxical notion. Every set in *M* has both particular special properties that identify it, and also general typical properties that it shares with almost all the other sets in *M*. It turns out to be possible in a precise way to make this distinction between special and generic properties perfectly explicit and formal. Then when we choose *a* to be a generic set (one with, so to speak, no special properties that distinguish it from any set in *M*), it follows that *N* is still a model for restricted set theory. The new element *a* we have introduced has no troublesome properties that can spoil the *M* we started with. At the same time *a* is nonconstructible. Any constructible set has a special character—the steps by which it can be constructed—and our *a* precisely lacks any such individuality.

To construct a model in which the continuum hypothesis is false we must add to *M* not just one new element *a* but a great many new elements. In fact, we must add an infinite number of them. We can actually do this in such a way that the elements we add have cardinality

$$\aleph_2 = 2^{\left(2^{\aleph_0}\right)}$$

from the viewpoint of the model *M*. Again a rough geometric analogy may be helpful: To a two-dimensional creature living embedded in a non-Euclidean surface it would be impossible to recognize that his world is part of a three-dimensional Euclidean space. In the present instance we, standing outside *M*, can see that we have thrown in only a countable infinity of new elements. They are such, however, that the counting cannot be done by any apparatus available in *M*

itself. Thus we obtain a new model *N'*, in which the continuum hypothesis is false. The new elements, which in *N'* play the role of real numbers (that is, points on a line segment), have cardinality greater than $2^{\aleph_0}$, and so there is now an infinite cardinal—namely $2^{\aleph_0}$—that is greater than $\aleph_0$ and yet smaller than $\mathfrak{c}$, since in our model *N'*, $\mathfrak{c}$ is equal to

$$2^{\left(2^{\aleph_0}\right)}.$$

Since we can construct a model of set theory in which the continuum hypothesis is false, it follows that we can add to our ordinary restricted set theory the assumption of the falsity of the continuum hypothesis; no contradiction can result that was not already present. In the same spirit we can construct models for set theory in which the axiom of choice fails. We can even be quite specific about which infinite sets it is possible to "choose from" and which are "too big to choose from."

Whereas Gödel produced his results with a single model (the constructible sets), we have in non-Cantorian set theory not one, but many models, each constructed with a particular purpose in mind. Perhaps more important than any of the models is the technique that enables one to construct them all: the notion of "generic" and the related notion of "forcing." Very roughly speaking, generic sets have only those properties they are "forced" to have in order to be setlike. In order to decide whether *a* is "forced" to have a certain property we must look at all of *N*. Yet *N* is not really defined until we have specified *a!* The recognition of how to make this seemingly circular argument noncircular is another key element in the new theory.

What does the history of geometry suggest for the future of set theory? The most remarkable thing about non-Euclidean geometry is that it turned out to be an essential prerequisite for Einstein's general theory of relativity. Riemann created Riemannian geometry for the purely abstract purpose of unifying, clarifying and deepening the non-Euclidean geometry of Lobachevsky, Bolyai and Gauss. This geometry turned out to be the indispensable tool for Einstein's revolutionary reinterpretation of the gravitational force.

Does this example justify an expectation that non-Cantorian set theory someday will find a currently unforeseeable application in the "real" (that is, nonmathematical) world? No one today would venture an answer. Certainly we can see (with hindsight) that geometry

GEOMETRY	STAGE OF DEVELOPMENT	SET THEORY
THALES, PYTHAGORAS	INTUITIVE BASIS FOR FIRST THEOREMS	CANTOR
ZENO	PARADOX REVEALED	RUSSELL
EUDOXUS, EUCLID	AXIOMATIC BASIS FOR STANDARD THEORY	ZERMELO, FRAENKEL, ETC.
DESCARTES, HILBERT	STANDARD THEORY SHOWN (RELATIVELY) CONSISTENT	GÖDEL
GAUSS, RIEMANN	DISCOVERY OF NONSTANDARD THEORIES	CURRENT WORK
MINKOWSKI, EINSTEIN	APPLICATION OF NONSTANDARD THEORY	? ?

ANALOGY IN DEVELOPMENT of geometry (*left*) and set theory (*right*) is traced historically. Nonstandard (**non-Euclidean**) geometry has been applied in such theories as Einstein's theory of relativity. Nonstandard set theory has yet to be applied in physics.

has always furnished the essential background in which physical events take place. In that sense it should perhaps have been expected that fundamental advances in geometry would find a physical application. Set theory does not seem today to have any such organic interrelationship with physics. Still, there have been some mathematicians (Stanislaw Ulam, for example) who have proposed that abstract set theory might furnish useful models for theoretical physics. At this stage the safest thing is to refuse to predict anything about the future—except that it is unpredictable.

31 GÖDEL'S PROOF

ERNEST NAGEL AND JAMES R. NEWMAN • June 1956

In 1931 a young mathematician of 25 named Kurt Gödel published in a German scientific periodical a paper which was read only by a few mathematicians. It bore the forbidding title: "On Formally Undecidable Propositions of *Principia Mathematica* and Related Systems." It dealt with a subject that has never attracted more than a small group of investigators, and its reasoning was so novel and complex that it was unintelligible even to most mathematicians. But Gödel's paper has become a landmark of science in the 20th century. As "Gödel's proof," its general conclusions have become known to many scientists, and appreciated to be of revolutionary importance. Gödel's achievement has been recognized by many honors; not long after his paper appeared the young man was invited from Vienna to join the Institute for Advanced Study at Princeton, and he has been a permanent member of the Institute since 1938. When Harvard University awarded him an honorary degree in 1952, the citation described his proof as one of the most important advances in logic in modern times.

Gödel attacked a central problem in the foundations of mathematics. The axiomatic method invented by the Greeks has always been regarded as the strongest foundation for erecting systems of mathematical thinking. This method, as every student of logic knows, consists in assuming certain propositions or axioms (*e.g.*, if equals be added to equals, the wholes are equal) and deriving other propositions or theorems from the axioms. Until recent times the only branch of mathematics that was considered by most students to be established on sound axiomatic foundations was geometry. But within the past two centuries powerful and rigorous systems of axioms have been developed for other branches of mathematics, including the familiar arithmetic of whole numbers. Mathematicians came to hope and believe that the whole realm of mathematical reasoning could be brought into order by way of the axiomatic method.

Gödel's paper put an end to this hope. He confronted mathematicians with proof that the axiomatic method has certain inherent limitations which rule out any possibility that even the ordinary arithmetic of whole numbers can ever be fully systematized by its means. What is more, his proofs brought the astounding and melancholy revelation that it is impossible to establish the logical consistency of any complex deductive system except by assuming principles of reasoning whose own internal consistency is as open to question as that of the system itself.

Gödel's paper was not, however, altogether negative. It introduced into the foundations of mathematics a new technique of analysis which is comparable in fertility with René Descartes's historic introduction of the algebraic method into geometry. Gödel's work initiated whole new branches of study in mathematical logic. It provoked a reappraisal of mathematical philosophies, and indeed of philosophies of knowledge in general.

His epoch-making paper is still not widely known, and its detailed demonstrations are too complex to be followed by a nonmathematician, but the main outlines of his argument and conclusions can be understood. This article will recount the background of the problem and the substance of Gödel's findings.

The New Mathematics

The 19th century witnessed a tremendous surge forward in mathematical research. Many fundamental problems that had long resisted solution were solved; new areas of mathematical study were created; foundations were newly built or rebuilt for various branches of the discipline. The most revolutionary development was the construction of new geometries by replacing certain of Euclid's axioms with different ones. In particular the modification of Euclid's parallel axiom led to immensely fruitful results [see "The Straight Line," by Kline; SCIENTIFIC AMERICAN, March, 1956]. It was this successful departure that stimulated the development of an axiomatic basis for other branches of mathematics which had been cultivated in a more or less intuitive manner. One important conclusion that emerged from this critical examination of the foundations of mathematics was that the traditional conception of mathematics as the "science of quantity" was inadequate and misleading. For it became evident that mathematics was most essentially concerned with drawing necessary conclusions from a given set of axioms (or postulates). It was thus recognized to be much more "abstract" and "formal" than had been traditionally supposed: more "abstract" because mathematical statements can be construed to be about anything whatsoever, not merely about some inherently circumscribed set of objects or traits of objects; more "formal" because the validity of a mathematical demonstration is grounded in the structure of statements rather than in the nature of a particular subject matter. The postulates of any branch of demonstrative mathematics are not inherently about space, quantity, apples, angles or budgets, and any special meaning that may be associated with the postulates' descriptive terms plays no essential role in the process of deriving theorems. The question that confronts a pure mathematician (as distinct from the scientist who

KURT GÖDEL was photographed in his office at the Institute for Advanced Study by Arnold Newman. Gödel was born in Czecho-slovakia in 1906. He received his doctorate from the University of Vienna in 1930 and served on its faculty until he came to the U. S.

employs mathematics in investigating a special subject matter) is not whether the postulates he assumes or the conclusions he deduces from them are true, but only whether the alleged conclusions are in fact the necessary logical consequences of the initial assumptions. This approach recalls Bertrand Russell's famous epigram: Pure mathematics is the subject in which we do not know what we are talking about, nor whether what we are saying is true.

A land of rigorous abstraction, empty of all familiar landmarks, is certainly not easy to get around in. But it offers compensations in the form of a new freedom of movement and fresh vistas. As mathematics became more abstract, men's minds were emancipated from habitual connotations of language and could construct novel systems of postulates. Formalization led in fact to a great variety of systems of considerable mathematical interest and value. Some of these systems, it must be admitted, did not lend themselves to interpretations as obviously intuitive ("common sense") as those of Euclidean geometry or arithmetic, but this fact caused no alarm. Intuition, for one thing, is an elastic faculty. Our children will have no difficulty in accepting as intuitively obvious the paradoxes of relativity, just as we do not boggle at ideas which were regarded as wholly unintuitive a couple of generations ago. Moreover intuition, as we all know, is not a safe guide: it cannot be used safely as a criterion of either truth or fruitfulness in scientific explorations.

However, the increased abstractness of mathematics also raised a more serious problem. When a set of axioms is taken to be about a definite and familiar domain of objects, it is usually possible to ascertain whether the axioms are indeed true of these objects, and if they are true, they must also be mutually consistent. But the abstract non-Euclidean axioms appeared to be plainly false as descriptions of space, and, for that matter, doubtfully true of anything. Thus the problem of establishing the internal consistency of non-Euclidean systems was formidable. In Riemannian geometry, for example, the famous parallel postulate of Euclid is replaced by the assumption that through a given point outside a line *no* parallel to the line can be drawn in the same plane. Now suppose the question: Is the Riemannian set of postulates consistent? They are apparently not true of the ordinary space of our experience. How then is their consistency to be tested? How can one prove they will not lead to contradictory theorems?

A general method for solving this problem was proposed. The underlying idea was to find a "model" for the postulates so that each postulate was converted into a true statement about the model. The procedure goes something like this. Let us take the word "class" to signify a collection of distinguishable elements, or "members." (For example, the class of prime numbers less than 10 is a collection consisting of 2, 3, 5 and 7 as members.) Suppose now we consider two purely abstract classes, K and L, concerning which these postulates are given:

1. Any two members of K are contained in just one member of L.

2. No member of K is contained in more than two members of L.

3. The members of K are not all contained in a single member of L.

4. Any two members of L contain just one member of K.

5. No member of L contains more than two members of K.

From this little set we can derive, by using customary rules of inference, certain theorems. For example, it can be shown that K contains just three members. But is the set a consistent one, so that mutually contradictory theorems can never be derived from it? This is where we invoke the help of a model, or interpretation, of the classes. Let K be the vertices of a triangle, and L its sides. Each of the five abstract postulates is then converted into a true statement: *e.g.*, the first postulate asserts that any two of the vertices are contained on just one side. In this way the set is proved to be consistent.

At first thought such a procedure may seem to suffice to establish the consistency of an abstract system such as plane Riemannian geometry. We may adopt a model embodying the Riemannian postulates in which the expression "plane" signifies the surface of a Euclidean sphere; the expression "point," a point on this surface; the expression "straight line," an arc of a great circle on this surface, and so on. Each Riemannian postulate can then be converted into a theorem of Euclid. For example, on this interpretation the Riemannian parallel postulate reads as follows: Through a point on the surface of a sphere, no arc of a great circle can be drawn parallel to a given arc of a great circle.

Unhappily this method is vulnerable to a serious objection; namely, that it attempts to solve a problem in one domain merely by shifting the problem to another (or, to put it another way, we invoke Euclid to demonstrate the consistency of a system which subverts Eu-

All gentlemen are polite.

No bankers are polite.

No gentlemen are bankers.

$$g \subset p$$
$$b \subset \bar{p}$$
$$\therefore\ g \subset \bar{b}$$

$$g\,\bar{p} = 0$$
$$b\,p = 0$$

$$g\,b = 0$$

SYMBOLIC LOGIC was invented in the middle of the 19th century by the English mathematician George Boole. In this illustration a syllogism is translated into his notation in two different ways. In the upper group of formulas, the symbol $\subset$ means "is contained in." Thus $g \subset p$ says that the class of gentlemen is included in the class of polite persons. In the equations below two letters together mean the class of things having both characteristics. For example, bp means the class of individuals who are bankers and polite. The second equation in the group says that this class has no members. A line above a letter means "not." (Not-p, for example, means impolite.)

clid). Riemannian geometry is proved to be consistent only if Euclidean geometry is consistent. Query, then: Is Euclidean geometry consistent? If we attempt to answer this question by invoking yet another model, we are no closer to our goal. In short, any proof obtained by this method will be only a "relative" proof of consistency, not an absolute proof.

So long as we can interpret a system by a model containing only a finite number of elements, we have no great difficulty in proving the consistency of its postulates. For example, the triangle model which we used to test the K and L class postulates is finite, and accordingly it is comparatively simple to determine by actual inspection whether the postulates are "true" and hence consistent. Unfortunately most of the postulate systems that constitute the foundations of important branches of mathematics cannot be mirrored in finite models; they can be satisfied only by nonfinite ones. In a well-known set of axioms for elementary arithmetic one of the axioms asserts that every integer in the sequence of whole numbers has an immediate successor which differs from any preceding integer. Obviously any model used to test the set of postulates must mirror the infinity of elements postulated by this axiom. It follows that the truth (and so the consistency) of the set cannot be established by inspection and enumeration. Apparently we have reached an impasse.

Russell's Paradox

It may be tempting to suggest at this point that we can be sure that a set of postulates is consistent, i.e., free from contradictions, if the basic notions employed are transparently "clear" and "certain." But the history of thought has not dealt kindly with the doctrine of intuitive knowledge implicit in this suggestion. In certain areas of mathematical research radical contradictions have turned up in spite of the "intuitive" clarity of the notions involved in the assumptions, and despite the seemingly consistent character of the intellectual constructions performed. Such contradictions (technically called "antinomies") have emerged, for example, in the theory of infinite numbers developed by Georg Cantor in the 19th century. His theory was built on the elementary and seemingly "clear" concept of class. Since modern systems in other branches of mathematics, particularly elementary arithmetic, have been built on the foundation of the theory of classes, it is pertinent to ask whether they, too, are not infected with contradictions.

In point of fact, Bertrand Russell constructed a contradiction within the framework of elementary logic itself. It is precisely analogous to the contradiction first developed in the Cantorian theory of infinite classes. Russell's antinomy can be stated as follows: All classes apparently may be divided into two groups: those which do not contain themselves as members, and those which do. An example of the first is the class of mathematicians, for patently the class itself is not a mathematician and is therefore not a member of itself. An example of the second is the class of all thinkable concepts, for the class of all thinkable concepts is itself a thinkable concept, and is therefore a member of itself. We shall call the first type of class "normal," and the second type "non-normal." Now let N stand for the class of all normal classes. We ask whether N itself is a normal class. If so, it is a member of itself. But in that case N is non-normal, because by definition a class which contains itself is non-normal. Yet if N is non-normal and thus a member of itself, it must be normal, because by definition all the members of N are normal. In short, N is normal if and only if

N is non-normal. This fatal contradiction results from an uncritical use of the apparently pellucid notion of class.

Other paradoxes were found later, each of them constructed by means of familiar and seemingly cogent modes of reasoning. Non-finite models by their very nature involve the use of possibly inconsistent sets of postulates. Thus it became clear that, although the model method for establishing the consistency of axioms is an invaluable mathematical tool, that method does not supply a final answer to the problem it was designed to resolve.

Hilbert's Meta-Mathematics

The eminent German mathematician David Hilbert then adopted the opposite approach of eschewing models and draining mathematics of any meaning whatever. In Hilbert's complete formalization, mathematical expressions are regarded simply as empty signs. The postulates and theorems constructed from the system of signs (called a calculus) are simply sequences of meaningless marks which are combined in strict agreement with explicitly stated rules. The derivation of theorems from postulates can be viewed as simply the transformation of one set of such sequences, or "strings," into another set of "strings," in accordance with precise rules of operation. In this manner Hilbert hoped to eliminate the danger of using any unavowed principles of reasoning.

Formalization is a difficult and tricky business, but it serves a valuable purpose. It reveals logical relations in naked clarity, as does a cut-away working model of a machine. One is able to see the structural patterns of various "strings" of signs: how they hang together, how they are combined, how they nest in one another, and so on. A page covered with the "meaningless" marks of such a formalized mathematics does not *assert* anything—it is simply an abstract design or a mosaic possessing a certain structure. But configurations of such a system can be described, and statements can be made about their various relations to one another. One may say that a "string" is pretty, or that it resembles another "string," or that one "string" appears to be made up of three others, and so on. Such statements will evidently be meaningful.

Now it is plain that any meaningful statements about a meaningless system do not themselves belong to that system. Hilbert assigned them to a separate realm which he called "meta-mathematics." Meta-mathematical statements

are statements *about* the signs and expressions of a formalized mathematical system: about the kinds and arrangements of such signs when they are combined to form longer strings of marks called "formulas," or about the relations between formulas which may obtain as a consequence of the rules of manipulation that have been specified for them.

A few examples will illustrate Hilbert's distinction between mathematics (a system of meaningless expressions) and meta-mathematics (statements about mathematics). Consider the arithmetical expression $2+3=5$. This expression belongs to mathematics and is constructed entirely out of elementary arithmetical signs. Now we may make a statement about the displayed expression, viz.: " $2+3=5$ ' is an arithmetical formula." The statement does not express an arithmetical fact: it belongs to meta-mathematics, because it characterizes the string of arithmetical signs. Similarly the expression $x=x$ belongs to mathematics, but the statement " 'x' is a variable" belongs to meta-mathematics. We may also make the following meta-mathematical statement: "The formula '0=0' is derivable from the formula 'x=x' by substituting the numeral '0' for the variable 'x'." This statement specifies in what manner one arithmetical formula can be obtained from another formula, and thereby describes how the two formulas are related to each other. Again, we may make the meta-mathematical statement: " '0≠0' is not a theorem." It says that the formula in question is not derivable from the axioms of arithmetic, or in other words, that a certain relation does not hold between the specified formulas of the system. Finally, the following statement also belongs to meta-mathematics: "Arithmetic is consistent" (i.e., it is not possible to derive from the axioms of arithmetic both the formula 0=0 and also the formula 0≠0).

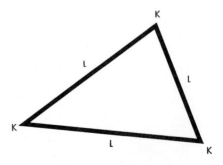

MODEL for a set of postulates about two classes, K and L, is a triangle whose vertices are the members of K and whose sides are the members of L. The geometrical model shows that the postulates are consistent.

Upon this foundation—separation of meta-mathematical descriptions from mathematics itself—Hilbert attempted to build a method of "absolute" proof of the internal consistency of mathematical systems. Specifically, he sought to develop a theory of proof which would yield demonstrations of consistency by an analysis of the purely structural features of expressions in completely formalized (or "uninterpreted") calculi. Such an analysis consists exclusively of noting the kinds and arrangements of signs in formulas and determining whether a given combination of signs can be obtained from others in accordance with the explicitly stated rules of operation. An absolute proof of the consistency of arithmetic, if one could be constructed, would consist in showing by meta-mathematical procedures of a "finitistic" (non-infinite) character that two "contradictory" formulas, such as $(0=0)$ and its negation, cannot both be derived from the axioms or initial formulas by valid rules of inference.

It may be useful, by way of illustration, to compare meta-mathematics as a theory of proof with the theory of chess. Chess is played with 32 pieces of specified design on a square board containing 64 square subdivisions, where the pieces may be moved in accordance with fixed rules. Neither the pieces, nor the squares, nor the positions of the pieces on the board signify anything *outside* the game. In this sense the pieces and their configurations on the board are "meaningless." Thus the game is analogous to a formalized mathematical calculus. The pieces and the squares of the board correspond to the elementary signs of the calculus; the initial positions of the pieces correspond to the axioms or initial formulas of the calculus; their subsequent positions correspond to formulas derived from the axioms (*i.e.*, to the theorems), and the rules of the game correspond to the rules of inference for the calculus. Now, though configurations of pieces on the board are "meaningless," statements about these configurations, like meta-mathematical statements about mathematical formulas, are quite meaningful. A "meta-chess" statement may assert that there are 20 possible opening moves for White, or that, given a certain configuration of pieces on the board with White to move, Black is mate in three moves. Moreover, one can prove general "meta-chess" theorems on the basis of the finite number of permissible configurations on the board. The meta-chess theorem about the number of possible opening moves for White can be established in this way,

and so can the meta-chess theorem that if White has only two Knights, it is impossible for White to mate Black. These and other "meta-chess" theorems can, in other words, be proved by finitistic methods of reasoning, consisting in the examination of each of a finite number of configurations that can occur under stated conditions. The aim of Hilbert's theory of proof, similarly, was to demonstrate by such finitistic methods the impossibility of deriving certain contradictory formulas in a calculus.

The Principia

It was Hilbert's approach, coupled with the formalization of logic itself in the famous *Principia Mathematica* by Alfred North Whitehead and Bertrand Russell, that led to the crisis to which Gödel supplied a final answer.

The grand object of *Principia*, published in 1910, was to demonstrate that mathematics is only a chapter of logic. But it made two contributions which are of particular interest to us here. First, following up work by the 19th-century pioneer George Boole, it supplied a system of symbols which permitted all statements of pure mathematics to be codified in a standard manner [see the article "Symbolic Logic," by John E. Pfeiffer, page 209 in this volume]. Secondly, it stated in explicit form most of the rules of formal

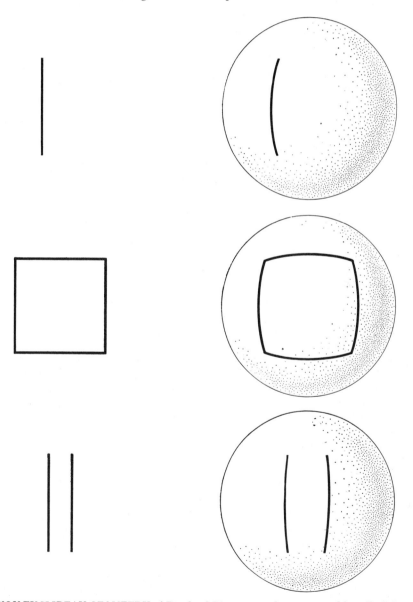

NON-EUCLIDEAN GEOMETRY of Bernhard Riemann can be represented by a Euclidean model. The plane becomes the surface of a Euclidean sphere, points on the plane become points on this surface, straight lines become great circles. Thus a portion of the plane bounded by segments of straight lines is depicted as a portion of the sphere bounded by parts of great circles (*center*). Two parallel line segments are two segments of great circles (*bottom*), and these, if extended, indeed intersect, thus contradicting the parallel postulate.

logic that are employed in mathematical proofs. Thus *Principia* provided an essential instrument for investigating the entire system of arithmetic as a system of "meaningless" marks which could be operated upon in accordance with explicitly stated rules.

We turn now to the formalization of a small portion of *Principia*, namely, the elementary logic of propositions. The task is to convert this fragment into a "meaningless" calculus of uninterpreted signs and to demonstrate a method of proving that the calculus is free from contradictions.

Four steps are involved. First we must specify the complete "vocabulary" of signs to be employed in the calculus. Second, we state the "formation rules" (the rules of "grammar") which indicate the combinations of signs permissible as formulas (or "sentences"). Third, we specify the "transformation rules," which tell how formulas may be derived from others. Finally, we select certain formulas as axioms which serve as foundations for the entire system. The "theorems" of the system are all the formulas, including the axioms, that can be derived from the axioms by applying the transformation rules. A "proof" consists of a finite sequence of legitimate formulas, each of which is either an axiom or is derivable from preceding formulas in the sequence by the transformation rules.

The vocabulary for the elementary logic of propositions (often also called the "sentential calculus") is extremely simple. The "sentential" variables (which correspond to sentences or statements) are certain letters: p, q, r and so on. Then there are several connectives: $\sim$, which stands for "not"; $\vee$, which stands for "or"; $\supset$, which stands for "if . . . then," and $\cdot$, which stands for "and." Parenthesis marks are used as signs of punctuation.

Each sentential variable counts as a formula, and the signs may be combined according to the formation rules to form other formulas: *e.g.*, $p \supset q$. If a given sentence $(p \supset q)$ is a formula, so is its negation $\sim (p \supset q)$. If two sentences, S_1 and S_2, are formulas, so is the combination $(S_1) \vee (S_2)$. Similar conventions apply to the other connectives.

For transformations there are just two rules. One, the rule of substitution, says that if a sentence containing sentential variables has been assumed, any formulas may be substituted everywhere for these variables, so that the new sentence will count as a logical consequence of the original one. For example, having accepted $p \supset p$ (if p, then p), we can

1	$(p \vee p) \supset p$ If either p or p, then p	If either Henry VIII was a boor or Henry VIII was a boor, then Henry VIII was a boor.
2	$p \supset (p \vee q)$ If p, then either p or q	If psychoanalysis is valid then either psychoanalysis is valid or headache powders are better.
3	$(p \vee q) \supset (q \vee p)$ If either p or q, then either q or p	If either Immanuel Kant was punctual or Hollywood is sinful then either Hollywood is sinful or Immanuel Kant was punctual.
4	$(p \supset q) \supset [(r \vee p) \supset (r \vee q)]$ If p implies q, then (either r or p) implies (either r or q)	If ducks waddle implies that $\sqrt{2}$ is a number then (either Churchill drinks brandy or ducks waddle) implies (either Churchill drinks brandy or $\sqrt{2}$ is a number).

SENTENTIAL CALCULUS, or the elementary logic of propositions, is based on four axioms. The nonsense statements illustrate how general is the "meaning" of the symbols.

always substitute q for p, obtaining as a theorem the formula $q \supset q$; or we may substitute $(p \vee q)$ for p, obtaining $(p \vee q) \supset (p \vee q)$. The other rule, that of detachment, simply says that if the sentences S_1 and $S_1 \supset S_2$ are logically true, we may also accept as logically true the sentence S_2.

The calculus has four axioms, essentially those of *Principia*, which are given in the table at the top of this page, along with nonsensical English sentences to illustrate their independence of meaning. The clumsiness of the translations, especially in the case of the fourth axiom, will perhaps help the reader to realize the advantages of using a special symbolism.

Search for a Proof

Each of these axioms may seem "obvious" and trivial. Nevertheless it is pos-

sible to derive from them with the help of the stated transformation rules an indefinitely large class of theorems which are far from obvious or trivial. However, at this point we are interested not in deriving theorems from the axioms but in showing that this set of axioms is not contradictory. We wish to prove that, using the transformation rules, it is impossible to derive from the axioms any formula S (*i.e.*, any expression which would normally count as a sentence) together with its negation $\sim$ S.

Now it can be shown that $p \supset (\sim p \supset q)$ (if p, then if not-p then q) is a theorem in the calculus. Let us suppose, for the sake of demonstration, that a formula S and its contradictory $\sim$ S were both deducible from the axioms, and test the consequences by means of this theorem. By substituting S for p in the theorem, as permitted by the rule of substitution, we first obtain

CONNECTIVES AND ELEMENTARY SIGNS

SIGNS	GÖDEL NUMBER	MEANING
$\sim$	1	not
$\vee$	2	or
$\supset$	3	If . . . then
$\exists$	4	There is an . . .
$=$	5	equals
0	6	zero
S	7	The next following number
(	8	punctuation mark
)	9	punctuation mark
,	10	punctuation mark

SENTENTIAL VARIABLES (EACH DESIGNATED BY A NUMBER GREATER THAN 10 AND DIVISIBLE BY 3)

VARIABLES	GÖDEL NUMBER	SAMPLE
p	12	Henry VIII was a boor.
q	15	Headache powders are better.
r	18	Ducks waddle.
etc.		

INDIVIDUAL VARIABLES (EACH DESIGNATED BY A NUMBER GREATER THAN 10 WHICH LEAVES A REMAINDER OF 1 WHEN DIVIDED BY 3)

VARIABLES	GÖDEL NUMBER	MEANING
x	13	a numerical variable
y	16	a numerical variable
z	19	a numerical variable
etc.		

PREDICATE VARIABLES (EACH DESIGNATED BY A NUMBER GREATER THAN 10 WHICH LEAVES A REMAINDER OF 2 WHEN DIVIDED BY 3)

VARIABLES	GÖDEL NUMBER	SAMPLE
P	14	Being a boor
Q	17	Being a headache powder
R	20	Being a duck
etc.		

ELEMENTARY GÖDEL NUMBERS are assigned to every symbol used in his system of symbolic logic in accordance with the orderly scheme which is illustrated in the table above.

$S \supset (\sim S \supset q)$. From this, assuming S to be demonstrably true, we could next obtain, by the detachment rule, $\sim S \supset q$. Finally, if we assume $\sim S$ also is demonstrable, by the detachment rule we would get q. Since we can substitute any formula whatsoever for q, this means that any formula whatsoever would be deducible from the axioms. Thus if both S and its contradictory $\sim S$ were deducible from the axioms, then *any* formula would be deducible. We arrive, then, at the conclusion that if the calculus is not consistent (*i.e.*, if both S and $\sim S$ are deducible) any theorem can be derived from the axioms. Accordingly, to prove the consistency of the calculus, our task is reduced to finding at least one formula which cannot be derived from the axioms.

The way this is done is to employ meta-mathematical reasoning upon the system before us. The actual procedure is elegant. It consists in finding a characteristic of formulas which satisfies the three following conditions. (1) it is common to all four axioms; (2) it is "hereditary," that is, any formula derived from the axioms (*i.e.*, any theorem) must also have the property; (3) there must be at least one formula which does not have the characteristic and is therefore not a theorem. If we succeed in this threefold task, we shall have an absolute proof of the consistency of the axioms. If we can find an array of signs that conforms to the requirements of being a formula but does not possess the specified characteristic, this formula cannot be a theorem. In other words, the finding of a single formula which is not a theorem suffices to establish the consistency of the system.

Let us choose as a characteristic of the required kind the property of being a "tautology." In common parlance a tautology is usually considered to be a redundant statement such as: "John is the father of Charles and Charles is a son of John." But in logic a tautology is defined as a statement which excludes no logical possibilities—*e.g.*, "Either it is raining or it is not raining." Another way of putting this is to say that a tautology is "true in all possible worlds." We apply this definition to formulas in the system we are considering. A formula is said to be a tautology if it is invariably true regardless of whether its elementary constituents (p, q, r and so on) are true or false. Now all four of our axioms plainly possess the property of being tautologous. For example, the first axiom, $(p \vee p) \supset p$, is true regardless of whether p is assumed to be true or is assumed to be false. The axiom says, for instance:

"If either Mount Rainier is 20,000 feet high or Mount Rainier is 20,000 feet high, then Mount Rainier is 20,000 feet high." It makes no difference whether Mount Rainier is actually 20,000 feet high or not: the statement is still true in either case. A similar demonstration can be made for the other axioms.

Next it is possible to prove that the property of being a tautology is hereditary under the transformation rules, though we shall not turn aside to give the demonstration. It follows that every formula properly derived from the axioms (*i.e.*, every theorem) must be a tautology. Having performed these two steps, we are ready to look for a formula which does not possess the characteristic of being a tautology. We do not have to look very hard. For example, $p \lor q$ fits the requirements. Clearly it is not a tautology; it is the same as saying: "Either John is a philosopher or Charles reads SCIENTIFIC AMERICAN." This is patently not a truth of logic; it is not a sentence that is true irrespective of the truth or falsity of its elementary constituents. Thus $p \lor q$, though it purports to be a gosling, is in fact a duckling; it is a formula but it is not a theorem.

We have achieved our goal. We have found at least one formula which is not a theorem, therefore the axioms must be consistent.

Gödel's Answer

The sentential calculus is an example of a mathematical system for which the objectives of Hilbert's theory of proof are fully realized. But this calculus codifies only a fragment of formal logic. The question remains: Can a formalized system embracing the whole of arithmetic be proved consistent in the sense of Hilbert's program?

This was the conundrum that Gödel answered. His paper in 1931 showed that all such efforts to prove arithmetic to be free from contradictions are doomed to failure.

His main conclusions were twofold. In the first place, he showed that it is impossible to establish a meta-mathematical proof of the consistency of a system comprehensive enough to contain the whole of arithmetic—unless, indeed, this proof itself employs rules of inference much more powerful than the transformation rules used in deriving theorems within the system. In short, one dragon is slain only to create another.

Gödel's second main conclusion was even more surprising and revolutionary, for it made evident a fundamental limitation in the power of the axiomatic method itself. Gödel showed that *Principia*, or any other system within which arithmetic can be developed, is essentially incomplete. In other words, given *any* consistent set of arithmetical axioms, there are true arithmetical statements which are not derivable from the set. A classic illustration of a mathematical "theorem" which has thwarted all attempts at proof is that of Christian Goldbach, stating that every even number is the sum of two primes. No even number has ever been found which is not the sum of two primes, yet no one has succeeded in finding a proof that the rule applies without exception to all even numbers. In reply to Gödel it might be suggested that the set of arithmetical axioms could be modified or expanded to make "underivable" statements derivable. But Gödel showed that this approach promises no final cure. That is, even if any finite number of other axioms is added, there will always be further arithmetical truths which are not formally derivable.

How did Gödel prove his conclusions? His paper is difficult. A reader must master 46 preliminary definitions, together with several important preliminary theorems, before he gets to the main results. We shall take a much easier road; nevertheless we hope at least to offer glimpses of the argument.

Gödel Numbers

Gödel first devised a method of assigning a number as a label for each elementary sign, each formula and each proof in a formalized system. To the elementary signs he attached as "Gödel numbers" the integers from 1 to 10; to the variables he assigned numbers according to certain rules [*see table, page 227*]. To see how a number is given to a formula of the system, let us take this formula: $(\exists x)\ (x = Sy)$, which reads literally "there is an x, such that x is the immediate successor of y" and in effect says that every number has an immediate successor. The numbers associated with the formula's 10 successive signs are, respectively, 8, 4, 13, 9, 8, 13, 5, 7, 16, 9 [*see table*]. Now these numbers are to be used as exponents, or powers, of the first 10 prime numbers (*i.e.*, 2, 3, 5 and so on). The prime numbers, raised to these powers, are multiplied together. Thus we get the number $2^8 \times 3^4 \times 5^{13} \times 7^9 \times 11^8 \times 13^{13} \times 17^5 \times 19^7 \times 23^{16} \times 29^9$. The product is the Gödel number of the formula. In the same way every formula can be represented by a single unique number.

We can assign a number to a sequence of formulas, such as may occur in some

A	100
B	4×25
C	$2^2 \times 5^2$
A	162
B	2×81
C	$2^1 \times 3^4$
D	1 4 ↓ ↓ ~ ∃
E	~∃

GÖDEL NUMBERS of formulas are constructed by raising the prime numbers, in sequence, to powers which are the Gödel numbers of the symbols involved. Thus 100 is not a Gödel number because its factors skip the prime number 3. On the other hand, 162 is the Gödel number for "there is not."

proof, by a similar process. Let us say that we have a sequence of two formulas, the second derived from the first. For example, by substituting 0 for y in the formula given above, we derive $(\exists x)\ (x = S0)$, which says that 0 has an immediate successor. Now the first and second formulas are identified by Gödel numbers which we shall call m and n, respectively. To label this sequence, we use the Gödel numbers m and n as exponents and multiply the first two primes (2 and 3) raised to these powers. That is to say, the Gödel number that identifies the sequence is $2^m \times 3^n$. In like manner we can give a number to any sequence of formulas or any other expression in the system.

What has been done so far is to establish a method for completely arithmetizing a formal system. The method is essentially a set of directions for making a one-to-one correspondence between specific numbers and the various elements or combinations of elements of the system. Once an expression is given, it can be uniquely numbered. But more than that, we can retranslate any Gödel number into the expression it represents by factoring it into its component prime numbers, which can be done in only one way, as we know from a famous theorem

A	125,000,000
B	$64 \times 125 \times 15{,}625$
C	$2^6 \times 3^5 \times 5^6$
D	$\begin{array}{ccc} 6 & 5 & 6 \\ \downarrow & \downarrow & \downarrow \\ 0 & = & 0 \end{array}$
E	$0 = 0$

ARITHMETICAL FORMULA "zero equals zero" has the Gödel number 125 million. Reading down from A to E, the illustration shows how the number is translated into the expression it represents; reading up, how the number for the formula is derived.

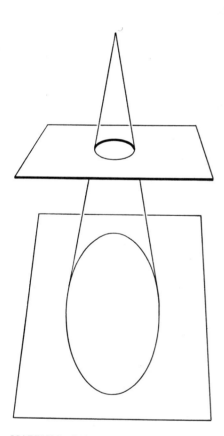

MAPPING of objects from one realm onto another is illustrated above. Points in the upper, horizontal plane can be uniquely mapped onto the lower plane, which slants downward from back to front, by drawing lines from a single point through the points of the upper plane and extending them until they intersect the lower plane. Thus a circle in the upper plane maps as an ellipse in the lower. Gödel mapped statements about arithmetic as expressions in arithmetic.

of arithmetic [*see figure on page 228*]. In other words, we can take the number apart as if it were a machine, see how it was constructed and what went into it, and we can dissect an expression or a proof in the same way.

This leads to the next step. It occurred to Gödel that meta-mathematical statements can be translated into arithmetical terms by a process analogous to mapping. In geography the spatial relations between points on the spherical earth can be projected onto a flat map; in mathematical physics relations between the properties of electric currents can be mapped in terms of the flow of fluids; in mathematics itself relations in geometry can be translated into algebra. Gödel saw that if complicated meta-mathematical statements about a system could be translated into, or mirrored by, arithmetical statements within the system itself, an important gain would be achieved in clarity of expression and facility of analysis. Plainly it would be easier to deal with arithmetical counterparts of complex logical relations than with the logical relations themselves. To cite a trivial analogy: If customers in a supermarket are given tickets with numbers determining the order in which they are to be waited on, it is a simple matter to discover, merely by scrutinizing the numbers, how many persons have been served, how many are waiting, who precedes whom and by how many customers, and so on.

What Gödel aimed at was nothing less than the complete arithmetization of meta-mathematics. If each meta-mathematical statement could be uniquely represented in the formal system by a formula expressing a relation between numbers, questions of logical dependence between meta-mathematical statements could be explored by examining the corresponding relations between integers. Gödel did in fact succeed brilliantly in mapping the meta-mathematics of arithmetic upon arithmetic itself. We need cite only one illustration of how a meta-mathematical statement can be made to correspond to a formula in the formal arithmetical system. Let us take the formula $(p \lor p) \supset p$. We may make the meta-mathematical statement that the formula $(p \lor p)$ is the initial part of this formula. Now we can represent this meta-mathematical statement by an arithmetical formula which says in effect that the Gödel number of the initial part is a factor of the Gödel number of the complete formula. Evidently this is so, for the Gödel number of $(p \lor p)$ is $2^8 \times 3^{12} \times 5^2 \times 7^{12} \times 11^9$, while the Gödel number of $(p$

$\lor p) \supset p$ is $2^8 \times 3^{12} \times 5^2 \times 7^{12} \times 11^9 \times 13^3 \times 17^{12}$.

The Undecidable Proposition

We have now arrived at the very heart of Gödel's analysis. He showed how to construct an arithmetical formula, whose Gödel number we shall suppose is h, which corresponds to the meta-mathematical statement, *viz.*: "The formula with Gödel number h is not demonstrable." In other words, this formula (call it G) in effect asserts its own indemonstrability, though it is a legitimate formula belonging to the formal system of arithmetic. Gödel then proceeded to examine the question whether G is or is not a demonstrable formula of arithmetic. He was able to show that G is demonstrable if, and only if, its negation, $\sim$ G, also is demonstrable. But if a formula and its negation are both derivable from a set of axioms, obviously the axioms are not consistent. It follows that if arithmetic is consistent, neither G nor its negation is demonstrable. That is to say, G is an undecidable formula of arithmetic. Now from this Gödel proved the indemonstrability of the proposition that arithmetic is consistent. It can be shown that a meta-mathematical statement of arithmetic's consistency corresponds to a certain arithmetical formula, A, and that the arithmetical formula A $\supset$ G (if A, then G) is demonstrable. Thus if A were demonstrable, G would be also. But we have just seen that G is not demonstrable. It follows that A is undecidable. In short, the consistency of arithmetic is undecidable by any meta-mathematical reasoning which can be represented within the formalism of arithmetic.

Gödel's analysis does not exclude a meta-mathematical demonstration of the consistency of arithmetic; indeed, such proofs have been constructed, notably by Gerhard Gentzen, a member of the Hilbert school. But these "proofs" are in a sense pointless, because they employ rules of inference whose own internal consistency is as much open to doubt as is the formal consistency of arithmetic itself. Gentzen's proof employs a rule of inference which in effect permits a formula to be derived from an infinite class of premises. And the employment of this non-finitistic meta-mathematical notion raises once more the difficulty which Hilbert's original program was intended to resolve.

There is another surprise coming. Although the formula G is undecidable, it can be shown by meta-mathematical reasoning that G is nevertheless a *true* arithmetical statement and expresses a property of the arithmetical integers. The argument for this conclusion is quite simple. We need recall only that Gödel mapped meta-mathematical statements upon arithmetical formulas in such a way that every true meta-mathematical statement corresponds to a true arithmetical formula. Now G corresponds to a meta-mathematical statement ("the formula with Gödel number h is not demonstrable") which, as we have seen, is true, unless arithmetic is inconsistent. It follows that G itself must be true. We have thus established an *arithmetical* truth by a *meta-mathematical* argument.

So we come to the finale of Gödel's amazing and profound intellectual symphony. Arithmetic is incomplete, in the transparent sense that there is at least one arithmetical truth which cannot be derived from the arithmetical axioms and yet can be established by a meta-mathematical argument outside the system. Moreover, arithmetic is *essentially* incomplete, for even if the true formula G were taken as an axiom and added to the original axioms, the augmented system would still not suffice to yield formally all the truths of arithmetic: we could still construct a true formula which would not be formally demonstrable within the system. And such would be the case no matter how often we repeated the process of adding axioms to the initial set.

This remarkable conclusion makes evident an inherent limitation in the axiomatic method. Contrary to previous assumptions, the vast "continent" of arithmetical truth cannot be brought into systematic order by way of specifying once for all a fixed set of axioms from which all true arithmetical statements would be formally derivable.

Men and Calculating Machines

The far-reaching import of Gödel's conclusions has not yet been fully fathomed. They show that the hope of finding an absolute proof of consistency for any deductive system expressing the whole of arithmetic cannot be realized, if such a proof must satisfy the finitistic requirements of Hilbert's original program. They also show that there is an endless number of true arithmetical statements which cannot be formally deduced from any specified set of axioms in accordance with a closed set of rules of inference. It follows that an axiomatic approach to the theory of numbers, for example, cannot exhaust the domain of arithmetic truth. Whether an all-inclusive general definition of mathematical or logical truth can be devised, and whether, as Gödel himself appears to believe, only a thoroughgoing Platonic realism can supply such a definition, are problems still under debate.

Gödel's conclusions have a bearing on the question whether a calculating machine can be constructed that would equal the human brain in mathematical reasoning. Present calculating machines have a fixed set of directives built into them, and they operate in a step-by-step manner. But in the light of Gödel's incompleteness theorem, there is an endless set of problems in elementary number theory for which such machines are inherently incapable of supplying answers, however complex their built-in mechanisms may be and however rapid their operations. The human brain may, to be sure, have built-in limitations of its own, and there may be mathematical problems which it is incapable of solving. But even so, the human brain appears to embody a structure of rules of operation which is far more powerful than the structure of currently conceived artificial machines. There is no immediate prospect of replacing the human mind by robots.

Gödel's proof should not be construed as an invitation to despair. The discovery that there are arithmetical truths which cannot be demonstrated formally does not mean that there are truths which are forever incapable of becoming known, or that a mystic intuition must replace cogent proof. It does mean that the resources of the human intellect have not been, and cannot be, fully formalized, and that new principles of demonstration forever await invention and discovery. We have seen that mathematical propositions which cannot be established by formal deduction from a given set of axioms may nevertheless be established by "informal" meta-mathematical reasoning.

Nor does the fact that it is impossible to construct a calculating machine equivalent to the human brain necessarily mean that we cannot hope to explain living matter and human reason in physical and chemical terms. The possibility of such explanations is neither precluded nor affirmed by Gödel's incompleteness theorem. The theorem does indicate that the structure and power of the human mind are far more complex and subtle than any non-living machine yet envisaged. Gödel's own work is a remarkable example of such complexity and subtlety. It is an occasion not for discouragement but for a renewed appreciation of the powers of creative reason.

V

THE
IMPORT
OF
MATHEMATICS

THE IMPORT
OF MATHEMATICS

INTRODUCTION

The subject matter contained in Sections III and IV is often described as "pure mathematics," whereas the material to be presented in this section would be labeled "applied mathematics." However these very terms are misleading. They suggest that there is a subject called mathematics, which is first erected by mathematicians for reasons having nothing to do with other human activities and is then applied to real problems. One might reasonably infer that the possibility of applying mathematics is fortuitous and a stroke of good luck for mankind. The truth is that mathematics is one of the sciences. Almost all of it was created as part and parcel of man's efforts to achieve two goals: the understanding of nature and the utilization of natural phenomena to improve the life of man. Not only the goals of mathematics but the specific problems, the themes, and even the suggestions on how to proceed were derived from real, largely physical investigations. The term "pure mathematics" is a contradiction of history and the term "applied mathematics" is redundant.

It is of course true that once a mathematical theme has been created to further some physical objective, mathematicians have felt free to investigate the theme itself. The justification for such efforts is twofold. Knowing that the mathematics represents a physical phenomenon, mathematicians might hope to deduce more physical knowledge about the very happening which gave rise to the mathematics. Secondly, it is characteristic of mathematics that its very abstractness enables it to represent quite diverse physical happenings. Water waves, sound waves, and radio waves are all represented in one partial differential equation known, in fact, as the wave equation. Hence the additional mathematical knowledge gained by further investigation of the wave equation, which was first developed in the investigation of sound waves, might prove useful in questions that could arise from the investigation of radio waves.

A mathematical theme is like a piece of oil-bearing land. Dark puddles on the surface may suggest that a particular spot be explored for oil, and if oil is discovered the value of the land is established. The proven worth of the land warrants further drilling in the expectation that more oil will be found if the drilling sites are not too far removed from the location of the original strike. Of course one might choose a very distant site because the drilling is easier there and still claim that he will strike oil. Some mathematicians have in fact defended worthless explorations by making this claim.

Today many mathematicians go further and argue that any mathematical theme they choose to pursue is worthwhile and they point to examples of arbitrarily chosen themes that proved subsequently to be just what scientists needed. Their argument is, in other words, that mathematicians who pursue ideas that have originated entirely in their own minds have in their wisdom anticipated the needs of scientists. But this has never happened.

The examples most often cited are Kepler's use of the ellipse to describe planetary paths about 1800 years after the conic sections were introduced into mathematics, and Einstein's use of Riemannian geometry and tensor analysis to build his theory of relativity many decades after these mathematical subjects were created. Let us look into these examples.

Kepler did indeed use the ellipse in place of a combination of circles and thereby simplified astronomy. But was the ellipse *just* what he really needed? The answer is negative. Kepler spent years in trying to fit a curve to the astronomical data on the path of Mars and he did think of the ellipse because it already existed in mathematics. When he found that the elliptical path did fit the observations well enough so that the departures from that path could be charged to experimental error he decided that the ellipse was correct. However the paths of the planets around the sun are not ellipses. If there were just the sun and only one planet in the sky and if each could be regarded as a perfect sphere, then the path of that planet would be truly elliptical. But the actual gravitational pull on any one planet is not that of the sun alone. It includes the pull of all the other planets and many moons. For this reason the path is not elliptical.

What about Einstein's use of Riemannian geometry and tensor analysis? Einstein started to work on the problem of accounting, by means of the structure of space, for motions which were presumed to be caused by the force of gravitation. In 1911 he made public a theory which treated a very special and artificial case and for which he had used rather simple mathematics. He knew of course that this work was not good enough. He discussed his difficulty with his colleague, a mathematician named George Pick, and Pick called his attention to Riemannian geometry and the tensor analysis of Ricci and Levi-Civita, which Pick thought might be helpful. Einstein then found another colleague and friend in Zurich, Marcel Grossmann, from whom he learned this mathematics. In a few years he was able to use it to formulate his general theory of relativity. Were Riemannian geometry and tensor analysis *just right* for the theory of relativity? Almost certainly not. There is ample reason to believe that Einstein merely did the best he could with the mathematics he found available. Ingenious as the *general* theory of relativity is, it is contrived; it is not too useful for the solution of astronomical problems because it is too complicated; and the evidence for it rests solely on the improved accuracy with which it predicts three astronomical phenomena. If the history of science teaches us anything, it teaches us that this theory will some day be superseded.

The point of the history of these two examples is that the concept of mathematics being just right for a scientific theory is unsound. The scientist wrestles with a problem. But the solution is not unique. In his efforts to build a theory he latches on to whatever mathematics may serve to build it. He makes use of the available tools, as a man might use a hatchet in place of an ax and do an adequate job. Was the hatchet, then, just right for the job?

It might seem that the preceding argument can be turned on itself. If the scientist can adopt available mathematical tools and develop a useful theory, even though the tool and theory are not unique, wouldn't it be wise for mathematicians to create as many tools as possible and thereby make many more aids available to scientists? In other words shouldn't pure mathematicians feel free to pursue any ideas that attract them because they would be increasing the mathematical apparatus available to scientists? The answer to this question is another question: "Where should one drill for oil?" The answer is, "on oil-bearing land."

That the conic sections, Riemannian geometry, and tensor analysis were at all useful, even though scientists were obliged to build their theories as best they could with these tools, is due to the fact that these subjects were physically motivated in the first place. Although we do not know the early history of the conic sections, the best-established theory is that they were developed during the construction of sundials. Moreover the fact that the conic sections can be used to focus light was known long before Apollonius devoted his classic work to that subject. These curves are in any case natural topics in the physically significant subject of Euclidean geometry. Since the conic sections were physically applicable, it is not surprising that Kepler, too, was able to make use of them.

The history of Riemannian geometry, like that of tensor analysis, is fully known. As we have previously related, the efforts of mathematicians to establish beyond question the physical soundness of Euclidean geometry culminated in the creation of non-Euclidean geometries which proved as useful as Euclidean geometry for representing the properties of physical space. This unexpected fact gave rise to the question, "Since these geometries differ from each other what are we really sure is true about physical space?" This question was Riemann's point of departure. In answering it he created more general geometries, now known as Riemannian geometries, which, because of their very nature and in view of our limited physical knowledge, could be as instrumental in representing physical space as Euclidean geometry. Is it then to be wondered that Einstein found Riemannian geometry useful? The physical relevance of Riemannian geometry does not detract from the ingenious use Einstein made of it; nevertheless its suitability was the consequence of work on the most fundamental physical problem that mathematicians have ever tackled, the nature of physical space.

The subject of tensor analysis was initiated by Eugenio Beltrami, Rudolf Lipschitz, and E. B. Christoffel, who followed up on Riemann's work. Beltrami and Lipschitz pursued the subject further in the context of theoretical mechanics. Ricci and Levi-Civita then recast and extended the work of all three men. Hence tensor analysis too was physically motivated. Thus the unexpected scientific uses of mathematical theories arise because the theories are physically grounded to begin with and not because they are in any way due to the prophetic insight of all-wise mathematicians who wrestle solely with their souls.

Whatever way one explains the marvelous applicability of mathematics, the power and extent of its accomplishments are the distinguishing features of modern civilization. The quest to understand our physical universe, with mathematics as the prime instrument, was begun by the ancient Greeks, the very people who fashioned mathematics itself. Their supreme achievement in what they called "disclosing the mathematical design of nature" was the first sound, quantitative theory of planetary motions, known as Ptolemaic theory. They also contributed the beginnings of mathematical optics, mechanics, the theory of musical sounds, hydrostatics, and mathematical geography. It is relevant that Euclid himself wrote books on the first three of these subjects, that Archimedes, the greatest of the Greek mathematicians, created the subject of hydrostatics, and that Ptolemy, who created trigonometry for use in his astronomy, wrote the definitive geography.

From the time of the decline of the Greek world, roughly about 300 A.D., to the rise of the modern European civilization about 1500 A.D., the progress in mathematics and science was sporadic and minor. However, from 1500 to the present, the mathematical investigation of nature has made unprecedented and rapidly accelerating progress. The significant achievements are far too numerous even to mention, and they range from pendulum motion to cosmology. Needless to say, all the great contributors to mathematics, many of whom were primarily physicists, participated in this work.

The greatest successes, all in the area of physics, fall into seven major classes: Newtonian mechanics, fluid motion (the term "fluid" covering liquids and gases), the theory of elasticity, electromagnetic theory, statistical mechanics, the theory of relativity, and quantum theory.

In this section, the articles by Dirac and Dyson are concerned with quantum theory: Dirac presents the development and main features of the theory, and Dyson, the use of group theory to bring order into the variety of elementary particles now believed to be in the nuclei of atoms. Einstein and Gamow, in their articles, discuss the theory of relativity. The biography of Maxwell in Section II gives some idea of his contributions to electromagnetic theory and statistical mechanics.

The mathematics explained or referred to in these articles is by no means elementary. Indeed, one of the accompaniments of the modern, deeper investigations of nature has been the need to employ increasingly sophisticated mathematical tools. Nature, as Augustin Fresnel once remarked, is not embarrassed by mathematical difficulties. Nor are mathematicians deterred.

Since the idea of a science and particularly a mathematical science is not an obvious one, it was only after some great successes were achieved in mathematical physics that the idea of building mathematical biological and social sciences occurred to some thinkers. In the course of the last hundred years these two sciences have developed rapidly. The initial approaches imitated those of mathematical physics. The basic methodology, the same as that introduced by Galileo in the physical sciences, is to find quantitative principles which seem to be fundamental properties of the phenomenon under investigation and to employ mathematical axioms and theorems in conjunction with these principles to deduce new information about the phenomenon. Mathematical approaches to biology and the social sciences are exemplified in the articles by Moore and Stone.

Biological and social phenomena are far more complicated than most physical phenomena because billions of cells in the one field and millions of people in the other determine the outcomes, and yet the individual participants do not all behave in the same way. Alternatively we may say that it is not possible to find fundamental properties, either of cells or of the behavior of people, that serve as the bases for deductions. The approach that has produced some useful knowledge is the use of statistical and probabilistic methods, which the mathematicians had already developed to estimate errors of measurement in astronomy. Statistical methods cancel the less significant individual variations and give what one might call a simplified, or smoothed out, account which is nevertheless valuable. Thus the statement that intelligence is normally distributed is a smoothed out description of the varieties of human intelligence (see Kac's article in Section III). The statement does not tell us how much intelligence John Jones possesses but it does tell us the distribution of intelligence among a million Joneses. Dalton describes a fine use of statistical methods in his article. The application of probability, often in conjunction with statistical information, does not yield what will happen, but what will most likely happen and a measure of the probability that it will happen. The probability of death at a given age is a simple example. As in statistical methods, the knowledge gained by the use of probability is not certain and reliable for the individual event, but it is valuable in dealing with large groups of people or many happenings of the same phenomenon. Some applications are described in the articles by Weaver and Kac in Section III, and some others will be mentioned shortly.

During the past 25 years several new classes of techniques have been introduced to treat social, industrial, scientific, and military problems. The current names for these classes are game theory, information theory, linear programming, and operations research. No new basic mathematical theory is involved; what distinguishes each of these new applied fields is the particular combination of several mathematical techniques. Thus game theory, even in its elementary applications, uses ordinary algebra, matrix theory, and probability.

The mathematician Émile Borel introduced game theory in 1921 to make predictions on the outcome of games. The idea was adopted, expanded, and applied to economic competition by the mathematician John von Neumann and the economist Oskar Morgenstern. It is now applied to all kinds of military and social problems. Throwing dice is a game, and probability theory alone can be used to predict the chance of throwing a seven. Poker is also a game, but beyond the probability of drawing cards to make a certain combination, the drawings of competitors and the responses these competitors may make to one's own bets have at least as much to do with success as what one holds in his own hand. The major theme of game theory is how to make rational decisions, in the face of competition from opponents who are also free to make various decisions. Thus game theory as applied to economic competition and military maneuvers is a serious business. The articles by Morgenstern and Rapoport elaborate on this subject.

In all communication, as in speaking or writing, and in the use of channels, such as the telephone, radio, and television, the primary objective is to transmit information. The subject of information theory seeks to make a science out of the process of communication. Common language, a product of historical movements, is in many cases overinformative. The statement "As I live and breathe" is clearly redundant and, unless the redundancy is intended for dramatic emphasis, should be shortened. On the other hand telephone and radio communication are often underinformative because the instruments introduce distortion. How much information must be transmitted for intelligibility? The problems investigated in information theory are described in Weaver's article. The mathematics employed are the theory of probability and much of analysis.

Linear programming, to be distinguished from programming a message to a computer, is a series of techniques used to solve what one might call the simpler algebraic problems of business and military logistics. A manufacturer can produce different amounts of several items. He may know the ranges of prices at which he can sell these items and how many he can sell at the various prices. It may also be true that there is a maximum number of any one or several items that can be sold no matter how low the price. How many should he produce and at what price should he sell them to maximize profit? Linear programming can be used to determine the best locations of factories (from such standpoints as accessibility of raw materials and convenience for shipping the finished product), the use of space in a factory, the locations of storage warehouses and sales outlets, the schedule of production either to achieve lowest cost or to maintain employment, and how much inventory to keep on various items in the light of demand and the amount of money tied up in the inventory. In all cases one seeks the best plan of operation in view of what might happen. The mathematics used are simple algebra, matrix theory, statistical techniques, and a bit of symbolic logic. The article by Cooper and Charnes will make the nature of linear programming clearer.

Operations research is a name for a conglomeration of techniques that include game theory, linear programming, probability, and indeed any mathematical technique that provides guidance in the operation of any large scale organization. In the application of these techniques to the management of corporations, tactics in warfare, prediction of the operation of a complex of man-machine systems, and the organization of production, all the factors that bear upon a problem are taken into account. Since operations research encompasses game theory and linear programming it is of course used for the more limited problems already described under these subjects. It replaces guesses by rational decisions and impulsive acts by strategy. In their article, Levinson and Brown describe the subject more fully.

The influences of mathematics on our civilization have generally been veiled from sight. Most people, although fully aware of the revolutionary influences of radio, do not know that the existence of radio waves was predicted mathematically and that, were it not for mathematics, these waves might never have been discovered. The latest influence, equally revolutionary in its effects, is very perceptible indeed. It is the electronic computer, a giant in size and capacity.

The electronic computer is the outcome of centuries of effort to speed up calculation. It is the successor of the abacus, logarithms, the slide rule and mechanically driven calculators. Once the marvelously rapid computer was devised, it was inevitable that man should seek other uses for it and he is gradually finding and exploring them. In general the computer performs any kind of symbolic information processing. Beyond its function in making enormous arithmetical calculations, the computer is now used to store and retrieve immense masses of data, to direct machinery in factories, to perform the multiple commercial operations of large businesses, to play games, and to educate young people. Many potential uses—to recognize patterns such as the letters of the alphabet, to respond to vocal directions, to translate foreign-language books, and even to reproduce itself—are being explored. In their articles, Davis, Ulam, Evans, Oettinger and Strachey recount the structure and uses of the computer. The biography of Babbage in Section II provides a description of the first large mechanical computer.

The efforts to increase the capabilities of the electronic computer have a twofold objective. The knowledge of the functioning of the human nerves and the brain is applied to improve the design of computers. However our understanding of the brain is far from complete: we do not know much about the physiology of brain actions, let alone what intelligence is. Hence as mathematicians and electronic engineers design new components for the computer they may also be discovering what must be taking place in the human brain. The goal of all basic research is ultimately knowledge about man himself, and the research on the computer has reached the stage at which the likening of computers to man is worthy of serious consideration. This theme is explored in Wiener's article on the self-regulating mechanism in man and in Kemeny's article on man as a machine.

The articles in this section cannot cover the thousands of valuable and impressive uses of mathematics. They are rather representative of what has been done in major scientific areas. But they may not only convince the reader of the marvelous power of mathematics, but generate pride that man, who made this mathematics, can achieve so much.

THE EVOLUTION OF THE PHYSICIST'S PICTURE OF NATURE

32

P. A. M. DIRAC · May 1963

In this article I should like to discuss the development of general physical theory: how it developed in the past and how one may expect it to develop in the future. One can look on this continual development as a process of evolution, a process that has been going on for several centuries.

The first main step in this process of evolution was brought about by Newton. Before Newton, people looked on the world as being essentially two-dimensional—the two dimensions in which one can walk about—and the up-and-down dimension seemed to be something essentially different. Newton showed how one can look on the up-and-down direction as being symmetrical with the other two directions, by bringing in gravitational forces and showing how they take their place in physical theory. One can say that Newton enabled us to pass from a picture with two-dimensional symmetry to a picture with three-dimensional symmetry.

Einstein made another step in the same direction, showing how one can pass from a picture with three-dimensional symmetry to a picture with four-dimensional symmetry. Einstein brought in time and showed how it plays a role that is in many ways symmetrical with the three space dimensions. However, this symmetry is not quite perfect. With

Einstein's picture one is led to think of the world from a four-dimensional point of view, but the four dimensions are not completely symmetrical. There are some directions in the four-dimensional picture that are different from others: directions that are called null directions, along which a ray of light can move; hence the four-dimensional picture is not completely symmetrical. Still, there is a great deal of symmetry among the four dimensions. The only lack of symmetry, so far as concerns the equations of physics, is in the appearance of a minus sign in the equations with respect to the time dimension as compared with the three space dimensions [see top equation on page 244].

We have, then, the development from the three-dimensional picture of the world to the four-dimensional picture. The reader will probably not be happy with this situation, because the world still appears three-dimensional to his consciousness. How can one bring this appearance into the four-dimensional picture that Einstein requires the physicist to have?

What appears to our consciousness is really a three-dimensional section of the four-dimensional picture. We must take a three-dimensional section to give us what appears to our consciousness at one time; at a later time we shall have a

different three-dimensional section. The task of the physicist consists largely of relating events in one of these sections to events in another section referring to a later time. Thus the picture with four-dimensional symmetry does not give us the whole situation. This becomes particularly important when one takes into account the developments that have been brought about by quantum theory. Quantum theory has taught us that we have to take the process of observation into account, and observations usually require us to bring in the three-dimensional sections of the four-dimensional picture of the universe.

The special theory of relativity, which Einstein introduced, requires us to put all the laws of physics into a form that displays four-dimensional symmetry. But when we use these laws to get results about observations, we have to bring in something additional to the four-dimensional symmetry, namely the three-dimensional sections that describe our consciousness of the universe at a certain time.

Einstein made another most important contribution to the development of our physical picture: he put forward the general theory of relativity, which requires us to suppose that the space of physics is curved. Before this physicists had always worked with a flat space, the three-dimensional flat space of Newton which was then extended to the four-dimensional flat space of special relativity. General relativity made a really important contribution to the evolution of our physical picture by requiring us to go over to curved space. The general requirements of this theory mean that all the laws of physics can be formulated in curved four-dimensional space, and that they show symmetry among the four dimensions. But again, when we want to bring in observations, as we must if we look at things from the point of view of quantum theory, we have to refer to a section of this four-dimensional space. With the four-dimensional space curved, any section that we make in it also has to be curved, because in general we cannot give a meaning to a flat section in a curved space. This leads us to a picture in which we have to take curved three-dimensional sections in the curved four-dimensional space and discuss observations in these sections.

During the past few years people have been trying to apply quantum ideas to gravitation as well as to the other phenomena of physics, and this has led to a rather unexpected development, namely that when one looks at gravitational theory from the point of view of the sections, one finds that there are some degrees of freedom that drop out of the theory. The gravitational field is a tensor field with 10 components. One finds that six of the components are adequate for describing everything of physical importance and the other four can be dropped out of the equations. One cannot, however, pick out the six important components from the complete set of 10 in any way that does not destroy the four-dimensional symmetry. Thus if one insists on preserving four-dimensional symmetry in the equations, one cannot adapt the theory of gravitation to a discussion of measurements in the way quantum theory requires without being forced to a more complicated description than is needed by the physical situation. This result has led me to doubt how fundamental the four-dimensional requirement in physics is. A few decades ago it seemed quite certain that one had to express the whole of physics in four-dimensional form. But now it seems that four-dimensional symmetry is not of such overriding importance, since the description of nature sometimes gets simplified when one departs from it.

Now I should like to proceed to the developments that have been brought about by quantum theory. Quantum theory is the discussion of very small things, and it has formed the main subject of physics for the past 60 years. During this period physicists have been amassing quite a lot of experimental information and developing a theory to correspond to it, and this combination of theory and experiment has led to important developments in the physicist's picture of the world.

The quantum first made its appearance when Planck discovered the need to suppose that the energy of electromagnetic waves can exist only in multiples of a certain unit, depending on the frequency of the waves, in order to explain the law of black-body radiation. Then Einstein discovered the same unit of energy occurring in the photoelectric effect. In this early work on quantum theory one simply had to accept the unit of energy without being able to incorporate it into a physical picture.

The first new picture that appeared was Bohr's picture of the atom. It was a picture in which we had electrons moving about in certain well-defined orbits and occasionally making a jump from one orbit to another. We could not picture how the jump took place. We just had to accept it as a kind of discontinuity. Bohr's picture of the atom worked only for special examples, essentially when there was only one electron that was of importance for the problem under consideration. Thus the picture was an incomplete and primitive one.

The big advance in the quantum theory came in 1925, with the discovery of quantum mechanics. This advance was brought about independently by two men, Heisenberg first and Schrödinger soon afterward, working from different points of view. Heisenberg worked keeping close to the experimental evidence about spectra that was being amassed at that time, and he found out how the experimental information could be fitted into a scheme that is now known as matrix mechanics. All the experimental data of spectroscopy fitted beautifully into the scheme of matrix mechanics, and this led to quite a different picture of the atomic world. Schrödinger worked from a more mathematical point of view, trying to find a beautiful theory for describ-

ISAAC NEWTON (1642–1727), with his law of gravitation, changed the physicist's picture of nature from one with two-dimensional symmetry to one with three-dimensional symmetry. This drawing of him was made in 1760 by James Macardel from a painting by Enoch Seeman.

ing atomic events, and was helped by De Broglie's ideas of waves associated with particles. He was able to extend De Broglie's ideas and to get a very beautiful equation, known as Schrödinger's wave equation, for describing atomic processes. Schrödinger got this equation by pure thought, looking for some beautiful generalization of De Broglie's ideas, and not by keeping close to the experimental development of the subject in the way Heisenberg did.

I might tell you the story I heard from Schrödinger of how, when he first got the idea for this equation, he immediately applied it to the behavior of the electron in the hydrogen atom, and then he got results that did not agree with experiment. The disagreement arose because at that time it was not known that the electron has a spin. That, of course, was a great disappointment to Schrödinger, and it caused him to abandon the work for some months. Then he noticed that if he applied the theory in a more approximate way, not taking into account the refinements required by relativity, to this rough approximation his work was in agreement with observation. He published his first paper with only this rough approximation, and in that way Schrödinger's wave equation was presented to the world. Afterward, of course, when people found out how to take into account correctly the spin of the electron, the discrepancy between the results of applying Schrödinger's relativistic equation and the experiments was completely cleared up.

I think there is a moral to this story, namely that it is more important to have beauty in one's equations than to have them fit experiment. If Schrödinger had been more confident of his work, he could have published it some months earlier, and he could have published a more accurate equation. That equation is now known as the Klein-Gordon equation, although it was really discovered by Schrödinger, and in fact was discovered by Schrödinger before he discovered his nonrelativistic treatment of the hydrogen atom. It seems that if one is working from the point of view of getting beauty in one's equations, and if one has really a sound insight, one is on a sure line of progress. If there is not complete agreement between the results of one's work and experiment, one should not allow oneself to be too discouraged, because the discrepancy may well be due to minor features that are not properly taken into account and that will get cleared up with further developments of the theory.

ALBERT EINSTEIN (1879–1955), with his special theory of relativity, changed the physicist's picture from one with three-dimensional symmetry to one with four-dimensional symmetry. This photograph of him and his wife and their daughter Margot was made in 1929.

That is how quantum mechanics was discovered. It led to a drastic change in the physicist's picture of the world, perhaps the biggest that has yet taken place. This change comes from our having to give up the deterministic picture we had always taken for granted. We are led to a theory that does not predict with certainty what is going to happen in the future but gives us information only about the probability of occurrence of various events. This giving up of determinacy has been a very controversial subject, and some people do not like it at all. Einstein in particular never liked it.

Although Einstein was one of the great contributors to the development of quantum mechanics, he still was always rather hostile to the form that quantum mechanics evolved into during his lifetime and that it still retains.

The hostility some people have to the giving up of the deterministic picture can be centered on a much discussed paper by Einstein, Podolsky and Rosen dealing with the difficulty one has in forming a consistent picture that still gives results according to the rules of quantum mechanics. The rules of quantum mechanics are quite definite. People

NIELS BOHR (1885–1962) introduced the idea that the electron moved about the nucleus in well-defined orbits. This photograph was made in 1922, nine years after the publication of his paper.

MAX PLANCK (1858–1947) introduced the idea that electromagnetic radiation consists of quanta, or particles. This photograph was made in 1913, 13 years after his original paper was published.

know how to calculate results and how to compare the results of their calculations with experiment. Everyone is agreed on the formalism. It works so well that nobody can afford to disagree with it. But still the picture that we are to set up behind this formalism is a subject of controversy.

I should like to suggest that one not worry too much about this controversy. I feel very strongly that the stage physics has reached at the present day is not the final stage. It is just one stage in the evolution of our picture of nature, and we should expect this process of evolution to continue in the future, as biological evolution continues into the future. The present stage of physical theory is merely a steppingstone toward the better stages we shall have in the future. One can be quite sure that there will be better stages simply because of the difficulties that occur in the physics of today.

I should now like to dwell a bit on the difficulties in the physics of the present day. The reader who is not an expert in the subject might get the idea that because of all these difficulties physical theory is in pretty poor shape and that the quantum theory is not much good. I should like to correct this impression by saying that quantum theory is an extremely good theory. It gives wonderful agreement with observation over a wide range of phenomena. There is no doubt that it is a good theory, and the only reason physicists talk so much about

the difficulties in it is that it is precisely the difficulties that are interesting. The successes of the theory are all taken for granted. One does not get anywhere simply by going over the successes again and again, whereas by talking over the difficulties people can hope to make some progress.

The difficulties in quantum theory are of two kinds. I might call them Class One difficulties and Class Two difficulties. Class One difficulties are the difficulties I have already mentioned: How can one form a consistent picture behind the rules for the present quantum theory? These Class One difficulties do not really worry the physicist. If the physicist knows how to calculate results and compare them with experiment, he is quite happy if the results agree with his experiments, and that is all he needs. It is only the philosopher, wanting to have a satisfying description of nature, who is bothered by Class One difficulties.

There are, in addition to the Class One difficulties, the Class Two difficulties, which stem from the fact that the present laws of quantum theory are not always adequate to give any results. If one pushes the laws to extreme conditions— to phenomena involving very high energies or very small distances—one sometimes gets results that are ambiguous or not really sensible at all. Then it is clear that one has reached the limits of application of the theory and that some further development is needed. The Class Two difficulties are important even for

the physicist, because they put a limitation on how far he can use the rules of quantum theory to get results comparable with experiment.

I should like to say a little more about the Class One difficulties. I feel that one should not be bothered with them too much, because they are difficulties that refer to the present stage in the development of our physical picture and are almost certain to change with future development. There is one strong reason, I think, why one can be quite confident that these difficulties will change. There are some fundamental constants in nature: the charge on the electron (designated e), Planck's constant divided by 2π (designated $\hbar$) and the velocity of light (c). From these fundamental constants one can construct a number that has no dimensions: the number $\hbar c/e^2$. That number is found by experiment to have the value 137, or something very close to 137. Now, there is no known reason why it should have this value rather than some other number. Various people have put forward ideas about it, but there is no accepted theory. Still, one can be fairly sure that someday physicists will solve the problem and explain why the number has this value. There will be a physics in the future that works when $\hbar c/e^2$ has the value 137 and that will not work when it has any other value.

The physics of the future, of course, cannot have the three quantities $\hbar$, e and c all as fundamental quantities. Only two of them can be fundamental, and the third must be derived from those two. It is almost certain that c will be one of the two fundamental ones. The velocity of light, c, is so important in the four-dimensional picture, and it plays such a fundamental role in the special theory of relativity, correlating our units of space and time, that it has to be fundamental. Then we are faced with the fact that of the two quantities $\hbar$ and e, one will be fundamental and one will be derived. If $\hbar$ is fundamental, e will have to be explained in some way in terms of the square root of $\hbar$, and it seems most unlikely that any fundamental theory can give e in terms of a square root, since square roots do not occur in basic equations. It is much more likely that e will be the fundamental quantity and that $\hbar$ will be explained in terms of e^2. Then there will be no square root in the basic equations. I think one is on safe ground if one makes the guess that in the physical picture we shall have at some future stage e and c will be fundamental quantities and $\hbar$ will be derived.

If $\hbar$ is a derived quantity instead of a fundamental one, our whole set of ideas about uncertainty will be altered: $\hbar$ is the fundamental quantity that occurs in the Heisenberg uncertainty relation connecting the amount of uncertainty in a position and in a momentum. This uncertainty relation cannot play a fundamental role in a theory in which $\hbar$ itself is not a fundamental quantity. I think one can make a safe guess that uncertainty relations in their present form will not survive in the physics of the future.

Of course there will not be a return to the determinism of classical physical theory. Evolution does not go backward. It will have to go forward. There will have to be some new development that is quite unexpected, that we cannot make a guess about, which will take us still further from classical ideas but which will alter completely the discussion of uncertainty relations. And when this new development occurs, people will find it all rather futile to have had so much of a discussion on the role of observation in the theory, because they will have then a much better point of view from which to look at things. So I shall say that if we can find a way to describe the uncertainty relations and the indeterminacy of present quantum mechanics that is satisfying to our philosophical ideas, we can count ourselves lucky. But if we cannot find such a way, it is nothing to be really disturbed about. We simply have to take into account that we are at a transitional stage and that perhaps it is quite impossible to get a satisfactory picture for this stage.

I have disposed of the Class One difficulties by saying that they are really not so important, that if one can make progress with them one can count oneself lucky, and that if one cannot it is nothing to be genuinely disturbed about. The Class Two difficulties are the really serious ones. They arise primarily from the fact that when we apply our quantum theory to fields in the way we have to if we are to make it agree with special relativity, interpreting it in terms of the three-dimensional sections I have mentioned, we have equations that at first look all right. But when one tries to solve them, one finds that they do not have any solutions. At this point we ought to say that we do not have a theory. But physicists are very ingenious about it, and they have found a way to make progress in spite of this obstacle. They find that when they try to solve the equations, the trouble is that certain quantities that ought to be finite are actually infinite. One gets integrals that diverge instead of converging to something definite. Physicists have found that there is a way to handle these infinities according to certain rules, which makes it possible to get definite results. This method is known as the renormalization method.

I shall merely explain the idea in words. We start out with a theory involving equations. In these equations there occur certain parameters: the charge of the electron, e, the mass of the electron, m, and things of a similar nature. One then finds that these quantities, which appear in the original equations, are not equal to the measured values of the charge and the mass of the electron. The measured values differ from these by certain correcting terms—$\triangle e$, $\triangle m$. and so on—so that the total charge is $e + \triangle e$ and the total mass $m + \triangle m$. These changes in charge and mass are brought about through the interaction of our elementary particle with other things. Then one says that $e + \triangle e$ and $m + \triangle m$, being the observed things, are the important things. The original e and m are just mathematical parameters; they are unobservable and therefore just tools one can discard when one has got far enough to bring in the things that one can com-

LOUIS DE BROGLIE (1892–) put forward the idea that particles are associated with waves. This photograph was made in 1929, five years after the appearance of his paper.

pare with observation. This would be a quite correct way to proceed if $\triangle e$ and $\triangle m$ were small (or even if they were not so small but finite) corrections. According to the actual theory, however, $\triangle e$ and $\triangle m$ are infinitely great. In spite of that fact one can still use the formalism and get results in terms of $e + \triangle e$ and $m + \triangle m$, which one can interpret by saying that the original e and m have to be minus infinity of a suitable amount to compensate for the $\triangle e$ and $\triangle m$ that are infinitely great. One can use the theory to get results that can be compared with experiment, in particular for electrodynamics. The surprising thing is that in the case of electrodynamics one gets results that are in extremely good agreement with experiment. The agreement applies to many significant figures—the kind of accuracy that previously one had only in astronomy. It is because of this good agreement that physicists do attach some value to the renormalization theory, in spite of its illogical character.

It seems to be quite impossible to put this theory on a mathematically sound basis. At one time physical theory was all built on mathematics that was inherently

sound. I do not say that physicists always use sound mathematics; they often use unsound steps in their calculations. But previously when they did so it was simply because of, one might say, laziness. They wanted to get results as quickly as possible without doing unnecessary work. It was always possible for the pure mathematician to come along and make the theory sound by bringing in further steps, and perhaps by introducing quite a lot of cumbersome notation and other things that are desirable from a mathematical point of view in order to get everything expressed rigorously but do not contribute to the physical ideas. The earlier mathematics could always be made sound in that way, but in the renormalization theory we have a theory that has defied all the attempts of the mathematician to make it sound. I am inclined to suspect that the renormalization theory is something that will not survive in the future, and that the remarkable agreement between its results and experiment should be looked on as a fluke.

This is perhaps not altogether surprising, because there have been similar flukes in the past. In fact, Bohr's elec-

tron-orbit theory was found to give very good agreement with observation as long as one confined oneself to one-electron problems. I think people will now say that this agreement was a fluke, because the basic ideas of Bohr's orbit theory have been superseded by something radically different. I believe the successes of the renormalization theory will be on the same footing as the successes of the Bohr orbit theory applied to one-electron problems.

The renormalization theory has removed some of these Class Two difficulties, if one can accept the illogical character of discarding infinities, but it does not remove all of them. There are a good many problems left over concerning particles other than those that come into electrodynamics: the new particles—mesons of various kinds and neutrinos. There the theory is still in a primitive stage. It is fairly certain that there will have to be drastic changes in our fundamental ideas before these problems can be solved.

One of the problems is the one I have already mentioned about accounting for the number 137. Other problems are how to introduce the fundamental length to physics in some natural way, how to explain the ratios of the masses of the elementary particles and how to explain their other properties. I believe separate ideas will be needed to solve these distinct problems and that they will be solved one at a time through successive stages in the future evolution of physics. At this point I find myself in disagreement with most physicists. They are inclined to think one master idea will be discovered that will solve all these problems together. I think it is asking too much to hope that anyone will be able to solve all these problems together. One should separate them one from another as much as possible and try to tackle them separately. And I believe the future development of physics will consist of solving them one at a time, and that after any one of them has been solved there will still be a great mystery about how to attack further ones.

I might perhaps discuss some ideas I have had about how one can possibly attack some of these problems. None of these ideas has been worked out very far, and I do not have much hope for any one of them. But I think they are worth mentioning briefly.

One of these ideas is to introduce something corresponding to the luminiferous ether, which was so popular among the physicists of the 19th century. I said earlier that physics does not evolve back-

$$ds^2 = c^2dt^2 - dx^2 - dy^2 - dz^2$$

FOUR-DIMENSIONAL SYMMETRY introduced by the special theory of relativity is not quite perfect. This equation is the expression for the invariant distance in four-dimensional space-time. The symbol s is the invariant distance; c, the speed of light; t, time; x, y and z, the three spatial dimensions. The d's are differentials. The lack of complete symmetry lies in the fact that the contribution from the time direction (c^2dt^2) does not have the same sign as the contributions from the three spatial directions $(-dx^2, -dy^2$ and $-dz^2)$.

$$\left(\frac{ih}{2\pi c}\frac{\partial}{\partial t} + \frac{e^2}{cr}\right)^2 \psi = \left[m^2c^2 - \frac{h^2}{4\pi^2}\left(\frac{\partial^2}{\partial x^2} + \frac{\partial^2}{\partial y^2} + \frac{\partial^2}{\partial z^2}\right)\right]\psi$$

SCHRÖDINGER'S FIRST WAVE EQUATION did not fit experimental results because it did not take into account the spin of the electron, which was not known at the time. The equation is a generalization of De Broglie's equation for the motion of a free electron. The symbol e represents the charge on the electron; i, the square root of minus one; h, Planck's constant; r, the distance from the nucleus; ψ, Schrödinger's wave function; m, the mass of the electron. The symbols resembling sixes turned backward are partial derivatives.

$$\left(E + \frac{e^2}{r}\right)\psi = -\frac{h^2}{8\pi^2 m}\left(\frac{\partial^2}{\partial x^2} + \frac{\partial^2}{\partial y^2} + \frac{\partial^2}{\partial z^2}\right)\psi$$

SCHRÖDINGER'S SECOND WAVE EQUATION is an approximation to the original equation, which does not take into account the refinements that are required by relativity.

ward. When I talk about reintroducing the ether, I do not mean to go back to the picture of the ether that one had in the 19th century, but I do mean to introduce a new picture of the ether that will conform to our present ideas of quantum theory. The objection to the old idea of the ether was that if you suppose it to be a fluid filling up the whole of space, in any place it has a definite velocity, which destroys the four-dimensional symmetry required by Einstein's special principle of relativity. Einstein's special relativity killed this idea of the ether.

But with our present quantum theory we no longer have to attach a definite velocity to any given physical thing, because the velocity is subject to uncertainty relations. The smaller the mass of the thing we are interested in, the more important are the uncertainty relations. Now, the ether will certainly have very little mass, so that uncertainty relations for it will be extremely important. The velocity of the ether at some particular place should therefore not be pictured as definite, because it will be subject to uncertainty relations and so may be anything over a wide range of values. In that way one can get over the difficulties of reconciling the existence of an ether with the special theory of relativity.

There is one important change this will make in our picture of a vacuum. We would like to think of a vacuum as a region in which we have complete symmetry between the four dimensions of space-time as required by special relativity. If there is an ether subject to uncertainty relations, it will not be possible to have this symmetry accurately. We can suppose that the velocity of the ether is equally likely to be anything within a wide range of values that would give the symmetry only approximately. We cannot in any precise way proceed to the limit of allowing all values for the velocity between plus and minus the velocity of light, which we would have to do in order to make the symmetry accurate. Thus the vacuum becomes a state that is unattainable. I do not think that this is a physical objection to the theory. It would mean that the vacuum is a state we can approach very closely. There is no limit as to how closely we can approach it, but we can never attain it. I believe that would be quite satisfactory to the experimental physicist. It would, however, mean a departure from the notion of the vacuum that we have in the quantum theory, where we start off with the vacuum state having exactly the symmetry required by special relativity.

That is one idea for the development of physics in the future that would

ERWIN SCHRÖDINGER (1887–1961) devised his wave equation by extending De Broglie's idea that waves are associated with particles to the electrons moving around the nucleus. This photograph was made in 1929, four years after he had published his second equation.

change our picture of the vacuum, but change it in a way that is not unacceptable to the experimental physicist. It has proved difficult to continue with the theory, because one would need to set up mathematically the uncertainty relations for the ether and so far some satisfactory theory along these lines has not been discovered. If it could be developed satisfactorily, it would give rise to a new kind of field in physical theory, which might help in explaining some of the elementary particles.

Another possible picture I should like to mention concerns the question of why all the electric charges that are observed in nature should be multiples of one elementary unit, e. Why does one not have a continuous distribution of charge occurring in nature? The picture I propose goes back to the idea of Faraday lines of force and involves a development of this idea. The Faraday lines of force are a way of picturing electric fields. If we have an electric field in any region of space, then according to Faraday we can draw a set of lines that have the direction of the electric field. The closeness of the lines to one another gives a measure of the strength of the field—they are close where the field is strong and less close where the field is weak. The Faraday lines of force give us a good picture of the electric field in classical theory.

When we go over to quantum theory, we bring a kind of discreteness into our basic picture. We can suppose that the continuous distribution of Faraday lines of force that we have in the classical picture is replaced by just a few discrete lines of force with no lines of force between them.

Now, the lines of force in the Faraday picture end where there are charges. Therefore with these quantized Faraday lines of force it would be reasonable to suppose the charge associated with each line, which has to lie at the end if the line of force has an end, is always the same (apart from its sign), and is always just the electronic charge, $-e$ or $+e$. This leads us to a picture of discrete Faraday lines of force, each associated with a charge, $-e$ or $+e$. There is a direction attached to each line, so that the ends of a line that has two ends are not the same, and there is a charge $+e$ at one end and a charge $-e$ at the other. We may have lines of force extending to infinity, of course, and then there is no charge.

If we suppose that these discrete Faraday lines of force are something basic in physics and lie at the bottom of our picture of the electromagnetic field, we shall have an explanation of why charges always occur in multiples of e. This happens because if we have any particle with some lines of force ending on it, the number of these lines must be a whole number. In that way we get a picture that is qualitatively quite reasonable.

We suppose these lines of force can move about. Some of them, forming closed loops or simply extending from minus infinity to infinity, will correspond to electromagnetic waves. Others will have ends, and the ends of these lines will be the charges. We may have a line of force sometimes breaking. When that happens, we have two ends appearing, and there must be charges at the two ends. This process—the breaking of a line of force—would be the picture for the creation of an electron (e^-) and a positron (e^+). It would be quite a reasonable picture, and if one could develop it, it would provide a theory in which e appears as a basic quantity. I have not yet found any reasonable system of equations of motion for these lines of force, and so I just put forward the idea as a possible physical picture we might have in the future.

There is one very attractive feature in this picture. It will quite alter the discussion of renormalization. The renormalization we have in our present quantum electrodynamics comes from starting off with what people call a bare electron—an electron without a charge on it. At a certain stage in the theory one brings in the charge and puts it on the electron, thereby making the electron interact with the electromagnetic field. This brings a perturbation into the equations and causes a change in the mass of the electron, the $\triangle m$, which is to be added to the previous mass of the electron. The procedure is rather roundabout because it starts off with the unphysical concept of the bare electron. Probably in the improved physical picture we shall have in the future the bare electron will not exist at all.

Now, that state of affairs is just what we have with the discrete lines of force. We can picture the lines of force as strings, and then the electron in the picture is the end of a string. The string itself is the Coulomb force around the electron. A bare electron means an electron without the Coulomb force around it. That is inconceivable with this picture, just as it is inconceivable to think of the end of a piece of string without thinking of the string itself. This, I think, is the kind of way in which we should try to develop our physical picture—to bring in ideas that make inconceivable the things we do not want to have. Again we have a picture that looks reasonable, but I have not found the proper equations for developing it.

I might mention a third picture with which I have been dealing lately. It involves departing from the picture of the electron as a point and thinking of it as a kind of sphere with a finite size. Of course, it is really quite an old idea to picture the electron as a sphere, but previously one had the difficulty of discussing a sphere that is subject to acceleration and to irregular motion. It will get distorted, and how is one to deal with the distortions? I propose that one should allow the electron to have, in general, an arbitrary shape and size. There will be some shapes and sizes in which it has less energy than in others, and it will tend to assume a spherical shape with a certain size in which the electron has the least energy.

This picture of the extended electron has been stimulated by the discovery of the mu meson, or muon, one of the new particles of physics. The muon has the surprising property of being almost identical with the electron except in one particular, namely, its mass is some 200 times greater than the mass of the electron. Apart from this disparity in mass the muon is remarkably similar to the electron, having, to an extremely high degree of accuracy, the same spin and the same magnetic moment in proportion to its mass as the electron does. This

WERNER HEISENBERG (1901–) **introduced matrix mechanics, which, like the Schrödinger theory, accounted for the motions of the electron. This photograph was made in 1929.**

leads to the suggestion that the muon should be looked on as an excited electron. If the electron is a point, picturing how it can be excited becomes quite awkward. But if the electron is the most stable state for an object of finite size, the muon might just be the next most stable state in which the object undergoes a kind of oscillation. That is an idea I have been working on recently. There are difficulties in the development of this idea, in particular the difficulty of bringing in the correct spin.

I have mentioned three possible ways in which one might think of developing our physical picture. No doubt there will be others that other people will think of. One hopes that sooner or later someone will find an idea that really fits and leads to a big development. I am rather pessimistic about it and am inclined to think none of them will be good enough. The future evolution of basic physics—that is to say, a development that will really solve one of the fundamental problems, such as bringing in the fundamental length or calculating the ratio of the masses—may require some much more drastic change in our physical picture. This would mean that in our present attempts to think of a new physical picture we are setting our imaginations to work in terms of inadequate physical concepts. If that is really the case, how can we hope to make progress in the future?

There is one other line along which one can still proceed by theoretical means. It seems to be one of the fundamental features of nature that fundamental physical laws are described in terms of a mathematical theory of great beauty and power, needing quite a high standard of mathematics for one to understand it. You may wonder: Why is nature constructed along these lines? One can only answer that our present knowledge seems to show that nature is so constructed. We simply have to accept it. One could perhaps describe the situation by saying that God is a mathematician of a very high order, and He used very advanced mathematics in constructing the universe. Our feeble attempts at mathematics enable us to understand a bit of the universe, and as we proceed to develop higher and higher mathematics we can hope to understand the universe better.

This view provides us with another way in which we can hope to make advances in our theories. Just by studying mathematics we can hope to make a guess at the kind of mathematics that will come into the physics of the future.

LINES OF FORCE in an electromagnetic field, if they are assumed to be discrete in the quantum theory, suggest why electric charges always occur in multiples of the charge of the electron. In Dirac's view, when a line of force has two ends, there is a particle with charge — e, perhaps an electron, at one end and a particle with charge + e, perhaps a positron, at the other end. When a closed line of force is broken, an electron-positron pair materializes.

A good many people are working on the mathematical basis of quantum theory, trying to understand the theory better and to make it more powerful and more beautiful. If someone can hit on the right lines along which to make this development, it may lead to a future advance in which people will first discover the equations and then, after examining them, gradually learn how to apply them. To some extent that corresponds with the line of development that occurred with Schrödinger's discovery of his wave equation. Schrödinger discovered the equation simply by looking for an equation with mathematical beauty. When the equation was first discovered, people saw that it fitted in certain ways, but the general principles according to which one should apply it were worked out only some two or three years later. It may well be that the next advance in physics will come about along these lines: people first discovering the equa-

tions and then needing a few years of development in order to find the physical ideas behind the equations. My own belief is that this is a more likely line of progress than trying to guess at physical pictures.

Of course, it may be that even this line of progress will fail, and then the only line left is the experimental one. Experimental physicists are continuing their work quite independently of theory, collecting a vast storehouse of information. Sooner or later there will be a new Heisenberg who will be able to pick out the important features of this information and see how to use them in a way similar to that in which Heisenberg used the experimental knowledge of spectra to build his matrix mechanics. It is inevitable that physics will develop ultimately along these lines, but we may have to wait quite a long time if people do not get bright ideas for developing the theoretical side.

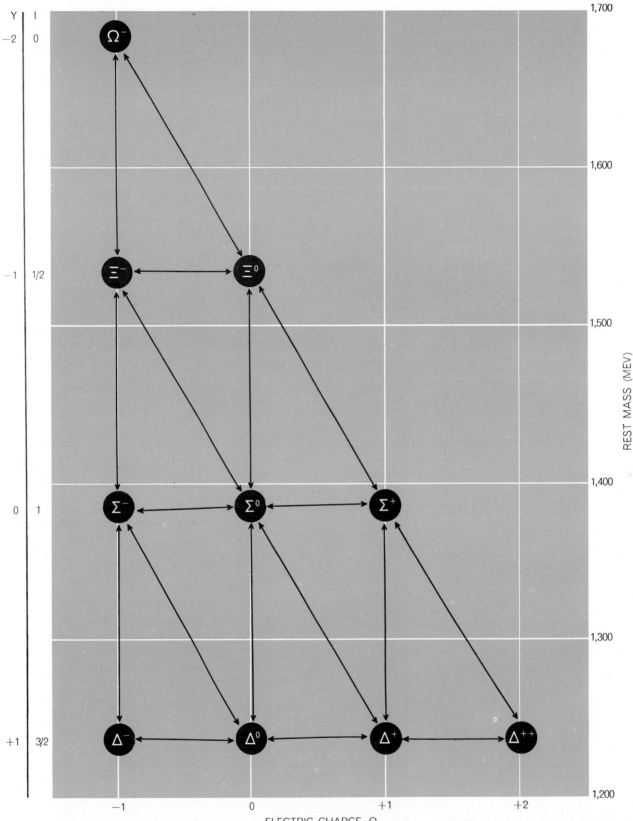

SUCCESS OF GROUP THEORY in the physics of fundamental particles was dramatized early this year with the discovery of the omega-minus (Ω^-) baryon at the Brookhaven National Laboratory. The existence of the omega minus had been predicted by the "eightfold way," a theory devised independently by Murray Gell-Mann and Yuval Ne'eman. The term "eightfold" refers to a classification scheme based on the mathematical theory of abstract groups. Previous theory had shown that "isotopic spin" symmetry (*black arrows*) connects families of particles with different values of electric charge (Q). The eightfold way invokes a new system of symmetries (*colored arrows*) to group together superfamilies of particles with different values of hypercharge (Y) and isotopic spin (I). The omega-minus baryon was needed to complete a superfamily of 10 members, of which nine members were previously known: a delta (Δ) quartet, a sigma (Σ) triplet and a xi (Ξ) doublet. The omega minus is the only baryon singlet with a negative electric charge, and its observed mass is within a few million electron volts (mev) of the mass predicted by theory.

33 MATHEMATICS IN THE PHYSICAL SCIENCES

FREEMAN J. DYSON · September 1964

In 1910 the mathematician Oswald Veblen and the physicist James Jeans were discussing the reform of the mathematical curriculum at Princeton University. "We may as well cut out group theory," said Jeans. "That is a subject which will never be of any use in physics." It is not recorded whether Veblen disputed Jeans's point, or whether he argued for the retention of group theory, on purely mathematical grounds. All we know is that group theory continued to be taught. And Veblen's disregard for Jeans's advice turned out to be of some importance to the history of science at Princeton. By an irony of fate group theory later grew into one of the central themes of physics, and it now dominates the thinking of all of us who are struggling to understand the fundamental particles of nature. It also happened by chance that Hermann Weyl and Eugene P. Wigner, who pioneered the group-theoretical point of view in physics from the 1920's to the present, were both Princeton professors.

This little story has several morals. The first moral is that scientists ought not to make off-the-cuff pronouncements concerning matters outside their special field of competence. Jeans provides us with a clear lesson on the evil effects of the habit of pontification. Starting from this unfortunate beginning with Veblen, he later went from bad to worse, becoming a successful popular writer and radio broadcaster, accepting a knighthood and ruining his professional reputation with suave and shallow speculations on religion and philosophy.

We ought not, however, to look so complacently on the decline and fall of Jeans. There, but for the grace of God, go we. After all, Jeans in 1910 was a respected physicist (although Princeton, aping the English custom in titles as in pseudo-Gothic architecture, called him professor of applied mathematics). He was neither more incompetent nor more ignorant than most of his colleagues. Very few men at that time had the slightest inkling of the fruitfulness that would result from the marriage of physics and group theory. So the second and more serious moral of our story is that the future of science is unpredictable. The place of mathematics in the physical sciences is not something that can be defined once and for all. The interrelations of mathematics with science are as rich and various as the texture of science itself.

One factor that has remained constant through all the twists and turns of the history of physical science is the decisive importance of mathematical imagination. Each century had its own particular preoccupations in science and its own particular style in mathematics. But in every century in which major advances were achieved the growth in physical understanding was guided by a combination of empirical observation with purely mathematical intuition. For a physicist mathematics is not just a tool by means of which phenomena can be calculated; it is the main source of concepts and principles by means of which new theories can be created.

All through the centuries the power of mathematics to mirror the behavior of the physical universe has been a source of wonder to physicists. The great 17th-century astronomer Johannes Kepler, discoverer of the laws of motion of the planets, expressed his wonder in theological terms: "Thus God himself was too kind to remain idle, and began to play the game of signatures, signing his likeness into the world; therefore I chance to think that all nature and the graceful sky are symbolized in the art of geometry." In the more idealistic 19th century the German physicist Heinrich Hertz, who first verified James Clerk Maxwell's electromagnetic equations by demonstrating the existence of radio waves, wrote: "One cannot escape the feeling that these mathematical formulae have an independent existence and an intelligence of their own, that they are wiser than we are, wiser even than their discoverers, that we get more out of them than was originally put into them." Lastly, in our rationalistic 20th century Eugene Wigner has expressed his puzzlement at the success of more modern mathematical ideas in his characteristically dry and modest manner: "We are in a position similar to that of a man who was provided with a bunch of keys and who, having to open several doors in succession, always hit on the right key on the first or second trial. He became skeptical concerning the uniqueness of the coordination between keys and doors."

The mathematics of Kepler, the mathematics of Hertz and of Wigner have almost nothing in common. Kepler was concerned with Euclidean geometry, circles and spheres and regular polyhedra. Hertz was thinking of partial differential equations. Wigner was writing about the use of complex numbers in quantum mechanics, and no doubt he was also thinking about (but not mentioning) his own triumphant introduction of group theory into many diverse areas of physics. Euclid, partial differential equations and group theory are three branches of mathematics so remote from each other that they seem to belong to different mathematical universes. And yet all three of them turn out to be intimately involved in our one physical universe. These are astonishing facts, understood fully by nobody. Only one conclusion seems to follow

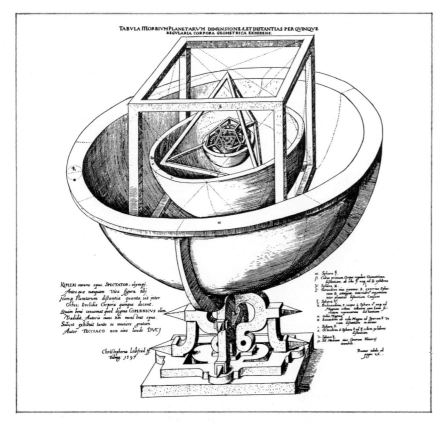

KEPLER'S MODEL OF THE SOLAR SYSTEM, published in 1596, was based on the five "perfect" solids of Euclidean geometry. The planetary orbits were successively inscribed in and circumscribed about an octahedron, an icosahedron, a dodecahedron, a tetrahedron and a cube. The model is a supreme example of misguided mathematical intuition. Although Kepler was aware of the discrepancies between his theory and the best observations of his time, he always regarded this model as one of his greatest achievements.

genuinely philosophical difficulties. The vast majority of working scientists, myself included, find comfort in the words of the French mathematician Henri Lebesgue: "In my opinion a mathematician, in so far as he is a mathematician, need not preoccupy himself with philosophy—an opinion, moreover, which has been expressed by many philosophers."

We are content to leave the philosophizing to giants such as Bohr and Wigner, while we amuse ourselves with the exploration of nature on a more superficial level. I shall accordingly not discuss further the ultimate reasons why mathematical concepts have come to be preeminent in physics. I shall beg the philosophical question, assuming as an article of faith that nature is to be understood in mathematical terms. The questions I shall address are practical ones relating to the way in which mathematical ideas react on physics. What are the standards of taste and judgment that mathematics imposes on the physicist? Which are the parts of mathematics that now offer hope for new physical understanding? In conclusion, since one concrete example is better than a mountain of prose, I shall sketch the role group theory has played in physics, leading up to the theory of fundamental particles known as the "eightfold way" [see "Strongly Interacting Particles," by Geoffrey F. Chew, Murray Gell-Mann, and Arthur H. Rosenfeld, SCIENTIFIC AMERICAN Offprint #296]. This theory, developed independently by Gell-Mann and Yuval Ne'eman, has been brilliantly vindicated by the discovery of the omega-minus particle.

Before plunging into the details of

with assurance from such facts. The human mind is not yet close to any complete understanding of the physical world, or of the mathematical world, or of the relations between them.

In this article I shall not attempt any deep philosophical discussion of the reasons why mathematics supplies so much power to physics. In each century it is only a few physicists—in our century perhaps only Albert Einstein, Weyl, Niels Bohr, P. W. Bridgman and Wigner—who dig deep enough into the foundations of our knowledge to reach

RATIO OF ORBITS	COPERNICAN VALUES	KEPLER'S MODEL	MODERN VALUES
MERCURY MAXIMUM / VENUS MINIMUM	.723	.707	.650
VENUS MAXIMUM / EARTH MINIMUM	.794	.795	.741
EARTH MAXIMUM / MARS MINIMUM	.757	.795	.735
MARS MAXIMUM / JUPITER MINIMUM	.333	.333	.337
JUPITER MAXIMUM / SATURN MINIMUM	.635	.577	.604

MERCURY   VENUS   EARTH

MARS

EXPLODED VIEW of Kepler's polyhedron model of the solar system (*right*) shows how each planetary orbit was supposed to occupy a spherical shell whose thickness corresponded to the difference between that planet's maximum and minimum distance from the sun. The table at left contains three sets of values for the ratio between each planet's maximum orbit and the next outer planet's minimum orbit. The first column gives the observational values obtained by Kepler from Copernicus. The second column gives the

present-day problems, I shall illustrate the effects of mathematical tastes and prejudices on physics with some historical examples. In trying to explain technical matters to a nontechnical audience, it is often helpful to examine past history and draw analogies between the problems of the past and those of the present. The reader should be warned not to take historical analogies too seriously. Very few active scientists are particularly well informed about the history of science, and almost none are directly guided in their work by historical analogies. In this respect scientists can be compared to politicians. The greatest politician of our century was probably Lenin, and he operated successfully within a historical viewpoint that was grossly limited and distorted. The only important historian of modern times to achieve high political office was François Guizot, prime minister of France during the 1840's, and all his historical understanding did not save him from mediocrity as a statesman. A good historian is too much committed to the past to be either a creative political leader or a creative scientist. In science at least, if a man

wishes to achieve greatness, he should follow the advice of William Blake: "Drive your cart and your plow over the bones of the dead."

The most spectacular example in physics of the successful use of mathematical imagination is still Einstein's theory of gravitation, otherwise known as the general theory of relativity. To build his theory Einstein used as his working material non-Euclidean geometry, a theory of curved spaces that had been invented during the 19th century. Einstein took the revolutionary step of identifying our physical space-time with a curved non-Euclidean space, so that the laws of physics became propositions in a geometry radically different from the classical flat-space geometry [see "Geometry," page 112]. All this was done by Einstein on the basis of very general arguments and aesthetic judgments. The observational tests of the theory were made only after it was essentially complete, and they did not play any part in the creative process. Einstein himself seems to have trusted his mathematical intuition so firmly that he had no feeling of nervousness about the outcome of the

observations. The positive results of the observations were, of course, decisive in convincing other physicists that he was right.

General relativity is the prime example of a physical theory built on a mathematical "leap in the dark." It might have remained undiscovered for a century if a man with Einstein's peculiar imagination had not lived. The same cannot be said of quantum mechanics, the other major achievement of 20th-century physics. Quantum mechanics was created independently by Werner Heisenberg and Erwin Schrödinger, working from quite different points of view, and its completion was a cooperative enterprise of many hands. Nevertheless, in quantum mechanics too the decisive step was a speculative jump of mathematical imagination, seen most clearly in the work of Schrödinger.

Schrödinger's work rested on a formal mathematical similarity between the theory of light rays and the theory of particle orbits, a similarity discovered some 90 years earlier by the Irish mathematician William Rowan Hamilton. Schrödinger observed that the theory of light rays is a special limiting case of

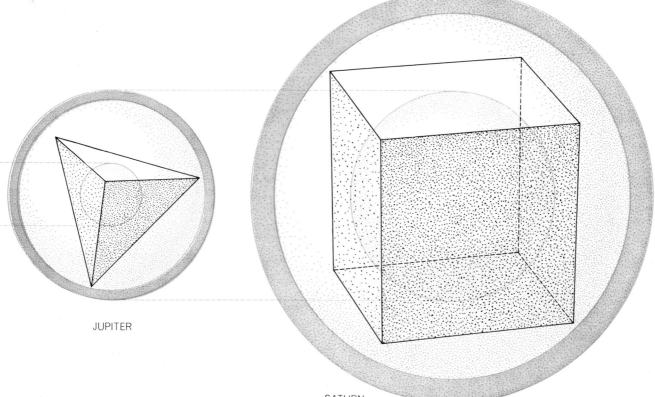

JUPITER

SATURN

theoretical values predicted by Kepler's polyhedron model. The third column gives the accepted modern values. Kepler cheated in the case of Mercury in order to account for the most conspicuous discrepancy between his theory and the Copernican values: although the four outer polyhedra are circumscribed around a planetary shell in the usual way (the shell touches the faces of the polyhedron), the octahedron is circumscribed around the shell of Mercury in a special way (the shell touches the edges of the octahedron).

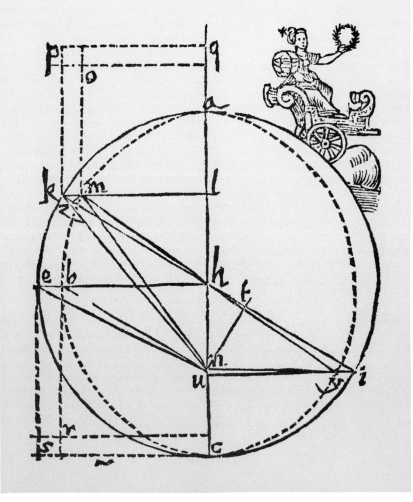

DISCOVERY OF ELLIPTICAL ORBIT FOR MARS was Kepler's great triumph after years of trying to make circular orbits satisfy Tycho Brahe's observations. In this diagram he shows that Mars sweeps out equal areas, measured from the sun at *n*, in equal times.

Ptolemy's system was that, since it was tailored in detail to fit the observed motions of each planet, it was immune to observational disproof. By the time of Ptolemy (A.D. 150) the vital force of Greek mathematics had been extinguished, and there were no new mathematical ideas to contest the stranglehold of Euclid's spheres and circles on the scientific imagination. Disturbed neither by new celestial observations nor by new mathematics, the 1,000-year night set in.

When Kepler in 1604 finally demolished the epicyclic cosmology by his discovery that planetary orbits are ellipses, he was not helped by any mathematical preconceptions favoring elliptical motions. On the contrary, he had to fight tooth and nail against his own mathematical prejudices, which were still uncompromisingly medieval. Only after years of struggling with various systems of epicycles did he overcome his conservative tastes enough to consider a system of ellipses. Such mathematical conservatism is the rule rather than the exception among the great minds of physics. The man who breaks out into a new era of thought is usually himself still a prisoner of the old. Even Isaac Newton, who invented the calculus as a mathematical vehicle for his epoch-making discoveries in physics and astronomy, preferred to express himself in archaic geometrical terms. His *Principia Mathematica* is written throughout in the language of classical Greek geometry. His assistant Henry Pemberton, who edited the third edition of the *Principia*, reports that Newton always expressed great admiration for the geometers of ancient Greece and censured himself for not following them more closely than he did. Lord Keynes, the economist, who made a hobby of collecting and studying Newton's unpublished manuscripts, summed up his impressions of Newton in the following words:

"In the eighteenth century and since, Newton came to be thought of as the first and greatest of the modern age of scientists, a rationalist, one who taught us to think on the lines of cold and untinctured reason. I do not see him in this light. I do not think any one who has pored over the contents of the box which he packed up when he finally left Cambridge in 1696 and which, though partly dispersed, have come down to us, can see him like that. Newton was not the first of the age of reason. He was the last of the magicians, the last of the Babylonians and Su-

the theory of light waves that had been established after Hamilton's time by Maxwell and Hertz. So Schrödinger argued: Why should there not be a theory of particle waves having the same relation to particle orbits as light waves have to light rays? This purely mathematical argument led him to construct the theory of particle waves, which is now called quantum mechanics. The theory was promptly checked against the experimentally known facts concerning the behavior of atoms, and the agreement was even more impressive than in the case of the general theory of relativity. As often happens in physics, a theory that had been based on some general mathematical arguments combined with a few experimental facts turned out to predict innumerable further experimental results with unfailing and uncanny accuracy.

General relativity and quantum mechanics are success stories, showing mathematical intuition in a fruitful and

liberating role. Unfortunately there is another side to the picture. Mathematical intuition is more often conservative than revolutionary, more often hampering than liberating. The worst of all the historic setbacks of physical science was the definitive adoption by Aristotle and Ptolemy of an earth-centered astronomy in which all heavenly bodies were supposed to move on spheres and circles. The Aristotelian astronomy benighted science almost completely for 1,800 years (250 B.C. to A.D. 1550). There were of course many reasons for this prolonged stagnation, but it must be admitted that the primary reason for the popularity of Aristotle's astronomy was a misguided mathematical intuition that held only spheres and circles to be aesthetically satisfactory.

Ptolemy explained the motions of the moon and planets by means of cycles and epicycles, that is to say, hierarchies of circles of various sizes moving one on another. The devastating feature of

merians, the last great mind which looked out on the visible and intellectual world with the same eyes as those who began to build our intellectual inheritance rather less than 10,000 years ago. Isaac Newton, a posthumous child born on Christmas Day, 1642, was the last wonder-child to whom the Magi could do sincere and appropriate homage."

The character of Newton and his devotion to alchemy and to ancient apocalyptic writings are a fascinating subject, but it does not concern us here. We are concerned only with his mathematical style and tastes and with the effect of his mathematics on his science. Everything we know concerning his attitude toward mathematics is consistent with Keynes's conclusions. There is little doubt that Newton, like Kepler, made his discoveries by overcoming deeply conservative mathematical prejudices.

From these various historical examples we can only conclude that mathematical intuition is both good and bad, both indispensable to creative work in physics and also totally untrustworthy. The reasons for this two-edged quality lie in the nature of mathematics itself. As the physicist Ernst Mach remarked: "The power of mathematics rests on its evasion of all unnecessary thought and on its wonderful saving of mental operations." A physicist builds theories with mathematical materials, because the mathematics enables him to imagine more than he can clearly think. The

physicist's art is to choose his materials and build with them an image of nature, knowing only vaguely and intuitively rather than rationally whether or not the materials are appropriate to his purpose. After the design of the theory is complete, rational criticism and experimental test will show if it is scientifically sound. In the process of theory-building, mathematical intuition is indispensable because the "evasion of unnecessary thought" gives freedom to the imagination; mathematical intuition is dangerous, because many situations in science demand for their understanding not the evasion of thought but thought.

I come now to discuss the present situation in physics. Without intending discourtesy to the experts in solid-state, nuclear spectroscopy and so forth, I use the word "physics" as an abbreviation for high-energy physics: the study of the fundamental particles. Physics (in this narrow sense) is now in an unusually happy situation. The latest generation of big accelerators has revealed during the past five years a whole new world of particles, with a quantity of detail and a richness of structure hardly anyone had expected. We must be profoundly thankful that the responsible physicists and politicians, not knowing that all these things were there, had the faith and courage 10 years ago to go ahead with building the machines. As

a result of their enterprise we now have a large amount of exact information about a world that is as new and strange as the world of atoms was in 1910. Just as in 1910, we have no comprehensive theory, and the theorists have complete freedom to make of the experimental data what they will.

In this situation the theoretical physicists choose their objectives and their methods according to criteria of mathematical taste. The primary question for a theorist is not yet "Will my theory work?" but rather "Is what I am doing a theory?" The material at hand for theoretical work consists of fragments of mathematics, cookbook rules of calculation and a few general principles surviving from earlier days. What combination of these items would deserve the name of a theory is a question of mathematical taste.

The three main methods of work in contemporary theory are called field theory, S-matrix theory and group theory. They are not mutually exclusive; at least there is no contradiction between the things that adherents of the different methods do, although there is sometimes a contradiction between the things they say. Probably all three points of view will in the end make fruitful contributions to the understanding of nature.

The three methods differ not only in their choice of mathematical material but also in the uses to which the ma-

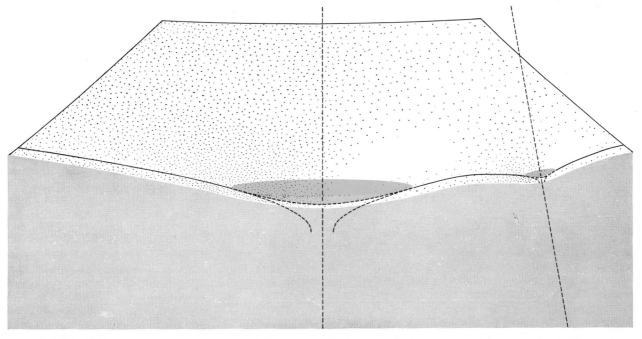

CURVATURE OF SPACE was postulated by Einstein on the basis of very general arguments and aesthetic judgments. To build his theory Einstein used as his working material non-Euclidean geometry, a theory of curved spaces that had been invented during the 19th century. In this representation two massive bodies are shown in two dimensions on a two-dimensional surface. The local curvature of space around the bodies accounts for their gravitational properties. In actuality physical space-time is four-dimensional.

terial is put. Field theory begins from a prejudice in favor of mathematical depth, a feeling that deep physical understanding and deep mathematics ought to go together. So the chosen mathematical material is the algebra of operators in Hilbert space, which is combined with various other difficult parts of mathematics in order to reach a structure that embodies some of the salient features of the real world. The emphasis is on a rigorous mathematical understanding of the theory, not on detailed comparison with experiment. Of the three methods, field theory is the remotest from experiment and the most mathematically strict, the most ambitious in its intellectual tone and the vaguest in its relevance to physics. I am myself addicted to it and am therefore particularly qualified to point out its limitations.

In S-matrix theory (the S stands for *Streu*, the German word for "scatter") the mathematical material is deliberately chosen to be as elementary as possible. It consists of the standard theory of analytic functions of complex variables, a theory whose essential fea-

tures have not changed since it was created by the French mathematician Augustin Cauchy early in the 19th century. S-matrix theory compensates for the weakness of its mathematical base by making heavy use of experimental data. The S-matrix theoretician typically aims to compute or predict the result of one experiment by making use of the results of others. Sometimes predictions are made from "first principles" independent of other experiments, and the hope is ultimately to deduce everything from first principles. One of the most pleasant and refreshing features of S-matrix theory is that the rules of the game can be changed as a calculation proceeds. The method as it now exists is transitional; one is not applying a cut-and-dried theory but rather creating a theory as one goes along by a process of trial and error. At every stage of the work the comparison with experiment will ruthlessly eliminate the unfit idea and leave room for truth to grow.

The success of S-matrix theory in interpreting experiments, and in giving guidance to experimenters, has been impressive. My own preference for field

theory is based on a personal taste that, judged by the evidence of history, cannot be considered reliable. I find S-matrix theory too simple, too lacking in mathematical depth, and I cannot believe that it is really all there is. If the S-matrix theory turned out to explain everything, then I would feel disappointed that the Creator had after all been rather unsophisticated. I realize, however, that He has a habit of being sophisticated in ways one does not expect.

I shall now discuss group theory, the third of the principal methods used in modern theoretical physics, in somewhat greater detail than the other two. The mathematical material here is a theory of considerable depth and power, mostly dating from the first quarter of the 20th century. The two main concepts are "group" and "representation." A group is a set of operations possessing the property that any two of them performed in succession are together equivalent to another operation belonging to the set. For example, the three-dimensional rotation group O_3 is defined as the set of all rotations of an ordinary three-dimensional space about a fixed center. Obviously, if R_1 and R_2 are any two such rotations, the combination of R_1 with R_2 can be duplicated by a third rotation, R_3. A representation of a group is a set of numbers and a rule of transformation of these numbers such that each operation of the group produces a well-defined transformation of the numbers. The transformations in a representation are restricted to being linear; that is to say, if a particular transformation sends p to p' and q to q', then it also sends $p + q$ to $p' + q'$. An example of a representation of O_3 is the set of three coordinates (x, y, z) that determine the position in space of any point P [*see illustration at left*]. When a rotation R is applied, the point P moves to a new position P' with coordinates x', y', z', and this determines the rule of transformation for x, y, z. This particular representation of O_3 is called the triplet representation, since there are three numbers involved in it.

The immense power of group theory in physics derives from two facts. First, the laws of quantum mechanics decree that whenever a physical object has a symmetry, there is a well-defined group (G) of operations that preserve the symmetry, and the possible quantum states of the object are then in exact correspondence with the representations of G. Second, the enumeration and

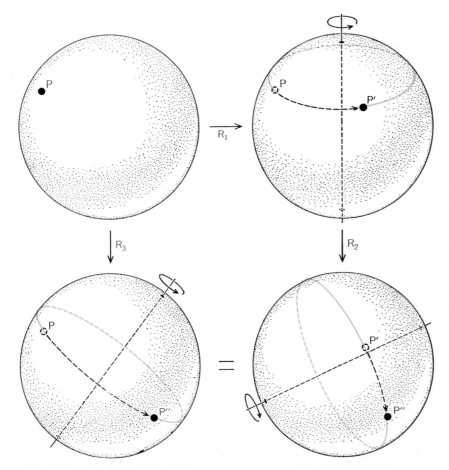

THREE-DIMENSIONAL ROTATION GROUP O_3 is defined as the set of all rotations of an ordinary three-dimensional space about a fixed center. If R_1 and R_2 are any two such rotations, the result of combining the two can be duplicated by a third rotation, R_3.

classification of all well-behaved groups and of their representations have been done by the mathematicians, once and for all, independently of the physical situation to which the groups may be applied. From these two facts results the possibility of making a purely abstract theory of the symmetries of fundamental particles, based on the abstract qualities of groups and representations and avoiding all arbitrary mechanical or dynamical models.

The crucial transition from concrete to abstract group theory is most easily explained by examples. An atom floating in a rarefied gas has no preferred direction in space and therefore has the symmetry of the ordinary rotation group O_3. Among the representations of O_3 there is the triplet representation. Those states of the atom that have one unit of spin belong to this representation and are called triplet states; they always occur precisely in groups of three with the same energy. Now let a magnetic field be turned on so as to destroy the rotational symmetry; the three equal energies are slightly split apart and the three states can be seen in a spectroscope as a visible triplet of spectral lines. Such a classification of states of the atom according to their rotational symmetry is the standard example of concrete group theory at work.

Now we jump to a different example. There are three kinds of fundamental particle called pions, one positively charged, one negatively charged and one neutral. They all have approximately the same mass and approximately the same nuclear interactions. Let us then imagine that they are a triplet representation of a group O_3', having exactly the same abstract structure as O_3 but having nothing to do with ordinary space rotations. We can then predict many of the properties of pions from abstract group theory alone without knowing anything about the intrinsic nature of the operations constituting O_3'. It turns out that all of these predicted properties of pions are correct. What is much more remarkable, these predictions were made on the basis of abstract group theory by Nicholas Kemmer in 1938, nine years before the first pion was discovered. The group O_3' (with some slight modification) is known in physics as the "isotopic-spin group."

Finally we come to the eightfold way, which gave us the key to the classification of the more recently discovered particles. The classification depends on a group U_3, which is larger and less familiar than O_3. To make U_3 under-

standable to nonmathematicians I shall introduce a mechanical model that bears the same relation to the abstract group U_3 as the rotations in three-dimensional space bear to the abstract group O_3. Needless to say, this mechanical model is not supposed to exist in the real world. It is intended only to illustrate the structure of U_3.

Consider a solar system in which the force of gravity varies directly with the

first power of distance instead of with the inverse-square law. Suppose the planets to be small, so that their mutual perturbations are negligible. Each planet then moves independently in an elliptical orbit with the sun at the center. The peculiar feature of these orbits is that they all have the same period, the outer planets moving faster than the inner ones. We call the period of each orbit a "year," so that the positions of

a

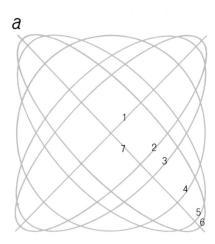

b

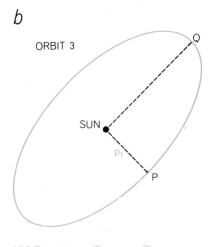

ORBIT 3

SUN

Q

P

p_1

ORBIT	1	2	3	4	5	6	7
p_1	0	1	$\sqrt{2}$	$\sqrt{5}$	$\sqrt{8}$	3	$\sqrt{10}$
q_2	$\sqrt{10}$	3	$\sqrt{8}$	$\sqrt{5}$	$\sqrt{2}$	1	0

ORBIT 3: $p_1 = \sqrt{2}$, $q_2 = \sqrt{8}$
$p_2 = q_1 = p_3 = q_3 = 0$

TOTAL ENERGY OF
ORBIT 3 $= [p_1{}^2 + q_2{}^2] = [2 + 8] = 10$

c

REPRESENTATION OF ORBITS
IN EIGHTFOLD WAY
$a_{12} = p_1 q_2 - p_2 q_1$
$a_{23} = p_2 q_3 - p_3 q_2 = 0$
$a_{31} = p_3 q_1 - p_1 q_3 = 0$
$S_{11} = p_1{}^2 + q_1{}^2$
$S_{22} = p_2{}^2 + q_2{}^2$
$S_{33} = p_3{}^2 + q_3{}^2 = 0$
$S_{12} = p_1 p_2 + q_1 q_2 = 0$
$S_{23} = p_2 p_3 + q_2 q_3 = 0$
$S_{31} = p_3 p_1 + q_3 q_1 = 0$

d

VALUES OF S_{11}, a_{12}, S_{22}

ORBIT	1	2	3	4	5	6	7
S_{11}	0	1	2	5	8	9	10
a_{12}	0	3	4	5	4	3	0
S_{22}	10	9	8	5	2	1	0

TOTAL ENERGY FOR
ALL ORBITS $= S_{11} + S_{22} = 10$

EIGHTFOLD-WAY MODEL bears the same relation to the abstract group SU_3 as rotations in three-dimensional space (*illustrated on page 254*) bear to the abstract group O_3. The model (*a*) shows seven planetary orbits that can be transformed into each other by operations belonging to the group SU_3, discussed in the text. That there are seven orbits is not significant; any number of others could be specified to satisfy the needs of this particular model. Orbit No. 3 is shown separately (*b*) to indicate how a planetary motion is defined by the points P and Q, with values p_1 and q_2. Normally six coordinates (three of p and three of q) are needed to define a point in space. But because of the special way the coordinate axes are chosen for this model, p_2 and q_1 are zero, and because the orbits all lie in a plane, the coordinates p_3 and q_3 are also zero. All the orbits have the same total energy $(p_1{}^2 + q_2{}^2 = 10)$ but different angular momenta, expressed in terms of the value a_{12}. In particular the two straight-line orbits (*1 and 7*) have zero angular momentum, whereas the circular orbit (*4*) has the most angular momentum. According to the eightfold way the seven orbits can be represented by sets of nine numbers, listed in *c*. It is evident that six of these numbers vanish because p_2, p_3, q_1 and q_3 are all zero. Thus only three components remain: S_{11}, a_{12}, S_{22}. When the appropriate values for p_1 and q_2 are inserted, the three components take the values shown in *d*. The values are such that they transform into each other when the operations of SU_3 symmetry are applied. This is possible, in part, because the total energy for all orbits is the same: $S_{11} + S_{22} = 10$.

all planets repeat themselves at yearly intervals.

The motion of a planet can be specified precisely by two points in space denoted (P, Q), P being the position of the planet now and Q being the position it will occupy three months later. Another planet traveling three months ahead of the first in the same orbit will be specified by (Q, $-P$), where $-P$ means the point diametrically opposite P. The total energy of either of these planets is given by ($OP^2 + OQ^2$), which is the sum of the squares of the distances of the points P and Q from the sun at O. The group U_3 (as exhibited by this particular model) is defined as the set of all transformations of the planetary motions, subject to the following three restrictions: (1) the transformations are linear; (2) the transformations leave the total energy of each motion unchanged, and (3) if two or more planets are moving in a given orbit, a transformation that takes one to a new orbit takes all.

If only the first two conditions were imposed, we would have the group of all linear transformations of (P, Q), leaving the sum ($OP^2 + OQ^2$) unchanged. This would be simply the rotation group O_6 in a space of six dimensions (three dimensions for P and three for Q). The group U_3 is thus a subgroup of O_6. The third restriction on U_3 can be stated in a more concise but equivalent form as follows: A transformation that takes the motion (P, Q) into (R, S) must also take (Q, $-P$) into (S, $-R$).

Two special kinds of transformation can easily be seen to belong to U_3. First, consider ordinary rotations operating on P and Q simultaneously. These obviously satisfy the three conditions. Hence the rotation group O_3 is a subgroup of U_3. Second, consider the transformations of time-displacement, in which each planet is transformed into the same planet at a fixed interval of time earlier or later. The time-displacements also belong to U_3 and form another subgroup (T) of U_3.

For application to physics it is convenient to reduce U_3 to a smaller group SU_3 (and when I write SU_3, I mean the group the professionals call SU_3/Z_3). One obtains SU_3 from U_3 by simply forgetting time. For SU_3 all motions belonging to the same orbit are regarded as identical, irrespective of the time. Whereas U_3 transforms a planetary motion into another planetary motion at a particular time, SU_3 transforms an orbit into an orbit without reference to time. In mathematical language SU_3 is the group U_3 with the subgroup T of time-

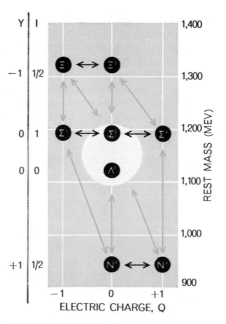

SUPERFAMILY OF EIGHT was the first grouping suggested by the eightfold way. It contains the eight most familiar baryons: the neutron (N⁰) and proton (N⁺)—also known as the nucleon doublet—the lambda (Λ) singlet, the original sigma (Σ) triplet and the original xi (Ξ) doublet. The sigma triplet and xi doublet that appear in the 10-member superfamily containing the omega minus (see page 248) are heavier particles with the same values of Y and I.

displacements removed from it. The representations of SU_3 are precisely those representations of U_3 that are independent of time.

Let us now look for simple representations of SU_3. A planetary motion (P, Q) is defined by the six coordinates (p_1, p_2, p_3, q_1, q_2, q_3) of P and Q. These coordinates by themselves define a representation of U_3 but, since they are time-dependent, not of SU_3. The simplest time-independent quantities (for reasons we need not go into) consist of p's and q's multiplied together in various combinations, as shown in the illustration on the preceding page. There are nine and only nine such quantities. Three of them are components of the angular momentum and are designated a_{12}, a_{23} and a_{31}; six are components of another kind that are related to the total energy of the system: S_{11}, S_{22}, S_{33}, S_{12}, S_{23}, S_{31}. (The subscripts indicate which of the p's and q's are involved in defining the quantity, thus $a_{12} = p_1 q_2 - p_2 q_1$ and $S_{12} = p_1 p_2 + q_1 q_2$.)

Because this representation of SU_3 involves nine quantities it is said to be nine-dimensional. The sum $S_{11} + S_{22} + S_{33}$, however, is the total energy of the system and does not transform at all

under any of the operations of U_3. When three quantities yield a constant sum, it is evident that only two of them are independent and that the third is always implied when any two are given. The three quantities S_{11}, S_{22} and S_{33} might be reduced to two independent quantities in various ways, but for technical reasons they are usually combined as follows: one quantity is expressed as $S_{11} - S_{22}$ and the other as $S_{33} - \frac{1}{2}(S_{11} + S_{22})$. As a result there are only five independent components of S rather than six, and these together with the three components of a yield a total of eight quantities that do in fact transform into each other under U_3. These eight quantities are time-independent and provide an eight-dimensional representation of SU_3. The representation so obtained is the simplest that exists and is the famous eightfold way.

Finally, let us imagine that the SU_3 symmetry in nature is not perfect. Suppose, for example, that the "three direction" (that is, the direction in which the coordinates have the values p_3 and q_3) is somehow different from the other two directions. In terms of our imaginary solar system this means that symmetry is preserved only when the orbits all lie in the same plane and is not preserved by rotations that carry the orbits off the plane. In this case the symmetry group U_3 will be replaced by its subgroup U_2, consisting only of those transformations of U_3 that leave the three directions unaltered. Under the operations of U_2 the eightfold way does not remain a unified representation. Its eight components split into subsets in the following manner:

$$S_{33} - \frac{1}{2}(S_{11} + S_{22}) \qquad \text{(a singlet)}$$

$$\left.\begin{array}{l} S_{23}, \ S_{31} \\ a_{23}, \ a_{31} \end{array}\right\} \qquad \text{(two doublets)}$$

$$(S_{11} - S_{22}), \ S_{12}, \ a_{12} \qquad \text{(a triplet)}$$

Each of these subsets forms a representation of U_2. In other words, the transformation defined by the singlet representation pertains to a unique subset of the total set: a subset of one member. Each of the two doublets represents a slightly larger subset: a subset of two members. Similarly, the triplet subset has three members.

Turning now to the actual physical world, compare this eight-member structure with the eight original baryons, the most familiar of the heavy "elementary" particles, which consist of the lambda (Λ) singlet, the proton-neutron (or nucleon) doublet, the xi (Ξ) doublet

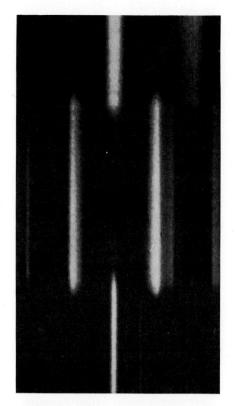

SPECTRAL LINE OF NIOBIUM (*bottom*) is split into three components when a magnetic field is turned on so as to destroy the rotational symmetry of the atoms. Two components are observed perpendicular to the magnetic field (*middle*) and a third is observed parallel to the magnetic field (*top*). The triplet lines correspond to three states of the atom that have one unit of spin each; these states always occur precisely in groups of three with the same energy. Such a classification of states of the atom according to their rotational symmetry is an example of applied group theory. Spectrograms were made in the Spectroscopy Laboratory of the Massachusetts Institute of Technology.

and the sigma (Σ) triplet. The agreement is exact.

In other representations of SU_3 there are 10, 27 or more members. Gell-Mann was the first to point out that the symmetry of a 10-member set could be satisfied by nine of the known baryons if they were augmented by a missing singlet that he named, in advance, the omega-minus (Ω^-) baryon. The known members of this 10-member set were a delta (Δ) quartet, another sigma triplet and another xi doublet. The predicted singlet was discovered in February in bubble-chamber photographs made at the Brookhaven National Laboratory.

The evidence is now overwhelming that an abstract symmetry with the structure of SU_3 actually exists in nature and dominates the behavior of the strongly interacting particles. The symmetry is not perfect, being broken by some relatively weak perturbation that reduces the group SU_3 to its subgroup U_2. The U_2 symmetry that remains is essentially identical with the abstract isotopic-spin symmetry discussed earlier. Our entire picture of the strongly interacting particles has been transformed from chaos to a considerable degree of order by these compellingly simple group-theoretical ideas.

Group theory is in many respects the most satisfactory of the three theoretical methods I have discussed. Unlike S-matrix theory, it has an elegant and impeccably rigorous mathematical basis; unlike field theory, it has clear and solid experimental support. What then is lacking? The trouble with group theory is that it leaves so much unexplained that one would like to explain. It isolates in a beautiful way those aspects of nature that can be understood in terms of abstract symmetry alone. It does not offer much hope of explaining the messier facts of life, the numerical values of particle lifetimes and interaction strengths—the great bulk of quantitative experimental data that is now waiting for explanation. The process of abstraction seems to have been too drastic, so that many essential and concrete features of the real world have been left out of consideration. Altogether group theory succeeds just because its aims are modest. It does not try to explain everything, and it does not seem likely that it will grow into a complete or comprehensive theory of the physical world.

We are left with three methods of work in theoretical physics: field theory, S-matrix theory and group theory. None of them really deserves the name of theory, if we mean by a theory something similar to the great theories of the past, for example general relativity or quantum mechanics. They are too vague, too partial or too fragmentary. This is of course only my personal judgment. Even if they succeed in their declared aims, they do not satisfy my aesthetic sense of what a theory ought to be. I am tempted to apply to them the term "Bridges of snow built across crevasses of ignorance" to describe my feelings of dissatisfaction. This splendid phrase is often useful for characterizing theoretical ideas with which one happens to be unsympathetic. It is well to remember, however, that it was first so used by the bigoted biometrician Karl Pearson in a diatribe against Gregor Mendel's laws of inheritance.

ON THE GENERALIZED THEORY OF GRAVITATION

34

ALBERT EINSTEIN • April 1950

HE editors of SCIENTIFIC AMERICAN have asked me to write about my recent work which has just been published. It is a mathematical investigation concerning the foundations of field physics.

Some readers may be puzzled: Didn't we learn all about the foundations of physics when we were still at school? The answer is "yes" or "no," depending on the interpretation. We have become acquainted with concepts and general relations that enable us to comprehend an immense range of experiences and make them accessible to mathematical treatment. In a certain sense these concepts and relations are probably even final. This is true, for example, of the laws of light refraction, of the relations of classical thermodynamics as far as it is based on the concepts of pressure, volume, temperature, heat and work, and of the hypothesis of the non-existence of a perpetual motion machine.

What, then, impels us to devise theory after theory? Why do we devise theories at all? The answer to the latter question is simply: Because we enjoy "comprehending," i.e., reducing phenomena by the process of logic to something already known or (apparently) evident. New theories are first of all necessary when we encounter new facts which cannot be "explained" by existing theories. But this motivation for setting up new theories is, so to speak, trivial, imposed from without. There is another, more subtle motive of no less importance. This is the striving toward unification and simplification of the premises of the theory as a whole (i.e., Mach's principle of economy, interpreted as a logical principle).

There exists a passion for comprehension, just as there exists a passion for music. That passion is rather common in children, but gets lost in most people later on. Without this passion, there would be neither mathematics nor natural science. Time and again the passion for understanding has led to the illusion that man is able to comprehend the objective world rationally, by pure thought, without any empirical foundations—in short, by metaphysics. I believe that every true theorist is a kind of tamed metaphysicist, no matter how pure a "positivist" he may fancy himself. The metaphysicist believes that the logically simple is also the real. The tamed metaphysicist believes that not all that is logically simple is embodied in experienced reality, but that the totality of all sensory experience can be "comprehended" on the basis of a conceptual system built on premises of great simplicity. The skeptic will say that this is a "miracle creed." Admittedly so, but it is a miracle creed which has been borne out to an amazing extent by the development of science.

The rise of atomism is a good example. How may Leucippus have conceived this bold idea? When water freezes and becomes ice—apparently something entirely different from water—why is it that the thawing of the ice forms something which seems indistinguishable from the original water? Leucippus is puzzled and looks for an "explanation." He is driven to the conclusion that in these transitions the "essence" of the thing has not changed at all. Maybe the thing consists of immutable particles and the change is only a change in their spatial arrangement. Could it not be that the same is true of all material objects which emerge again and again with nearly identical qualities?

This idea is not entirely lost during the long hibernation of occidental thought. Two thousand years after Leucippus, Bernoulli wonders why gas exerts pressure on the walls of a container. Should this be "explained" by mutual repulsion of the parts of the gas, in the sense of Newtonian mechanics? This hypothesis appears absurd, for the gas pressure depends on the temperature, all other things being equal. To assume that the Newtonian forces of interaction depend on temperature is contrary to the spirit of Newtonian mechanics. Since Bernoulli is aware of the concept of atomism, he is bound to conclude that the atoms (or molecules) collide with the walls of the container and in doing so exert pressure. After all, one has to assume that atoms are in motion; how else can one account for the varying temperature of gases?

A simple mechanical consideration shows that this pressure depends only on the kinetic energy of the particles and on their density in space. This should have led the physicists of that age to the conclusion that heat consists in random motion of the atoms. Had they taken this consideration as seriously as it deserved to be taken, the development of the theory of heat—in particular the discovery of the equivalence of heat and mechanical energy—would have been considerably facilitated.

This example is meant to illustrate two things. The theoretical idea (atomism in this case) does not arise apart from and independent of experience; nor can it be derived from experience by a purely logical procedure. It is produced by a creative act. Once a theoretical idea has been acquired, one does well to hold fast to it until it leads to an untenable conclusion.

S FOR my latest theoretical work, I do not feel justified in giving a detailed account of it before a wide group of readers interested in science. That should be done only with theories which have been adequately confirmed by experience. So far it is primarily the simplicity of its premises and its intimate connection with what is already known (*viz.*, the laws of the pure gravitational field) that speak in favor of the theory to be discussed here. It may, however, be of interest to a wide group of readers to become acquainted with the train of thought which can lead to endeavors of such an extremely speculative nature. Moreover, it will be shown what kinds of difficulties are encountered and in what sense they have been overcome.

In Newtonian physics the elementary theoretical concept on which the theoretical description of material bodies is based is the material point, or particle. Thus matter is considered *a priori* to be discontinuous. This makes it necessary to consider the action of material points on one another as "action at a distance." Since the latter concept seems quite contrary to everyday experience, it is only natural that the contemporaries of Newton—and indeed Newton himself—found it difficult to accept. Owing to the almost miraculous success of the Newtonian system, however, the succeeding generations of physicists became used to the idea of action at a distance. Any doubt was buried for a long time to come.

But when, in the second half of the 19th century, the laws of electrodynamics became known, it turned out that these laws could not be satisfactorily incorporated into the Newtonian system. It is fascinating to muse: Would Faraday have discovered the law of electromagnetic induction if he had received a regular college education? Unencumbered by the traditional way of thinking, he felt that the introduction of the "field" as an independent element of reality helped him to coordinate the experimental facts. It was Maxwell who fully comprehended the significance of the field concept; he made the fundamental discovery that the laws of electrodynamics found their natural expression in the differential equations for the electric

and magnetic fields. These equations implied the existence of waves, whose properties corresponded to those of light as far as they were known at that time.

This incorporation of optics into the theory of electromagnetism represents one of the greatest triumphs in the striving toward unification of the foundations of physics; Maxwell achieved this unification by purely theoretical arguments, long before it was corroborated by Hertz' experimental work. The new insight made it possible to dispense with the hypothesis of action at a distance, at least in the realm of electromagnetic phenomena; the intermediary field now appeared as the only carrier of electromagnetic interaction between bodies, and the field's behavior was completely determined by contiguous processes, expressed by differential equations.

Now a question arose: Since the field exists even in a vacuum, should one conceive of the field as a state of a "carrier," or should it rather be endowed with an independent existence not reducible to anything else? In other words, is there an "ether" which carries the field; the ether being considered in the undulatory state, for example, when it carries light waves?

The question has a natural answer: Because one cannot dispense with the field concept, it is preferable not to introduce in addition a carrier with hypothetical properties. However, the pathfinders who first recognized the indispensability of the field concept were still too strongly imbued with the mechanistic tradition of thought to accept unhesitatingly this simple point of view. But in the course of the following decades this view imperceptibly took hold.

The introduction of the field as an elementary concept gave rise to an inconsistency of the theory as a whole. Maxwell's theory, although adequately describing the behavior of electrically charged particles in their interaction with one another, does not explain the behavior of electrical densities, *i.e.*, it does not provide a theory of the particles themselves. They must therefore be treated as mass points on the basis of the old theory. The combination of the idea of a continuous field with that of material points discontinuous in space appears inconsistent. A consistent field theory requires continuity of all elements of the theory, not only in time but also in space, and in all points of space. Hence the material particle has no place as a fundamental concept in a field theory. Thus even apart from the fact that gravitation is not included, Maxwell's electrodynamics cannot be considered a complete theory.

Maxwell's equations for empty space remain unchanged if the spatial coordinates and the time are subjected to a particular kind of linear transformations—the Lorentz transformations ("covariance" with respect to Lorentz transformations). Covariance also holds, of course, for a transformation which is

composed of two or more such transformations; this is called the "group" property of Lorentz transformations.

Maxwell's equations imply the "Lorentz group," but the Lorentz group does not imply Maxwell's equations. The Lorentz group may indeed be defined independently of Maxwell's equations as a group of linear transformations which leave a particular value of the velocity—the velocity of light—invariant. These transformations hold for the transition from one "inertial system" to another which is in uniform motion relative to the first. The most conspicuous novel property of this transformation group is that it does away with the absolute character of the concept of simultaneity of events distant from each other in space. On this account it is to be expected that all equations of physics are covariant with respect to Lorentz transformations (special theory of relativity). Thus it came about that Maxwell's equations led to a heuristic principle valid far beyond the range of the applicability or even validity of the equations themselves.

Special relativity has this in common with Newtonian mechanics: The laws of both theories are supposed to hold only with respect to certain coordinate systems: those known as "inertial systems." An inertial system is a system in a state of motion such that "force-free" material points within it are not accelerated with respect to the coordinate system. However, this definition is empty if there is no independent means for recognizing the absence of forces. But such a means of recognition does not exist if gravitation is considered as a "field."

Let A be a system uniformly accelerated with respect to an "inertial system" I. Material points, not accelerated with respect to I, are accelerated with respect to A, the acceleration of all the points being equal in magnitude and direction. They behave as if a gravitational field exists with respect to A, for it is a characteristic property of the gravitational field that the acceleration is independent of the particular nature of the body. There is no reason to exclude the possibility of interpreting this behavior as the effect of a true" gravitational field (*principle of equivalence*). This interpretation implies that A is an "inertial system," even though it is accelerated with respect to another inertial system. (It is essential for this argument that the introduction of independent gravitational fields is considered justified even though no masses generating the field are defined. Therefore, to Newton such an argument would not have appeared convincing.) Thus the concepts of inertial system, the law of inertia and the law of motion are deprived of their concrete meaning—not only in classical mechanics but also in special relativity. Moreover, following up this train of thought, it turns out that with respect to A time cannot be measured by identical clocks; indeed, even the immediate physical significance of coordinate differences is generally lost In view of all these difficulties, should one not try, after all, to hold on to the concept of the inertial system, relinquishing the attempt to explain the fundamental character of the gravitational phenomena which manifest themselves in the Newtonian system as the equivalence of inert and gravitational mass? Those who trust in the comprehensibility of nature must answer: No.

HIS is the gist of the principle of equivalence: In order to account for the equality of inert and gravitational mass within the theory it is necessary to admit non-linear transformations of the four coordinates. That is, the group of Lorentz transformations and hence the set of the "permissible" coordinate systems has to be extended.

What group of coordinate transformations can then be substituted for the group of Lorentz transformations? Mathematics suggests an answer which is based on the fundamental investigations of Gauss and Riemann: namely, that the appropriate substitute is the group of all continuous (analytical) transformations of the coordinates. Under these transformations the only thing that remains invariant is the fact that neighboring points have nearly the same coordinates; the coordinate system expresses only the topological order of the points in space (including its four-dimensional character). The equations expressing the laws of nature must be covariant with respect to all continuous transformations of the coordinates. This is the principle of general relativity.

The procedure just described overcomes a deficiency in the foundations of mechanics which had already been noticed by Newton and was criticized by Leibnitz and, two centuries later, by Mach: Inertia resists acceleration, but acceleration relative to what? Within the frame of classical mechanics the only answer is: Inertia resists acceleration *relative to space*. This is a physical property of space—space acts on objects, but objects do not act on space. Such is probably the deeper meaning of Newton's assertion *spatium est absolutum* (space is absolute). But the idea disturbed some, in particular Leibnitz, who did not ascribe an independent existence to space but considered it merely a property of "things" (contiguity of physical objects). Had his justified doubts won out at that time, it hardly would have been a boon to physics, for the empirical and theoretical foundations necessary to follow up his idea were not available in the 17th century.

According to general relativity, the concept of space detached from any physical content does not exist. The phys-

ical reality of space is represented by a field whose components are continuous functions of four independent variables —the coordinates of space and time. It is just this particular kind of dependence that expresses the spatial character of physical reality

Since the theory of general relativity implies the representation of physical reality by a *continuous* field, the concept of particles or material points cannot play a fundamental part, nor can the concept of motion. The particle can only appear as a limited region in space in which the field strength or the energy density are particularly high.

A relativistic theory has to answer two questions: 1) What is the mathematical character of the field? 2) What equations hold for this field?

Concerning the first question: From the mathematical point of view the field is essentially characterized by the way its components transform if a coordinate transformation is applied. Concerning the second question: The equations must determine the field *to a sufficient extent* while satisfying the postulates of general relativity. Whether or not this requirement can be satisfied depends on the choice of the field-type.

The attempt to comprehend the correlations among the empirical data on the basis of such a highly abstract program may at first appear almost hopeless. The procedure amounts, in fact, to putting the question: What most simple property can be required from what most simple object (field) while preserving the principle of general relativity? Viewed from the standpoint of formal logic, the dual character of the question appears calamitous, quite apart from the vagueness of the concept "simple." Moreover, from the standpoint of physics there is nothing to warrant the assumption that a theory which is "logically simple" should also be "true."

Yet every theory is speculative. When the basic concepts of a theory are comparatively "close to experience" (*e.g.*, the concepts of force, pressure, mass), its speculative character is not so easily discernible. If, however, a theory is such as to require the application of complicated logical processes in order to reach conclusions from the premises that can be confronted with observation, everybody becomes conscious of the speculative nature of the theory. In such a case an almost irresistible feeling of aversion arises in people who are inexperienced in epistemological analysis and who are unaware of the precarious nature of theoretical thinking in those fields with which they are familiar.

On the other hand, it must be conceded that a theory has an important advantage if its basic concepts and fundamental hypotheses are "close to experience," and greater confidence in such a theory is certainly justified. There is less danger of going completely astray, particularly since it takes so much less

time and effort to disprove such theories by experience. Yet more and more, as the depth of our knowledge increases, we must give up this advantage in our quest for logical simplicity and uniformity in the foundations of physical theory. It has to be admitted that general relativity has gone further than previous physical theories in relinquishing "closeness to experience" of fundamental concepts in order to attain logical simplicity. This holds already for the theory of gravitation, and it is even more true of the new generalization, which is an attempt to comprise the properties of the total field. In the generalized theory the procedure of deriving from the premises of the theory conclusions that can be confronted with empirical data is so difficult that so far no such result has been obtained. In favor of this theory are, at this point, its logical simplicity and its "rigidity." Rigidity means here that the theory is either true or false, but not modifiable.

HE greatest inner difficulty impeding the development of the theory of relativity is the dual nature of the problem, indicated by the two questions we have asked. This duality is the reason why the development of the theory has taken place in two steps so widely separated in time. The first of these steps, the theory of gravitation, is based on the principle of equivalence discussed above and rests on the following consideration: According to the theory of special relativity, light has a constant velocity of propagation. If a light ray in a vacuum starts from a point, designated by the coordinates x_1, x_2 and x_3 in a three dimensional coordinate system, at the time x_4, it spreads as a spherical wave and reaches a neighboring point $(x_1+dx_1, x_2+dx_2, x_3+dx_3)$ at the time x_4+dx_4. Introducing the velocity of light, c, we write the expression:

$$\sqrt{dx_1{}^2+dx_2{}^2+dx_3{}^2}=c\,dx_4$$

This can also be written in the form:

$$dx_1{}^2+dx_2{}^2+dx_3{}^2-c^2\,dx_4{}^2=0$$

This expression represents an objective relation between neighboring space-time points in four dimensions, and it holds for all inertial systems, provided the coordinate transformations are restricted to those of special relativity. The relation loses this form, however, if arbitrary continuous transformations of the coordinates are admitted in accordance with the principle of general relativity. The relation then assumes the more general form:

$$\sum_{ik} g_{ik}\,dx_i\,dx_k=0$$

The g_{ik} are certain functions of the coordinates which transform in a definite way if a continuous coordinate transformation is applied. According to the principle of equivalence, these g_{ik} functions describe a particular kind of gravitational field: a field which can be obtained by transformation of "field-free" space. The g_{ik} satisfy a particular law of transformation. Mathematically speaking, they are the components of a "tensor" with a property of symmetry which is preserved in all transformations; the symmetrical property is expressed as follows:

$$g_{ik} = g_{ki}$$

The idea suggests itself: May we not ascribe objective meaning to such a symmetrical tensor, even though the field *cannot* be obtained from the empty space of special relativity by a mere coordinate transformation? Although we cannot expect that such a symmetrical tensor will describe the most general field, it may well describe the particular case of the "pure gravitational field." Thus it is evident what kind of field, at least for a special case, general relativity has to postulate: a symmetrical tensor field.

Hence only the second question is left: What kind of general covariant field law can be postulated for a symmetrical tensor field?

This question has not been difficult to answer in our time, since the necessary mathematical conceptions were already at hand in the form of the metric theory of surfaces, created a century ago by Gauss and extended by Riemann to manifolds of an arbitrary number of dimensions. The result of this purely formal investigation has been amazing in many respects. The differential equations which can be postulated as field law for g_{ik} cannot be of lower than second order, *i.e.*, they must at least contain the second derivatives of the g_{ik} with respect to the coordinates. Assuming that no higher than second derivatives appear in the field law, *it is mathematically determined by the principle of general relativity*. The system of equations can be written in the form:

$$R_{ik} = 0$$

The R_{ik} transform in the same manner as the g_{ik}, *i.e.*, they too form a symmetrical tensor.

These differential equations completely replace the Newtonian theory of the motion of celestial bodies provided the masses are represented as singularities of the field. In other words, they contain the law of force as well as the law of motion while eliminating "inertial systems."

The fact that the masses appear as singularities indicates that these masses themselves cannot be explained by symmetrical g_{ik} fields, or "gravitational fields." Not even the fact that only *positive* gravitating masses exist can be deduced from this theory. Evidently a complete relativistic field theory must be based on a field of more complex nature,

that is, a generalization of the symmetrical tensor field.

BEFORE considering such a generalization, two remarks pertaining to gravitational theory are essential for the explanation to follow. The first observation is that the principle of general relativity imposes exceedingly strong restrictions on the theoretical possibilities. Without this restrictive principle it would be practically impossible for anybody to hit on the gravitational equations, not even by using the principle of special relativity, even though one knows that the field has to be described by a symmetrical tensor. No amount of collection of facts could lead to these equations unless the principle of general relativity were used. This is the reason why all attempts to obtain a deeper knowledge of the foundations of physics seem doomed to me unless the basic concepts are in accordance with general relativity from the beginning. This situation makes it difficult to use our empirical knowledge, however comprehensive, in looking for the fundamental concepts and relations of physics, and it forces us to apply free speculation to a much greater extent than is presently assumed by most physicists. I do not see any reason to assume that the heuristic significance of the principle of general relativity is restricted to gravitation and that the rest of physics can be dealt with separately on the basis of special relativity, with the hope that later on the whole may be fitted consistently into a general relativistic scheme. I do not think that such an attitude, although historically understandable, can be objectively justified. The comparative smallness of what we know today as gravitational effects is not a conclusive reason for ignoring the principle of general relativity in theoretical investigations of a fundamental character. In other words, I do not believe that it is justifiable to ask: What would physics look like without gravitation?

The second point we must note is that the equations of gravitation are 10 differential equations for the 10 components of the symmetrical tensor g_{ik}. In the case of a non-general relativistic theory, a system is ordinarily not overdetermined if the number of equations is equal to the number of unknown functions. The manifold of solutions is such that within the general solution a certain number of functions of three variables can be chosen arbitrarily. For a general relativistic theory this cannot be expected as a matter of course. Free choice with respect to the coordinate system implies that out of the 10 functions of a solution, or components of the field, four can be made to assume prescribed values

by a suitable choice of the coordinate system. In other words, the principle of general relativity implies that the number of functions to be determined by differential equations is not 10 but $10 - 4 = 6$. For these six functions only six independent differential equations may be postulated. Only six out of the 10 differential equations of the gravitational field ought to be independent of each other, while the remaining four must be connected to those six by means of four relations (identities). And indeed there exist among the left-hand sides, R_{ik}, of the 10 gravitational equations four identities—"Bianchi's identities"—which assure their "compatibility."

In a case like this—when the number of field variables is equal to the number of differential equations—compatibility is always assured if the equations can be obtained from a variational principle. This is indeed the case for the gravitational equations.

However, the 10 differential equations cannot be entirely replaced by six. The system of equations is indeed "overdetermined," but due to the existence of the identities it is overdetermined in such a way that its compatibility is not lost, *i.e.*, the manifold of solutions is not critically restricted. The fact that the equations of gravitation imply the law of motion for the masses is intimately connected with this (permissible) overdetermination.

After this preparation it is now easy to understand the nature of the present investigation without entering into the details of its mathematics. The problem is to set up a relativistic theory for the total field. The most important clue to its solution is that there exists already the solution for the special case of the pure gravitational field. The theory we are looking for must therefore be a generalization of the theory of the gravitational field. The first question is: What is the natural generalization of the symmetrical tensor field?

This question cannot be answered by itself, but only in connection with the other question: What generalization of the field is going to provide the most natural theoretical system? The answer on which the theory under discussion is based is that the symmetrical tensor field must be replaced by a non-symmetrical one. This means that the condition $g_{ik} = g_{ki}$ for the field components must be dropped. In that case the field has 16 instead of 10 independent components.

There remains the task of setting up the relativistic differential equations for a non-symmetrical tensor field. In the attempt to solve this problem one meets with a difficulty which does not arise in the case of the symmetrical field. The principle of general relativity does not suffice to determine completely the field equations, mainly because the transformation law of the symmetrical part of the field alone does not involve the components of the antisymmetrical part or *vice versa.* Probably this is the reason why this kind of generalization of the field has hardly ever been tried before. The combination of the two parts of the field can only be shown to be a natural procedure if in the formalism of the theory only the total field plays a role, and not the symmetrical and antisymmetrical parts separately.

It turned out that this requirement can indeed be satisfied in a natural way. But even this requirement, together with the principle of general relativity, is still not sufficient to determine uniquely the field equations. Let us remember that the system of equations must satisfy a further condition: the equations must be compatible. It has been mentioned above that this condition is satisfied if the equations can be derived from a variational principle.

This has indeed been achieved, although not in so natural a way as in the case of the symmetrical field. It has been disturbing to find that it can be achieved in two different ways. These variational principles furnished two systems of equations—let us denote them by E_1 and E_2—which were different from each other (although only slightly so), each of them exhibiting specific imperfections. Consequently even the condition of compatibility was insufficient to determine the system of equations uniquely.

It was, in fact, the formal defects of the systems E_1 and E_2 that indicated a possible way out. There exists a third system of equations, E_3, which is free of the formal defects of the systems E_1 and E_2 and represents a combination of them in the sense that every solution of E_3 is a solution of E_1 as well as of E_2. This suggests that E_3 may be the system we have been looking for. Why not postulate E_3, then, as the system of equations? Such a procedure is not justified without further analysis, since the compatibility of E_1 and that of E_2 do not imply compatibility of the stronger system E_3, where the number of equations exceeds the number of field components by four.

An independent consideration shows that irrespective of the question of compatibility the stronger system, E_3, is the only really natural generalization of the equations of gravitation.

But E_3 is not a compatible system in the same sense as are the systems E_1 and E_2, whose compatibility is assured by a sufficient number of identities, which means that every field that satisfies the equations for a definite value of the time has a continuous extension representing a solution in four-dimensional space. The system E_3, however, is not extensible in the same way. Using the language of classical mechanics we might say: In the case of the system E_3 the "initial condition" cannot be freely chosen. What really matters is the answer to the question: Is the manifold of solutions for the system E_3 as extensive as must be required

for a physical theory? This purely mathematical problem is as yet unsolved.

The skeptic will say: "It may well be true that this system of equations is reasonable from a logical standpoint. But this does not prove that it corresponds to nature." You are right, dear skeptic. Experience alone can decide on truth. Yet we have achieved something if we have succeeded in formulating a meaningful and precise question. Affirmation or refutation will not be easy, in spite of an abundance of known empirical facts. The derivation, from the equations, of conclusions which can be confronted with experience will require painstaking efforts and probably new mathematical methods.

35 GRAVITY

GEORGE GAMOW • March 1961

In the days when civilized men believed that the world was flat they had no reason to think about gravity. There was "up" and "down." All material things tended naturally to move downward, or to fall, and no one thought to ask why. The notion of absolute up and down directions persisted into the Middle Ages, when it was still invoked to prove that the earth could not be round.

The first ray of light to pierce the mist of scholastic ideas about falling bodies issued from the work of Galileo Galilei. Since free fall was too fast to measure directly, Galileo decided to dilute the motion by studying bodies placed on an inclined plane. He argued —and at the time it was a novel argument—that since a ball resting on a horizontal surface does not move at all, and since a ball falling parallel to a vertical surface moves as fast as it would if the surface were not there, a ball on an inclined surface should roll with an intermediate speed depending on the angle of inclination. Letting balls roll down planes tilted at various angles, he observed their rates of travel and the distances covered in different time intervals, which he measured with a water clock. The experiments showed that at any angle the speed increases in direct proportion to time (counted from the moment of release) and that the distance covered increases in proportion to the square of the time. Galileo also observed that a massive iron ball and a much lighter wooden ball roll down side by side if released simultaneously from the same height on the same inclined plane.

As another way to dilute free fall he employed simple pendulums—weights suspended by thin strings. Here the steepness of the arc along which the weight travels is adjusted by changing the length of the string. Pendulums of the same length proved to have the same period of oscillation even when the weight was varied, a result in agreement with the outcome of the inclined-plane experiments. From all these observations Galileo was led to infer that in free fall all material bodies, light or heavy, also move in exactly the same way. This idea directly contradicted the opinion of the then prevailing Aristotelian school of philosophy, which held that heavier bodies fall faster than light ones. According to the celebrated legend, which may or may not be true, Galileo climbed the leaning tower of Pisa and dropped a light and a heavy ball, which hit the ground simultaneously, to the consternation of contemporary philosophers.

Newton's Law of Gravity

These studies laid the foundation for the science of mechanics. The main structure was erected by Isaac Newton, who was born the year Galileo died. With his laws of motion Newton introduced the notions of force and of inertial mass. When a force is applied to material bodies, it changes their speed or direction of motion or both. Their inertial mass opposes these changes. Newton stated that the rate of change of velocity (acceleration) of an object is directly proportional to the force acting on it and inversely proportional to its mass. Doubling the force doubles the acceleration; doubling the mass cuts the acceleration in half; if both force and mass are doubled, the acceleration is unchanged.

In the light of this law Galileo's conclusion about free-falling bodies implies a fact that is usually taken for granted, but which is actually very curious; namely, the weight of a body (that is, the gravitational pull of the earth upon it) is strictly proportional to its inertial mass. Otherwise an iron and a wooden ball of the same size would not fall at the same rate. If the two objects have the same acceleration when they are dropped, the inertial mass opposing a change of motion in the iron ball must be greater than that in the wooden ball in exactly the same proportion that the downward force on the iron ball is greater. This proportionality is far from trivial; in fact, it holds true only for gravity and not for other familiar forces such as those of electricity and magnetism. Thus while an electron and a proton would fall with equal acceleration in a gravitational field, when these particles are placed in an electric field the electron is accelerated 1,836 times faster.

From his analysis of balls (or apples) that fall toward the earth Newton went on to consider gravitation in wider terms. His line of thought is demonstrated by a very interesting discussion in his *Principia*. Suppose, he said, we shoot a bullet horizontally from the top of a mountain so high that it rises above the atmosphere [*see illustration on page 265*]. The bullet will follow a curved trajectory and hit the surface of the earth some distance away from the base of the mountain. The greater the muzzle velocity, the farther away from the mountain the bullet will land. At a sufficiently high initial velocity the bullet will come to earth at a point directly opposite the mountain; at still higher velocity it will never hit the ground but will continue to revolve around the earth like a little moon. If, Newton argued, it is possible in this way to make an artificial satellite, why not assume that the motion of the natural moon is also a free fall? And if the moon revolves around the earth because of the earth's gravitational attraction, is it not logical to assume that the earth itself is held in orbit around the sun by the force of the sun's gravity? Then is this not also true for all the other planets and their satellites? So originated the profoundly important idea of universal gravitation, which states that all material bodies in the universe attract one another with forces determined by their masses and mutual distances.

To establish the exact relation of force to mass and distance, Newton began by assuming that, since the force between the earth and each body near its surface is proportional to the inertial mass of the body, the force should also be proportional to the inertial mass of the earth. This immediately explained why the gravitational attraction between bodies of small mass, such as two apples, had never been noticed. It was too weak. Not until half a century after Newton's death was the existence of such a force demonstrated experimentally by another British genius, Henry Cavendish.

Having postulated that the gravitational attraction between two bodies is proportional to the product of their masses, Newton then investigated the

dependence on distance. He compared the force necessary to hold the moon in its orbit at the distance of 60 earth radii with the force on an apple at the distance of only one radius from the center of the earth. It is important to realize here that the great difference in mass between the two bodies does not affect the validity of the comparison. As a matter of fact, an apple placed at the moon's distance and given its orbital velocity will move around the earth exactly as the moon does; by the same token, if one could suspend the moon from a branch, it would fall to the ground exactly as fast as apples do. Newton's mathematical analysis showed that the force of gravity decreases as the square of the distances between the attracting bodies.

He could now write the formula for gravitational force: $F = G (M_1 M_2)/d^2$. G is the constant of proportionality, or

the gravitational constant. It is a very small number; if the masses are measured in grams and the distance in centimeters, G is approximately .000000066. This means that a pair of one-gram weights separated by one centimeter attract each other with a force a little

PRINCIPLE OF EQUIVALENCE enunciated by Einstein states that accelerated motion produces effects indistinguishable from those of a gravitational field. If an observer in a uniformly accelerating spaceship simultaneously releases two balls of different weight, he will see them fall toward the floor at the same rate. An outside observer would say that the balls continue to move upward (*broken line*) with the speed of the ship at the moment of release, while the floor, moving up at an accelerating rate, overtakes them.

more than six hundred-millionths of a dyne, or about six hundred-billionths of the weight of a gram.

Combining the law of gravitation with his laws of motion, Newton was able to derive mathematically the rules governing planetary motion that had been discovered by Johannes Kepler. In the memorable era that followed, Newton and his successors explained the motions of celestial bodies down to the most minute details. But the nature of gravitational interaction, and in particular the reason for the mysterious proportionality between gravitational mass and inertial mass, remained completely hidden for more than 200 years.

Einstein's Law of Gravity

Then, in 1914, Albert Einstein lifted the veil. The ideas he put forward grew out of his formulation of the special theory of relativity a decade earlier. That theory is based on the postulate that no observations made inside an enclosed chamber can answer the question of whether the chamber is at rest or moving along a straight line at constant speed. Thus a person in the situation of the author as he writes these lines—in an inside cabin of the S.S. *Queen Elizabeth* sailing on a smooth sea—can perform no experiment, mechanical, optical or any other kind, that will tell him whether the ship is really moving or still in port. But let a storm come up and the situation changes painfully; the deviation from uniform motion is all too apparent.

In order to deal with the problem of nonuniform motion Einstein imagined a laboratory in a spaceship located far from any large gravitating masses. If the vehicle is at rest, or in uniform motion with respect to distant stars, the observers inside, and all their instruments that are not secured to the walls, will float freely. There will be no up and no down. As soon as the rocket motors are started and the ship accelerates, however, instruments and people will be pressed to the wall opposite the direction of motion. This wall will become the floor, the opposite wall will become the ceiling and the people will be able to stand up and move about much as they do on the ground. In fact, if the acceleration is equal to the acceleration of gravity on the surface of the earth, the passengers may well believe that their ship is still standing on its launching pad.

Suppose one of the passengers simultaneously releases two spheres, one of iron and one of wood, which he has been holding next to each other in his hands.

What "actually" happens can be described as follows: While the spheres were held they were undergoing accelerated motion, along with the observer and the whole ship. When they are released, they are no longer driven by the rocket engines. Now they will move side by side, each with a velocity equal to that of the spaceship at the moment of release. The ship itself, however, will continuously gain speed and the "floor" of the ship will quickly overtake the two spheres and hit them simultaneously.

To the observer inside the ship the experiment will look different. He will see the balls drop and hit the "floor" at the same time. Recalling Galileo's demonstration from the leaning tower of Pisa, he will be persuaded that an ordinary gravitational field exists in his space laboratory.

Both descriptions of the observed event are correct; the equivalence of the two points of view is the foundation of Einstein's relativistic theory of gravity. This so-called principle of equivalence

between observations carried out in an accelerated chamber and in a "real" gravitational field would be trivial, however, if it applied only to mechanical phenomena. Einstein's deep insight was that the principle is quite general and holds also for optical and other electromagnetic phenomena.

Imagine a beam of light propagating across the space laboratory in a "horizontal" direction. Its path can be traced by means of a series of vertical fluorescent glass plates spaced at equal distances [see illustration on page 267]. Again what actually happens is that the beam travels in a straight line at constant speed, while the glass plates move across its path at an ever increasing speed. The beam takes the same time to travel from each plate to the next, but the plates move farther during each successive interval. Hence the pattern of fluorescent spots shows the floor approaching the light beam at an increasing rate. If the observer inside the chamber draws a line through the spots, it will look to him like

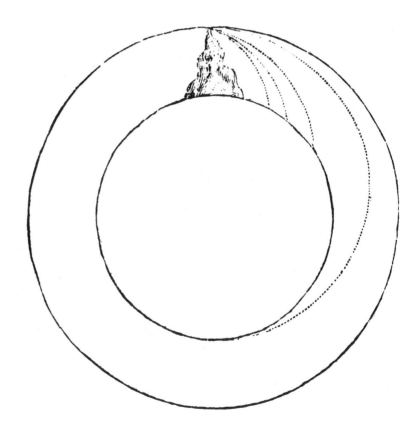

ARTIFICIAL SATELLITE was envisaged as a thought experiment by Isaac Newton in his *Principia*, from which this diagram is reproduced. Bullet fired horizontally from a mountaintop falls farther from base as its muzzle velocity is increased. At sufficiently high speed it circles the earth, suggesting that the moon is also falling in the earth's gravitational field.

a parabola bending toward the floor. Since he considers acceleration phenomena as being caused by gravity, he will say that a light ray is bent when propagating through a gravitational field.

Thus, concluded Einstein, if the principle of equivalence holds in all of physics, light rays from distant stars that pass close to the sun on their way to the earth should bend toward the sun. This prediction was brilliantly confirmed in 1919 by a party of British astronomers observing a total solar eclipse in Africa. With the obscuring sunlight extinguished by the moon, stars near the edge of the solar disk were seen to be displaced about 1.75 seconds of arc away from the sun.

Relativistic Merry-Go-Round

Let us next consider another type of accelerated motion—uniform rotation. (A body moving at constant speed on a circular path is accelerated because of its continuous change of direction.) Im-

agine a merry-go-round with a curtain around it so that people inside cannot tell by looking at the surroundings that it is rotating. If the merry-go-round is turning, the observers will be aware of centrifugal force, which pushes them out toward the rim. A ball placed on the platform will roll away from the center. The centrifugal force acting on any object on the platform will be proportional to the inertial mass of the object, so that here again the effect of accelerated motion can be considered as equivalent to that of a gravitational field. It is a peculiar field, to be sure; it is quite different from the field on the surface of the earth or of any other spherical body. The force is directed away from the center of the system, not toward it; and instead of decreasing as the square of the distance from the center, it increases proportionately to that distance. Moreover, the field has cylindrical symmetry around a central axis rather than spherical symmetry around a central point. Nevertheless, the equivalence principle

holds, and the field can be interpreted as being caused by gravitating mass distributed at large distances all around the symmetry axis.

How will light propagate through this field? Suppose a light source that sends out rays in all directions is located at a point, A, on the periphery of the rotating disk, and is observed at a second point, B, also on the periphery. According to the basic law of optics, light always propagates along the shortest path. But what is the shortest path between A and B? To measure the length of various lines connecting the points A and B the observer uses the old-fashioned but always safe method of counting the number of yardsticks that can be placed end to end along the line [see illustration on page 268].

As we watch the experiment from outside, we recall the special theory of relativity, which tells us that moving yardsticks shrink in the direction of their motion. Therefore we see that if the observer measures along the "true" straight

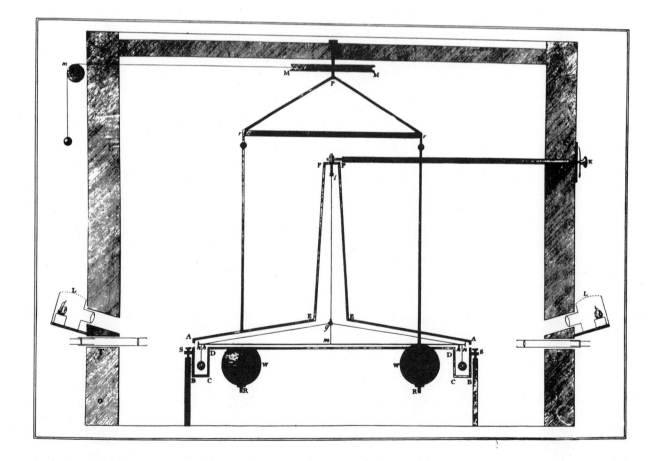

TORSION BALANCE was used by the British physicist Henry Cavendish to measure gravitational attraction between small masses. In this diagram, reproduced from his paper in the *Philosophical Transactions of the Royal Society*, two-inch lead spheres (*x*) are attached to beam suspended by torsion wire (*lg*). Twelve-inch spheres (*W*) are placed so as to twist the beam first in one direction and then in the other. Turning is observed through system of lenses at each side. Total rotation is measure of attractive force.

line from A to B, his sticks will contract and he will need more of them to measure that line than if the platform were not moving. Now an interesting point arises. The closer a yardstick is to the center of the merry-go-round, the less its linear velocity and therefore the smaller

its contraction. By bending the line of yardsticks toward the center the observer decreases the number he needs to go from A to B. Although the "actual" distance is somewhat longer, the increase is more than compensated for by the smaller shrinkage of each yardstick. A

light ray following this shortest path, heading inward at the start of its journey and then bending outward, can be considered to be deflected by the apparent gravitational field, which is directed radially outward.

Before leaving the merry-go-round let us consider one more experiment. A pair of identical clocks are placed on the platform, one near the center and the other at the edge. As in the case of the yardsticks, the outer clock is moving faster than the inner one, and again special relativity predicts a difference in their behavior. In addition to causing yardsticks to contract, motion makes clocks run slow. Therefore the outer clock will lose time with respect to the inner one. Now the observer who interprets the acceleration effects in terms of a gravitational field will say that the clock placed in the higher gravitational potential (that is, in the direction in which gravitational force acts) runs slower.

Although we cannot go into details here, Einstein's argument shows that the same effect is expected in a normal gravitational field such as that on the earth. Here the field is directed downward, so that a clock at sea level runs slower than one on top of a mountain. The slowing down applies equally to all other physical, chemical and biological phenomena, and a typist working on the first floor of the Empire State Building will age slower than her twin sister working on the top floor. Stronger fields produce greater retardation. A clock on the surface of the sun would run .0001 per cent slower than a terrestrial clock.

Obviously we cannot put a clock on the sun, but we can watch the rate of atomic vibrations that produce the various lines in the solar spectrum. If these natural clocks are slowed down, the light they emit should be shifted toward the low-frequency, or red, end of the spectrum. This "gravitational red shift" was predicted by Einstein. Such a shift is indeed found in the lines of the solar spectrum, but it is so small as to be almost at the limit of observational precision. Spectra of the much denser white-dwarf stars, where the red shift is expected to be 40 times larger than on the sun, agree quite well with the theory.

Astronomical evidence is not so satisfying as experiments that can be performed in a terrestrial laboratory. Until a couple of years ago, however, there seemed to be no hope of measuring the minute difference predicted between clocks at different heights in the earth's gravitational field. Then R. L. Mössbauer, working at the University of

CURVATURE OF LIGHT is detected by observer in accelerating rocket. To an observer outside, the light beam travels along a straight, horizontal path and crosses each successive plate of glass at a point nearer the floor because of the upward acceleration of the plates.

CENTRIFUGAL FIELD OF FORCE, such as the one on a rotating merry-go-round, can also be interpreted in terms of gravitating mass. As explained in the text, an observer on the platform
would find that a curved line is the shortest distance between
points on the periphery. Since light rays travel along the shortest
path, or geodesic, they are expected to curve in this type of field.

Munich, found a way to produce nuclear
gamma rays of very pure frequency and
to measure extremely small changes in
their frequency [see "The Mössbauer
Effect," by Sergio De Benedetti; SCIEN-
TIFIC AMERICAN, April, 1960]. Seizing
on the new opportunity, several workers
proceeded to show that two nuclear
"clocks" separated by only a few tens of
feet in the earth's field run at measurably
different rates, and the difference is ex-

actly that predicted by Einstein, within
the limits of experimental error. Still another verification, if any more are needed, will almost certainly be obtained
when an atomic clock in an artificial
satellite is compared with one on the
ground.

So we see that in a gravitational field
clocks run slow, light rays bend in the
direction of the field and a straight line
is not the shortest distance between two

points. Yet how can one define "straight
line" other than as the path of light in
a vacuum, or the shortest distance between two points? Einstein's idea was to
retain this definition. Instead of saying
that light rays and shortest distances are
curved, he suggested that space itself
(more accurately space-time) is curved.
It is difficult to conceive of a curved
three-dimensional space, let alone a
curved four-dimensional space-time, but

some idea of what it means can be gained from an analogy with two-dimensional surfaces. The Euclidean geometry we all learned at school pertains to figures that can be drawn on a plane. If geometrical figures are drawn on curved surfaces, for example a sphere or a surface shaped like a saddle [see illustration on this page], many of the Euclidean theorems do not hold.

In particular, the sum of the angles of a plane triangle is equal to 180 degrees. In a spherical triangle the sum of the angles is greater than 180 degrees, and in a triangle drawn on a saddle surface it is less. True, the lines forming triangles on spherical and saddle surfaces are not straight from the three-dimensional point of view, but they are the "straightest" (i.e., shortest) lines between the points if one is confined to the surface in question. Mathematicians call such lines geodesic lines, or simply geodesics.

In three-dimensional space a geodesic line is by definition the path along which a light ray would propagate. Consider a triangle formed by three such geodesics. If the sum of the angles is equal to 180 degrees, the space is said to be flat. If the sum is more than 180 degrees, we say that the space is spherelike, or positively curved; if it is less than 180 degrees, we say that it is saddle-like, or negatively curved. Because of the bending of light toward the sun, astronomers located on earth, Mars and Venus would

measure more than 180 degrees in the angles of the triangle formed by light rays traveling between the planets [see illustration on page 270]. Hence we can say that the space around the sun is positively curved. On the other hand, in the merry-go-round type of gravitational field, the sum of angles of a triangle is less than 180 degrees, and this space is curved in the negative sense.

The foregoing arguments represent the foundation of Einstein's theory of gravity. In the Newtonian view the sun produces in the space around it a field of force that makes the planets move along curved trajectories instead of straight lines. In Einstein's picture space itself becomes curved and the planets move along the straightest (geodesic) lines in that curved space. Here we are speaking of geodesics in the four-dimensional space-time continuum [see illustration on page 271]. It would, of course, be wrong to say that the orbits themselves are geodesic lines in three-dimensional space.

Einstein's interpretation of gravity as the curvature of space-time does not lead to exactly the same results as those of the classical Newtonian theory. We have already mentioned the bending of light. The relativistic theory also gives slightly different answers for the motions of material bodies. For example, it explained the difference between the calculated and observed rates of precession of the major axis of Mercury's orbit,

which represented a long-standing mystery of classical celestial mechanics.

Gravity Waves

Newton's law of gravitational interaction between masses is quite similar to the law of electrostatic interaction between charges, and Einstein's theory of the gravitational field has many common elements with James Clerk Maxwell's theory of the electromagnetic field. So it is natural to expect that an oscillating mass should give rise to gravitational waves just as an oscillating electric charge produces electromagnetic waves. In a famous article published in 1918 Einstein indeed obtained solutions of his basic equation of general relativity that represent such gravitational disturbances propagating through space with the velocity of light. If they exist, gravitational waves must carry energy; but their intensity, or the amount of energy they transport, is extremely small. For example, the earth, in its orbital motion around the sun, should emit about .001 watt, which would result in its falling a millionth of a centimeter toward the sun in a billion years!

No one has yet thought of a way to detect waves so weak. In fact, some theorists, among them Sir Arthur Eddington, have suggested that gravitational waves do not represent any physical reality at all but are simply a mathematical fiction that can be eliminated from the equation by a suitable choice of space-time co-ordinates. More thorough analysis indicates, however, that this is not the case and that gravitational waves, weak though they may be, are real.

Are gravitational waves divided into discrete energy packets, or quanta, as electromagnetic waves are? This question, which is as old as the quantum theory, was finally answered two years ago by the British physicist P. A. M. Dirac. He succeeded in quantizing the gravitational-field equation and showed that the energy of gravity quanta, or "gravitons," is equal to Planck's constant, h, times their frequency—the same expression that gives the energy of light quanta or photons. The spin of the graviton, however, is twice the spin of the photon.

Because of their weakness gravitational waves are of no importance in celestial mechanics. But might not gravitons play some role in the physics of elementary particles? These ultimate bits of matter interact in a variety of ways, by means of the emission or absorption of appropriate "field quanta." Thus electromag-

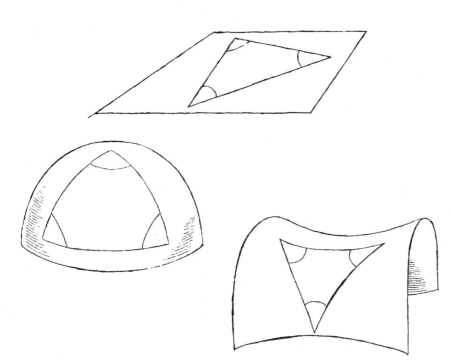

SPACE CURVATURE is illustrated in two dimensions. In flat space (top) the angles of a triangle total 180 degrees; in spherelike or positively curved space (middle), more than 180 degrees; in saddle-like or negatively curved space (bottom), less than 180 degrees.

netic interactions (for example the attraction of oppositely charged bodies) involve the emission or absorption of photons; presumably gravitational interactions are similarly related to gravitons. In the past few years it has become clear that the interactions of matter fall into distinct classes: (1) strong interactions, which include electromagnetic forces; (2) weak interactions such as the "beta decay" of a radioactive nucleus, in which an electron and a neutrino are emitted; (3) gravitational interactions, which are vastly weaker than the ones called "weak."

The strength of an interaction is related to the rate, or probability, of the emission or absorption of its quantum. For example, a nucleus takes about 10^{-12} second (a millionth of a billionth of a second) to emit a photon. In comparison the beta decay of a neutron takes 12 minutes—about 10^{14} times longer. It can be calculated that the time necessary for the emission of a graviton by a nucleus is 10^{60} seconds, or 10^{53} years! This is slower than the weak interaction by a factor of 10^{58}.

Now, neutrinos are themselves particles with an extremely low probability of absorption, that is, interaction, with other types of matter [see "The Neutrino," by Philip Morrison; SCIENTIFIC AMERICAN Offprint #230]. They have no charge and no mass. As long ago as 1933 Niels Bohr inquired: "What is the difference between [neutrinos] and the quanta of gravitational waves?" In the so-called weak interactions neutrinos are emitted together with other particles. What about processes involving only neutrinos—say, the emission of a neutrino-antineutrino pair by an excited nucleus? No one has detected such events, but they may occur, perhaps on the same time scale as the gravitational interaction. A pair of neutrinos would furnish a spin of two, the value calculated for the graviton by Dirac. All this is, of course, the sheerest speculation, but a connection between neutrinos and gravity is an exciting theoretical possibility.

Gravity and Electromagnetism

In the laboratory diary of Michael Faraday appears the following entry in 1849: "Gravity. Surely this force must be capable of an experimental relation to electricity, magnetism and other forces, so as to build it up with them in reciprocal action and equivalent effect. Consider for a moment how to set about touching this matter by facts and trial." The numerous experiments he undertook to discover such a relation were

fruitless, and he concludes that part of his diary with the words: "Here end my trials for the present. The results are negative. They do not shake my strong feeling of the existence of a relation between gravity and electricity, though they give no proof that such a relation exists." Subsequent experimental efforts have not been any more successful.

A theoretical attack aimed at bringing the electromagnetic field into line with the gravitational field was undertaken by Einstein. Having reduced gravity to the geometrical properties of a space-time continuum, he became convinced that the electromagnetic field must also have some purely geometrical interpretation. However, the "unified field" theory, which grew out of this conviction, had hard going, and Einstein died without producing anything so simple, elegant and convincing as his earlier work. Today fewer and fewer physicists are working at unified-field theory; most are persuaded that the effort to geometrize the electromagnetic field is futile. It seems, at least to the author, that the true relation between gravitational and electromagnetic forces is to be found only through an understanding of the nature of elementary particles—an understanding of why there exist particles with just certain inertial masses and not others—and of the relation between the masses and the electric and magnetic properties of the particles.

As a sample of one of the basic questions in this field, consider again the relative strength of gravitational and electromagnetic interactions. Instead of comparing the times required for emission of quanta, let us compare the actual strength of the electrostatic and gravitational forces between a pair of middleweight particles, say pi mesons. Computation shows that the ratio of electrostatic to gravitational force equals the

square of the charge on an electron divided by the square of the mass of the particles times the gravitational constant: $e^2 / M^2 G$. For two pi mesons the value is 10^{40}. Any theory that claims to describe the relation between electromagnetism and gravity must explain this ratio. It should be pointed out that the ratio is a pure number, one that remains unchanged no matter what system of units is used for measuring the various physical quantities. Such dimensionless constants, which can be derived in a purely mathematical way, often turn up in theoretical formulas, but they are usually small numbers such as 2π, $5/3$ and the like.

How can one derive mathematically a constant as large as 10^{40}? Some 20 years ago Dirac made an interesting proposal. He suggested that the figure 10^{40} is in fact not a constant, but a variable that changes with time and is connected with the age of the universe. According to the evolutionary cosmology, which holds that the universe originated with a "big bang," the universe is now about 5×10^9 years, or 10^{17} seconds, old. Of course, a year or a second is an arbitrary unit, and we would prefer an elementary time interval that can be derived from the basic properties of matter and light. A reasonable one is the length of time required by light to travel a distance equal to the radius of an elementary particle. Since all the particles have radii of about 3×10^{-13} centimeter, and since the velocity of light is 3×10^{10} centimeters per second, this elementary time unit is 3×10^{-13} divided by 3×10^{10}, or 10^{-23} second. To express the age of the universe in this elementary time unit we divide its age in seconds, 10^{17}, by 10^{-23} and obtain the number 10^{40}! Thus, said Dirac, the large ratio of electric to gravitational forces is characteristic of the present age of the universe. When

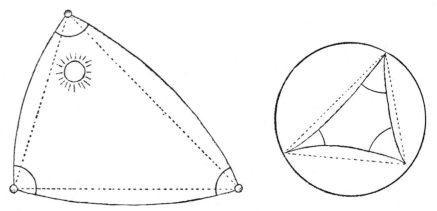

SIGN OF SPACE CURVATURE depends on type of gravitational field. Observers on three planets (*left*) would detect positive curvature because of deflection of light rays by the sun. Observers on periphery of merry-go-round (*right*) would detect negative curvature.

the universe was half as old as it is now, this ratio was also half of its present value. Since there are good reasons to assume that the elementary electric charge does not change with time, Dirac concluded that the gravitational constant must be decreasing, and that this decrease may be associated with the expansion of the universe and the steady rarefaction of the material that fills it.

If the gravitational constant really has been decreasing, or in other words if the force of gravity has been growing weaker, then our solar system must have been expanding along with the universe. In earlier times the earth would have been nearer the sun and therefore hotter than it is now. When Dirac put forward the idea, the solar system was thought to be about three billion years old. Edward Teller, now at the University of California, pointed out that on such a time scale the earth would have been 50 degrees hotter than the boiling point of water during the Cambrian era, when well-developed marine life existed. Now it seems that the solar system may be five billion or more years old, in which case the Cambrian oceans, though hot, would not have been vaporized. So the objection loses its force, provided that Cambrian plants and animals could live in very hot water.

Antigravity

In one of his stories H. G. Wells describes a British inventor, Mr. Cavor, who found a material, called cavorite, that was impenetrable to the force of gravity. Just as sheet copper can shield an object against electric forces and sheet iron can shield against magnetism, a sheet of cavorite placed under a material body would shield it from the gravitational pull of the earth. Mr. Cavor built a large gondola surrounded by cavorite shutters. One night when the moon was high, he got into the ship, closed the shutters facing the ground and opened those facing the moon. Cut off from terrestrial gravity and subjected only to the attraction of the moon, the gondola soared into space and eventually deposited Mr. Cavor on the surface of our satellite.

Why is such an invention impossible? Or is it? There is a profound similarity between Newton's law of universal gravity and the laws that govern the interactions of electric charges and magnetic poles. If one can shield electric and magnetic forces, why not gravity? To answer this question we must consider the mechanism of electric and magnetic shielding. Each atom or molecule in any piece of matter is a system of positive and negative electric charges; in conducting metals there are numbers of negative electrons that are free to move through the crystal lattice of positively charged ions. When a metal is placed in an electric field, the free electrons move to one side of the material, giving it a negative charge and leaving the opposite side positive. This polarization produces a new electric field, which is directed opposite to the original field. Thus the two can cancel each other. Similarly, magnetic shielding depends on the fact that the atoms of magnetic materials are tiny magnets, with north and south poles that line up so as to produce a field that opposes an external magnetic field. Here also the shielding effect arises from polarization of atomic particles.

Gravitational polarization, which

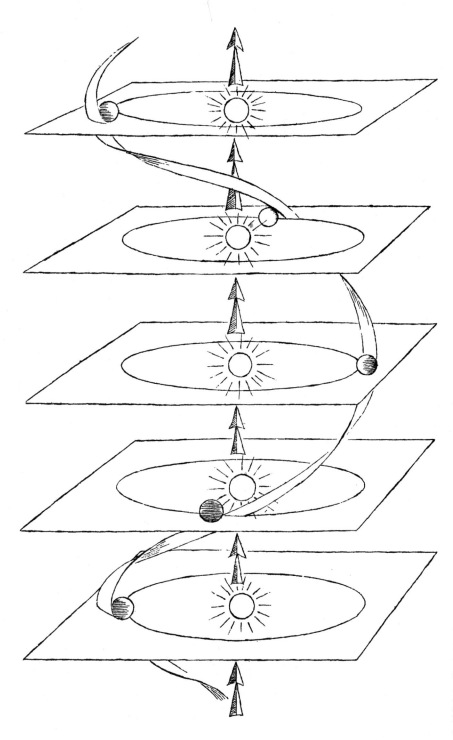

FOUR-DIMENSIONAL PATH (*spiral*) of a planet in space-time is a geodesic. It is rendered schematically by showing space in two dimensions and measuring time vertically.

could make possible shielding against the force of gravity, requires that matter be constituted of two kinds of particles: some with positive gravitational mass, which are attracted by the earth, and some with negative gravitational mass, which are repelled. Positive and negative electric charges and north and south magnetic poles are equally abundant in nature, but particles with negative gravitational mass are as yet unknown, at least within the structure of ordinary atoms and molecules. Therefore ordinary matter cannot be gravitationally polarized and cannot act as a gravity shield.

There is, however, another kind of matter—antimatter—that in many ways is the reverse of ordinary matter, including its electric and magnetic properties. Perhaps antiparticles also have negative mass. At first sight this might seem an easy point to decide. One has only to watch a horizontal beam of antineutrons, say, emerging from an accelerator and see whether the beam bends down or up in the gravitational field of the earth. In practice the experiment cannot be done. The particles produced by accelerators move almost at the speed of light; in a kilometer of horizontal travel gravity would bend them, whether up or down, only about 10^{-12} centimeter, the diameter of an atomic nucleus. Nor can they be slowed down by letting them collide with the nuclei of a "moderator" material, as neutrons are slowed in atomic piles. If antiparticles collide with their ordinary counterparts, both disappear in material annihilation. Thus from the experimental point of view the question as to the sign of the gravitational mass of antiparticles remains painfully open.

From the theoretical point of view it is open too, since we do not have a theory that relates gravitational and electromagnetic interactions. If a future experiment should demonstrate that antiparticles do have a negative gravitational mass, it will deliver a mortal blow to the entire relativistic theory of gravity by disproving the principle of equivalence. An antiapple might fall up in a true gravitational field, but it could hardly do so in Einstein's accelerated spaceship If it did, an outside observer would see it moving at twice the acceleration of the ship, with no force at all acting on it. The discovery of antigravity would therefore force upon us a choice between Newton's law of inertia and Einstein's equivalence principle. The author earnestly hopes that this will not come to pass.

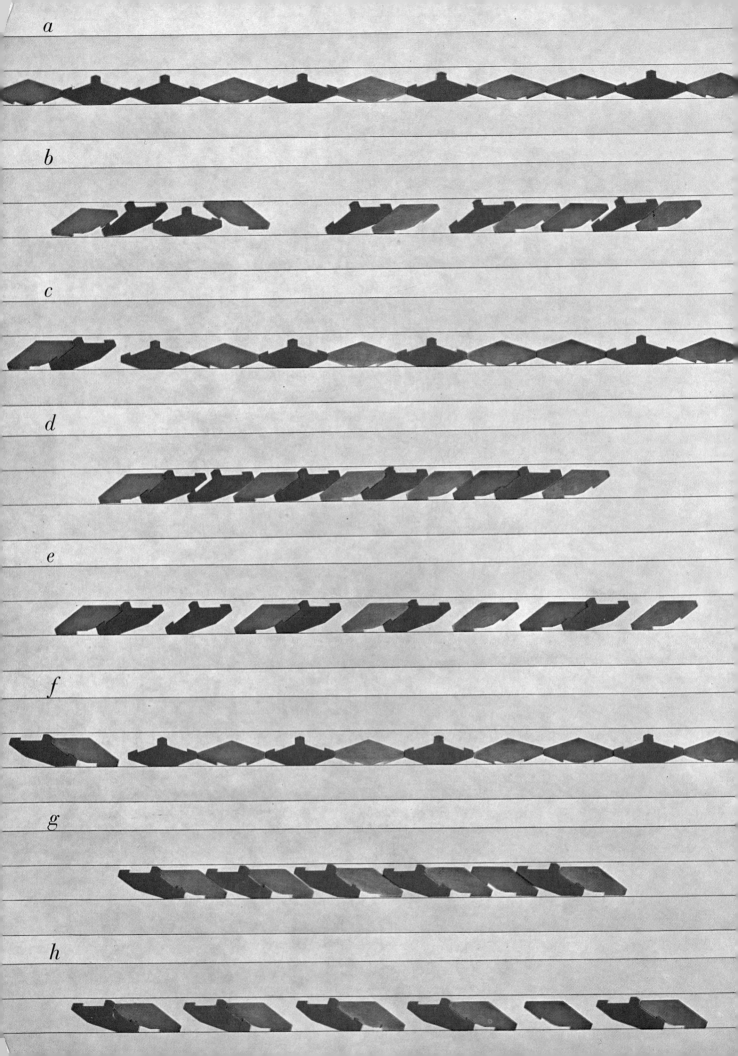

a

b

c

d

e

f

g

h

MATHEMATICS IN THE BIOLOGICAL SCIENCES

36

EDWARD F. MOORE · September 1964

René Descartes looked on animals (and the human body, but not the soul) as devices that could be explained in mechanical terms. Once when he was tutoring Queen Christina of Sweden, she challenged him with the question: But how can a machine reproduce itself? The same question is being asked today by mathematicians who reflect on the capabilities and limitations of machines. In their efforts to construct a detailed mathematical theory of self-reproduction they apply mathematical methods to the study of a process that has always seemed uniquely biological.

Such applications of mathematics have been rare. Whereas physics and mathematics have flowered together over the past 300 years, closely related to each other and mutually stimulating [see "Mathematics in the Physical Sciences," page 249], original mathematical thought has done little for biology. I can think of a few exceptions. Thomas Malthus created a mathematical model in which population multiplies in a geometric progression while the food supply increases only arithmetically, precipitating a "struggle for existence." Both Charles Darwin and Alfred Russel Wallace, on reading Malthus, saw in that struggle the mechanism with which to explain natural selection. An essentially mathematical idea, in other words, can be said to have contributed to the development of the central concept of biological evolution.

As for contributions by biology to mathematics, they too have been rare. One of the most notable has been in the area of population genetics. R. A. Fisher of Britain and Sewall Wright of the U.S. developed mathematical models to show how the rules of heredity combine with the laws of chance to cause a given gene to survive or die out in a population. Wright's extremely sophisticated model was based on diffusion theory, and it led William Feller of Princeton University to explore new areas of mathematics.

In their everyday work, of course, biologists do make use of mathematics. Like other investigators, biologists must subject their results to statistical tests (some of them developed by Fisher), and they customarily display the relations they discover in the form of the curves of analytic geometry. The mathematical equations of thermodynamics are familiar to biochemists. Statistical techniques have played a role in the deciphering of the genetic code and in the mapping of genes. The fact remains that all this is conventional mathematics. Although there have been a number of deliberate attempts to establish a "mathematical biology," most of these efforts seem not to fulfill their early promise. It is possible, however, that new mathematical studies utilizing computers may accomplish more than could be done in the past with necessarily oversimplified models of biological processes.

The special value of mathematics to biology lies not in its use as a tool but in its power to abstract and thus to lay bare fundamental problems and the relations between superficially distinct entities and processes. Organisms are machines, albeit highly organized machines. It seems to me that the significant encounter between mathematics and biology will stem from the logical examination of problems in machine theory that turn out to have relevance to fundamental problems in biology, and it is to speculations of this kind that this article will be largely confined.

Claude E. Shannon of the Massachusetts Institute of Technology and John McCarthy of Stanford University once pointed out that when men find machine analogues for the human body, the machines they pick necessarily reflect their times. Descartes compared the body to intricate water clocks and fountains; earlier in this century the brain was regarded as a telephone central office; more recently the electronic computer has been the preferred machine to which to compare an organism. Perhaps for this reason most of the workers who have recently explored the relations between organism and machine have concentrated on the central nervous system. They have tended to ask two questions: Can one explain the brain as a kind of computer? Can one

SELF-REPRODUCTION is one of the biological processes that have been subjected to mathematical analysis. The little red and blue "creatures" in the photographs on the opposite page are the two kinds of part of an elementary self-reproducing machine designed by the geneticist L. S. Penrose. If the parts are placed in a plastic tray (a) and the tray is shaken end to end, the parts are jostled but they do not link up (b). But if a blue-red "seed," or "machine," is introduced (c) and the parts are shaken again, the seed imparts a tilt to the other parts, which link to form more blue-red units (d); these machines are spread apart for better visibility in e. Now if a red-blue seed is introduced instead (f), shaking produces only red-blue machines (g, h): the machine "breeds true." Penrose's creatures were made of plywood; these were made of aluminum at the Bell Telephone Laboratories.

build a computer that "thinks" like a brain?

There have been several lines of approach, but central to most of them has been the concept of the "automaton," which is in effect an idealized machine or machine part or, when the analogy to neurophysiological processes is being pressed, an idealized organism or part of an organism, such as a cell. In automaton theory one deals not with the internal workings of the automaton but with its external manifestations. In the words of the late John von Neumann, the elements of a machine or an organism "are viewed as automatisms, the inner structure of which need not be disclosed, but which are assumed to react to certain unambiguously defined stimuli, by certain unambiguously defined responses."

One of the most useful of such abstract machines is the "finite-state machine," or "finite automaton." It is a "black box" that has a finite number of discrete internal "states." It also commonly has a finite number of possible inputs and possible outputs. The state and the output at any time T depend in some arbitrary way on the previous state and input at time $T - 1$. Confronted with a finite automaton and a set of rules for its transitions from state to state, one can determine from its starting state and the input sequence what the state and output of the automaton will be at any specified time. The rules can be presented in the form of a table or diagram [see top illustration on page 278]. It is important in dealing with finite-state machines to understand the concept of state. The state of an automaton that is an abstract model of a combination lock is not "locked" or "open," for example; it is the situation of the lock's innards—the positions of the various unseen gears and levers, which change with each twist of the visible dial [see bottom illustration on page 278].

In 1943 Warren S. McCulloch and W. S. Pitts of the Massachusetts Institute of Technology developed an abstract and highly simplified model of the basic element of a biological nervous system: the neuron, or nerve cell. It was in effect a finite automaton with only two possible states—firing or not firing. By combining these modules, or formal neurons, they set up models of nervous systems, and later S. C. Kleene of the University of Wisconsin proved a general theorem characterizing the kinds of behavior that can be expected of networks of McCulloch-Pitts neurons.

A MATHEMATICAL MODEL OF THE NERVE IMPULSE

The most frequent subjects of mathematical modeling in the biological sciences are neurons, or nerve cells, and networks of neurons. Some models, as Edward F. Moore indicates in the accompanying article, leave biological fact far behind. Other models, however, seek to explain the actual functioning of nerve cells or fibers. The classic example is the model of the nerve impulse that was developed by A. L. Hodgkin and A. F. Huxley of the University of Cambridge.

The signal that travels down the cable-like axon of a nerve cell is an electrical pulse about 100 millivolts in amplitude and one millisecond in duration. The impulse is propagated at constant velocity and shape by a mechanism that regenerates the pulse at each point along the axon; the energy for this regeneration comes from the distribution of ions between the inside and the outside of the axon. Potassium ions are more concentrated inside the axon, and if the axon membrane were permeable only to potassium, the potential difference across it would be the potassium equilibrium potential (E_K) of about 75 millivolts, with the inside of the axon negative. Sodium ions are more concentrated outside, and if the membrane were permeable only to sodium, the voltage across it would be the sodium equilibrium potential (E_{Na}) of about 50 millivolts, with the inside of the axon positive. What happens is that the permeability of the membrane to ions undergoes dramatic changes in response to changes in potential. In its resting state the membrane is moderately permeable to potassium and the potential is about −60 millivolts. If an artificial stimulus or an advancing nerve impulse reduces this potential, the membrane momentarily becomes highly permeable to sodium ions, which enter the axon; the potential in this active region momentarily becomes positive. Almost immediately, then, the sodium permeability is shut off and the potassium permeability increases, restoring the membrane potential to its resting value as the nerve impulse moves on down the axon.

A number of investigators in Britain and the U.S. established that the propagation of the nerve impulse, or action potential, is essentially an electrical process described by the nonlinear partial differential equation shown in the middle illustration at left. The equation says that the current (I_m) across any segment of the membrane (color) equals the difference between the longitudinal currents flowing into and out of that segment, and that this in turn is equal to the membrane capacitance current

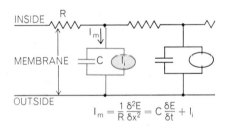

NERVE IMPULSE is a wavelike variation of potential difference across the nerve-axon membrane. Sodium ions enter the axon during the rising phase of the impulse and potassium ions leave during the falling phase.

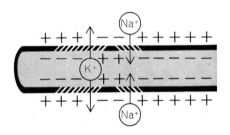

$$I_m = \frac{1}{R}\frac{\delta^2 E}{\delta x^2} = C\frac{\delta E}{\delta t} + I_i$$

CABLE ANALOGUE of nerve axon has longitudinal resistances, membrane capacitances and ionic-current elements (I_i).

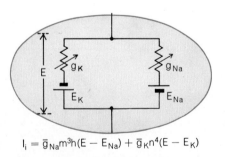

$$I_i = \bar{g}_{Na}m^3 h(E - E_{Na}) + \bar{g}_K n^4(E - E_K)$$

IONIC-CURRENT ELEMENTS have potassium and sodium batteries, each with a variable resistance. E is membrane potential.

plus the current carried by ions moving through the membrane. The dependence of this ionic current on the membrane potential was still unknown until 1949, when Hodgkin and Bernhard Katz discovered the effect of the sodium-potassium sequence on the rising and falling phases of the impulse. In 1952 Hodgkin and Huxley, using a technique originated by K. S. Cole at the Marine Biological Laboratory at Woods Hole, Mass., measured the ionic current when the membrane potential was held constant. From these data they deduced the laws governing the dependence of sodium and potassium permeability on membrane potential, and they formulated the laws in a set of differential equations.

The active nonlinear element that accounts for the ionic current is shown in the bottom illustration at left. The equation with it shows how the ionic current is the product of the electrochemical driving force for each ion and its specific conductance. The sodium and potassium conductances depend on three dimensionless, experimentally determined variables: m, h and n. These variables obey the nonlinear differential equations shown in the top illustration at right. The time constants (τ) and steady-state values in the equations are functions only of the membrane potential. Five equations—these three and the two previously described—together form the Hodgkin-Huxley model.

If one assumes that a potential pulse travels with a constant velocity, solution of the equations yields the wave form of the impulse and produces an adequate description of other observed phenomena. In order to inspect the transient buildup of the pulse from a stimulus, however, one needs a more general solution. Recently Fred Dodge, James Cooley and Hirsh Cohen at the International Business Machines Research Center have carried out a computer calculation in which they replaced the five equations with difference equations. One of their results is the set of curves in the top illustration, showing the relation between sodium and potassium conductances and potential. The three-dimensional graph in the bottom illustration exhibits the formation of the pulse as it tends toward a fixed shape and constant velocity. This new method of solving the equations should also make it possible to study the propagation of the nerve impulse in axons that branch or otherwise change in geometry.

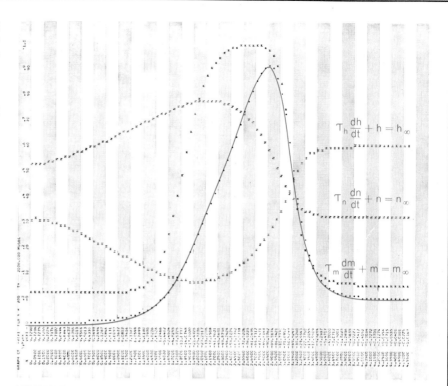

$$\tau_h \frac{dh}{dt} + h = h_\infty$$

$$\tau_n \frac{dn}{dt} + n = n_\infty$$

$$\tau_m \frac{dm}{dt} + m = m_\infty$$

COMPUTER PRINT-OUT shows how the membrane potential and effective conductances of sodium and potassium vary along the axon at a fixed time. The distance scale runs from 0 (*left*) to 4.55 centimeters. The potential curve is delineated by asterisks (with a curve added for clarity) on a scale of 0 to 90 millivolts, 0 corresponding to the membrane's resting potential of —60 millivolts. The three curves consisting of letters are the variables representing changes in ionic conductance of the membrane: M (sodium activation), H (sodium inactivation) and N (potassium activation). Their values lie between 0 and 1. These variables obey the nonlinear differential equations shown with each curve. The voltage-dependent time constants and the steady-state values in each equation were obtained experimentally.

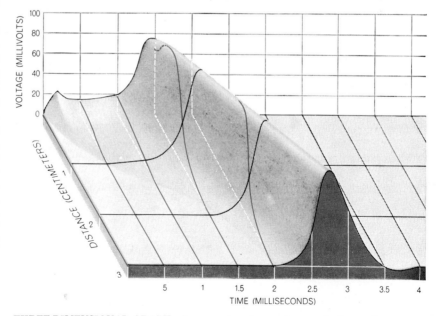

THREE-DIMENSIONAL GRAPH of a nerve impulse moving out in time and space was constructed from a series of curves generated by a computer, which gave the voltage as a function of distance along the axon at successive time intervals (*colored curves*). The black curves show the voltage as a function of time. The graph shows how a short stimulus (.2 millisecond) triggers a change in potential that hovers around the threshold and then flares into an action potential, and how the nerve impulse attains its constant shape and velocity.

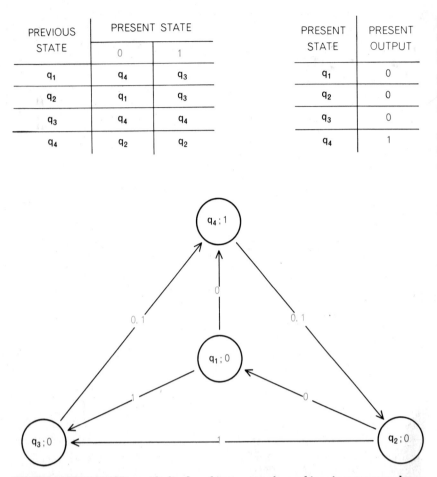

PREVIOUS STATE	PRESENT STATE	
	0	1
q_1	q_4	q_3
q_2	q_1	q_3
q_3	q_4	q_4
q_4	q_2	q_2

PRESENT STATE	PRESENT OUTPUT
q_1	0
q_2	0
q_3	0
q_4	1

FINITE AUTOMATON is an idealized machine or part of a machine; in automaton theory it is the basic building block of systems ranging from neural networks and computer circuits to self-reproducing machines. An automaton can be described by two tables. One (*top left*) shows the change in state in a unit of time depending on input (*color*). The other (*top right*) shows the output associated with each state. The description can be diagrammed (*bottom*). Vertices give the states and outputs; edges give transitions for each input (*color*).

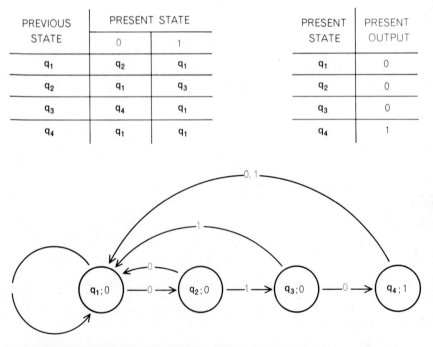

PREVIOUS STATE	PRESENT STATE	
	0	1
q_1	q_2	q_1
q_2	q_1	q_3
q_3	q_4	q_1
q_4	q_1	q_1

PRESENT STATE	PRESENT OUTPUT
q_1	0
q_2	0
q_3	0
q_4	1

COMBINATION LOCK can be described in finite-automaton terms. The input sequence is the combination. In this simple example the combination is 0, 1, 0; output 1 is "unlocked."

Kleene's theorem has since been applied directly to arbitrary finite-state machines, without considering neurons. What began as an attempt to analyze the nervous system therefore led eventually to theoretical advances in logic and electrical engineering.

The British logician A. M. Turing took a different approach to the "thinking machine" problem. Without making any assumptions about the physiology of the brain, he sought to define in logical terms an automaton that could in principle carry out any precisely definable computation. A Turing machine works by performing a very large number of exceedingly simple operations. It is an automaton with a finite number of states but supplied with an infinitely long "tape." Its instructions are written on a finite portion of the tape; given enough time and enough steps, the "head" of the machine reads these instructions and prints out its answer on more of the same tape. Turing showed that a "universal" machine could even be designed to perform any possible computation. If it is supplied with descriptions of a task and of a machine that could perform that task, it will figure out how to do the job itself and proceed to do it.

Both the McCulloch-Pitts neurological model and the more abstract Turing machine have stimulated interesting speculations on the nature of thinking and on the extreme capabilities of machines. Automaton theorists have, for example, tried to mimic the ability of biological systems to repair themselves and to perform reliably in spite of having unreliable components. Von Neumann showed how one could make a machine that would function properly, even if some of its parts failed, by introducing redundancy: by providing multiple logic elements in a computer, for instance, and multiple pathways among them. Both self-repair and redundancy are of obvious importance in computer and other electronic technologies and are currently under serious investigation.

The fact remains that a biological neuron is not a simple on-off switch that is either firing or not firing at any given time, and that computers are not "thinking machines." There are probably better ways to build computers than to imitate what we think we understand of the brain, and better ways to improve that understanding than by oversimplifying the behavior of neurons. It has sometimes seemed to me that the effort to design oversimplified neurons

A MODEL OF ENERGY TRANSFER IN PREDATION

Ecology, the study of interactions between organisms and their environment, is a field of biology that has seen an increasing application of what might be called "constructive" mathematics, or mathematics designed to create models that in turn lead to predictions and biological insights. This is a brief account of one such piece of work, an investigation of predation by L. B. Slobodkin of the University of Michigan. Slobodkin experimented with laboratory populations of the minute freshwater crustacean *Daphnia*, measuring the caloric content of a population, of its food (algae) and of the *Daphnia* taken as "prey" (simply by removing them from the tank) at various rates. He reasoned as follows:

If the energy income, or input, per unit time to a steady-state population is I, and if in the absence of predation the "standing crop," or caloric content of the population, is P, and if the cost in calories to maintain one calorie of crop for one day is c, then

$$I = cP .$$

If there is predation, the standing crop P' will be reduced; assuming that the energy input is constant, there will be a change (Δc) in the cost, so that under predation

$$I = (c + \Delta c)P' = cP' + \Delta cP' .$$

The last term in the equation represents the effect of predation. If one considers this effect in a different way, then

$$I = cP' + \sum \frac{Y_i}{E_{pi}} .$$

The new expression is a summation of as many different kinds of yield (Y_i) as are involved, divided by E_{pi}. The latter is a dimensionless number, a "regression coefficient" inserted to avoid converting I into Y without taking into account the events implied by the switch from algae (I) to *Daphnia* (Y). Inspection of the equation shows that a high E_{pi} will make for a low drain on the population for a given amount of yield. Having measured I, P' and Y_i, Slobodkin

solved equations for c and the various values of E_{pi}. High E_{pi} values turned out to be associated with older *Daphnia*. This implied that E_{pi} should be equivalent to some biologically meaningful expression.

Now, if one assigns to each dying animal the energy required to replace it, the sum of the replacement costs of all animals dying in a given interval in a steady-state population should precisely equal the energy income to the population in that interval. So if K_i is the cost of replacing an animal of age i, and if D_i such animals die in a unit of time, then in the absence of predation

$$I = \sum K_i D_i = cP ,$$

and in the presence of predation

$$I = \sum K_i' D_i' = cP' + \Delta cP' .$$

Now suppose only one kind of prey is taken, k. Then by manipulating equations one can write

$$E_{pk} = \frac{Y_k}{\sum K_i' D_i' - \frac{P'}{P} \sum K_i D_i} .$$

This equation implies that predation on animals that are about to die any-

way minimizes the difference between the two death distributions and is therefore best for both the predator and the prey. It provides the predator with a maximum steady yield and at the same time enables the population to withstand predation. In nature, then, both predator and prey might be expected to evolve toward a relation in which the animals taken as yield will have maximum E_{pi}. For the predator this means taking the biggest and weakest animals it can get; for the prey it suggests a life pattern in which the causes of death other than predation accumulate at the age level normally taken by the chief predator.

The regression coefficient E_{pi}, which Slobodkin calls "population efficiency," leads to new questions about actual predator behavior and the mechanism of aging; it suggests a theory even though it makes no unique numerical prediction. In this it is unlike another concept of efficiency, Y/I, or "ecological efficiency," which has a fairly constant maximum value in various populations [*see illustration*]. There is as yet no explanation for this value, although it is predictable. The ratio Y/I, in other words, still awaits constructive mathematical analysis.

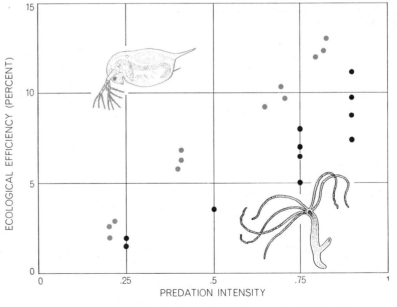

ECOLOGICAL EFFICIENCY tends to reach a maximum value of 7 to 13 percent, whether in **Daphnia pulex** (*color*) or in species of the coelenterate **Hydra** (*black*).

as a step toward "thinking machines" is comparable to an early attempt to build artificial feathers to enable men to fly: a bird's flight reveals some fundamental principles of aerodynamics that are pertinent to aircraft design, but the details are significantly different. As for describing brain function in logical terms, that appears to be far beyond our present capabilities. Von Neumann suggested that the simplest possible description of a specific mode of operation of the brain may be a diagram of all the nerve connections themselves! There may be a mathematical logic that can explain the brain, but it is surely orders of magnitude more complex than anything mathematicians have yet devised.

Is there perhaps some characteristic of living things that is more amenable to logical analysis? Self-reproduction is a good possibility. Certainly it is the most primitive aspect of life. Most organisms do not "think," and many have no nervous system at all, but all organisms do reproduce themselves. There is a good chance, then, that self-reproduction will turn out to be much simpler logically than thinking is. If one could uncover a logical scheme of reproduction, one should at least be able to identify the important problems in the process and perhaps even some of the ways in which those problems can be solved; this might in turn tell the biologist what to look for and perhaps throw light on some of the biological processes that are now under intensive investigation.

Von Neumann was the first to consider in detail how to make a machine reproduce itself. The task he set himself, as he once stated it, was: "Can one build an aggregate out of [simple] elements in such a manner that if it is put into a reservoir, in which there float all these elements in large numbers, it will then begin to construct other aggregates, each of which will at the end turn out to be another automaton exactly like the original one?" He proceeded to show that this was feasible: that a properly instructed machine placed in a "stockroom" environment would wander around assembling the parts with which to reproduce itself, and that there would in time be two and then four, eight and 16 machines and so on as long as the parts held out and space was available.

At first this sounds quite impossible and even ridiculous. Is it not, however, perhaps just a matter of degree? If a small crystalline "seed" composed of a few molecules of a substance is introduced into an environment of many of the same molecules at the appropriate temperature and pressure, the seed causes more molecules to be assembled in the same crystalline configuration. Seen in this light, crystal growth is self-reproduction. So is the closing of a zipper: two little hooks are brought together in an environment consisting of more hooks, arranged in a row, and a runner; all the other hooks join in sequence to form a series of two-hook "machines," a sort of one-dimensional crystal.

These are, to be sure, trivial examples, because each involves one simple change in state: from amorphous to crystalline, from open to closed. How about the punched card of a business machine? It is a "machine" and it reproduces itself—with the help, to be sure, of a complex environment: the card-punching equipment, which supplies most of the organization required for duplicating the card. (Note, however, that whereas some one-celled organisms can reproduce in a simple nutrient medium, higher organisms may be dependent on a complex environment that contains, for instance, such complex elements as vitamins.) The real problem, then, is to produce a complicated machine in a simple environment—a machine with a large number of parts, perhaps, but not very many kinds (or "states") of parts. This is what von Neumann accomplished with his model of self-reproduction.

One might still ask if von Neumann's model bears any significant relation to biological reproduction. One of the first logical difficulties he encountered provides a good example of such a relation, as does the way in which he solved it. He quickly realized that the instructions that tell the machine how to construct a copy of itself cannot be complete. To be complete they would have to describe not only the automaton but also the instructions themselves; there would be a blueprint of the blueprint, and this could go on in an infinite regress. The way to get around this problem is to provide two machines that operate on the blueprint in two ways. One is a blueprint-copier (C). The other is a blueprint-obeyer (O). They are combined, along with a sequencing device (s) that turns each on at the proper time, with the blueprint describing all three elements ($B_{C + o + s}$). The complete machine can be symbolized as $C + O + s + B_{C + o + s}$. Presented with the blueprint for the total machine, C copies it and O follows it to build C, O and s.

Recent findings in the chemistry of genetics reveal some striking parallels between von Neumann's elements and processes in the living cell. B is a set of genes composed of deoxyribonucleic acid (DNA), which encodes hereditary characteristics. C is the enzyme DNA polymerase, which catalyzes the replication of a strand of DNA and so

X	Y	Z	O	X	Y	Z	O
X	Z	Y	X	X	Z	Y	X
O	O	O	O	O	O	O	O
X	Y	Z	X	Y	Z	O	O
X	Z	Y	X	Z	Y	X	O

TESSELLATION is a plane subdivided into square cells. This array is a configuration of 40 cells, shown in states designated X, Y, Z and O (quiescent). The total configuration contains three "copies" of a seven-cell configuration (color). A copy must be a "disjoint subset"; the fourth set like the others (black outline) is not a copy because it is not disjoint.

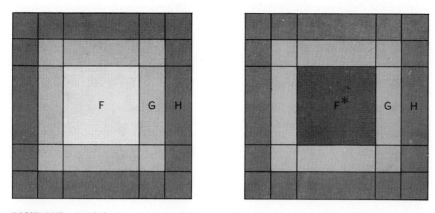

CONFIGURATIONS of two arrays of the same size are shown as of time *T*. The configurations of the two inner arrays are different from each other. (The drawings show inner arrays of one particular size but they could be any size.) The configurations marked *G*, the hollow squares of neighbors of the inner arrays, are similar to each other. So are the *H*'s.

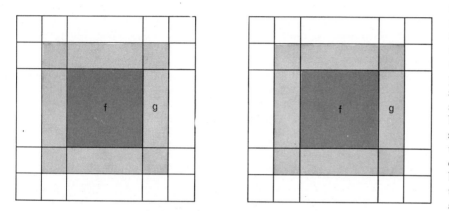

NEW CONFIGURATIONS of the arrays shown at the top of the page are shown here at *T* + 1. The inner arrays have been mapped into a new configuration that is the same for each of them. The intermediate arrays are also similar to each other. The state of the outer arrays cannot be specified. Two arrays that differ as in the illustration at the top of the page and are followed by identical arrays, as here, are said to be "mutually erasable."

copies the genes. *O* is the system of messenger ribonucleic acid (RNA), enzymes and ribosomes that assembles amino acids according to the prescription of the DNA to synthesize enzymes and other proteins and thereby build the new cell.

Von Neumann's early models were "kinematic" in that they dealt with physical parts in motion, but they were not actually built. Some less general kinematic models have been demonstrated, however. In one, designed by Homer Jacobson of Brooklyn College, the self-reproducing machine is a train of toy railroad cars; the cars are the individual parts and control is accomplished by circuits mounted in each car. When a train of different kinds of cars arranged in a particular sequence is placed on a track layout, it moves around bumping into unattached cars, rearranging them when necessary by using sidings and coupling them in its

own image. Jacobson designed one such train model that would work for arbitrary trains of any length, and he actually built a simpler demonstration model in which a train two cars long can reproduce itself.

The British geneticist L. S. Penrose took a different approach, stimulated in part by his speculations on the manner in which the genetic material might replicate. In its most elementary form Penrose's machine has two kinds of part, *A* and *B*, simple cutouts shaped so that they can hook together in either of two ways. If an *AB* machine is placed on a tray with a number of *A*'s and *B*'s and the tray is shaken, a number of new *AB* units are formed; the first machine acts as a seed [*see illustration on page 274*]. If the seed is a *BA* machine, the reproduced pairs will be more *BA*'s.

Kinematic models have the virtue of realism and dramatic impact, but they are exceedingly hard to deal with math-

ematically. In his later work von Neumann turned to an abstract model; he discarded the hardware, thereby avoiding all problems of mechanical movement, fit and manipulation and setting himself a more purely logical and mathematical task rather than one in mechanical or electrical engineering. For his stockroom he substituted a mathematical environment: a tessellation, or plane subdivided into square cells. In each cell he placed one of his elementary parts: a finite-state machine. Von Neumann's machines have no inputs or outputs but only a number of permissible states. The list of these states and the rules governing transitions from one state to another are the same for all the cells, although different cells can be in different states at any one time. Each machine is deterministic and synchronous: at each integer-valued time *T* (except in the initial condition, or at $T = 0$) the state of each cell depends only on its own and its neighbors' states at time $T - 1$. There is a special state known as the "quiescent" state; all but a finite number of cells are in this state, which has the special property that if any cell and all its neighbors are quiescent at time $T - 1$, that cell will be quiescent at *T*. The entire system—tessellation space, cell machines, allowable states and transition rules—is called a "tessellation structure." A finite block of cells, or "array," is called a "configuration" when the states of its cells are specified.

What have all these definitions to do with machines and reproduction? Consider the entire tessellation space as an extremely abstract environment—one in which space and time are quantized and both motion and other forms of gradual change are replaced by successions of discrete states, the transitions between which are prescribed by definite rules. Within this environment there are configurations of square cells; these are our "machines," and it is these machines that can be made to be self-reproducing. The individual cells are the elementary parts—perhaps molecules. Their changing states can be thought of as different quantum states—energy levels or chemical-activation states—and geometrical positions. The rules for transitions between states are the physical and chemical laws of this environment that determine how the cells change and relate to one another. The quiescent-state cells are unused raw materials, and the rule for quiescent states says in effect that no cell separated from a configuration will suddenly flare into activity; a machine "reaches out" to surrounding materials through local action only.

The problem, therefore, is to build a tessellation structure with individual cells that have a small number of states (fairly simple parts, in other words), to choose the transition rules and then to arrange cells into a configuration that will in time reproduce itself. It is a task somewhat like writing a program for a digital computer. Von Neumann set a further requirement: Each configuration must contain a universal Turing machine. He then worked out most of the details for a self-reproducing configuration of some 200,000 cells with 29 permissible states. Since his death in 1957 others have continued to work with tessellation models, examining the details of their construction and attempting to draw conclusions, in the form of provable theorems, as to the logic of reproduction.

One question that I asked was: How fast can a population of self-reproducing configurations grow? The answer is that

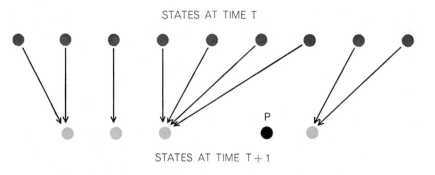

STATES AT TIME T

P

STATES AT TIME T + 1

NUMBER OF POSSIBLE STATES for the array illustrated below decreases between time T and $T + 1$ as a result of erasure and of shrinkage at the boundary layer (*see text*). It can be shown that the loss by erasure is larger than the loss by shrinkage. There will therefore be an extra state at $T + 1$; it is P, the Garden of Eden configuration.

it cannot grow exponentially—cannot keep doubling with each generation, for instance. The population of a two-dimensional tessellation cannot at any time be larger than the square of the time. Let us formulate that statement as a theorem: If a self-reproducing configuration is capable of reproducing $f(T)$ offspring by time T, then there exists a positive constant k such that $f(T) \leq kT^2$.

(The symbol $\leq$ means "is less than or equal to.")

The proof is as follows: Let c be the self-reproducing configuration and let the smallest square array able to contain a copy of c be of size $D \times D$. Then at each time T the total number of nonquiescent cells is at most $(2T + D)^2$, since the square array can only grow by one cell on each side with each unit of time. If r is the number of cells in c, then

$$f(T) \leq \frac{(2T + D)^2}{r}.$$

This inequality expression can be simplified in a few more steps to reach the conclusion of the theorem. The situation is Malthusian: the population is limited by the space available, since the nonquiescent region has a velocity of propagation that cannot exceed a fixed constant.

Another important question is this: Can every configuration reproduce itself? It turns out that there are configurations that cannot occur except at the outset, at $T = 0$. Such a configuration is nonconstructible, in the sense that there is no configuration that can give rise to it by means of the specified rules of transition. John W. Tukey of Princeton University suggested calling such a block of cells, which can have had no predecessor state, a "Garden of Eden" configuration. Since such configurations cannot be produced by any other configuration, they cannot reproduce themselves. An investigation of the conditions under which they can occur therefore helps to define fundamental limitations on the ability of machines to reproduce themselves.

These conditions involve the ability to perform something called "erasing."

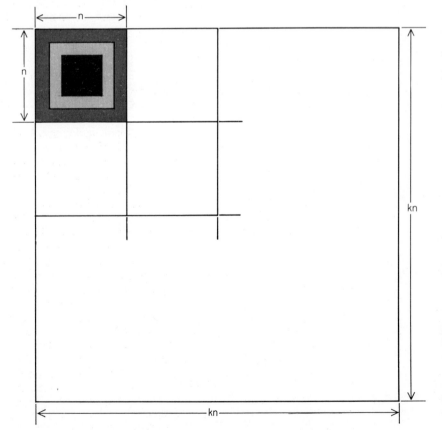

"GARDEN OF EDEN" THEOREM (*see text*) is proved with the help of this diagram. The small array of size $n \times n$ has an erasable configuration. The large array is of size $kn \times kn$. (The integer k is 4 in the illustration but would actually be much larger.) This drawing shows the array as of time T. At $T + 1$ it will be reduced in size to $(kn - 2) \times (kn - 2)$.

When a blackboard has been erased, there is no way of telling what was written there. Computer designers apply the term "erasing" to an operation on computer memory elements that puts them into a standard state regardless of what was stored there before the erasing. In general, erasing is an irreversible process; after it occurs it is impossible to determine the preceding states from which the present state could have arisen. There must, then, have been at least two possible preceding states that could go through transitions putting them into the same present state. In the case of tessellation structures it is necessary to define erasing somewhat more formally to make sure that the information as to past state is really erased and not merely shifted away to neighboring states.

To establish such a definition consider the two configurations in the upper illustration on page 281. The configurations of the two nine-cell inner arrays are different at a given time; call them F and F°. At the same time the configurations of the intermediate arrays—the hollow squares of immediate neighbors of the inner arrays—are both G; that is, one intermediate array is a copy of the other. The same is true of the configurations of the outer arrays: both are H. Now consider the configurations into which these arrays will have been mapped after one unit of time [see lower illustration on page 281]. If, in these $T + 1$ arrays, the configurations f and g of both the inner and the intermediate arrays are copies of each other, then the two original configurations are said to have been "mutually erasable"— they were different and have become alike. Note that one cannot specify the final configuration of the outer array because the states of its cells are affected by exterior cells that have not been considered in this definition; its function has been simply to "protect" the intermediate array. A configuration, then, will be said to be erasable if there is another configuration such that the two are mutually erasable. It further follows from this definition that if an erasable configuration of any shape is contained within a rectangular array, that rectangular array is also erasable. As a result one can consider this problem in terms of square arrays, which are easier to work with than those of irregular shape.

It is now possible to state a theorem: In a tessellation structure for which there exist erasable configurations, there exist Garden of Eden configurations. (Although one might construct a tessellation without erasable configurations, such a structure would be essentially trivial.)

I shall sketch the intuitive proof of this theorem rather than give the detailed proof. Let n be an integer such that there is an array of size $n \times n$ that has an erasable configuration. Then consider a larger array of size $kn \times kn$ [see illustration on page 282]. Each of the k^2 arrays of size $n \times n$ is the proper size to contain a copy of an erasable configuration; k is chosen to be large enough so that there will often be many such erasable configurations in the large array. If A states are permissible for each cell, then the whole array can have $A^{(kn)^2}$ possible configurations at time T. Consider next the array into which this first array is mapped after one unit of time. Remember that one cannot specify the states of the outer hollow square at $T + 1$. There are therefore fewer possible states available to the $T + 1$ array: $A^{(kn-2)^2}$.

Now, if in the original $kn \times kn$ array there was one $n \times n$ array with an erasable configuration, then two possible states—those of the erasable configuration and of the one mutually erasable with it—will both map into only one possible state at $T + 1$. If there were two copies of an erasable configuration, their four possible states will map into only one possible state. In general, if there were s copies of the erasable configuration at time T, there will be 2^s states mapping into one state at $T + 1$. This situation is diagrammed in the illustration on page 282. Now it is only necessary to show that the loss in the number of states due to erasure must be larger than the loss due to shrinkage of the outer boundary cells—that is, the loss due to the difference between $A^{(kn)^2}$ and $A^{(kn-2)^2}$.

Consider the logarithms of the numbers of states rather than the numbers themselves. The logarithm of the ratio that indicates boundary-layer loss increases approximately linearly with k. But the logarithm of the number of states lost by erasure increases with the number of erasable configurations, and therefore approximately with the area of the array, or with the square of k. For a large k, then, more states will surely be lost by erasure than by shrinkage at the boundary layer. Therefore there must exist a state P at time $T + 1$ that cannot be reached from any of the states at time T.

This state P is the Garden of Eden configuration of the theorem. It is a conceivable state but one that cannot be reached from any previous state. It corresponds to a machine that can be described as an arrangement of the available parts but that cannot be built out of those parts. Since it is a machine that cannot arise by reproduction, it must be a machine that cannot reproduce itself.

The two theorems I have discussed may suffice to give some idea of the manner in which a process such as reproduction can be abstracted and made amenable to mathematical treatment. This is not to suggest that there is necessarily a close relation between a tessellation model of self-reproduction and biological reproduction; that certainly remains to be shown. Yet, as I proposed earlier in this article, it seems likely that manipulation of machine models should at least help by identifying difficulties or establishing criteria for biological processes.

To take just one example: Life on earth is now generally assumed to have originated through the chance interaction of nonliving materials. How likely would this be? Perhaps one could learn from tessellation models just how complicated an assemblage of parts must be in order to have the property of self-reproduction and the further property of being able to undergo evolution into more complicated descendants. Jacobson, the investigator who worked with toy-train machines, made a start in this direction, characterizing complexity in terms of "bits" of information.

Even if machine self-reproduction finally proves quite inapplicable to biology, it may nevertheless be of surpassing interest—for its own sake. Let us return for a moment to von Neumann's stockroom model of a self-reproducing machine. What if we devise such a machine not for an arbitrary stockroom but for some natural environment? Such a machine—really an artificial living plant—would make its own parts out of natural materials and then assemble those parts to reproduce itself. In the process it would extract substances from its environment and refine and concentrate them. A plant designed to reproduce in the oceans, for instance, might build itself largely out of magnesium, which is present in sea water, and could be harvested for its magnesium content. Nobody has yet done the engineering design work required to build such a machine, but I think it will someday be built.

MATHEMATICS IN
THE SOCIAL SCIENCES

37

RICHARD STONE · September 1964

Some 75 years ago the American economist Irving Fisher stated that the entire world's literature contained scarcely 50 worthwhile books and articles on mathematical economics. Today the situation is different, not only in economics but also in all the other social sciences: each year sees thousands of additions to a mountain of mathematical literature. The reason is a growing appreciation of the advantages that come from expressing in mathematical terms concepts that were once dealt with only verbally.

The progress has been greater in some areas of study than in others. The entire subject matter of demography and economics, for example, is so aggressively quantitative that a wider application of mathematics to these fields has been inescapable. But in every one of the social sciences it has become increasingly evident that an exclusively verbal description of complex systems and their interrelations—and more significantly the framing of theories about such systems—results in generalizations that are difficult to analyze, compare and apply. These difficulties are greatly reduced when mathematical expressions are substituted for words. For one thing, a number of problems that had seemed to be completely unrelated—for instance

the analysis of educational systems and the programming of capital investments —prove to be mathematically identical. For another, even in subjects whose concepts are rather vague and in which precise information is hard to find, mathematics can provide a means of obtaining valuable insights.

At the risk of enormous oversimplification it can be said that the social sciences, for all their diversity, are concerned with only two major areas of investigation. The first of these is the precise description of how social systems work and how their different parts are interrelated, whether the subject is cross-cousin marriage in a tribal society or the contribution of the steel industry to the total output of a technologically advanced nation. Studies of this kind investigate and analyze structure. The second area of investigation is concerned with control, that is, the effect of conscious aims on the operations of social structures and an examination of the rational processes that underlie the formulation of policy. These studies investigate and analyze decisions.

In both fields the same kinds of mathematics are applied to similar problems. Where empirical analysis of discrete observations is necessary much use is made of finite mathematics: in particu-

lar matrices, matrix algebra and difference equations. Where, on the other hand, purely theoretical analysis is desired and the data provide a continuum rather than discrete "bits," the use of the infinitesimal calculus—in particular differential equations—has many advantages. The examples that follow, drawn from the investigation of many kinds of structure, demonstrate the application of both kinds of mathematical method.

Among its many investigations the discipline of demography requires analysis of the structure and probable development of populations. To project the future structure of any population, assuming a constant pattern of births and survivals, we need three sets of data: (1) the numbers of people of different ages alive at a certain date; (2) the numbers surviving over a chosen time interval immediately following that date, and (3) the numbers born during that same time interval to the members of the different age-groups. This third set of data, by the way, exemplifies the kind of imprecision that can creep into quantifications of social science. In real life husbands and wives often belong to different age-groups, and the wife's childbearing capacity is a function of this factor as well as of her own fertility. In

FOUR MAJOR CIRCUITS, constituting a mathematical model of the British economy, are made to interact in the manner illustrated on the opposite page. At the heart of the model lies the circuit of real flows (*solid colored arrows*). Consumption demands and the rate of growth in these demands, together with exports and their rate of growth, combine (*middle right*) to determine the level of investment demands necessary to produce the required growth of output. Output levels themselves are composed of three "final" demands (for consumption, investment and exports) plus all intermediate demands for raw materials and fuels. Given the levels of output and the total labor force, industrial distributions of labor and capital are determined from the consideration that resources be used efficiently. The foreign-trade circuit (*light colored arrows*)

has a similar two-part start and, in addition to the obvious interactions of foreign prices and balances of trade on imports, has its effects both on domestic output levels and on domestic prices. The price circuit (*gray arrows*) shows an immediate interaction with consumption demands and a feedback, derived from considerations of wages, labor productivity and value added in the production sector (*middle left*), so that domestic prices and total consumers' expenditure are recalculated at the end of a cycle of calculations. Finally, because labor skills are as important as capital equipment, the fourth circuit (*black arrows*) sets forth interrelated factors of education and training that interact both with the total labor force (in terms of productivity and demands for skills) and with consumption demands (in terms of expenditures on education).

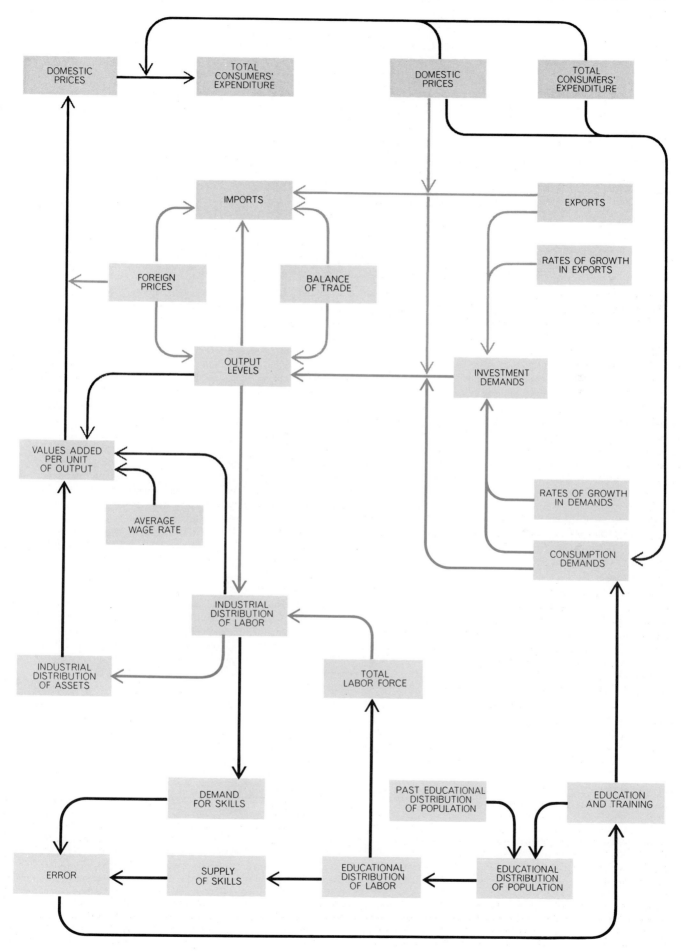

a

AGE	FEMALES (1940)	SURVIVING FEMALES (1955)	SURVIVING DAUGHTERS (1940–1954)
0–14	14,459	16,428	4,651
15–29	15,264	14,258	10,403
30–44	11,346	14,837	1,374

b

AGE	AGE 0–14	AGE 0–14	AGE 15–29	AGE 30–44
0–14	14,459 (A)	$\frac{4,651}{A}$	$\frac{10,403}{B}$	$\frac{1,374}{C}$
15–29	15,264 (B)	$\frac{14,258}{A}$	0	0
30–44	11,346 (C)	0	$\frac{14,837}{B}$	0

FUTURE POPULATIONS can be calculated by the use of matrix algebra. In this example it is assumed that the pattern of births and deaths remains constant over a 45-year period, and the calculation is confined to the future composition of the female population contained in three broad age-groups. The figures are samples and projections based on the 1940 U.S. Census; arrayed in tabular form (*a*) they show in three successive columns the numbers within each of three female age-groups in 1940, the numbers in each of these

the mathematical model we will take up here, however, the children are assigned according to the age-group of the wife alone.

In this kind of analysis of the process of change the changes from one time period to the next are most conveniently presented in a square array, or matrix [*see illustration at top of these two pages*]. The first step is to arrange the information about the age composition of the population in a single column of figures. Next, a square grid of rows and columns—the matrix proper—is constructed, with one row and one column for each age-group in the adjacent population column. Across the top row of the matrix are entered the number of children born to mothers in each age-group during the chosen time interval. Then the number of individuals in each age-group that are alive at the end of the chosen time interval, and have thus advanced from one age-group to the next, are entered diagonally on the grid, from top left to bottom right, in the spaces just below the main diagonal.

The information is now ready to be manipulated. By dividing the number of newborn individuals and the number of surviving individuals shown in each column of the matrix by the total number of people in the adjacent age-group column, a coefficient of birthrates and survival rates is obtained; these coefficients can be arrayed in a second matrix. If the figures in the age-group column are now multiplied by the coefficient matrix, the resulting totals in each age-group will show the estimated composition of the population at the end of the chosen time interval. Assume that this has been an interval of x years; if an estimate of population composition at the end of $2x$ years is desired, the original age-group figures are multiplied by the coefficient matrix raised to the power of 2. If a $3x$-year projection is desired, raise the multiplier to the power of 3, and so forth. In this

example the manipulation of figures has been simply called multiplication. Mathematicians will realize that the actual process is premultiplication of the column by the coefficient matrix. The reason is that the commutative law of arithmetic does not apply to matrix multiplication [see "Number," page 89].

Projections of this kind assume that the pattern of births and survivals remains unchanged throughout the period of the estimate; this is another example of the differences between models and reality. Nonetheless, even the unreality is illuminating. Manipulation of this rigid model demonstrates that, if a human population actually achieved a fixed pattern of births and deaths, it would eventually attain a stable age composition and a steady rate of growth.

In actuality, of course, an unchanging matrix of coefficients is an extreme improbability: the birthrate and death rate are subject to chance or to systematic influences or to both. The investigator therefore works toward an approximation of reality by manipulating the values in the coefficient matrix, a process known as complicating the model. It is not difficult to work out conditions in which a population would tend to attain an upper or a lower limit,

and thus a demographer's device can be extended to the study of problems in such fields as ecology and epidemiology.

Another point is worth reemphasis: the very process of mathematization helps to demonstrate that a certain unity exists in the structure of many apparently different problems. The population-projection matrix described here has been presented in a demographic context. A precisely similar projection can be made for populations of inanimate objects, such as telegraph poles, railroad cars or apartment buildings, and the model can then be used to study problems of industrial inventory or urban renewal. In such cases investment rates are substituted for birthrates and obsolescence for death. Whatever the age composition of the original stock, the model will show the replacements (and extensions) needed to keep the stock on any selected time path.

Another kind of structure, the investigation of which is the delight of ethnologists, is kinship—with its associated complex patterns of marriage and descent, clans, phratries and tribes and eventually considerations of class structure and social mobility. In such studies difference equations often provide a

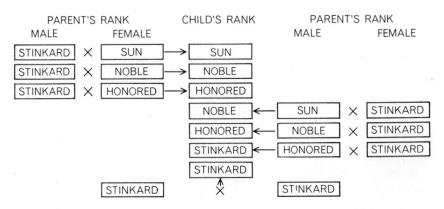

MARITAL CUSTOM among the Natchez Indians of North America required that one partner in each match be a proletarian Stinkard. The table lists the seven possible unions and

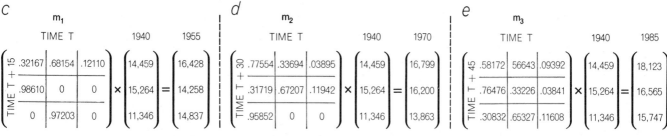

groups still alive in 1955 and finally the number of daughters born to each group during the same period. These figures are next arrayed in a square matrix (*b*) and then converted into a matrix of coefficients (*c*). When the coefficient matrix and the 1940 age-

groups are now multiplied, the result (*the column of numbers under 1955 at "c"*) is the predicted female population for that year. A multiplication of the square and cube of the coefficient matrix, in turn ("*d*" and "*e*") yields predictions for the years 1970 and 1985.

convenient way to manipulate the data. A classic example of social stratification reportedly existed among the Natchez, an American Indian tribe of the Mississippi basin. Fundamentally there were two classes among the Natchez: the aristocrats and the proletarians. The aristocrats were subdivided into three ranks, with Suns at the top, Nobles in the middle and Honoreds—still aristocrats but only a cut above the proletarian Stinkards—at the bottom.

As European travelers described the Natchez society, a kind of continuous social ferment was built into it by the marriage rules. At least one partner in any marriage—husband or wife—was always drawn from the Stinkard class. At the same time a child born into the aristocracy had the rank of its mother. Thus the child of a Sun, a Noble or an Honored mother and a Stinkard father was a Sun, a Noble or an Honored. The child of a Stinkard mother and a Sun father, however, inherited a rank one level below his father's and was only a Noble. This downgrading was progressive, so that the issue of a Stinkard mother and a Noble father was an Honored, and of a Stinkard mother and an Honored father a common Stinkard. At the bottom of the social heap Stinkard

and Stinkard produced Stinkard [*see illustration at bottom of these two pages*].

The Natchez tribe has long since disappeared, but students of class structure have continued to wonder if such a complex social system could possess any natural stability. To mathematize the problem it is necessary to assume that the population is stable, that each Natchez individual married once and only once and that each marriage produced one boy and one girl. Using these values in a mathematical model, it is soon evident that a stable class structure is impossible unless Suns and Nobles are initially absent from the population. Otherwise a few generations produce such a numerous aristocracy that there are no longer enough proletarian marriage partners to go around.

The behavior of the model suggests that the real Natchez did not in fact have a stable class structure. The inadequacy of the actual observations, however, makes it impossible to be sure. Manipulation of the model to allow for possible variations in the number of marriages per individual, or the comparative productivity, say, of Sun-Stinkard v. Stinkard-Stinkard marriages, or such completely unmodeled elements as a rapidly expanding population due to

a Natchez policy of conquest and assimilation, might yield significantly different results.

In a completely different area of study, economists who wish to examine such matters as rate of growth face the task of reducing innumerable transactions concerned with production, consumption, accumulation and foreign trade to some kind of order. One way to achieve such order is to view the economy as a vast system of interlocking accounts; in theory an enormous square matrix could be set up to do this, with each row-and-column pair representing a single account. Incoming revenue would be shown in the rows and outgoing costs in the columns. In actuality, if all the flows in an economic system were recorded in detail in a single matrix, the resulting array of rows and columns would be impossibly large and unmanageable. The solution is a selective consolidation of accounts into major classes. One such consolidation, applicable to a closed economy, reduces a complex picture to three interlocking accounts: one for production, one for consumption and one for accumulation [*see illustration on next page*].

In a model economy of this kind the

	INITIAL POPULATION	GENERATION 1	GENERATION 2	GENERATION 3	GENERATION 4	GENERATION 5
SUN	10	10	10	10	10	10
NOBLE	20	30	40	50	60	70
HONORED	40	60	90	130	180	240
TOTAL	70	100	140	190	250	320
STINKARD	500	470	430	380	320	250
TOTAL	570	570	570	570	570	570
	G	G + 1	G + 2	G + 3	G + 4	G + 5
SUN	S	S	S	S	S	S
NOBLE	N	N + S	N + 2S	N + 3S	N + 4S	N + 5S
HONORED	H	H + N	H + 2N + S	H + 3N + 3S	H + 4N + 6S	H + 5N + 10S

the rank of their issue. At first glance the system seems plausible. But mathematical analysis of a sample population (in this case containing 70 aristocrats and 500 proletarians at the start) shows a deficiency in Stinkard marriage partners after only four generations.

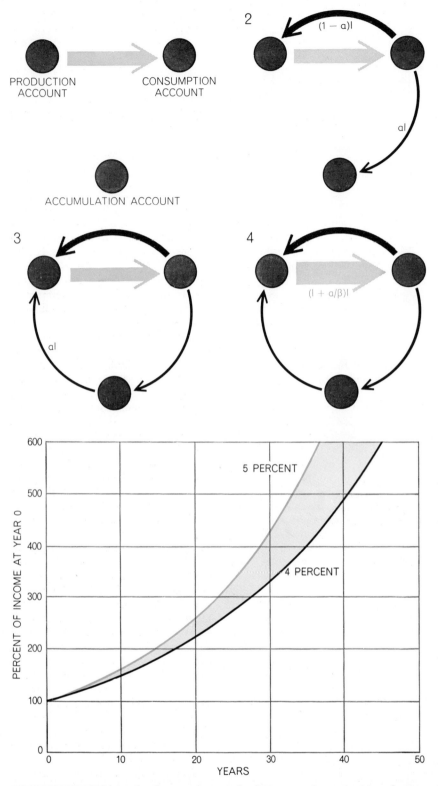

KEYNESIAN VIEW of a closed economy states that income equals consumption plus savings and that savings equal investment. When production, consumption and savings are interlocked in a model (*top illustration*), the growth of such a closed economy can be traced as the movement of income to the consumption account (*1*), which produces a two-way flow of outlay (*2*) into consumption spending and into savings. The second flow continues (*3*) from accumulation to production, increasing capital equipment and thereby stimulating greater production (*4, enlarged arrow*). If the rate of economic growth is to be increased, either more income must be saved and invested or greater efficiency must be achieved in the funds invested per unit of output. The importance of even slight rate increases, for example in the case of underdeveloped economies, is shown (*bottom illustration*) by comparison of a 1 percent difference between two rates of growth during a 50-year period.

production account receives money from the consumption account in exchange for sales of consumption goods and services and from the accumulation account in exchange for sales of investment goods. The production account then proceeds to pay out to the consumption account the value of its sales in the form of income. This income is the only revenue the consumption account receives; within that account the revenue is divided into two unequal parts. The larger part is spent on additional consumption goods and services (with a resulting flow back into the production account) and the rest goes into savings (with a resulting flow back into the accumulation account). To close the system the accumulation account then pays these savings into the production account in return for further investment goods.

Two of the assumptions in this model are obvious. The first is that total income is exactly equal to the sum expended on consumption goods and savings. The second is that savings, in turn, are exactly equal to expenditures on investment goods. Two other assumptions, although less immediately apparent, prove on examination to be the key relations in this closed-economy model. One of these is that the economy's inhabitants save a fixed proportion of their income (here called α). The other is that a fixed coefficient of proportionality exists between expenditures on investment goods, to wit additional capital, and increased yields from the production account, to wit additional production. This coefficient is here called β.

Any closed economy that is based on these assumptions can only grow at the constant rate represented by α/β. If it is to increase its rate of growth, the system must either save and invest a larger proportion of its income (that is, increase α) or contrive to use less capital per unit of output (that is, reduce β) or both. As an example, let these relations be quantified as follows: α is a savings rate of 10 percent of income and β is a capital-to-output ratio of 2.5. Under these circumstances α/β will yield a growth rate of 4 percent. But if the value of α can be increased to 12.5 percent, or if the value of β can be reduced to 2 percent, the economy's rate of growth will rise from 4 percent to 5.

A final example of the use of mathematics in describing and analyzing social situations can be found in the area of education. Concern over an adequate future supply of teachers, for in-

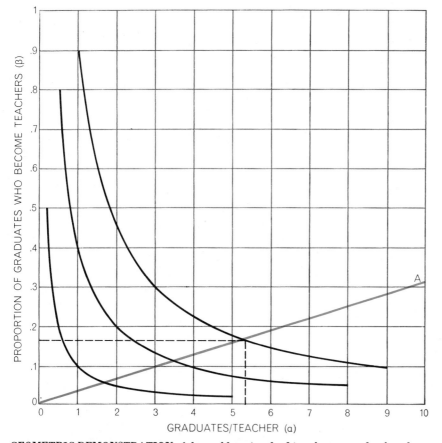

GEOMETRIC DEMONSTRATION of the problems involved in a future supply of teachers, as a first step, shows that all the possible rates of growth for the stockpile of teachers are interactions between the number of students each teacher can bring to the graduate level and the proportion of graduates who then become teachers. For each growth rate a separate hyperbolic curve (*black*) will plot all the possible combinations of these related factors. A separate calculation, in turn, establishes a linear relation between these same two factors in response to the varying stimuli of higher and lower rates of pay for teachers. When this linear relation is inserted in the graph (*straight colored line*), its intersections with the family of hyperbolas pinpoint specific values for each of the two factors in each instance. It is then possible to make another calculation that will show the corresponding rates of pay.

circumstance prevents any significant manipulation of γ, but courses of action are still possible with regard to α and β. What might be achieved by raising teachers' wages? Such an action would certainly bring more graduates into the teaching profession (thus affecting β) and might also improve morale and increase teacher efficiency (thus affecting α).

Indeed, it can be imagined that both α and β are related hyperbolically to pay; that is, at very low rates of pay the teachers would do no work and no graduates would enter the profession, whereas at very high rates both the teachers' efficiency and the number of graduate careerists would approach upper limits. In such a case the relation between α and β is linear, and this linear relation, when it is inserted in the geometric construction, enables corresponding rates of pay to be calculated for various values of α and β.

All the preceding examples are concerned with describing the world as it is without considering the mechanisms that determine how it comes to be that way. This latter consideration introduces the area of decisions. To a large extent the maintenance and modification of social patterns depend on innumerable private and public decisions consciously undertaken in the hope of achieving certain ends, and therefore the study of the decision process is an essential part of the social sciences.

To a large extent the decision process can be formulated and analyzed mathematically. In addition to the classical techniques of mathematics today's decision-maker can draw on such new methods as linear programming, game theory and statistical decision theory. As a preliminary, however, it is necessary to distinguish between decisions made under conditions of certainty and those made under conditions of uncertainty. And within these two categories it is necessary to distinguish between decisions that relate to a single period and those that involve a course of action over several periods.

An example of the first category and subcategory—a single-stage decision taken under conditions of certainty—can be found in the dietitian's problem of devising an adequate diet at minimum cost. This problem defines an adequate diet in terms of certain minimum quantities of such nutritional factors as proteins, carbohydrates and fats, vitamins, caloric content and the like. Various foods, with fixed prices, contain these nutritional elements in known

stance, requires analysis of the way teachers and graduates interact. In the simplest kind of case it can be taken as self-evident that the number of graduates produced by any educational system is in some way proportional to the number of teachers engaged in the system. An increase in the number of teachers, in turn, depends on the proportion (supposedly constant) of graduates of the system who become teachers and the proportion (also supposedly constant) of the existing teacher pool that is lost to the profession through death, retirement or resignation.

The ratio of graduates produced per teacher, in this example, may be designated α, the proportion of graduates who become teachers designated β and the lost-to-the-profession proportion designated γ. It is then easy to devise an equation for the net growth of teachers and graduates (designated δ). The equation is $\delta = \alpha\beta - \gamma$. At first glance it

seems that nothing but the obvious has been mathematized. All the equation says is that if more teachers are wanted, it is necessary either (1) to arrange for the existing number of teachers to turn out a greater number of graduates (that is, increase α), or (2) to persuade a greater number of graduates to enter the teaching profession (that is, increase β), or (3) to diminish the wastage rate in the existing stock of teachers (that is, reduce γ), or finally (4) to do all three at once.

Actually more than the obvious has been achieved by reducing the problem to mathematical relations. When these various interacting considerations are expressed geometrically [see illustration above], it becomes possible to examine still other interactions. Suppose the social situation is such that little or nothing can be done to reduce teacher wastage; no board of education, say, will reemploy retired teachers. Such a

quantities. The question is: How much of each foodstuff should be bought in order to meet the nutritional requirement at minimum cost?

Because the function to be minimized in this problem is linear, the solution requires the technique of linear programming. If a simplified case—involving only two foodstuffs and three nutritional elements—is taken, the problem can also be interpreted geometrically as a construction of two axes, one for each foodstuff [*see illustration at left*]. With n foods the same geometric construction can be thought of as repeated in n dimensions; as n increases, the number of calculations needed to find a solution also increases.

In practice the solution of the minimum-cost diet problem usually turns out to involve very few foods and to offer a far from acceptable diet. The reason for this is that the problem is usually too narrowly formulated; for example, the bulk of the food that constitutes the minimum-cost diet is not taken into account, and this bulk often turns out to be very large. As has recently been found, if a limit is put on the weight of the food to be consumed

Column headers

PRODUCTION ACCOUNTS | INCOME AND OUTLAY ACCOUNTS

Groups: COMMODITIES (1–4) · INDUSTRIES (5–8) · CONSUMERS' GOODS AND SERVICES (9–11) · GOVERNMENT PURPOSES (12–14) · INDIRECT TAXES AND SUBSIDIES · INSTITUTIONAL SECTORS

Column labels: 1 FUEL AND POWER; 2 METALS, ENGINEERING, CONSTRUCTION; 3 AGRICULTURE, MANUFACTURING; 4 SERVICES; 5 FUEL AND POWER; 6 METALS, ENGINEERING, CONSTRUCTION; 7 AGRICULTURE, MANUFACTURING; 8 SERVICES; 9 FOOD, DRINK, TOBACCO; 10 CLOTHING AND HOUSEHOLD; 11 OTHER; 12 DEFENSE; 13 HEALTH, EDUCATION, CHILD CARE; 14 OTHER

Account	Item	#	1	2	3	4	5	6	7	8	9	10	11	12	13	14
COMMODITIES	FUEL AND POWER	1	0	0	0	0	590	353	274	476	0	647	94	74	46	41
	METALS, ENGINEERING, CONSTRUCTION	2	0	0	0	0	235	6,077	750	756	0	373	88	637	62	98
	AGRICULTURE, MANUFACTURING	3	0	0	0	0	72	693	4,032	882	4,046	1,363	381	28	147	39
	SERVICES	4	0	0	0	0	281	1,724	1,767	367	1,478	878	2,569	23	266	67
INDUSTRIES	FUEL AND POWER	5	2,686	4	12	0	0	0	0	0	0	0	0	0	0	0
	METALS, ENGINEERING, CONSTRUCTION	6	5	15,349	74	17	0	0	0	0	0	0	0	0	0	0
	AGRICULTURE, MANUFACTURING	7	12	43	11,769	12	0	0	0	0	0	0	0	0	0	0
	SERVICES	8	0	25	4	10,640	0	0	0	0	0	0	0	0	0	0
CONSUMERS' GOODS AND SERVICES	FOOD, DRINK, TOBACCO	9	0	0	0	0	0	0	0	0	0	0	0	0	0	0
	CLOTHING AND HOUSEHOLD	10	0	0	0	0	0	0	0	0	0	0	0	0	0	0
	OTHER	11	0	0	0	0	0	0	0	0	0	0	0	0	0	0
GOVERNMENT PURPOSES	DEFENSE	12	0	0	0	0	0	0	0	0	0	0	0	0	0	0
	HEALTH, EDUCATION, CHILD CARE	13	0	0	0	0	0	0	0	0	0	0	0	0	0	0
	OTHER	14	0	0	0	0	0	0	0	0	0	0	0	0	0	0
INDIRECT TAXES AND SUBSIDIES	INDIRECT TAXES	15	1	49	85	0	53	76	126	604	1,221	471	372	10	20	14
	LESS SUBSIDIES	16	0	0	0	0	-3	0	-257	-111	0	-118	0	0	0	0
INSTITUTIONAL SECTORS	DISTRIBUTION OF PROPERTY INCOME	17	0	0	0	0	101	1,401	1,369	1,899	0	524	0	0	0	0
	PRIVATE SECTOR	18	0	0	0	0	792	4,341	2,408	5,028	0	86	118	718	921	699
	PUBLIC SECTOR	19	0	0	0	0	0	0	0	0	0	0	0	0	0	0
COMMODITIES (replacements)	FUEL AND POWER	20	0	0	0	0	0	0	0	0	0	0	0	0	0	0
	METALS, ENGINEERING, CONSTRUCTION	21	0	0	0	0	0	0	0	0	0	0	0	0	0	0
	AGRICULTURE, MANUFACTURING	22	0	0	0	0	0	0	0	0	0	0	0	0	0	0
INDUSTRIES REPLACEMENTS	FUEL AND POWER	23	0	0	0	0	185	0	0	0	0	0	0	0	0	0
	METALS, ENGINEERING, CONSTRUCTION	24	0	0	0	0	0	184	0	0	0	0	0	0	0	0
	AGRICULTURE, MANUFACTURING	25	0	0	0	0	0	0	312	0	0	0	0	0	0	0
	SERVICES	26	0	0	0	0	0	0	0	416	0	0	0	0	0	0
INDUSTRIES, EXTENSIONS	FUEL AND POWER	27	0	0	0	0	70	0	0	0	0	0	0	0	0	0
	METALS, ENGINEERING, CONSTRUCTION	28	0	0	0	0	0	119	0	0	0	0	0	0	0	0
	AGRICULTURE, MANUFACTURING	29	0	0	0	0	0	0	91	0	0	0	0	0	0	0
	SERVICES	30	0	0	0	0	0	0	0	209	0	0	0	0	0	0
CONSUMERS, REPLACEMENTS	DWELLINGS	31	0	0	0	0	0	0	0	0	0	132	0	0	0	0
	DURABLES	32	0	0	0	0	0	0	0	0	0	227	337	0	0	0
CONSUMERS, EXTENSIONS	DWELLINGS	33	0	0	0	0	0	0	0	0	0	164	0	0	0	0
	DURABLES	34	0	0	0	0	0	0	0	0	0	171	234	0	0	0
GOVT. REPLACEMENTS	ALL SOCIAL CAPITAL	35	0	0	0	0	0	0	0	0	0	0	0	1	42	20
GOVT. EXTENSIONS	ALL SOCIAL CAPITAL	36	0	0	0	0	0	0	0	0	0	0	0	0	44	26
INSTITUTIONAL SECTORS	CHANGES IN ASSETS AND CLAIMS	37	0	0	0	0	-7	-83	-81	-112	0	0	0	0	0	0
	PRIVATE SECTOR	38	0	0	0	0	0	0	0	0	0	0	0	0	0	0
	PUBLIC SECTOR	39	0	0	0	0	0	0	0	0	0	0	0	0	0	0
REST OF THE WORLD ACCOUNT		40	145	665	1,308	347	333	560	1,045	255	296	0	277	120	0	26
TOTAL OUTGOINGS			2,849	16,135	13,252	11,016	2,702	15,445	11,836	10,669	7,041	4,918	4,470	1,611	1,548	1,030

Left-margin account braces: PRODUCTION ACCOUNTS; INCOME AND OUTLAY ACCOUNTS; CAPITAL-TRANSACTION ACCOUNTS.

MATRIX MODEL of the British economy presents the accruals and disbursements for the year 1960 within the four national accounts. These four are here subdivided into 40 groups; in the author's larger model there are 253 such subdivisions. The accounting nature of the model is shown (*color*) for entry No. 10, a consumers' subdivision of the "Production accounts" that summarizes clothing and household transactions. At the intersection of row 10 and column 18 is entered the total amount (4,918 million pounds) spent by consumers on clothing and household items. Column 10, in turn, presents the component parts of this expenditure.

each day, a much more varied diet emerges with no appreciable increase in cost. This problem of narrow formulation illustrates a feature that is characteristic of all complex calculations: mathematical methods are literal methods. They solve problems as they are formulated; it is up to the investigator to see that they are formulated sensibly.

In any decision made under conditions of uncertainty, what was previously a known (or supposedly known) magnitude has been replaced by an entire distribution of magnitudes. The problem is to find out the nature of this distribution and decide how it should influence the decision. Questions of this kind involve the fields of probability and statistics. A classic example is the tossing of heads and tails with a "biased" coin. Under normal circumstances the probability of an ordinary coin's falling heads up at a single throw is, for all practical purposes, 1/2, and the probability of two consecutive heads-up falls, in turn, is 1/4. Obviously a trick coin with two heads would not yield the same probability: the single-throw prospect for heads would improve from 1/2 to 1. Imagine, in place of this brutal

CAPITAL-TRANSACTION ACCOUNTS

			INDUSTRIES, REPLACEMENTS			INDUSTRIES, EXTENSIONS				CONSUMERS, REPLACEMENTS		CONSUMERS, EXTENSIONS		GOVT. REP.	GOVT. EXT.	INSTITUTIONAL SECTORS		CHANGES IN ASSETS AND CLAIMS		REST OF THE WORLD ACCOUNT				
17	18	19	20	21	22	23	24	25	26	27	28	29	30	31	32	33	34	35	36	37	38	39	40	TOTAL INCOMINGS
0	0	0	−6	0	0	38	0	0	0	52	0	0	0	0	0	0	0	0	0	0	0	0	170	2,849
0	0	0	0	339	0	142	174	289	331	262	430	298	737	107	262	646	410	63	274	0	0	0	2,295	16,135
0	0	0	0	0	230	0	0	6	0	0	0	3	0	0	33	0	47	0	0	0	0	0	1,250	13,252
0	0	0	0	0	0	5	4	11	65	1	2	0	60	25	169	0	217	0	1	0	0	0	1,036	11,016
0	0	0	0	0	0	0	0	0	0	0	0	0	0	0	0	0	0	0	0	0	0	0	0	2,702
0	0	0	0	0	0	0	0	0	0	0	0	0	0	0	0	0	0	0	0	0	0	0	0	15,445
0	0	0	0	0	0	0	0	0	0	0	0	0	0	0	0	0	0	0	0	0	0	0	0	11,836
0	0	0	0	0	0	0	0	0	0	0	0	0	0	0	0	0	0	0	0	0	0	0	0	10,669
0	7,041	0	0	0	0	0	0	0	0	0	0	0	0	0	0	0	0	0	0	0	0	0	0	7,041
0	4,918	0	0	0	0	0	0	0	0	0	0	0	0	0	0	0	0	0	0	0	0	0	0	4,918
0	4,255	0	0	0	0	0	0	0	0	0	0	0	0	0	0	0	0	0	0	0	0	0	215	4,470
0	0	1,611	0	0	0	0	0	0	0	0	0	0	0	0	0	0	0	0	0	0	0	0	0	1,611
0	0	1,548	0	0	0	0	0	0	0	0	0	0	0	0	0	0	0	0	0	0	0	0	0	1,548
0	0	1,030	0	0	0	0	0	0	0	0	0	0	0	0	0	0	0	0	0	0	0	0	0	1,030
0	0	0	0	0	1	0	6	6	20	1	7	8	29	0	100	0	125	0	0	0	0	0	0	3,405
0	0	0	0	0	0	0	0	0	0	0	0	0	0	0	0	0	0	0	0	0	0	0	0	−489
0	0	0	0	0	0	0	0	0	0	0	0	0	0	0	0	0	0	0	0	0	0	0	179	5,473
,139	0	1,650	0	0	0	0	0	0	0	0	0	0	0	0	0	0	0	0	0	0	0	0	0	22,900
666	3,624	0	0	0	0	0	0	0	0	0	0	0	0	0	0	0	0	0	0	0	0	0	0	5,874
0	0	0	0	0	0	0	0	0	0	0	0	0	0	0	0	0	0	0	0	−6	0	0	0	−6
0	0	0	0	0	0	0	0	0	0	0	0	0	0	0	0	0	0	0	0	357	0	0	0	357
0	0	0	0	0	0	0	0	0	0	0	0	0	0	0	0	0	0	0	0	240	0	0	0	240
0	0	0	0	0	0	0	0	0	0	0	0	0	0	0	0	0	0	0	0	0	0	0	0	185
0	0	0	0	0	0	0	0	0	0	0	0	0	0	0	0	0	0	0	0	0	0	0	0	184
0	0	0	0	0	0	0	0	0	0	0	0	0	0	0	0	0	0	0	0	0	0	0	0	312
0	0	0	0	0	0	0	0	0	0	0	0	0	0	0	0	0	0	0	0	0	0	0	0	416
0	0	0	0	0	0	0	0	0	0	0	0	0	0	0	0	0	0	0	0	246	0	0	0	316
0	0	0	0	0	0	0	0	0	0	0	0	0	0	0	0	0	0	0	0	320	0	0	0	439
0	0	0	0	0	0	0	0	0	0	0	0	0	0	0	0	0	0	0	0	218	0	0	0	309
0	0	0	0	0	0	0	0	0	0	0	0	0	0	0	0	0	0	0	0	617	0	0	0	826
0	0	0	0	0	0	0	0	0	0	0	0	0	0	0	0	0	0	0	0	0	0	0	0	132
0	0	0	0	0	0	0	0	0	0	0	0	0	0	0	0	0	0	0	0	0	0	0	0	564
0	0	0	0	0	0	0	0	0	0	0	0	0	0	0	0	0	0	0	0	0	293	189	0	646
0	0	0	0	0	0	0	0	0	0	0	0	0	0	0	0	0	0	0	0	0	394	0	0	799
0	0	0	0	0	0	0	0	0	0	0	0	0	0	0	0	0	0	0	0	0	0	0	0	63
0	0	0	0	0	0	0	0	0	0	0	0	0	0	0	0	0	0	0	0	0	0	205	0	275
0	0	0	0	0	0	0	0	0	0	0	0	0	0	0	0	0	0	0	0	0	2,213	−282	0	1,648
0	3,062	0	0	0	0	0	0	0	0	0	0	0	0	0	0	0	0	0	0	0	0	74	0	3,136
0	0	−51	0	0	0	0	0	0	0	0	0	0	0	0	0	0	0	0	0	0	236	0	1	186
0	0	86	0	18	9	0	0	0	0	0	0	0	0	0	0	0	0	0	0	−344	0	0	0	5,146
,473	22,900	5,874	−6	357	240	185	184	312	416	316	439	309	826	132	564	646	799	63	275	1,648	3,136	186	5,146	

First entry (647 million pounds) is the total spent for household heating and lighting: coal, coke, gas, electricity and oil. Negative entry at row 16 (−118 million pounds) represents housing subsidies paid by government. Another entry, at row 18 (86 million pounds), is the total paid in salaries to domestic servants during 1960. Author's larger model deals in more detail not only with the different branches of industry (a 31 × 31 square matrix stands in place of the 4 × 4 square matrix shown here at the intersection of rows 1, 2, 3 and 4 and columns 5, 6, 7 and 8) but also with the consumption, accumulation and foreign transactions of the economy.

kind of bias, a coin so ingeniously contrived that the probability of obtaining a head at a single throw ranges evenly between the limits of 0 and 1. As Pierre Simon de Laplace established with his law of succession, the chance of obtaining a head at each of two throws with such a coin is not 1/4 but 1/3.

What has happened, of course, is that a different distribution of magnitudes has been substituted for the usual distribution. In the real world no such coins exist; however, the real world abounds with opportunities for deci-sions under conditions of uncertainty where a failure to examine the assumptions about the kind of distribution proves to be quite as hazardous as betting blindly against a biased coin.

The combination of theories and facts in the social sciences will produce useful models of real situations. If a model, in turn, is combined with a set of aims, the product that results is a policy. It is because of this, I think, that large quantitative models of national economic systems, intended for practical use, are at present being built in many countries. An economy can be viewed as a system that transforms information into decisions. Today a quantitative economic model, if it is made detailed enough and reliable enough, should be able to provide much useful information for decision-makers.

For the past four years my colleagues and I at the University of Cambridge have been working on such a device, a computable model of the British economy. We now have a working prototype which, although still much in need of improvement, shows that the task is a manageable one. As a first step we constructed a model for a steady state of economic growth starting from a future year that for the moment we have arbitrarily set as 1970 [see illustration on page 285]. This model is based on specific assumptions about the British standard of living in 1970 and about the economy's rate of growth thereafter. The economic consequences of these assumptions are set out as a series of balances. First are the balances of supply and demand for the 31 product groups distinguished in our model. Second are the balances of revenues and costs in the corresponding branches of production. Three others complete the series: the balance of supply and demand for labor, the balance of saving and investment and the balance of the external account (Britain's foreign trade).

The variables in the model are the entries in a square matrix consisting of 253 pairs of rows and columns (each of which represents a balancing account, showing the incomings and outgoings of some branch or sector of the economy), and the prices and quantities associated with these entries [see "Input-Output Economics," by Wassily W. Leontief; SCIENTIFIC AMERICAN Offprint #610]. The entire series of entries we call the "social-accounting matrix," or SAM; a summary presentation of SAM's row-and-column entries appears on the preceding two pages. Working within such a framework at least assures us results

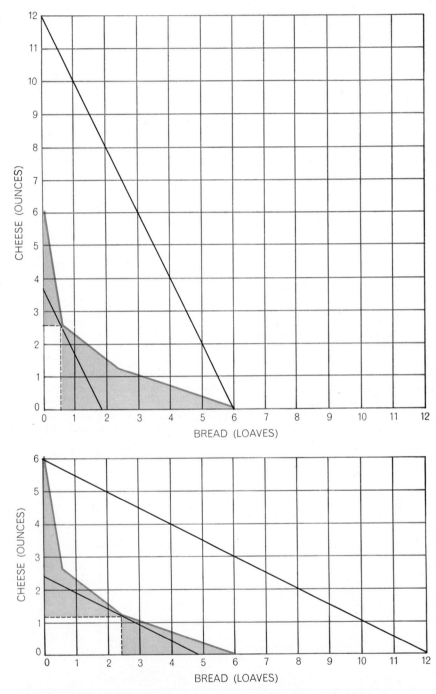

MINIMUM-COST DIET demonstrates that even decisions made under conditions of certainty are not always palatable. The example assumes that three required nutrient factors are present in varying proportions in both bread and cheese (two ounces of cheese, in this case, contain as much protein as six loaves of bread do). Plotting the three proportions on a graph produces a convex boundary (*solid colored line*), any point on which satisfies all constraints regarding nutrient demands. Now the least expensive combination of the two foodstuffs must be found. If 12 ounces of cheese cost the same as six loaves of bread (*upper graph*), the minimum-cost diet is reasonable: more than two ounces of cheese go with every half-loaf of bread. But if the price ratio is reversed (*lower graph*), the minimum-cost diet proves to contain an unacceptable bulk of cheap bread in proportion to expensive cheese.

that are consistent in an arithmetic and accounting sense.

Operating the model involves a computer run. The input required to obtain a set of output balances consists of 5,000 to 6,000 numerical statements; the run involves about 30 million multiplications. The Atlas computer we use needs only 22 seconds to do these multiplications. Indeed, only the development of electronic computers has made macromodels of this kind possible. A generation ago, when the discipline of econometrics was coming into being with the help of desk calculators, such models would have been unthinkable. Twenty-two seconds of work for Atlas is the equivalent of 60 man-years with a desk calculator.

Now that SAM is operating, although much refinement lies ahead, we have begun work on our second task. This is: Given the present state of the British economy, what are the changes that are needed to bring tomorrow's economy, so to speak, more in line with our projection for 1970—the day after tomorrow? Eventually we hope to make these two parts of the model interact.

In this connection, one of the main advantages of economic models is that they can be made to work out the implications of any assumptions we choose to make. We can, for example, establish a "closed" system and observe how this will develop "naturally" in the future; given an initial set of values, the model will trace out the future paths of a number of variables. In moving from today's facts toward 1970's assumptions, however, our interest frequently centers on ways to bring about a state of affairs that does not seem to happen naturally.

There are many such problem sectors: how to reduce unemployment, say, or how to increase the proportion of college and postcollege graduates in the population, or how to avoid recurrent balance-of-payment crises. For each of these cases we must open our model at some point and introduce into it a new feature: a precise statement of aims. The model will then show how the system balances out on the assumption that these aims are met. Meanwhile, as we increase the size of our original model, we have to decide whether it is more practical just to add categories or to set up submodels instead. The submodel solution seems the most promising. It is possible to imagine a decentralized system in which, for instance, the submodel for the fuel and power industries or for financial activities was maintained and operated by fuel or financial specialists who had the necessary knowledge at their fingertips. Another advantage of the submodel method is that situations could be represented that involve changes in the individual branches of production; the fixed input-output relations that are built into a single model effectively rule out such manipulations.

Although SAM was confined to the economic aspects of British society at the start, it has shown an inevitable tendency to spread. In assessing the parts played by labor, capital and invention in producing goods and services, for example, it was necessary to consider not only different skills but also social attitudes toward research and innovation. The former has led us to the study of the education and training systems in which skills are learned, whereas the latter has led us into the field of social psychology. Before the end we may be facing a model of the entire British socioeconomic system.

In the real world such systems may not keep on an even course, either because of an inherent tendency to oscillate or because they have only a limited capacity for recovering from the succession of natural shocks to which they are inevitably subject. But like their biological and engineering counterparts, socioeconomic systems possess automatic control mechanisms (an example of this in economics is the price mechanism). Often, however, these mechanisms do not function very well, partly because they are based on limited aims and partly because they work with limited information. This is why in every country efforts are made, in greater or lesser degree, to design devices that will improve the control mechanisms.

I observed above that combining a model with a set of aims produces a policy. When a policy is combined with control systems, the combination gives rise to a plan of action. The plan in turn combines with events to give all of us our experience of socioeconomic life. This experience feeds back to modify the theories we accept, the facts we consider relevant, the aims that appeal to us and the controls we regard as efficient. By modifying these factors, experience serves to modify our models, our policies and our plans. And so it goes. We can hope that someday, thanks to the tools of mathematics, decisions may come to rest a little more on knowledge and a little less on guesswork and that the world in which we live will function a little better and be less at the mercy of unforeseen events.

38 THE PRACTICE OF QUALITY CONTROL

A. G. DALTON · March 1953

STATISTICAL quality control has been employed to some extent for a quarter of a century, but only recently have the mists surrounding the rather formidable adjective "statistical" begun to clear. And only recently has industry generally come to see the potentialities of such methods for the solution of production problems.

What kind of problems? Let us consider a simple operation such as boiling eggs. Some people like their eggs boiled hard, some soft, some medium. Probably the most common desire is for medium-boiled eggs. Various mechanical egg-timing devices on the market indicate that the generally accepted average time for boiling an egg neither too hard nor too soft is three and a half minutes. However, even if we consistently boil our eggs for precisely that length of time, they don't always turn out medium boiled. Sometimes they are too congealed, at other times too runny.

Undoubtedly variations in the size or weight of eggs have much to do with this variability. Differences in the age of the eggs, in their original temperature, in the number of eggs put into the pot at one time, in the amount of water, in the atmospheric pressure, in the length of time they remain unopened after cooking—all these factors may influence whether they turn out medium boiled or not. If it seemed worth while, we could go to some lengths to find out how much these many variables might be controlled to produce more uniformly cooked eggs. We might establish a number of control points for individual variables: the size or weight of the eggs, their temperature immediately before boiling, and so forth. Some controls might have an important influence on the quality of the end product, others a

negligible effect; all would cost something in time, effort and money. Through such experiments we can weigh the costs of controlling undesirable variables against the benefits. Will we enjoy our eggs more? Will we, if we are restaurateurs, sell more? Will we have fewer complaints and fewer eggs returned to the kitchen?

This problem of achieving a desired uniformity of product or service is a common one in industry, applying to baked plastics and machined gears, to toasters and bicycles, to railroad schedules and telephones. In industry, of course, the problem is much more complicated than in the home, but essentially it yields to the same methods we might have used to determine why eggs boiled for equal lengths of time don't always come out alike.

THE NEED FOR statistical quality control derives from the inability of hens and manufacturers to make two or more things exactly alike, however hard they may try. It is these differences among units of product that cause trouble. If large enough, particularly in materials or subassembly parts, the variations may make fabrication or assembly difficult, costly or impossible. Even if small enough to go undetected, they may still lead to customer dissatisfaction. This dissatisfaction may mean only that the customer, a creature of habit, is disturbed by changes in product. Such changes may have nothing to do with actual quality, but they are all part of the problem.

Differences in product may come from one or both of two general types of causes. One kind is the normal, chance variability of materials, machines, temperatures, atmospheric conditions, temperatures, man-

ual operations, measuring devices and other factors entering into the manufacture of an item. These variations are inherent to some degree in all processes converting raw materials into useful products, and it usually costs something to reduce their effects. The other category covers other-than-chance causes of variations, as opposed to expected random fluctuations. This group includes extraordinary variations in materials or machine operation, interruptions of the power supply, operators' carelessness or lack of skill, rough handling, poor organization of the work, and so on. Harmful combinations of chance causes also may be included in this category. Once identified, the other-than-chance causes can often be eliminated at little or no expense.

The first step in the problem of improving the uniformity of a product is to determine what kinds of differences are occurring and to what extent. The only way to find out is by inspection, which is a problem in itself. To inspect every single item produced is often impracticable, sometimes would be damaging to the product and in any case would still leave the reliability of the results open to question, because of inevitable errors of measurement and judgment. Hence inspection is often restricted to random samples, and the results are interpreted by application of the laws of probability. The effect of human error is reduced and reliability greatly improved by this method.

Further complicating the problem is the fact that every product has many characteristics, in each of which some differences will occur. Pencils, for instance, have weight, length, thickness, color, hardness of graphite, hardness of wood and other properties. The only

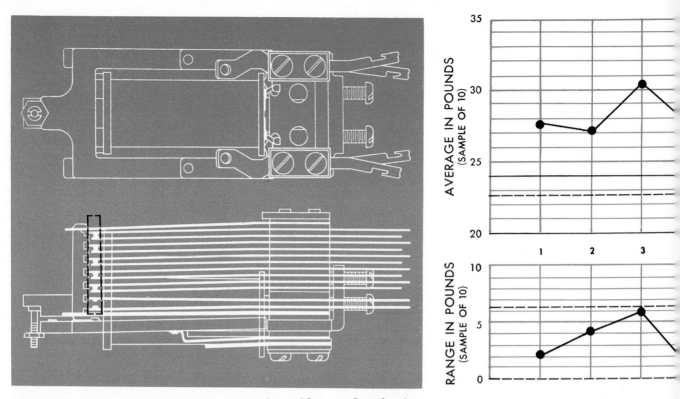

CHART is used to control the strength of the welds which fasten the contacts to the springs of an electric relay. At the left is a drawing of the relay from the top and side; the contacts are within the dotted black line at the far left. The curves at the right reflect the changes in the average strength of welds made by one machine over a period of 18 hours. Once an hour a sample of 10 welded contacts is taken from the output of each machine for testing. The test consists of measuring the number of pounds of force required to

variable of concern to consumers may be the hardness of the point. To the manufacturer, however, irregularities in length may be sufficient to disrupt packaging; variations in the wood may introduce tooling difficulties. Fortunately product characteristics are not all of equal importance, and their variabilities are not all likely to be of the same magnitude. With reliable inspection reports before us, we can proceed to sort them out and by statistical analysis find out what, if anything, we should do about the variations in our product.

IN ITS simplest form this analysis means plotting the inspection results on charts and comparing their distribution pattern with a normal law curve, in which the values are distributed uniformly around the average. The analyst selects upper and lower control limits, such that if any inspection results fall outside the limits, it is assumed that other-than-chance causes are affecting the process. Once in a great while this assumption may be incorrect, but the margin of error is comfortingly small.

Thus from the charts we can see whether variations in product derive from chance causes inherent in the process or from other-than-chance causes. If all are chance variations, but some are large enough to trouble us or our customers, we have only two choices of action. We can live with the condition so long as we can sell the product; or we can change the process, weighing the penalties of not changing it against the often considerable costs of improving it. If, as is more likely, many of the troublesome variations are due to other-than-chance causes, then a series of exploratory actions should be undertaken.

Control points, involving some kind of informative inspection and record keeping, can be set up at almost every step of production from raw materials to finished product, to find out at what stage things are going wrong. Since even the simplest product may undergo many stages, the cost of analyzing the product at every stage might well be prohibitive. Hence engineering judgment must step in to select the most promising points of control; i.e., those which will result in the largest saving of waste. After experiments on the usefulness of various control points, the most effective are retained as routine inspection stations.

We shall consider here three important applications of statistical quality control: (1) to give warning of abnormal behavior in a process, (2) to diagnose the underlying causes of a wasteful process, and (3) to establish economical inspection plans.

AS AN EXAMPLE of the first, let me cite a process in the manufacture of a product used in the Bell Telephone System. The product is the electric relays, made in the millions by the Western Electric Company, whose function is to make, break or transfer electrical circuits in telephone offices. These relays have a number of contact springs, which are pulled together or separated as the relay is electrically energized or released. The contact points, often of semiprecious metal, are electrically welded to the ends of the relay springs and must withstand millions of shocks and slight rubbings as the relay releases and operates over a normal lifetime. If one of these points broke off, it might interrupt telephone service and mean a major job of replacement or repair. Specifications have been established defining the strength of a satisfactory weld in terms of the minimum pull required to break a contact point loose from the spring. The problem is, how can we be sure that the process is consistently producing welds that meet this specification?

At each welding machine we establish a control station which will let us know immediately when the machine or any other element in the process falters. The operations at a control station are as follows. A sample of 10 units is selected from each hour's production. The welded contacts are torn from the springs, and the amount of force required in each instance is recorded. The results are plotted on a chart to provide a continuing record of two things: (1) the average strength of each 10-unit sample,

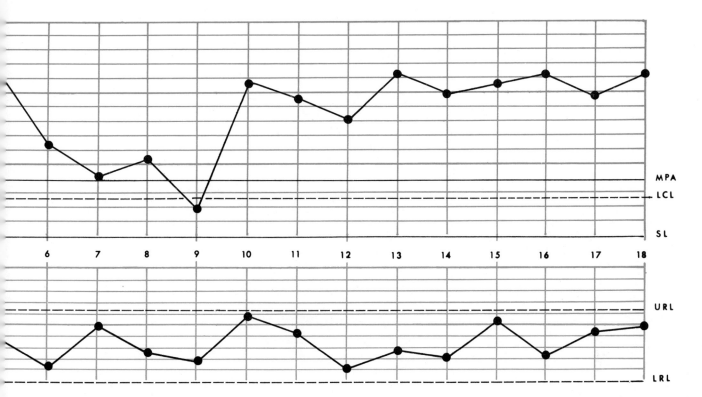

tear each contact from its spring. The curve at the top indicates how the average strength of the sample welds varied. The letters MPA at the far right stand for the minimum permissible average for the process; LCL, for the lower control limit; SL for the specification mini- mum limit for a single weld. At the ninth hour the aver- age strength of the sample welds fell below the lower control limit; corrective action was then taken. The bot- tom curve shows range of the samples. URL stands for upper range control limit; LRL for lower range limit.

and (2) the range from the strongest to the weakest unit. Statistical control lim- its also are put on the chart. The control limits are so calculated that if any aver- age value falls outside them, it indicates that the margin between the average strength and the minimum required is too narrow. The control limits for range are so calculated that when units begin to fall outside these limits, this also in- dicates that other-than-chance causes have intervened. Only when both the average and the range stay within their respective control limits is there ade- quate assurance that the welds made during the period in which the sample was taken are satisfactory. Whenever an average or range value of a sample falls outside the control limits, we know that we must stop the welding machine and look for the causes.

At this stage of manufacture the spring plus welded contact has some cash value, but the value is very small in comparison with the cost of the com- pleted relay. Therefore, the cost of maintaining a system of control at each welding machine represents a very small insurance payment against the much greater penalties that would be paid if defective parts were not detected and went on into the finished product. More- over, so long as the samples are statis- tically satisfactory, we need not inter- rupt operation of the process or reset the welding machines, which means a saving

in time, labor and the useful life of the machines.

THIS EXAMPLE shows how statis- tical quality control can provide re- liable warning signals on a production line. The following example will illus- trate the second application: how statis- tical methods are used to diagnose and eliminate the causes of abnormally low production yields in a simple product— in this case carbon inserts for a tiny protector block. These blocks are used to protect home telephones from light- ning discharge or an accidental power contact with the telephone lines. It was found that in the manufacture of these inserts the basic cause of rejections was irregularity in their dimensions. Several operations are involved, including mold- ing the carbon, two separate firings, ce- menting in a porcelain cup and gauging for size. The major losses occurred dur- ing inspection after the second firing, in which about 60 per cent of the inserts were rejected for shrinkage and softness. A more informative inspection procedure was instituted, and statistical analyses of the results showed that the trouble was in the average value rather than in the range of values after this step in the process. To raise the average, changes were made in processing the carbon powder and in the molding dies. The re- sult was a harder insert, with a more favorable average length and no harmful

increase in the spread between the high- est and lowest values. The changes re- duced losses after the second firing from about 60 per cent to .2 per cent.

For the statistical analyses six experi- mental control points had been estab- lished. Four of these were kept, to give early warnings of any temporary hitch in the process. The total time spent in investigating and statistically analyzing the problem was less than three months. The results: a reduction of waste from 75 to 15 per cent, an increase in yield from 5,000 satisfactory units a day to 25,000, and reduction of the labor force by three operators and five inspectors.

Experience indicates that these spec- tacular results from a relatively inex- pensive study are by no means excep- tional. Almost limitless opportunities exist throughout industry for securing impressive benefits from the use of sta- tistical quality control in diagnosing harmful irregularities.

A THIRD area for the use of statisti- cal quality control is in planning economical inspection procedures. In- spection per se adds nothing to a prod- uct and is often regarded as a necessary evil. In many instances it gets this bad name from being used so extensively as a sorting operation to separate bad units from good. Occasionally this may be economical, but not often. It is economi- cal only when a manufacturing plant is unable to produce a high enough percentage of acceptable items, and the cost of improving the facilities to a point where sorting operations are unnecessary exceeds the cost of sorting. In sorting operations as much or even more inspection time is usually expended on good items as on bad, giving rise to the age-old question, "Why don't we confine inspections to the bad units and stop wasting money looking at the good ones?" While statistical quality control cannot entirely eliminate such waste, it

can often substantially reduce inspection costs on "good product."

When a plant's output regularly contains an acceptably small percentage of defects, inspection can safely be limited to those operations necessary to verify maintenance of this performance. Sampling inspections of this kind are essentially informative. They can be made very sensitive to any change in the manufacturing process and will thus provide timely warnings of any imminent degradation of product. They are

also far cheaper than sorting inspections, since they involve looking at or measuring a relatively small percentage of the output.

It is important to recognize, however, that any sampling plan involves the risk that the sample may not be truly representative. If the quality of the sample is below that of the lot from which it comes, the lot may be rejected unnecessarily. On the other hand, if the sample is better than the lot as a whole, the consumer may get a product of marginal

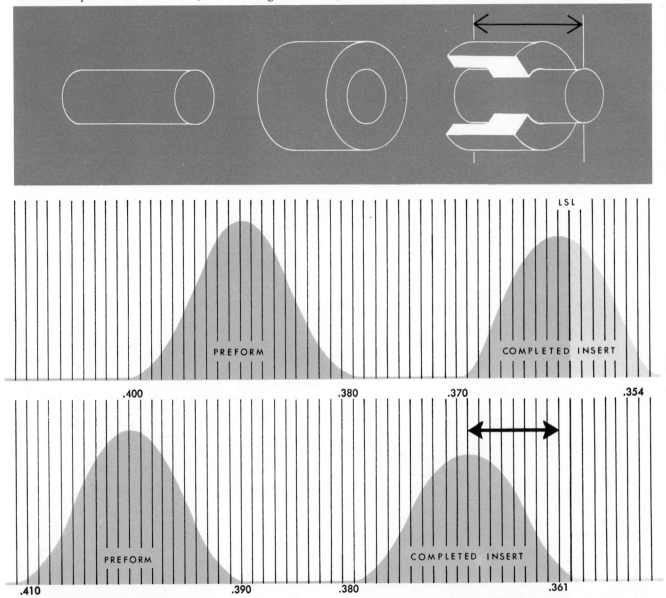

DISTRIBUTION CURVES were used to study the production of carbon inserts for protector blocks, used to protect telephones from lightning. At the upper right is a cutaway drawing of the insert; its length is indicated by the black arrow above it. The insert is made with a carbon rod (*top left*) which is given two firing operations and is then cemented into a porcelain cup (*top center*). The over-all length of the insert is given in fractions of an inch by the horizontal coordinate of the chart. The two curves in the top chart show the distribution of the lengths of sample inserts taken from one month's production. The curve labeled "preform" gives the distribution of the lengths before the inserts were

fired; the curve labeled "completed insert" gives the distribution after firing. The letters LSL at the top of the chart stand for lower specification limit. It was found that a large number of completed inserts were rejected because their lengths were below this limit (*light blue area on curve at upper right of chart*). By altering the manufacturing process so that the distribution of the preform inserts was moved to the left, as shown at the bottom, the distribution of the completed inserts was also shifted to a more favorable position and the rejects were sharply curtailed. The black arrow above the curve at lower right shows the distance the distribution pattern of the completed inserts was shifted.

quality. Sampling inspections can be used to protect the "lot" quality or the "average" quality. In either case random samples are drawn from specific lots, and a lot is accepted when the number of defects in the sample is no greater than an allowable number. That number is based on a calculated risk chosen as tolerable. If the allowable number of defects is exceeded, each unit in the lot is then inspected individually.

Sometimes a system of double sampling is used. Instead of accepting or rejecting a lot on the basis of a single sample, the inspector first takes a smaller sample and applies a stricter test: *i.e.*, it must have fewer defective items. If this standard is met, the lot is accepted, and the inspection effort is minimal. If the first sample does not meet this strict test, a second sample is taken, usually of substantially larger size, and for both samples combined the allowable number of defective items is larger. Double sampling, properly applied, usually results in a net saving in the number of units that have to be inspected.

Double sampling in turn may be extended to multiple or sequential sampling, using a larger series of sampling trials. However, in many instances the greater complexity, the chances for misapplication and the extra bookkeeping tend to cancel the theoretical economies of sequential sampling.

In any of these sampling procedures the relationship between lot sizes and sample sizes is not constant. From a small lot one needs a relatively larger percentage sample than from a large one. When a process consistently produces well above the quality requirement, it is usually advantageous to sample large lots, because the chances of a lot's being rejected are small. When the process is less consistent or dependable it may be better to test small lots.

When sampling plans are properly applied, the economies in inspection time are not the only benefits. Sampling inspections also provide a continuing historical record of the capabilities of a process or a machine, which may be helpful to engineers planning the production of similar products. Such records can help consumers as well, for when a producer can furnish evidence that the quality of a product is consistently controlled at the specified level, his customers can reduce or eliminate their own inspections of incoming products.

STATISTICAL quality control is invaluable for giving warning of impending trouble, and its warnings must be heeded. However drastic it may seem to have to curtail or stop production and search for the remedy, it must be remembered that the cheapest thing to do about an unsatisfactory product is not to make it.

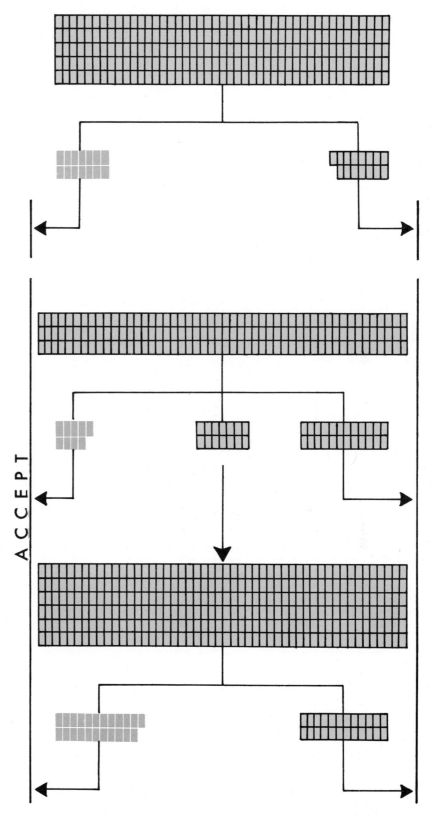

SINGLE AND DOUBLE SAMPLING are illustrated by this chart. In single sampling (*top*) a sample of 225 items might be taken from a much larger lot. If 14 or fewer were defective, the lot would be accepted; if 15 or more were defective, it would be rejected. In double sampling (*bottom*) the initial sample would be smaller, perhaps 150 items. If 9 or fewer were defective, the lot would be accepted; if 24 or more were defective, it would be rejected. If, however, from 10 to 23 were defective, a second sample, in this case one twice as large as the first, would be taken. Then if 23 or fewer defective units were found in the first and second samples combined, the lot would be accepted; if 24 or more were found, it would be rejected.

39 THE THEORY OF GAMES

OSKAR MORGENSTERN · May 1949

THE analogy between games of strategy and economic and social behavior is so obvious that it finds wide expression in the thinking and even the language of business and politics. Phrases such as "a political deal" and "playing the stock market" are familiar reflections of this. The connection between games and these other activities is more than superficial. When they are examined by the methods of modern mathematics, it becomes evident that many of the forms of economic and social behavior are strictly identical with—not merely analogous to—games of strategy. Thus the mathematical study of games offers the possibility of new insights and precision in the study of economics.

The theory of probability arose from a study of lowly games of chance and from the desire of professional gamblers to find ways of taking advantage of the odds. Far more difficult problems are presented by games of strategy such as poker, bridge and chess. In these games, where the outcome no longer depends on chance alone but also on the acts of other players and on their expectations of one's own present and future acts, a player must choose among relatively complex strategies. Mathematically, these problems remained not only unsolved, but even untouched.

Gottfried Wilhelm Leibnitz, the German philosopher and mathematician, seems to have recognized that a study of games of strategy would form the basis of a theory of society. On the other hand, many efforts along quite different lines were made by philosophers and economists to provide a theory for "rational behavior" for individuals, business corporations, or even for entire communities.

Such a theory must be quantitative, which means that it must ultimately assume a mathematical character. A theory of games fulfilling these requirements would take into account that participants in a game vary in information and intelligence, that they have various expectations about the other players' behavior, and that different paths of reaching their goal may be open to them. The theory must also allow for the fact that the position of a player (or, equivalently, of an economic individual or a firm) is often adversely affected if his opponent finds out his intentions. The player has to take steps to protect himself against this contingency, and the theory must indicate how he should proceed most efficiently—and what his countermeasures would mean to the other players.

Why should such a theory be of interest to the sociologist and, in particular, to the economist? Does not the economics of today have an adequate model in mechanics, with its notions of forces, of equilibrium and stability? Physics is, indeed, at the bottom of current efforts to provide a statement of rational economic behavior, whether it is mathematically formulated or not. But many important situations that arise at all levels in economics find no counterpart whatever in physics.

A typical example is the fixing of wage rates between workers and employers when both groups have found it to their advantage to combine into unions and associations. Current economics cannot tell us, except in a general manner, under what circumstances such combinations will arise, who will profit, and by how much. The two groups have opposing interests, but do not have separate means to pursue their contrary aims. They must finally come to some agreement, which may turn out to be more advantageous to one side than to the other. In settling their differences they will feint, bluff, use persuasion; they will try to discover each other's strategies and prevent discovery of their own. Under such circumstances a theory of rational behavior will have to tell a participant how much a given effort will be worth in view of the obstacles encountered, the obstacles being the behavior of his opponents and the influence of the chance factor.

Monopoly and monopolistic market forms—that is, trading among only a few individuals or firms on one side of the market at least—are characteristic of all social economies. They involve serious feuds and fights, a very different picture from the general, "free" competition with which classical economic theory usually deals. On the orthodox theory, the individual is supposed to face prices and other conditions that are fixed, and is supposed to be in a position to control all the variables, so that his profit or utility depends only on his own actions. Actually, however, when there are only a few individuals, or many individuals organized into a few combinations, the outcome never depends on the actions of the individual alone. No single person has control of all the variables, but only of a few.

The case of an individual acting in strict isolation can be described mathematically as a simple maximum problem —that is, finding the behavior formula that will yield the maximum value or return. The cases involving combinations are of an entirely different mathematical and logical structure. Indeed, they present a peculiar mixture of maximum problems, creating a profound mathematical question for which there is no parallel in physical science or even in classical mathematics.

Yet this is the level at which the problem of economic behavior needs to be attacked. Clearly it is far more realistic to investigate from the outset the nature of the all-pervading struggles and fights in economic and social life, rather than to deal with an essentially artificial, atomistic, "free" competition where men are supposed to act like automatons confronted by rigidly given conditions.

THE theory of games defines the solution of each game of strategy as the distribution or distributions of payments to be made by every player as a function of all other individuals' behavior. The solution thus has to tell each player, striving for his maximum advantage, how to behave in all conceivable circumstances, allowing for all and any behavior of all the other players. Obviously this concept of a solution is very comprehensive, and finding such a solution for each type of game, as well as computing it numerically for each particular instance, poses enormous mathematical difficulties. The theory makes important use of mathematical logic, as well as combinatorics (the study of possible ways of combining and ordering objects) and set theory (the techniques for dealing with any collection of objects which have one or more exactly specified properties in common). This domain of modern mathematics is one of exceptional rigor. But it is believed that great mathematical discoveries are required to make a break-through into the field of social phenomena.

A single individual, playing alone, faces the simplest maximum problem; his best strategy is the one that brings him the predetermined maximum gain. Consider a two-person game: Each player wishes to win a maximum, but he can do this only at the expense of the other. This situation results in a zero-sum game, since the sum of one player's gains and the other's losses (a negative number) is zero. One player has to design a strategy that will assure him of the maximum advantage. But the same is true of the other, who naturally wishes to minimize the first player's gain, thereby maximizing his own. This clear-cut opposition of interest introduces an entirely new concept, the so-called "minimax" problem.

SOME games have an optimal "pure" strategy. In other words, there is a sequence of moves such that the player using it will have the safest strategy possible, whatever his opponent does. His position will not deteriorate even if his strategy is found out. In such "strictly determined" games, every move—and hence every position resulting from a series of moves— is out in the open. Both players have complete information. The mathematical expression of this condition is that the function describing the outcome of a game has a "saddle point." This mathematical term is based on an analogy with the shape of a saddle, which can be regarded as the intersection of two curves at a single point. One curve in a saddle is the one in which the rider sits; the other is the one that fits over the horse's back and slopes down over its sides. The seat of the saddle represents the "maximum" curve, and its low point is the "maximin." The curve that straddles the horse's back is the "minimum" curve, and its high point is the "minimax." The point at which the two curves meet at the center of the saddle is the "saddle point." In the theory of games, the somewhat more special saddle point is the intersection of two particular strategies.

The mathematical values of the strategies involved in a hypothetical game of this kind are represented in the diagram on this page. This shows a simple game between two players, A and B, each of whom has available three possible strategies. There are nine possible combinations of moves by A and B. The numbers in the boxes represent A's gains or losses

for all combined strategies and, since this is a zero-sum game, their negatives represent B's losses or gains. A's minimax strategy is A-2, because if he follows that sequence of moves, he is sure to win at least two units no matter what B does. Similarly, B's minimax strategy is B-1, because then he cannot possibly lose more than two units whatever A's plan of action. If a spy informed A that B was planning to use B-1, A could make no profit from that information. The point where the A-2 row intersects the B-1 column is the saddle point for this game.

It may seem that B has no business playing such a game, since he must lose two units even with his best strategy, and any other strategy exposes him to even heavier loss. At best he can win only a single unit, and then only if A makes a mistake. Yet all strictly determined games are of this nature. A simple example is ticktacktoe. In perfectly played ticktacktoe every game would result in a tie. A more complex example is chess, which has a saddle point and a pure strategy. Chess is exciting because the number of possible moves and posi-

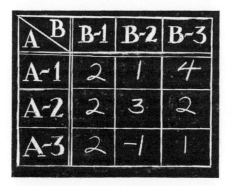

GAME OF STRATEGY between two players, each with three possible strategies, has nine possible results. Numbers in boxes represent A's gains or losses for each combination of plays by both players.

tions is so great that the finding of that strategy is beyond the powers of even the best calculating machines.

Other two-person, zero-sum games, however, have no single best possible strategy. This group includes games ranging from matching pennies to bridge and poker—and most military situations. These games, in which it would be disastrous if a player's strategy were discovered by his opponent, are not strictly determined. The player's principal concern is to protect his strategy from discovery. Do safe and good strategies exist for "not strictly determined" games, so that their choice would make the games again strictly determined? Can a player in such a game find strategies other than "pure" strategies which would make his behavior completely "rational"? Mathematically speaking, does a saddle point always exist?

It does, and the proof was originally established in 1927 by the mathematician John von Neumann, the originator of the theory of games, now at the Institute for Advanced Study in Princeton. He used various basic tools of modern mathematics, including the so-called fixed-point theorem of the Dutch mathematician L. E. J. Brouwer. Von Neumann proved, by a complex but rigorous application of this theorem to the theory of games, that there is a single "stable" or rational course of action that represents the best strategy or saddle point even in not strictly determined games.

This principle can also be demonstrated in practical terms. Observation shows that in games where the discovery of a player's plan of action would have dangerous consequences, he can protect himself by avoiding the consistent use of a pure strategy and choosing it with a certain probability only. This substitution of a statistical strategy makes discovery by the opponent impossible. Since the player's chief aim must be to prevent any leakage of information from himself to the other player, the best way to accomplish this is not to have the information oneself. Thus, instead of choosing a precise course of action, the various possible alternatives are considered with different probabilities.

It is in the nature of probability that individual events cannot be predicted, so that the strategy actually used will remain a secret up to the decisive moment, even to the player himself, and necessarily to his opponent as well. This type of indecision is a well-known empirical fact. Wherever there is an advantage in not having one's intentions found out—obviously a very common occurrence—people will be evasive, try to create uncertainty in the minds of others, produce doubts, and at the same time try to pierce the veil of secrecy thrown over their opponents' operations.

The example *par excellence* is poker. In a much simpler form, this type of behavior is illustrated in the game of matching pennies. Here the best strategy is to show heads or tails at random, taking care only to play each half the time. Since the same strategy is available to the opponent, both players will break even if they play long enough and both know this principle. The calculation of the best strategy grows in difficulty as the number of possible moves increases: *e.g.*, in the Italian game called morra, in which each player shows one, two or three fingers and simultaneously calls out his guess as to the sum of fingers shown by himself and his opponent, a player has nine possible strategies. His safest course is to guess a total of four fingers every time, and to vary his own moves so that out of every 12 games he shows one finger five times, two fingers four times and three fingers three times. If he plays according to this mixture of strategies, he will at least break even, no matter what his opponent does.

LET us apply these principles to a simple economic problem. Suppose that two manufacturers are competing for a given consumer market, and that each is considering three different sales strategies. The matrix on this page specifies the possible values of the respective strategies to manufacturer A: This situation does not have a single best strategy. If A chooses strategy A-1, B can limit his profit to one unit by using strategy B-2 or B-3; if A chooses strategy A-2 or A-3, B can deprive him of any profit by choosing strategy B-1. Thus each manufacturer stands to lose if he concentrates on a single sales technique and his rival discovers his plan. Analysis shows that A will lose unless he uses a combination of A-1, A-2 and A-3, each a third of the time. On the other hand, if manufacturer B fails to employ his best mixed strategy—B-1 a ninth of the time, B-2 two ninths of the time, and B-3 two thirds of the time—his competitor will gain. These mixed strategies are the safest strategies. They should be used whenever each manufacturer does not know what the other will do.

An example which illustrates in statistical terms many of the conflicts of choices involved in everyday life is the famous story of Sherlock Holmes' pursuit by his archenemy, Professor Moriarty, in Conan Doyle's story, "The Final Problem." Holmes has planned to take a train from London to Dover and thence make his escape to the Continent. Just as the Dover train is pulling out of Victoria Station, Moriarty rushes on the platform and the two men see each other. Moriarty is left at the station. He charters a special train to continue the chase. The detective is faced with the problem of outguessing his pursuer. Should he get off at Canterbury—the only intermediate stop—or go all the way to Dover? And what should Moriarty do? In effect, this situation can be treated as a rather unusual version of matching pennies—a "match" occurring if the two men decide to go to the same place and meet there. It is assumed that such a meeting would mean the death of Sherlock Holmes; therefore it has an arbitrarily assigned value of 100 to Moriarty. If Holmes goes to Dover and makes his way to the Continent, it is obviously a defeat for the professor, but—also obviously—not as great a defeat as death would be for the detective. Hence, a value of minus 50 to Moriarty is given to this eventuality. Finally, if Holmes leaves the train at Canterbury and Moriarty goes on to Dover, the chase is not over and the temporary outcome can be considered a draw. According to the theory of games, the odds are 60 to 40 in favor of the professor.

In the story, of course, this game is played only once: Sherlock Holmes, deducing that Moriarty will go to Dover, gets off at Canterbury and watches triumphantly as the professor's pursuing train speeds past the intermediate station. If the game were continued, however, Holmes' look of triumph would hardly be justified. On the assumption that Moriarty persisted in the chase, calculations indicate that the great detective was actually as good as 40 per cent dead when his train left Victoria Station!

The theory of games has already been applied to a number of practical problems. Situations similar to that of Holmes are being analyzed in that branch of operational research which deals with military tactics, the possible courses of action being various dispositions of troops or combinations of measures and countermeasures. The handling of the more complex situations that exist in economics is expected to require the aid of calculating machines. For example, two competing automobile manufacturers may each have a large number of strategies involving the choice of various body designs, the addition of new accessories, the best times to announce new models

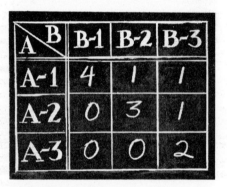

BUSINESS RIVALRY between two firms with three strategies each again diagrams A's possible gains. No single strategy is best if the opponent discovers it; hence the rivals must use a mixture of all three.

and price changes, and so on. It has been estimated that the calculations for a game in which one manufacturer had 100 possible strategies and his competitor had 200 (a not uncommon situation) would take about a year on an electronic computer.

If we now make the transition to games involving three or more persons, a fundamentally new phenomenon emerges—namely, the tendency among some players to combine against others, or equivalently in markets to form trade unions, cartels and trusts. Such coalitions will be successful only if they offer the individual members more than they could get acting separately. Games where that is the case are called essential. Coalitions will then oppose each other in the manner of individual players in a two-person game. A coalition will have a value for the players who form it, and they may therefore require payments or "compensations" from newcomers who want to enter the coalition and share in its proceeds. As a rule a great deal of bargaining will precede the determination of the system of distribution of gains or profits among the members of the coalition.

Basically, the formation of a coalition expresses the fundamental tendency toward monopoly, which is thus found to be deeply characteristic of social and economic life. Indeed, Adam Smith already had noted the tendency of businessmen to "conspire" against the common welfare, as he stated it, by getting together into groups for better exploitation. Important chapters of American economic history deal with the efforts of government to break conspiracies of various kinds in order to limit the power of trusts and other amalgamations. When these are broken—if at all—they tend to arise again, so a continuous watchfulness is necessary.

The powerful forces working toward monopoly ought therefore to be at the very center of economic studies. They should replace the preoccupation with a nonexistent pure or free competition where nobody has any perceptible influence on anything, and where all data are assumed to be immutably given. Since this is the imaginary setup from which current economic theory starts, it encounters insuperable difficulties when it enters the realm of monopolistic competition. It is not surprising, therefore, that classical economics has failed to yield a general theory that embraces all economic situations.

THE approach to the coalition problem in the theory of games can be shown by a three-person situation in which it is assumed that a player can achieve a gain in any given play only if he joins with one other player. The gains and losses that would result for the individual players in the case of each possible coalition are shown in the diagram on page 303. Thus if A and B form a coalition, each gains a half unit and C loses one unit. What keeps the players in the game is that they all stand a chance of profit; each player's problem is to succeed in forming a coalition with one of the other two on any given deal. This simplified situation illustrates in essence much of the conflict that occurs in modern economic life.

Now the important characteristic of this type of game is that there is no single "best" solution for any individual player. A, for example, can gain as much by forming a coalition with C as with B. Therefore all three of the possible distributions of payments, taken together, must be viewed as the solution of this three-person game.

There are, of course, many other distribution schemes that might be considered by the players. For example, one of the partners in a coalition could make a deal with the third player whereby both improved their positions (the third player reducing his losses) at the expense of the other partner. What is to prevent the participants in the game from considering all these other possibilities?

The question can be answered by introducing the concept of "domination." In mathematical terminology the various possible schemes for distribution of payments are called "imputations." One imputation is said to dominate another if it is clearly more advantageous to all the players in a given coalition. It is found, as shown in the three-person game described above, that the imputations belonging to a solution do not dominate each other: in this case all three imputations have an equal chance of being chosen; none is most advantageous to the players in each coalition. While it is extremely difficult to prove mathematically that such a solution would exist for every game with arbitrarily many players, the principle can be expected to hold true.

Now it is also found that while the imputations belonging to the solution do not dominate each other, individually they are not free from domination by imputations outside the solution. In other words, there are always outside schemes from which some of the players could profit. But any and every imputation outside the solution is dominated by one belonging to the solution, so that it will be rejected as too risky. It will be considered unsafe not to conform to the accepted standard of behavior, and only one of the imputations which are part of the solution will materialize.

These examples give an idea of the great complexity of social and economic organization. In this realm "stability" is far more involved than it is in the physical sciences, where a solution is usually given by a number or a set of numbers. In essential games, in economics and in warfare, there is instead a set of alternatives, none of which is clearly better than another or all others. One imputation in a set is not more stable than any other, because every one may be threatened by one outside the solution. But each has a certain stability because it is protected by other potential imputations in the solution against upsets from outside. Collectively they eliminate the danger of revolutions. The balance is most delicate, however, and it becomes more sensitive as the number of players increases. These higher-order games may have many solutions instead of a single one, and while there is no conflict within an individual solution, the various solutions or standards of behavior may well conflict with one another.

This multiplicity of solutions may be interpreted as a mathematical formula-

tion of the undisputed fact that on the same physical background of economic and social culture utterly different types of society can be established. Within each society, in turn, there is possible considerable variation in the distribution of income, privileges and other advantages—which corresponds to the multiplicity of imputations or distribution schemes in a single solution in a game.

The theory also yields insight into even more delicate social phenomena. Although it assumes that every player has full information, discrimination may exist: two players may make a third player "tabu," assigning him a fixed payment and excluding him from all negotiations and coalitions. Yet this arrangement need not lead to complete exploitation of the third player. In practical economic life, for example, cartels do not annihilate all outside firms, although it would not be a technically difficult operation. Rather, in deference to socially accepted standards of behavior they allow certain outsiders a share in the industry, so as not to attract undue at-

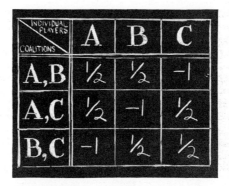

COALITION GAME with three players produces still another matrix. Here gains or losses to players resulting from various possible coalitions are shown in vertical columns. Player must form partnership to win.

tention—and to be able to point out to the government and the public that "competition" exists in the particular industry.

It is surprising and extremely significant that, although the theory of games was developed without any specific consideration of such situations, the fact that they exist was derived from general theorems by purely mathematical methods. Furthermore, the theory shows—again purely mathematically—that certain privileges, even if anchored in the rules of a game (or of a society), cannot always be maintained by the privileged if they come into conflict with the accepted standard of behavior. A privileged person or group may have to give up his entire "bonus" in order to survive economically.

These and many other implications can be derived from the study of simple

three-person games. Games of more than three players provide further interesting insights—but at the price of great and, in many cases, still insuperable mathematical difficulties. The almost unimaginable complexity involved may be illustrated by poker, the game which, above all others, furnishes a model for economic and social situations. The subtleties of poker and the countless number of available strategies—*e.g.*, the technique of purposely being caught bluffing now and then so that future bluffs may be successful—prevent the thorough analysis that would be necessary to throw light on corresponding problems in practical everyday affairs. The matrix of possible strategies for poker is so large that it has not even been calculated, much less drawn. Consider a radically simplified version of the game which assumes a deck of only three cards, a one-card, no-draw hand, only two players, three bids between them (the first player gets two, the second one), and no overbetting. Even this watered-down version of poker involves a matrix of 1,728 boxes, and computing a single best possible strategy for each player to an accuracy of about 10 per cent might require almost two billion multiplications and additions.

BUT even with its present limitations the theory of games has made it possible to analyze problems beyond the scope of previous economic theory. Besides those already indicated, the problems now being explored include the application of the mathematics for a game involving seven persons to the best location of plants in a particular industry, the relation between labor unions and management, the nature of monopoly.

The initial problem in the theory of games was to give precision to the notion of "rational behavior." Qualitative or philosophical arguments have led nowhere; the new quantitative approach may point in the right direction. Applications are still limited, but the approach is in the scientific tradition of proceeding step by step, instead of attempting to include all phenomena in a great general solution. We all hope eventually to discover truly scientific theories that will tell us exactly how to stabilize employment, increase national income and distribute it adequately. But we must first obtain precision and mastery in a limited field, and then proceed to increasingly greater problems. There are no short cuts in economics.

THE USE AND MISUSE OF GAME THEORY

40

ANATOL RAPOPORT · December 1962

We live in an age of belief—belief in the omnipotence of science. This belief is bolstered by the fact that the problems scientists are called on to solve are for the most part selected by the scientists themselves. For example, our Department of Defense did not one day decide that it wanted an atomic bomb and then order the scientists to make one. On the contrary, it was Albert Einstein, a scientist, who told Franklin D. Roosevelt, a decision maker, that such a bomb was possible. Today, in greater measure than ever before, scientists sit at the decision makers' elbows and guide the formulation of problems in such a way that scientific solutions are feasible. Problems that do not promise scientific solutions generally tend to go unformulated. Hence the faith in the omnipotence of science.

The self-amplifying prestige of science among decision makers has been further amplified in this period by the popularization of a scientific aid to the task of decision making itself. This is game theory—a mathematical technique for the analysis of conflict first propounded by the late John Von Neumann in 1927 and brought to wide notice by Von Neumann and Oskar Morgenstern in 1944 in a book entitled *Theory of Games and Economic Behavior*. Now, game theory is an intellectual achievement of superlative originality and has opened a large new field of research. Unfortunately this is not the way game theory has been embraced in certain quarters where Francis Bacon's dictum "Knowledge is power" is interpreted in its primitive, brutal sense. The decision makers in our society are overwhelmingly preoccupied with power conflict, be it in business, in politics or in the military. Game theory is a "science of conflict." What could this new science be

but a reservoir of power for those who get there fastest with the mostest?

A thorough understanding of game theory should dim these greedy hopes. Knowledge of game theory does not make any one a better card player, businessman or military strategist, because game theory is not primarily concerned with disclosing the optimum strategy for any particular conflict situation. It is concerned with the logic of conflict, that is, with the theory of strategy. In this lies both the strength and the limitation of the technique. Its strength derives from the powerful and intricate mathematical apparatus that it can bring to bear on the strategic analysis of certain conflict situations. The limitations are those inherent in the range of conflicts to which this analysis can be successfully applied.

No one will doubt that the logic of strategy does not apply to certain conflicts. For example, there are no strategic considerations in a dogfight. Such a conflict is better thought of as being a sequence of events, each of which triggers the next. A growl is a stimulus for a countergrowl, which in turn stimulates the baring of teeth, sudden thrusts and so on. Signals stimulate postures; postures stimulate actions. Human quarrels, where symbolic rather than physical injuries are mutually stimulated, are frequently also of this sort. Conflicts of this kind can be called fights. The motivation in a fight is hostility. The goal is to eliminate the opponent, who appears as a noxious stimulus, not as another ego, whose goals and strategies, even though hostile, must be taken into account. Intellect, in the sense of calculating capacity, foresight and comparison of alternative courses of action, need not and usually does not play any part in a fight.

Game theory applies to a very different type of conflict, now technically called a game. The well-known games such as poker, chess, ticktacktoe and so forth are games in the strict technical sense. But what makes parlor games games is not their entertainment value or detachment from real life. They are games because they are instances of formalized conflict: there is conflict of interest between two or more parties; each party has at certain specified times a range of choices of what to do prescribed by the rules; and the outcome representing the sum total of choices made by all parties, and in each case involving consideration of the choice made by or open to the other parties, determines an assignment of pay-offs to each party. By extension, any conflict so conducted falls into the category of games, as defined in game theory. Nor does it matter whether the rules are results of common agreement, as in parlor games, or simply of restraints imposed by the situation. Even if no rules of warfare are recognized, a military situation can still be considered as a game if the range of choices open to each opponent at any given stage can be exactly specified.

Let us see how chess and poker each fulfill these requirements. In chess the conflict of interest is, of course, implied

Bark and counterbark

in each player's desire to win. The range of choices consists for each player of all the legal moves open to him when it is his turn to move. The outcome is determined by all the choices of both players. The pay-offs are usually in psychological satisfaction or dissatisfaction. In poker the situation is much, but not entirely, the same. The choices are (at specified times) whether or not to stay in; which cards, if any, to throw off; whether or not to raise and by how much and so on. The outcome of each round is the designation of one of the players as the winner. Pay-offs are usually in money.

Poker differs from chess in one important respect. In a poker game there is an extra (invisible) player, who makes just one choice at the beginning of each round. This choice is important in determining the outcome, but the player who makes it has no interest in the game and does not get any pay-off. The player's name is Chance, and his choice is among the nearly 100 million trillion trillion trillion trillion trillion (10^{68}) arrangements of the deck at the beginning of each round. Chance makes no further choices during the round; the rest is up to the players. One can argue that Chance continues to interfere, for example by causing lapses of memory, directing or misdirecting the attention of the players and so forth. But game theory is concerned only with what perfect players would do.

Although Chance may thus play a part, the game as defined by game theory is clearly distinguished from gambling as treated by the much older and better-known mathematics of gambling. The latter has considerable historical importance, since it is in the context of gambling theory that the mathematical theory of probability was first developed some 300 years ago. This theory has since been incorporated into all branches of science where laws of chance must be taken into account, as in the physics of small particles, genetics, actuarial science, economics, experimental psychology and the psychology of mass be-

havior. For the gambler the mathematical theory of probability makes possible a precise calculation of the odds. This often calls for considerable mathematical sophistication. It is irrelevant, however, to the playing of the game; it is relevant only in deciding whether or not to play. The gambling problem is solved when the odds of the possible outcomes have been calculated. If there are several such outcomes, the gains or losses associated with each are multiplied by the corresponding probabilities and the products are added (with proper signs attached). The resulting number is the expected gain; that is, what can be reasonably expected over a long series of bets when the bets are placed according to the odds offered. A rational gambler is one who accepts or offers the gambles in such a way as to maximize his expected gain. All gambling houses are rational gamblers. That is why they stay in business.

The inadequacy of gambling theory as a guide in a true game is shown clearly in the well-known fact that the rational gambler is likely to meet with disaster in a poker game. The rational gambler will make his decisions strictly in accordance with the odds. He will never bluff, and he will bet in proportion to the strength of his hand. As a result he will betray his hand to his opponents, and they will use the information to his disadvantage.

Gambling theory is of even less use to the ticktacktoe player. Ticktacktoe is a game in which there is a best move in every conceivable situation. Chance, we know, is not involved at all in some games. To be sure, chance is involved in all card games but, as the example of poker shows, something else is involved, namely a strategic skill that is not part of gambling theory at all.

Consider what goes on in the mind of a chess player: If I play Knight to Queen's Bishop's 4, thus threatening his rook, he can reply Rook to King's 2, check. In that case I have the choice of either interposing the Bishop or King

The omnipotent scientist

to Queen's 1. On the other hand, he can ignore the threat to the rook and reply with a counterthreat by Bishop to Knight's 5, in which case I have the following choices . . .

The stronger the player, the longer this chain of reasoning is likely to be. But because of the limitations on how much we can hold in our minds at one time, the chain of reasoning must stop somewhere. For the chess player it stops a few moves ahead of the situation at hand, at a set of possible new situations among which he must choose. The one situation that will actually occur depends partly on his own choices and partly on the choices available to the opponent (over whom the first player has no control). Two decisions are involved in the choice of action: first, which situations may actually occur? Second, which of all those situations is to be preferred?

Now, these questions can be answered without ambiguity if the game is thought out to the end. In a game such as chess, however, it is out of the question to foresee all the alternatives to the end (except where checkmates or clear wins are foreseen as forced). The good chess player then does the next best thing: he calculates the relative values of the various possible future positions according to his experience in evaluating such positions. How then does he know which position will be actually arrived at, seeing that he controls only his own moves, not those of the opponent? Chess players recognize two chess philosophies.

Bite and counterbite

Escalated conflict

Playing the stock market or a slot machine involves no game theory

One is "playing the board," the other is "playing the opponent."

Playing the opponent makes chess akin to psychological warfare. The great chess master José Capablanca tells in his memoirs of an incident that illustrates the drama of such conflicts. In a tournament in 1918 he was matched with Frank J. Marshall, the U.S. champion. Marshall offered an unexpected response to Capablanca's accustomed opening attack, and the play proceeded not at all in line with the usual variations of this opening. Capablanca suspected that Marshall had discovered a new variation in the attack and had kept this knowledge as a secret weapon, to be used only at the most propitious time, namely in an international tournament with the eyes of the chess world on his play against a truly formidable opponent. Capablanca had been picked as the victim of the new strategy.

"The lust of battle, however," Capablanca continues, "had been aroused within me. I felt that my judgment and skill were being challenged by a player who had every reason to fear both (as shown by the records of our previous encounters), but who wanted to take advantage of the element of surprise and of the fact of my being unfamiliar with a

Psychological warfare in chess

Advanced psychological warfare in chess

thing to which he had devoted many nights of toil.... I considered the position then and decided that I was in honor bound ... to accept the challenge."

He did and went on to win the game. Capablanca's decision was based on taking into account his opponent's thought processes, not only those pertaining to the game but also Marshall's ambitions, his opinion of Capablanca's prowess, his single-mindedness and so on. Capablanca was playing the opponent.

Although the drama of games of strategy is strongly linked with the psychological aspects of the conflict, game theory is not concerned with these aspects. Game theory, so to speak, plays the board. It is concerned only with the logical aspects of strategy. It prescribes the same line of play against a master as it does against a beginner. When a stragetic game is completely analyzed by game-theory methods, nothing is left of the game. Ticktacktoe is a good example. This game is not played by adults because it has been completely analyzed. Analysis shows that every game of ticktacktoe must end in a draw. Checkers is in almost the same state, although only exceptionally good players know all the relevant strategies. A generation ago it was thought that chess too was approaching the "draw death." But new discoveries and particularly the introduction of psychological warfare into chess, notably by the Russian masters, has given the game a reprieve. Nevertheless H. A. Simon and Allen Newell of the Carnegie Institute of Technology have seriously predicted that within 10 years the world's chess champion will be an electronic computer. The prediction was made more than three years ago. There is still a good chance that it will come true.

Is the aim of game theory, then, to reveal the logic of every formalized game so that each player's best strategy is discovered and the game as a whole is killed because its outcome in every instance will be known in advance? This is by no means the case. The class of games for which such an analysis can

be carried through even in principle, let alone the prodigious difficulty of doing it in practice, is only a very small class.

Games of this class are known as games of perfect information. They are games in which it is impossible to have military secrets. Chess is such a game. Whatever the surprise Marshall thought he had prepared for Capablanca, he was not hiding something that could not be discovered by any chess player. He only hoped that it would be overlooked because of human limitations.

Not all games are games of perfect information. Poker is definitely not such a game. The essence of poker is in the circumstance that no player knows the entire situation and must be guided by guesses of what the situation is and what the others will do. Both chess and poker are "zero-sum" games in the sense that what one player wins the other or others necessarily lose. Not all games are of this sort either.

To understand the differences among these various classes of games, let us look at some examples from each class. The essential idea to be demonstrated is that each type of situation requires a different type of reasoning.

An improbably elementary situation in business competition will serve to illustrate the class of games of perfect information. The situation is otherwise a two-person zero-sum game. The Castor Company, an old, established firm, is being squeezed by Pollux, Incorporated, an aggressive newcomer. The Castor people guide their policies by the balance sheet, which is projected one year ahead. The Pollux people also guide their policies by a balance sheet, not their own but the Castor Company's. Their aim is to put Castor out of business, so they consider Castor's losses their gains and vice versa, regardless of what their own balance shows. Both are faced with a decision, namely whether or not to undertake an extensive advertising campaign. The outcome depends on what both firms do, each having control over only its own decision. Assume, however, that both firms have enough information to know what the outcomes will be, given both decisions [*see matrix at left in bottom illustration on page 308*].

From Castor's point of view, a better or a worse outcome corresponds to each of its decisions, depending on what Pollux does. Of the two worse outcomes associated with Castor's two possible decisions, $3 million in the red and $1 million in the red (both occurring if Pollux advertises), clearly the second is preferred. Castor's manager now puts himself into the shoes of Pollux' manager and asks what Pollux would do if Castor chose the lesser of the two evils. Clearly Pollux would choose to advertise to prevent the outcome that would be better for Castor ($1 million in the black). Getting back into his own shoes, Castor's manager now asks what he would do knowing that this was Pollux' decision. Again the answer is advertise. Exactly similar reasoning leads Pollux to its decision, which is advertise. Each has chosen the better of the two worse alternatives. In the language of game theory this is called the minimax (the maximum of the minima). This solution is always prescribed no matter how many alternatives there are, provided that the gains of one are the losses of the other and provided that what is the "best of the worst" for one is also the "best of the worst" for the other. In this case the game has a saddle point (named after the position on the saddle that is lowest with respect to front and back and highest with respect to right and left). Game theory shows that whenever a saddle point exists, neither party can improve the outcome for itself (or worsen it for the other). The outcome is forced, as it is in ticktacktoe.

The next situation is quite different. It is a two-person zero-sum game, again involving the choice of two strategies on each side. In this case, however, the choices must be made in the absence of the information that guides the opponent's decision. Appropriately this is a military situation enveloped in the fog of battle.

A commander of a division must decide which of two sectors to attack. A breakthrough would be more valuable in one than in the other, but the more valuable sector is also likely to be more strongly defended. The defending commander also has a problem: which sector to reinforce. It would seem obvious that the more critical sector should be reinforced at the expense of the secondary one. But it is clear to the defending commander that the problem is more complicated. Secrecy is of the essence. If he does exactly what the enemy expects him to do, which is to reinforce the critical sector, will this not be to the enemy's advantage? Will not the attacker, knowing that the important sector is more strongly defended, attack the weaker one, where a breakthrough, even though less valuable, is more certain? Should the defender therefore not do the opposite of what the enemy expects and reinforce the secondary sector, since that

is where the enemy, wishing to avoid the stronger sector, will probably attack? But then is not the enemy smart enough to figure this out and so attack the primary center and achieve a breakthrough where it counts?

The attacking commander is going through the same tortuous calculations. Should he attack the secondary sector because the primary one is more likely to be strongly defended or should he attack the primary one because the enemy expects him to avoid it?

In despair the attacking commander calls in a game theorist for consultation. If the game theorist is to help him, the

general must assign numerical values to each of the four outcomes; that is, he must estimate (in relative units) how much each outcome is "worth" to him. He assigns the values shown in the top illustration on the next page. Working with these figures, the game theorist will advise the general as follows: "Roll a die. If ace or six comes up, attack sector 1, otherwise attack sector 2."

If the defending commander assigns the same values (but with opposite signs, since he is the enemy) to the four outcomes, his game theorist will advise him to throw two pennies and reinforce sector 1 if they both come up heads,

Game theory in "Tosca": Tosca double-crosses Scarpia

Scarpia derives satisfaction from the thought of what is going to happen

Tosca and Cavaradossi discover the double double cross

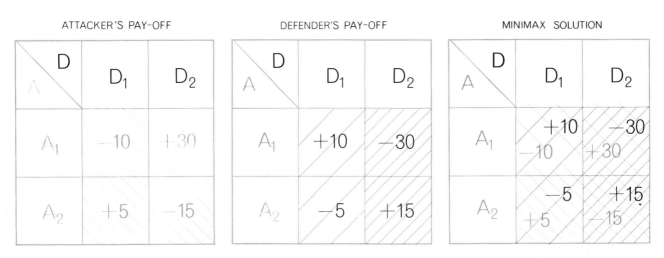

ATTACKER'S PAY-OFF   DEFENDER'S PAY-OFF   MINIMAX SOLUTION

TWO-PERSON ZERO-SUM GAME of an attacking (*A*) and a defending commander (*D*), in which neither possesses the information that guides his opponent's decisions, is summarized in these three matrices. The first commander has the choice of attacking a primary sector (*A₁*) or a secondary sector (*A₂*). The matrix at left shows the values he assigns to the four possibilities. The second commander has the choice of defending either sector. The matrix at center shows his assigned values. As the number of diagonal lines in each matrix square indicates, the first commander should decide by chance, using two-to-one odds in favor of the secondary sector; likewise for the defending commander, except that the odds are three to one. These results are combined in the matrix at right.

otherwise he should reinforce sector 2.

The solutions seem bizarre, because we think of tossing coins to make decisions only in matters of complete indifference. To be sure, a tossed-coin decision is sometimes used to settle an argument, but we do not think of such decisions as being rational and do not hire experts to figure them out. Nevertheless, the game theorists' decisions are offered not only as rational decisions but also as the best possible ones under the circumstances.

To see why this is so, imagine playing the game of button-button. You hide a button in one hand and your opponent tries to guess which. He wins a penny if he guesses right and loses a penny if he guesses wrong. What is your best pattern of choices of where to hide the button in a series of successive plays? You will certainly not choose the same hand every time; your opponent will quickly find this out. Nor will you alternate between the two hands; he will find this out too. It is reasonable to conclude (and it can be proved mathematically) that the best pattern is no pattern. The best way to ensure this is to abdicate your role as decision maker and let chance decide for you. Coin tossing as a guide to strategy is in this case not an act of desperation but a rational policy.

In the button-button game the payoffs are exactly symmetrical. This is why decisions should be made by a toss of a fair coin. If the pay-offs were not symmetrical—for example, if there were more advantage in guessing when the coin was in the right hand—this bias would have to be taken into account. It would be reflected in letting some biased chance device make the decision. Game theory provides the method of computing the bias that maximizes the long-run expected gain.

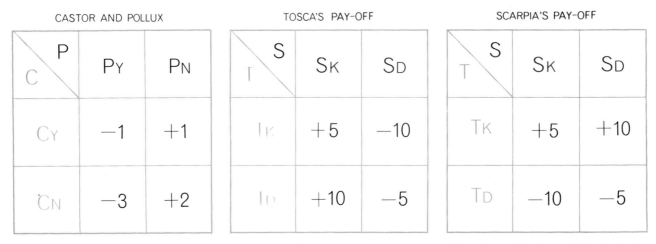

CASTOR AND POLLUX   TOSCA'S PAY-OFF   SCARPIA'S PAY-OFF

ZERO-SUM AND NONZERO-SUM GAMES are represented in these three game-theory matrices. The matrix at left is that of the two-person zero-sum game of perfect information discussed in the text. The matrix tabulates the results for Castor Company (in millions of dollars) of any combination of decisions; e.g., if Castor and Pollux, Incorporated, both advertise (*Cy and Py*), Castor loses $1 million. For Pollux, which will decide on the basis of the effect on Castor, this is a positive pay-off. Tosca and Scarpia are involved in a nonzero-sum game (also discussed in the text), that is, a gain for one does not imply a loss for the other. Tosca's line of reasoning can be determined from the matrix at center: if she keeps her bargain with Scarpia (*Tk*), then she loses everything if he double-crosses her (*Sd*); her gain is greatest and her loss least if she double-crosses him (*Td*). Scarpia, as the matrix at right indicates, reasons along the same line, in reverse. They both lose equally; if they had trusted each other, they would have gained equally.

The attacker's game theorist, then, has figured out that the attacker stands the best chance if he allows chance to decide, using two-to-one odds in favor of sector 2. This is the meaning of rolling a die and allowing four sides out of six to determine the second sector. This is the best the attacker can do against the best the defender can do. The defender's best is to let chance decide, using three-to-one odds in favor of sector 2. Game theory here prescribes not the one best strategy for the specific occasion but the best mixture of strategies for this kind of occasion. If the two commanders were confronted with the same. situation many times, these decisions would give each of them the maximum pay-offs they can get in these circumstances if both play rationally.

At this point one may protest that it is difficult, if not impossible, to assign numerical values to the outcome of real situations. Moreover, identical situations do not recur, and so the long-run expected gain has no meaning. There is much force in these objections. We can only say that game theory has gone just so far in baring the essentials of strategic conflict. What it has left undone should not be charged against it. In what follows some further inadequacies of game theory will become apparent. Paradoxically, in these inadequacies lies most of the value of the theory. The shortcomings show clearly how far strategic thinking can go.

In the next class of games to be illustrated there are choices open to the two parties where the gain of one does not imply loss for the other and vice versa. Our "nonzero-sum" game is a tale of lust and betrayal. In Puccini's opera *Tosca* the chief of police Scarpia has condemned Tosca's lover Cavaradossi to death but offers to save him in exchange for Tosca's favors. Tosca consents, the agreement being that Cavaradossi will go through a pretended execution. Scarpia and Tosca double-cross each other. She stabs him as he is about to embrace her, and he has not given the order to the firing squad to use blank cartridges.

The problem is to decide whether or not it was to the best advantage of each party to double-cross the other. Again we must assign numerical values to the outcome, taking into account what each outcome is worth both to Tosca and to Scarpia [*see two matrices at right in bottom illustration on opposite page*].

The values, although arbitrary, present the situation reasonably. If the bargain is kept, Tosca's satisfaction of getting her lover back is marred by her surrender to the chief of police. Scarpia's satisfaction in possessing Tosca will be marred by having had to reprieve a hated rival. If Tosca double-crosses Scarpia and gets away with it, she will win most (+ 10) and he will lose most (− 10), and vice versa. When both double-cross each other, both lose, but not so much as each would have lost had he or she been the sucker. For example, the dying Scarpia (we assume) derives some satisfaction from the thought of what is going to happen just before the final curtain, when Tosca rushes to her fallen lover and finds him riddled with bullets.

Let us now arrive at a decision from Tosca's point of view: whether to keep the bargain or to kill Scarpia. Tosca has no illusions about Scarpia's integrity. But she is not sure of what he will do, so she considers both possibilities: If he keeps the bargain, I am better off double-crossing him, since I will get Cavaradossi without Scarpia if I do and Cavaradossi with Scarpia if I don't. If he double-crosses me, I am certainly better off double-crossing him. It stands to reason that I should kill him whatever he does.

Scarpia reasons in exactly the same way: If she keeps the bargain, I am better off double-crossing her, since I will get rid of Cavaradossi if I do and have to put up with him if I don't. If she double-crosses me, I certainly should see to it that I am avenged. The execution, therefore, must go on.

The result is the denouement we know. Tosca and Scarpia both get − 5. If they had trusted each other and had kept the trust, each would have got + 5.

The shortcoming of strategic thinking becomes obvious in this example. Evidently more is required than the calculation of one's own pay-offs if the best decisions are to be made in conflict situations. Game theory can still treat the foregoing case satisfactorily by introducing the notion of a coalition. If Tosca and Scarpia realize that the interests of both will be best served if both keep the bargain, they need not both be losers. Coalitions, however, bring headaches of their own, as will be seen in the next example.

Abe, Bob and Charlie are to divide a dollar. The decision as to how to divide it is to be by majority vote. Abe and Bob form a coalition and agree to split the dollar evenly between them and so freeze Charlie out. The rules of the game allow bargaining. Charlie approaches Bob

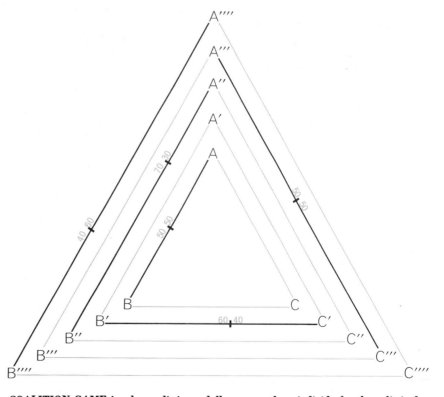

COALITION GAME involves splitting a dollar among three individuals; the split is decided by majority vote. Abe and Bob (*A and B*) form a coalition that excludes Charlie (*C*). Charlie then (*C'*) offers Bob (*B'*) 60 cents of the dollar, and so on. Any division is inherently unstable because two can always do better for themselves than can three, and two can enforce any division. No game-theory strategy will guarantee a division satisfactory to all.

Maximum in the military application of game theory

Minimum

of the worst outcomes. When both choose the minimax, neither firm can improve its position. Had one of the generals used such a decision, he would have been clearly at a disadvantage. Military secrecy introduces an element of randomness to confound the enemy and brings in a different kind of reasoning. Such reasoning would have been useless in the Castor and Pollux example, because in their case each knew what the other's best decision had to be, and this knowledge made no difference to either. The difference between the two situations is immediately apparent to the game theorist. In the first case the minimax choice of one player is also the minimax choice of the other, in the second case it is not.

Consider the Tosca-Scarpia game. Here both parties have the same minimax choice, which, in fact, they choose. The outcome is bad for both. Why is this? Again the answer is clear to the game theorist. Tosca and Scarpia were playing the game as if it were a zero-sum game, a game in which what one party wins the other necessarily loses. If we examine the pay-offs, we find that this is not the case. Both parties could have improved their pay-offs by moving from the minimax solution to the coalition solution (keeping the bargain and getting + 5 each). Life would be simple if advantage in conflicts could always be obtained by forming and keeping proper coalitions. But the dilemma plaguing Abe, Bob and Charlie deprives us of that hope also. Moreover, both the Tosca-Scarpia game and the divide-the-dollar game reveal that decisions based on calculated self-interest can lead to disaster.

Whether game theory leads to clear-cut solutions, to vague solutions or to impasses, it does achieve one thing. In bringing techniques of logical and mathematical analysis to bear on problems involving conflicts of interest, game theory gives men an opportunity to bring conflicts up from the level of fights, where the intellect is beclouded by passions, to the level of games, where the intellect has a chance to operate. This is in itself no mean achievement, but it is not the most important one. The most important achievement of game theory, in my opinion, is that game-theory analysis reveals its own limitations. Because this negative aspect is far less understood than the positive aspect, it will be useful to delve somewhat deeper into the matter.

The importance of game theory for decision making and for social science can be best understood in the light of the

with a proposition. He offers Bob 60 cents of the dollar if Bob will shift his vote to freeze Abe out. Abe does not like this arrangement, so he offers Bob 70 cents to shift his vote again to freeze Charlie out. Bob is about to rejoice in his good fortune, which he attributes to his bargaining shrewdness, when he notices that Abe and Charlie are off in a corner. Bob is shrewd enough to guess what they are discussing, and he is right. They are discussing the folly of respectively getting 30 cents and nothing when they have the power to freeze Bob out and split the dollar between them. In fact, they do this. Bob now approaches Abe hat in hand and offers him 60 cents if he will come back. The question is: Should Abe accept the offer?

The game-theory solutions to problems of this sort are extremely involved and need not be pursued here. Instead let us try to summarize in general terms the values and limitations of the game-theory approach to human conflict.

The value of game theory is not in the specific solutions it offers in highly simplified and idealized situations, which may occur in formalized games but hardly ever do in real life. Rather, the prime value of the theory is that it lays bare the different kinds of reasoning that apply in different kinds of conflict.

Let us go back to our examples and compare them. The decisions made by Castor and Pollux were clear-cut, and they were the best decisions on the basis of the knowledge at hand. As we have seen, both firms were guided by the principle of the minimax, choosing the best

history of science. Scientists have been able to avoid much futile squandering of effort because the very foundations of science rest on categorical statements about what cannot be done. For example, thermodynamics shows that perpetual-motion machines are impossible. The principles of biology assert the impossibility of a spontaneous generation of life and of the transmission of acquired characteristics; the uncertainty principle places absolute limits on the precision of certain measurements conducted simultaneously; great mathematical discoveries have revealed the impossibility of solving certain problems.

Absolute as these impossibilities are, they are not absolutely absolute but are so only in certain specific contexts. Progress in science is the generalization of contexts. Thus the conservation of mechanical energy can be circumvented by converting other forms of energy into mechanical energy. The simpler conservation law is violated, but it is re-established in a more general thermodynamic context. In this form it can again be seemingly violated, but it is again re-established in the still broader context of $E = mc^2$. Angles can be mechanically trisected by instruments more complicated than the straightedge and the compass. Life can probably be synthesized, but not in the form of maggots springing from rotting meat; acquired characteristics can probably be genetically transmitted, but not by exercising muscles.

The negative verdicts of science have often been accompanied by positive codicils. The power conferred by science, then, resides in the knowledge of what cannot be done and, by implication, of what can be done and of what it takes to do it.

The knowledge we derive from game theory is of the same kind. Starting with the simplest type of game, for example two-person zero-sum games with saddle points, we learn from game-theory analysis that the outcome of such games is predetermined. This leads to a verdict of impossibility: neither player can do better than his best. Once these bests are discovered, it is useless to play such a game. If war were a two-person zero-sum game with a saddle point, the outcome of each war could conceivably be calculated in advance and the war would not need to be fought. (The conclusion that wars need to be fought because they are not two-person zero-sum games with saddle points is not warranted!)

Examining now the two-person zero-sum game without a saddle point, we

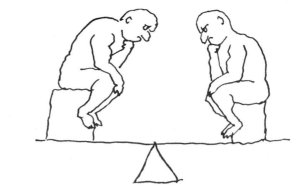

Strategic thinking in a two-person zero-sum situation with a saddle point

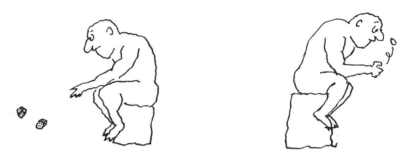

Strategic thinking in a two-person zero-sum situation without a saddle point

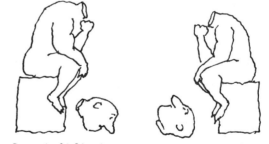

Strategic thinking in a two-person nonzero-sum situation

Strategic thinking in a three-person constant-sum situation with a coalition

Communication is a prerequisite for the resolution of conflict

arrive at another verdict of impossibility: It is impossible to prescribe a best strategy in such a game. It is still possible, however, to prescribe a best mixture of strategies. The meaning of a strategy mixture and the advantage of using it can be understood only in a certain context, namely in the context of an expected gain. This in turn requires that our concept of preference be defined with a certain degree of specificity. To choose the best strategy in a saddle-point game it is necessary only to rank-order the preferences for the possible outcomes. To choose the best strategy mixture an interval scale (like that of temperature) must be assigned to our preferences. Unless this more precise quantification of preferences can be made, rational decisions cannot be made in the context of a game without a saddle point.

I have often wondered to what extent decision makers who have been "sold" on game theory have understood this last verdict of impossibility, which is no less categorical than the verdict on squaring the circle with classical tools. I have seen many research proposals and listened to long discussions of how hot and cold wars can be "gamed." Allowing for the moment that hot and cold wars are zero-sum games (which they are not!), the assignment of "utilities" to outcomes must be made on an interval scale. There is the problem. Of course, this problem can be bypassed, and the utilities can be assigned one way or another, so that we can get on with the gaming, which is the most fun. But of what practical use are results based on arbitrary assumptions?

That is not all. By far the most important conflicts that plague the human race do not fit into the two-person zero-sum category at all. The Tosca-Scarpia game and the Abe-Bob-Charlie game are much more realistic models of human conflicts, namely dramas, in which individuals strive for advantage and come to grief. In these games there are neither pure nor mixed strategies that are best in the sense of guaranteeing the biggest pay-offs under the constraints of the game. No argument addressed individually to Tosca or to Scarpia will convince either that it is better to keep the bargain than to double-cross the other. Only an argument addressed to both at once has this force. Only collective rationality will help them to avoid the trap of the double double cross.

Similarly we can tell nothing to Abe, Bob or Charlie about how to behave to best advantage. We can only tell them collectively to settle the matter in accordance with some pre-existing social norm. (For example, they can take 33 cents apiece and donate one to charity.) This solution is based on an ethical principle and not on strategic considerations.

The role of social norms in games with more than two players was not missed by Von Neumann and Morgenstern. The importance of honesty, social responsibility and kindred virtues has been pointed out by sages since the dawn of history. Game theory, however, gives us another perspective on these matters. It shows how the "hardheaded" analysis of conflicts (with which game theory starts) comes to an impasse, how paradoxical conclusions cannot be avoided unless the situation is reformulated in another context and unless other, extra-game-theory concepts are invoked. Thus acquaintance with these deeper aspects of game theory reveals that the poker game is not the most general or the most sophisticated model of conflict, nor the most relevant in application, as professional strategists often implicitly assume.

Game theory, when it is pursued beyond its elementary paradox-free formulations, teaches us what we must be able to do in order to bring the intellect to bear on a science of human conflict. To analyze a conflict scientifically, we must be able to agree on relative values (to assign utilities). We must learn to be perceptive (evaluate the other's assignment of utilities). Furthermore, in order to engage in a conflict thus formalized, we must be able to communicate (give a credible indication to the other of how we assign utilities to outcomes). At times we must learn the meaning of trust, or else both we and our opponents will invariably lose in games of the Tosca-Scarpia type. At times we must be able to convince the other that he ought to play according to certain rules or even that he ought to play a different game. To convince the other we must get him to listen to us, and this cannot usually be done if we ourselves do not listen. Therefore we must learn to listen in the broadest sense of listening, in the sense of assuming for a while the other's world outlook, because only in this way will we make sense of what he is saying.

All these skills are related not to know-how but to wisdom. It may happen that if we acquire the necessary wisdom, many of the conflicts that the strategy experts in their professional zeal insist on formulating as battles of wits (or, worse, as battles of wills) will be resolved of their own accord.

Another prerequisite is the assignment of utilities to outcomes

41

THE MATHEMATICS
OF COMMUNICATION

WARREN WEAVER · July 1949

HOW do men communicate, one with another? The spoken word, either direct or by telephone or radio; the written or printed word, transmitted by hand, by post, by telegraph, or in any other way—these are obvious and common forms of communication. But there are many others. A nod or a wink, a drumbeat in the jungle, a gesture pictured on a television screen, the blinking of a signal light, a bit of music that reminds one of an event in the past, puffs of smoke in the desert air, the movements and posturing in a ballet—all of these are means men use to convey ideas.

The word communication, in fact, will be used here in a very broad sense to include all of the procedures by which one mind can affect another. Although the language used will often refer specifically to the communication of speech, practically everything said applies equally to music, to pictures, to a variety of other methods of conveying information.

In communication there seem to be problems at three levels: 1) technical, 2) semantic, and 3) influential.

The technical problems are concerned with the accuracy of transference of information from sender to receiver. They are inherent in all forms of communication, whether by sets of discrete symbols (written speech), or by a varying signal (telephonic or radio transmission of voice or music), or by a varying two-dimensional pattern (television).

The semantic problems are concerned with the interpretation of meaning by the receiver, as compared with the intended meaning of the sender. This is a very deep and involved situation, even when one deals only with the relatively simple problems of communicating through speech. For example, if Mr. X is suspected not to understand what Mr. Y says, then it is not possible, by having Mr. Y do nothing but talk further with Mr. X, completely to clarify this situation in any finite time. If Mr. Y says "Do you now understand me?" and Mr. X says "Certainly I do," this is not necessarily a certification that understanding has been achieved. It may just be that Mr. X did not understand the question. If this sounds silly, try it again as "Czy pan mnie rozumie?" with the answer "Hai wakkate imasu." In the restricted field of speech communication, the difficulty may be reduced to a tolerable size, but never completely eliminated, by "explanations." They are presumably never more than approximations to the ideas being explained, but are understandable when phrased in language that has previously been made reasonably clear by usage. For example, it does not take long to make the symbol for "yes" in any language understandable.

The problems of influence or effectiveness are concerned with the success with which the meaning conveyed to the receiver leads to the desired conduct on his part. It may seem at first glance undesirably narrow to imply that the purpose of all communication is to influence the conduct of the receiver. But with any reasonably broad definition of conduct, it is clear that communication either affects conduct or is without any discernible and provable effect at all.

One might be inclined to think that the technical problems involve only the engineering details of good design of a communication system, while the semantic and the effectiveness problems contain most if not all of the philosophical content of the general problem of communication. To see that this is not the case, we must now examine some important recent work in the mathematical theory of communication.

THIS is by no means a wholly new theory. As the mathematician John von Neumann has pointed out, the 19th-century Austrian physicist Ludwig Boltzmann suggested that some concepts of statistical mechanics were applicable to the concept of information. Other scientists, notably the late Norbert Wiener of the Massachusetts Institute of Technology, have made profound contributions. The work which will be here reported is that of Claude Shannon of the Bell Telephone Laboratories, which was preceded by that of H. Nyquist and R. V. L. Hartley in the same organization. This work applies in the first instance only to the technical problem, but the theory has broader significance. To begin with, meaning and effectiveness are inevitably restricted by the theoretical limits of accuracy in symbol transmission. Even more significant, a theoretical analysis of the technical problem reveals that it overlaps the semantic and the effectiveness problems more than one might suspect.

A communication system is symbolically represented in the drawing on pages 314 and 315. The information source selects a desired message out of a set of possible messages. (As will be shown, this is a particularly important function.) The transmitter changes this message into a signal which is sent over the communication channel to the receiver.

The receiver is a sort of inverse transmitter, changing the transmitted signal back into a message, and handing this message on to the destination. When I talk to you, my brain is the information source, yours the destination; my vocal system is the transmitter, and your ear with the eighth nerve is the receiver.

In the process of transmitting the signal, it is unfortunately characteristic that certain things not intended by the information source are added to the signal. These unwanted additions may be distortions of sound (in telephony, for example), or static (in radio), or distortions in the shape or shading of a picture (television), or errors in transmission (telegraphy or facsimile). All these changes in the signal may be called noise.

The questions to be studied in a communication system have to do with the amount of information, the capacity of the communication channel, the coding process that may be used to change a message into a signal and the effects of noise.

First off, we have to be clear about

the rather strange way in which, in this theory, the word "information" is used; for it has a special sense which, among other things, must not be confused at all with meaning. It is surprising but true that, from the present viewpoint, two messages, one heavily loaded with meaning and the other pure nonsense, can be equivalent as regards information.

In fact, in this new theory the word information relates not so much to what you *do* say, as to what you *could* say. That is, information is a measure of your freedom of choice when you select a message. If you are confronted with a very elementary situation where you have to choose one of two alternative messages, then it is arbitrarily said that the information associated with this situation is unity. The concept of information applies not to the individual messages, as the concept of meaning would, but rather to the situation as a whole, the unit information indicating that in this situation one has an amount of freedom of choice, in selecting a message, which it is convenient to regard as a standard or unit amount. The two messages between which one must choose in such a selection can be anything one likes. One might be the King James version of the Bible, and the other might be "Yes."

THE remarks thus far relate to artificially simple situations where the information source is free to choose only among several definite messages—like a man picking out one of a set of standard birthday-greeting telegrams. A more natural and more important situation is that in which the information source makes a sequence of choices from some set of elementary symbols, the selected sequence then forming the message. Thus a man may pick out one word after another, these individually selected words then adding up to the message.

Obviously probability plays a major role in the generation of the message, and the choices of the successive symbols depend upon the preceding choices. Thus, if we are concerned with English speech, and if the last symbol chosen is "the," then the probability that the next word will be an article, or a verb form other than a verbal, is very small. After the three words "in the event," the probability for "that" as the next word is fairly high, and for "elephant" as the next word is very low. Similarly, the probability is low for such a sequence of words as "Constantinople fishing nasty pink." Incidentally, it is low, but not zero, for it is perfectly possible to think of a passage in which one sentence closes with "Constantinople fishing," and the next begins with "Nasty pink." (We might observe in passing that the sequence under discussion *has* occurred in a single good English sentence, namely the one second preceding.)

As a matter of fact, Shannon has shown that when letters or words chosen at random are set down in sequences dictated by probability considerations alone, they tend to arrange themselves in meaningful words and phrases (*see illustration on page 316*).

Now let us return to the idea of information. The quantity which uniquely meets the natural requirements that one sets up for a measure of information turns out to be exactly that which is known in thermodynamics as entropy, or the degree of randomness, or of "shuffledness" if you will, in a situation. It is expressed in terms of the various probabilities involved.

To those who have studied the physical sciences, it is most significant that an entropy-like expression appears in communication theory as a measure of information. The concept of entropy, introduced by the German physicist Rudolf Clausius nearly 100 years ago, closely associated with the name of Boltzmann, and given deep meaning by Willard Gibbs of Yale in his classic work on statistical mechanics, has become so basic and pervasive a concept that Sir Arthur Eddington remarked: "The law that entropy always increases—the second law of thermodynamics—holds, I think, the supreme position among the laws of Nature."

Thus when one meets the concept of entropy in communication theory, he has a right to be rather excited. That information should be measured by entropy is, after all, natural when we remember that information is associated with the amount of freedom of choice we have in constructing messages. Thus one can say of a communication source, just as he would also say of a thermodynamic ensemble: "This situation is highly organized; it is not characterized by a large degree of randomness or of choice—that is to say, the information, or the entropy, is low."

We must keep in mind that in the mathematical theory of communication we are concerned not with the meaning of individual messages but with the whole statistical nature of the information source. Thus one is not surprised that the capacity of a channel of communication is to be described in terms of the amount of information it can transmit, or better, in terms of its ability to transmit what is produced out of a source of a given information.

The transmitter may take a written message and use some code to encipher this message into, say, a sequence of numbers, these numbers then being sent over the channel as the signal. Thus one says, in general, that the function of the transmitter is to encode, and that of the receiver to decode, the message. The theory provides for very sophisticated transmitters and receivers—such, for example, as possess "memories," so that the way they encode a certain symbol of the message depends not only upon this one symbol but also upon previous symbols of the message and the way they have been encoded.

We are now in a position to state the fundamental theorem for a noiseless channel transmitting discrete symbols. This theorem relates to a communication channel which has a capacity of C units per second, accepting signals from an information source of H units per second. The theorem states that by devising proper coding procedures for the transmitter it is possible to transmit symbols over the channel at an average rate

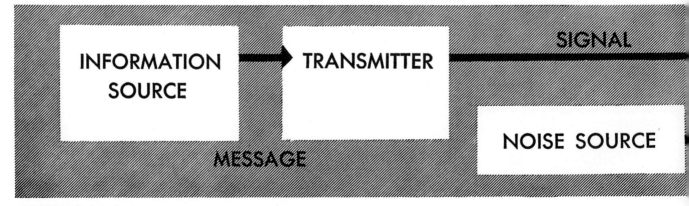

A COMMUNICATION SYSTEM may be reduced to these fundamental elements. In telephony the signal is a varying electric current, and the channel is a wire. In speech the signal is varying sound pressure, and the

which is nearly C/H, but which, no matter how clever the coding, can never be made to exceed C/H.

VIEWED superficially, say in rough analogy to the use of transformers to match impedances in electrical circuits, it seems very natural, although certainly pretty neat, to have this theorem which says that efficient coding is that which matches the statistical characteristics of information source and channel. But when it is examined in detail for any one of the vast array of situations to which this result applies, one realizes how deep and powerful this theory is.

How does noise affect information? Information, we must steadily remember, is a measure of one's freedom of choice in selecting a message. The greater this freedom of choice, the greater is the uncertainty that the message actually selected is some particular one. Thus greater freedom of choice, greater uncertainty and greater information all go hand in hand.

If noise is introduced, then the received message contains certain distortions, certain errors, certain extraneous material, that would certainly lead to increased uncertainty. But if the uncertainty is increased, the information is increased, and this sounds as though the noise were beneficial!

It is true that when there is noise, the received signal is selected out of a more varied set of signals than was intended by the sender. This situation beautifully illustrates the semantic trap into which one can fall if he does not remember that "information" is used here with a special meaning that measures freedom of choice and hence uncertainty as to what choice has been made. Uncertainty that arises by virtue of freedom of choice on the part of the sender is desirable uncertainty. Uncertainty that arises because of errors or because of the influence of noise is undesirable uncertainty. To get the useful information in the received signal we must subtract the spurious portion. This is accomplished, in the theory, by establishing a quantity known as the "equivocation," meaning the amount of ambiguity introduced by noise. One then refines or extends the previous definition of the capacity of a noiseless channel, and states that the capacity of a noisy channel is defined to be equal to the maximum rate at which useful information (*i.e.*, total uncertainty minus noise uncertainty) can be transmitted over the channel.

Now, finally, we can state the great central theorem of this whole communication theory. Suppose a noisy channel of capacity C is accepting information from a source of entropy H, entropy corresponding to the number of possible messages from the source. If the channel capacity C is equal to or larger than H, then by devising appropriate coding systems the output of the source can be transmitted over the channel with as little error as one pleases. But if the channel capacity C is less than H, the entropy of the source, then it is impossible to devise codes which reduce the error frequency as low as one may please.

However clever one is with the coding process, it will always be true that after the signal is received there remains some undesirable uncertainty about what the message was; and this undesirable uncertainty—this noise or equivocation—will always be equal to or greater than H minus C. But there is always at least one code capable of reducing this undesirable uncertainty down to a value that exceeds H minus C by a small amount.

This powerful theorem gives a precise and almost startlingly simple description of the utmost dependability one can ever obtain from a communication channel which operates in the presence of noise. One must think a long time, and consider many applications, before he fully realizes how powerful and general this amazingly compact theorem really is. One single application can be indicated here, but in order to do so, we must go back for a moment to the idea of the information of a source.

Having calculated the entropy (or the information, or the freedom of choice) of a certain information source, one can compare it to the maximum value this entropy could have, subject only to the condition that the source continue to employ the same symbols. The ratio of the actual to the maximum entropy is called the relative entropy of the source. If the relative entropy of a certain source is, say, eight-tenths, this means roughly that this source is, in its choice of symbols to form a message, about 80 per cent as free as it could possibly be with these same symbols. One minus the relative entropy is called the "redundancy." That is to say, this fraction of the message is unnecessary in the sense that if it were missing the message would still be essentially complete, or at least could be completed.

It is most interesting to note that the redundancy of English is just about 50 per cent. In other words, about half of the letters or words we choose in writing or speaking are under our free choice, and about half are really controlled by the statistical structure of the language, although we are not ordinarily aware of it. Incidentally, this is just about the minimum of freedom (or relative entropy) in the choice of letters that one must have to be able to construct satisfactory crossword puzzles. In a language that had only 20 per cent of freedom, or 80 per cent redundancy, it would be impossible to construct crossword puzzles in sufficient complexity and number to make the game popular.

Now since English is about 50 per cent redundant, it would be possible to save about one-half the time of ordinary telegraphy by a proper encoding process, provided one transmitted over a noiseless channel. When there is noise on a channel, however, there is some real advantage in not using a coding process that eliminates all of the redundancy. For the remaining redundancy helps combat the noise. It is the high redundancy of English, for example, that makes it easy to correct errors in spelling that have arisen during transmission.

THE communication systems dealt with so far involve the use of a dis-

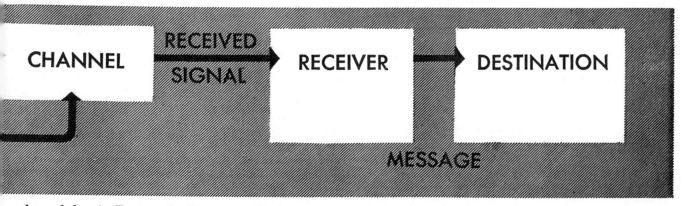

channel the air. Frequently things not intended by the information source are impressed on the signal. The static of radio is one example; distortion in telephony is another. All these additions may be called noise.

crete set of symbols—say letters—only moderately numerous. One might well expect that the theory would become almost indefinitely more complicated when it seeks to deal with continuous messages such as those of the speaking voice, with its continuous variation of pitch and energy. As is often the case, however, a very interesting mathematical theorem comes to the rescue. As a practical matter, one is always interested in a continuous signal which is built up of simple harmonic constituents, not of all frequencies but only of those that lie wholly within a band from zero to, say, W cycles per second. Thus very satisfactory communication can be achieved over a telephone channel that handles frequencies up to about 4,000, although the human voice does contain higher frequencies. With frequencies up to 10,000 or 12,000, high-fidelity radio transmission of symphonic music is possible.

The theorem that helps us is one which states that a continuous signal, T seconds in duration and band-limited in frequency to the range from zero to W, can be completely specified by stating 2TW numbers. This is really a remarkable theorem. Ordinarily a continuous curve can be defined only approximately by a finite number of points. But if the curve is built up out of simple harmonic constituents of a limited number of frequencies, as a complex sound is built up out of a limited number of pure tones, then a finite number of quantities is all that is necessary to define the curve completely.

Thanks partly to this theorem, and partly to the essential nature of the situation, it turns out that the extended theory of continuous communication is somewhat more difficult and complicated mathematically, but not essentially different from the theory for discrete symbols. Many of the statements for the discrete case require no modification for the continuous case, and others require only minor change.

The mathematical theory of communication is so general that one does not need to say what kinds of symbols are being considered—whether written letters or words, or musical notes, or spoken words, or symphonic music, or pictures. The relationships it reveals apply to all these and to other forms of communication. The theory is so imaginatively motivated that it deals with the real inner core of the communication problem.

One evidence of its generality is that the theory contributes importantly to, and in fact is really the basic theory of, cryptography, which is of course a form of coding. In a similar way, the theory contributes to the problem of translation from one language to another, although the complete story here clearly requires consideration of meaning, as well as of information. Similarly, the ideas developed in this work connect

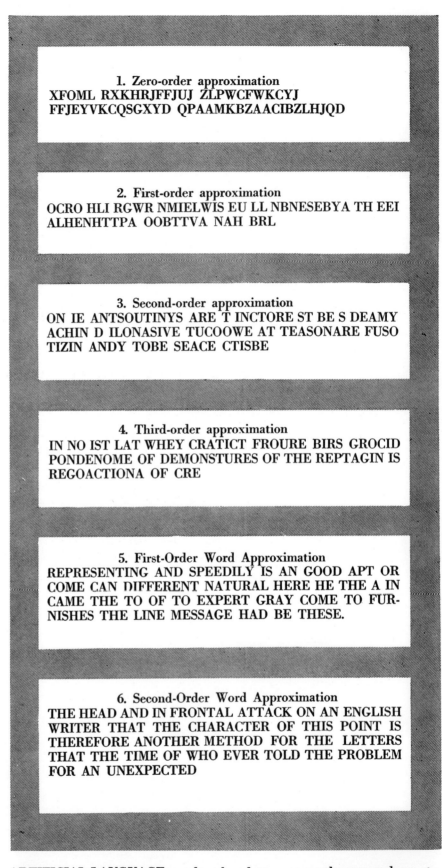

1. Zero-order approximation
XFOML RXKHRJFFJUJ ZLPWCFWKCYJ FFJEYVKCQSGXYD QPAAMKBZAACIBZLHJQD

2. First-order approximation
OCRO HLI RGWR NMIELWIS EU LL NBNESEBYA TH EEI ALHENHTTPA OOBTTVA NAH BRL

3. Second-order approximation
ON IE ANTSOUTINYS ARE T INCTORE ST BE S DEAMY ACHIN D ILONASIVE TUCOOWE AT TEASONARE FUSO TIZIN ANDY TOBE SEACE CTISBE

4. Third-order approximation
IN NO IST LAT WHEY CRATICT FROURE BIRS GROCID PONDENOME OF DEMONSTURES OF THE REPTAGIN IS REGOACTIONA OF CRE

5. First-Order Word Approximation
REPRESENTING AND SPEEDILY IS AN GOOD APT OR COME CAN DIFFERENT NATURAL HERE HE THE A IN CAME THE TO OF TO EXPERT GRAY COME TO FURNISHES THE LINE MESSAGE HAD BE THESE.

6. Second-Order Word Approximation
THE HEAD AND IN FRONTAL ATTACK ON AN ENGLISH WRITER THAT THE CHARACTER OF THIS POINT IS THEREFORE ANOTHER METHOD FOR THE LETTERS THAT THE TIME OF WHO EVER TOLD THE PROBLEM FOR AN UNEXPECTED

ARTIFICIAL LANGUAGE results when letters or words are set down statistically. 1. Twenty-six letters and one space are chosen at random. 2. Letters are chosen according to their frequency in English. 3. Letters are chosen according to the frequency with which they follow other letters. 4. Letters are chosen according to frequency with which they follow two other letters. Remaining examples do the same with words instead of letters.

so closely with the problem of the logical design of computing machines that it is no surprise that Shannon has written a paper on the design of a computer that would be capable of playing a skillful game of chess. And it is of further pertinence to the present contention that his paper closes with the remark that either one must say that such a computer "thinks," or one must substantially modify the conventional implication of the verb "to think."

The theory goes further. Though ostensibly applicable only to problems at the technical level, it is helpful and suggestive at the levels of semantics and effectiveness as well. The formal diagram of a communication system on pages 314 and 315 can, in all likelihood, be extended to include the central issues of meaning and effectiveness.

Thus when one moves to those levels it may prove to be essential to take account of the statistical characteristics of the destination. One can imagine, as an addition to the diagram, another box labeled "Semantic Receiver" interposed between the engineering receiver (which changes signals to messages) and the destination. This semantic receiver subjects the message to a second decoding, the demand on this one being that it must match the statistical semantic characteristics of the message to the statistical semantic capacities of the totality of receivers, or of that subset of receivers which constitutes the audience one wishes to affect.

Similarly one can imagine another box in the diagram which, inserted between the information source and the transmitter, would be labeled "Semantic Noise" (not to be confused with "engineering noise"). This would represent distortions of meaning introduced by the information source, such as a speaker, which are not intentional but nevertheless affect the destination, or listener. And the problem of semantic decoding must take this semantic noise into account. It is also possible to think of a treatment or adjustment of the original message that would make the sum of message meaning plus semantic noise equal to the desired total message meaning at the destination.

ANOTHER way in which the theory can be helpful in improving communication is suggested by the fact that error and confusion arise and fidelity decreases when, no matter how good the coding, one tries to crowd too much over a channel. A general theory at all levels will surely have to take into account not only the capacity of the channel but also (even the words are right!) the capacity of the audience. If you overcrowd the capacity of the audience, it is probably true, by direct analogy, that you do not fill the audience up and then waste only the remainder by spilling. More likely, and again by direct analogy, you force a general error and confusion.

The concept of information developed in this theory at first seems disappointing and bizarre—disappointing because it has nothing to do with meaning, and bizarre because it deals not with a single message but rather with the statistical character of a whole ensemble of messages, bizarre also because in these statistical terms the words information and uncertainty find themselves partners.

But we have seen upon further examination of the theory that this analysis has so penetratingly cleared the air that one is now perhaps for the first time ready for a real theory of meaning. An engineering communication theory is just like a very proper and discreet girl at the telegraph office accepting your telegram. She pays no attention to the meaning, whether it be sad or joyous or embarrassing. But she must be prepared to deal intelligently with all messages that come to her desk. This idea that a communication system ought to try to deal with all possible messages, and that the intelligent way to try is to base design on the statistical character of the source, is surely not without significance for communication in general. Language must be designed, or developed, with a view to the totality of things that man may wish to say; but not being able to accomplish everything, it should do as well as possible as often as possible. That is to say, it too should deal with its task statistically.

This study reveals facts about the statistical structure of the English language, as an example, which must seem significant to students of every phase of language and communication. It suggests, as a particularly promising lead, the application of probability theory to semantic studies. Especially pertinent is the powerful body of probability theory dealing with what mathematicians call the Markoff processes, whereby past events influence present probabilities, since this theory is specifically adapted to handle one of the most significant but difficult aspects of meaning, namely the influence of context. One has the vague feeling that information and meaning may prove to be something like a pair of canonically conjugate variables in quantum theory, that is, that information and meaning may be subject to some joint restriction that compels the sacrifice of one if you insist on having much of the other.

Or perhaps meaning may be shown to be analogous to one of the quantities on which the entropy of a thermodynamic ensemble depends. Here Eddington has another apt comment:

"Suppose that we were asked to arrange the following in two categories—*distance, mass, electric force, entropy, beauty, melody.*

"I think there are the strongest grounds for placing entropy alongside beauty and melody, and not with the first three. Entropy is only found when the parts are viewed in association, and it is by viewing or hearing the parts in association that beauty and melody are discerned. All three are features of arrangement. It is a pregnant thought that one of these three associates should be able to figure as a commonplace quantity of science. The reason why this stranger can pass itself off among the aborigines of the physical world is that it is able to speak their language, *viz.*, the language of arithmetic."

One feels sure that Eddington would have been willing to include the word meaning along with beauty and melody; and one suspects he would have been thrilled to see, in this theory, that entropy not only speaks the language of arithmetic; it also speaks the language of language.

42 LINEAR PROGRAMMING

WILLIAM W. COOPER AND ABRAHAM CHARNES · August 1954

Imagine that you are manufacturing a product at a number of factories and must freight it to markets in many different parts of the country. How would you go about calculating the pattern of shipments that would deliver the goods from your many warehouses to the many markets at the lowest possible freight cost?

By common sense and trial and error you might readily work out a reasonable schedule. But even a non-mathematician can see that to find the best solution among the infinite number of possible solutions would be a far more formidable problem.

We shall describe in this article a recently developed technique in applied mathematics which makes it possible to solve such problems in a relatively short time by means of simple computations. The theory of linear programming was developed by John von Neumann, G. B. Dantzig, T. C. Koopmans and a few other mathematicians, statisticians and economists. It was first applied as an operating tool by Marshall Wood and his staff in the Air Force's Project SCOOP (Scientific Computation of Optimum Programs). One of its applications was in the Berlin air lift. As a result of work by the Air Force group and others in linear programming and related developments, such as the theory of games, statistical decision theory and input-output analysis, truly scientific methods of analysis are now being applied to many problems in business and logistics which used to be considered beyond the scope of such analyses. In this article we shall confine ourselves to linear programming and explain the principle with a sample problem.

Linear programming derived its name from the fact that the typical problems with which it deals are stated mathematically in the form of linear equations. (Actually "linear" is too narrow a name for the technique, for it may be applied to nonlinear problems as well.) In essence it is a method for considering a number of variables simultaneously and calculating the best possible solution of a given problem within the stated limitations. Any manufacturer will at once appreciate that this is a precise statement of his own problem. In deciding what particular items to manufacture, and in what quantities, he must take into account a great complex of factors: the capacities of his machines, the cost and salability of the various items, and so on. To make matters worse, each subdivision of his problem has its own complexities; for instance, he may have to choose among several possible processes for making a particular item. And all the factors and decisions may interlock and react upon one another in unexpected ways. In the circumstances, the best that any management can hope to achieve is a reasonably workable compromise. With linear programming, however, it becomes possible to locate definitely the optimum solutions among all the available ones, both in the realm of over-all policy and in departmental detail.

To illustrate the method let us take a highly simplified hypothetical case. We have a factory that can make two products, which for simplicity's sake we shall name "widgets" and "gadgets." The factory has three machines—one "bounder" and two "rounders." The same machines can be used to make widgets or gadgets. Each product must first be roughed out on the bounder and then rounded on one of the rounders. There are two possible processes for making each product: We can use the bounder and rounder No. 1 or the bounder and rounder No. 2 for either a widget or a gadget. Let us name the respective processes for the widget One and Two, and for the gadget Three and Four. The key variables are the times involved. To make a widget by Process One requires .002 of an hour on the bounder and .003 of an hour on rounder 1; by Process Two, .002 of an hour on the bounder and .004 of an hour on rounder 2. A gadget by Process Three takes .005 of an hour on the bounder and .008 of an hour on rounder 1; by Process Four, .005 of an hour on the bounder and .010 of an hour on rounder 2. Finally, we know that the capacities of the machines for the period we are considering (say six months) are 1,000 hours of operation on the bounder, 600 hours on rounder 1 and 800 hours on rounder 2.

All this information is summarized at the top of the opposite page. A production superintendent might call this a flow chart; we can think of it as a model which specifies conditions, or constraints, that will govern any production decision we must make. Now it is readily apparent that we can translate these facts into an algebraic model. If we let x_1 represent the unknown number of widgets to be made by Process One, x_2 the number of widgets by Process Two, and x_3 and x_4 the numbers of gadgets to be made by Processes Three and Four, we can write all the information in an algebraic table [*middle of opposite page*]. The inequality sign before the numbers representing hours of capacity on the machines is the well-known symbol meaning "no more than." What this table means is simply that we can make no more widgets and/or gadgets than the capacities of the respective machines will allow. But with the conditions stated in this form, we are now in a position to consider the variables simultaneously and to calculate solutions which will satisfy the constraints. A solution will be called a linear program; linearity here refers to the fact that the available capacity on each machine is used up *in proportion to* the number of items run through it.

It is important to note here that the unknowns x_1, x_2, x_3 or x_4 may be zero but none of them can be a negative number. Of course it is obvious that we cannot produce a minus number of products. But in mathematics the exclusion of negative values must be carefully noted. In fact, the successful development of the theory of linear programming required extensive study of the effects that this restriction would have on traditional methods of solving and analyzing equations.

Having stated the constraints, we can proceed to find the best production schedule attainable within these limitations. What we mean by "best" will of course depend on what criterion we choose to apply. We might decide to seek the schedule that would produce the largest possible number of items, or the one that would use the greatest possible amount of the machines' available running time. But ordinarily the objective would be the greatest possible profit. Let us assume that the profit on each widget produced by Process One is 85 cents, on each widget by Process Two 70 cents, on each gadget by Process Three $1.60, and on each gadget by Process Four $1.30. We then get this equation: Total Profit $= .85x_1 + .70x_2 + 1.60x_3 + 1.30x_4$.

From this information we could calculate the number of each item we should produce to realize the largest possible total profit within the machines' capacity. (Be it noted that gadgets, though yielding a larger per unit profit, should not necessarily pre-empt the machines, for widgets take less time to produce.)

The problem as so far outlined, however, is much too simple to represent an actual situation. To come closer to a real problem we should at least introduce a sales factor. Let us suppose, therefore, that our factory has orders for 450,000 widgets. Elementary arithmetic will show that our present machine capacity cannot turn them out within the time limit. We have enough capacity on the bounder for 500,000 widgets (1,000 hours divided by .002 of an hour per widget) but our two rounders combined could finish no more than 400,000. We

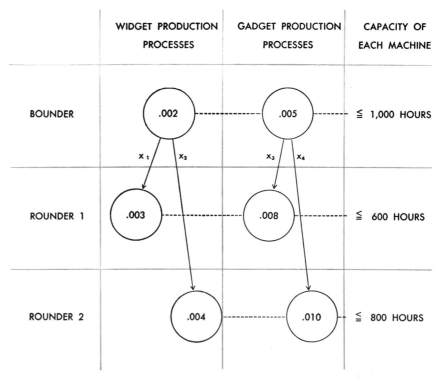

GRAPHIC MODEL depicts the restrictions on production of "widgets" and "gadgets" by three machines: one "bounder" and two "rounders." The numbers in the circles indicate the fraction of an hour required for each machine to perform its function on each part.

BOUNDER	$.002x_1$	+	$.002x_2$	+	$.005x_3$	+	$.005x_4$	$\leqq$ 1,000 HOURS
ROUNDER 1	$.003x_1$			+	$.008x_3$			$\leqq$ 600 HOURS
ROUNDER 2			$.004x_2$			+	$.010x_4$	$\leqq$ 800 HOURS

ALGEBRAIC MODEL of the same conditions represents as x_1, x_2, x_3 and x_4 the numbers of items produced by the processes indicated by arrows in the graphic model. The blank spaces in each column can be disregarded because they represent zero in each case.

BOUNDER	$.002x_1 + .002x_2 + .002x'_1 + .005x_3 + .005x_4 + .005x'_3$	$\leqq$ 1,000 HOURS
ROUNDER 1	$.003x_1$ $\quad + \quad$ $.008x_3$	$\leqq$ 600 HOURS
ROUNDER 2	$.004x_2$ $\quad + \quad$ $.010x_4$	$\leqq$ 800 HOURS
ROUNDER 1 (OVERTIME)	$.003x'_1$ $\quad + \quad$ $.008x'_3$	$\leqq$ 200 HOURS
CONTRACT	x_1 + x_2 + x'_1	$\geqq$ 450,000 WIDGETS

COMPLETED MODEL is based on the assumption of additional capacity for one of the machines. This is overtime on rounder 1. Now two new processes are introduced: x'_1 and x'_3. The sign before 450,000 widgets means at least this number must be produced.

must obtain more rounder capacity, and this may be done by authorizing overtime on one or both of the rounders. Suppose, then, we arrange for 200 hours of overtime on the faster of our two rounders (.003 of an hour per widget). Because of higher labor costs for overtime, the profit per widget will be reduced from the usual 85 cents to 60 cents during the overtime period, and if we should use any of the overtime capacity for making gadgets, the unit profit on them will drop from $1.60 to $1.40.

The constraints governing this expansion of the problem are summarized in the algebraic table above (the new symbols x'_1 and x'_3 represent the number of widgets and of gadgets, respectively, to be turned out on rounder 1 during the overtime period). Given the unit profit figures, we are now prepared to calculate the most profitable possible employment of the machines.

The answer can be computed by one of several methods. The most general, devised by Dantzig, is called the simplex method. Certain special methods which are more efficient for the kind of problem being considered here were developed by the authors of this article. These systems, though too involved and lengthy to be explained in detail here, require only simple arithmetical operations which can easily be carried out by clerks or commercially available computers. The simplex method starts from zero use of the machines' capacity, and the computation proceeds by a series of specified steps, each of which advances closer to the ultimate answer.

The answer in this case is that we should produce no gadgets but should make 466,667 widgets, finishing 200,000 on rounder 1 at straight time, another 200,000 on rounder 2 at straight time and the remaining 66,667 at overtime on rounder 1. The total profit will be $350,000. Our system of calculation tells us that it is not possible to devise a production schedule which will yield a larger total profit within our restrictions.

It is possible that there may be other programs which would provide as much (but no more) profit. If there are, the analyst can quickly find them. He can also determine the second best or third best program, and so on. Thus the method is not only powerful but also flexible; it can offer management a range of choices based on different considerations. Furthermore, linear programming methods can be extended to analyze the effects of any change in the restrictions—an improvement in efficiency, an increase or reduction in cost, an increase in capacity. These methods employ a "dual theorem," whereby a maximizing problem (such as the maximization of profits in the case we have been considering) is viewed as the reverse of a related minimizing problem. In this case the minimizing problem is concerned with the worth of the machine capacities. Using the same set of facts and calculations, it is possible to show precisely how much more profitable it is to employ overtime on rounder 1 than on rounder 2. If the overtime on rounder 1 were increased to 300 hours instead of 200 hours, the maximum profit would be $370,000 instead of $350,000. But an increase of overtime from 300 to 301 hours would be worthless, for at that point the possible rounder output would exceed the capacity of the bounder.

In short, linear programming may be applied not only to finding the best program within given restrictions but also to assessing the advisability of changing the restrictions themselves.

The hypothetical problem outlined in this article was simplified to illustrate some of the basic elements of the technique. In any real-life problem the factors at play are both more numerous and more difficult to identify. It is as important to locate the truly pertinent factors as it is to construct the correct mathematical model for dealing with them. The application of linear programming is full of pitfalls. To evaluate the various features of a problem and determine which should be included in the model requires understanding collaboration between the mathematical analyst and the operations people actually working at the job.

The range of problems to which linear programming may be applied is very wide. As we have already indicated, the Air Force has employed it in problems of logistics. In industry the method is solving problems not only in production but even in such matters as devising the most effective salary pattern for executives—a pattern which will not only meet competition for their services from outside but will also avoid inconsistencies within the company.

Through the dual theorem, linear programming has been related to the theory of games; it is thereby enabled to take probabilities as well as known restrictions into account. It also has fundamental, though indirect, connections with statistical decision theory, which the late Abraham Wald related to the theory of games shortly before his recent death in an airplane crash. All three of these disciplines are contributing to one another's progress. Indeed, our own chief interest in linear programming is to develop generalizations which will enlarge the scope of the technique.

It has been highly satisfying to us to see how often research on a particular problem has led to methods of much more general application, sometimes in altogether unexpected fields. For instance, the work we did in adapting linear programming to the problem of the executives' salary schedule opened a new path for studying the field of statistical regression and correlation analysis. Similarly, an investigation of certain problems in economic measurement and management science has paved the way for new approaches in totally unrelated fields of work in engineering and physics, such as plasticity and elasticity.

As research on these new tools of scientific analysis continues, we can expect to find many new uses for them. But what is perhaps most remarkable is the great and continuing revolution that science and technology have wrought in mathematics. As the mathematician and writer Eric Temple Bell has said in his book *The Development of Mathematics*:

"As the sciences . . . became more and more exact, they made constantly increasing demands on mathematical inventiveness, and were mainly responsible for a large part of the enormous expansion of all mathematics since 1637. Again, as industry and invention became increasingly scientific after the industrial revolution of the late 18th and early 19th centuries, they too stimulated mathematical creation. . . . The time curve of mathematical productivity [shoots up] with ever greater rapidity. . . ."

43 OPERATIONS RESEARCH

HORACE C. LEVINSON AND ARTHUR A. BROWN · March 1951

WORLD WAR II developed a new military use of science, christened operations research (in the U. S.) or operational research (in Britain). Unlike all previous applications of science to warfare, which were concerned almost entirely with the development of weapons, operations research is concerned with the use of weapons. Its province is the tactical and strategical aspects of military operations: it deals with methods of locating enemy submarines, for example, rather than with the technology of the torpedo or the bomb. What it does is to apply scientific method, including mathematical techniques, to the analysis of situations and of the efficiency of various systems of organization for coping with them.

Obviously this approach can be applied to business and governmental organizations just as well as to military ones, and since the war it has been used fruitfully to solve some business and industrial problems. In Britain the Government has made considerable use of it, and workers in the field have formed an Operational Research Club. In the U. S. there is now a Committee on Operations Research, organized by the National Research Council to further the development and use of operations research for nonmilitary purposes. Since 1948 a course on nonmilitary uses of it has been given at the Massachusetts Institute of Technology in collaboration with the Navy. On the military side, the Army, the Navy, the Air Force and the Joint Chiefs of Staff all have operations research organizations.

OPERATIONS research was born in the Battle of Britain. The British Government was exploring every available means to defend the country against the disastrous German bombings. The British had a skillful but small air force and they had radar. Could radar make up for the smallness of the Royal Air Force? How could the radar interception system be used to maximum advantage; how should the antennas be distributed, the signals organized, and so on? The Government called in half a dozen scientists of various disciplines to answer these questions. By collecting the relevant facts and analyzing them with the general methodology of science, these men devised a new operating technique that doubled the effectiveness of the air defense system.

Impressed with this spectacular success, Britain organized similar teams to tackle many other military problems. The U. S. armed forces likewise put operations research groups to work soon after this nation entered the war. The work of these teams in both countries paid high dividends in deciding such questions as the most effective altitudes at which planes should fly in hunting submarines, the best payload division between fuel, instruments and armament, the best search pattern. One short operations research study showed that planes attacking submarines could increase their effectiveness fivefold by changing the depth at which depth charges were set to go off. In the famous Allied anti-submarine campaign in the Bay of Biscay, British and U. S. operations research teams working together designed a patrol system which succeeded in sighting practically every submarine that came in or out of the Bay and sank about a quarter of those it attacked.

Operations research can handle very diverse problems, but to be eligible for solution the problem must satisfy two conditions: 1) it must be expressible in numbers or quantities, and 2) the data must be adaptable to the available techniques. If the data are statistical, for example, they must come from operations that are roughly similar and must be extensive enough to permit some sort of statistical regularity or law to show itself. Let us consider a couple of actual military examples.

Early in the war it was the conventional military view that in an airplane squadron it was most important to have as many planes as possible in fit condition to take to the air at all times. The RAF had set as a standard that no less than 70 per cent of a squadron's planes should be fit to fly; this percentage was called the maintenance efficiency. Since it was very difficult to keep up to this standard, the problem was given for study to Cecil Gordon, a member of an operations research team.

Gordon took a completely fresh approach. He was a biologist, and he decided there was a usable analogy between the life cycles of human beings and of aircraft. Flying, he reasoned, breeds disrepair and the necessity for repair; repair breeds readiness for flight; readiness for flight, given the opportunity, breeds flying, and so the cycle starts again. But in a military squadron it is not readiness for flight that you want: you want flying. An airplane on the ground is only potentially valuable—useless until you need to fly it.

Gordon lived with the squadron for a while, determined the rate at which flying time generated repair time and assimilated every significant feature of the squadron's operations and the life cycle of a plane. As the result of all this he came to a startling conclusion: the old criterion of maintenance efficiency was wrong. What counted was the percentage of demand for flying met by the planes and the amount of flying accomplished per maintenance man-hour. The upshot was that the target percentage of aircraft kept fit for flying was cut from 70 per cent to around 35 per cent, with a large increase in battle time and squadron efficiency.

The other example concerns the problem of the Japanese Kamikazes (suicide planes) that threatened our ships in the Pacific. The question was whether a ship should maneuver violently to spoil the aim of the diving Kamikaze or keep steady to improve the aim of its own defensive anti-aircraft fire. The operations research group that undertook to find the answer had the records of 477 attacks to study. In 172 cases the suicide plane had succeeded in hitting the ship, and in 27 cases the ship had been sunk. The scientists discovered that the effectiveness of the two types of defensive tactics depended on the size of the ship. Violent evasive maneuvers obviously have only a slight effect on the aim of anti-aircraft gunners in the case of a large ship but a very pronounced effect on their aim in a small ship. What is the net result when the effects on the aim of attacking Kamikazes are taken into account? After considerable study the group concluded that a large ship, when attacked by a diving Kamikaze, should change course violently and a small ship slowly. It also found that a ship should present its beam to an attacking plane that came in from a high dive and turn its bow or stern to a plane diving from a low altitude. In presenting its beam to a Kamikaze a ship could concentrate more anti-aircraft fire on it, but in the case of a low-diving plane the effect of the increased fire power was more than offset, the study showed, by the larger target offered by the ship. The operations research team's recommendations later proved their value in battle: ships that followed its suggestions were hit about 29 per cent of the time when attacked and those that did not observe these rules were hit about 47 per cent of the time.

OPERATIONS research makes use of such mathematical and statistical concepts as the variable, the statistical constant, the function and probability. Its military applications also introduced a number of new concepts, examples of which are exchange rate and sweep rate. The exchange rate of course is the ratio of one's own losses to those of the enemy, but when the losses are not in directly comparable units, a complex analysis may be necessary to determine the true value of an operation in the over-all picture.

The notion of sweep rate grew out of the problem of searching for enemy ships or submarines. Any search tool (a broom, a rake, a flashlight beam, a radar beam) essentially explores a field of targets whose exact locations are unknown. Its effectiveness is measured by its sweep width and its sweep rate. It has a certain probability, depending on these factors, of picking up a target at any given point. A new broom, which "sweeps clean," has a sweep width equal to its actual width, and the probability that it will pick up an object within these limits is 1, representing certainty. A rake swept over an area of small leaves has an irregular detection probability curve, and a man hunting a target at night with sweeps of a flashlight may have still another probability pattern.

Suppose that a plane, flying back and forth at a given speed without crossing its own path, is searching an area of ocean for submarines. To compute the sweep width you multiply the number of submarines assumed to be in the area by the distance flown by the plane, and then divide this product into the product of the number of submarines actually detected and the total number of square miles searched. This number, the sweep width, multiplied by the speed of the plane, gives the sweep rate.

This seems a lot of computing, and one is inclined to ask what is accomplished by it. The answer is that sweep rates are sensitive measures of the efficiency of the searching operation. If the sweep rate of a command of airplanes searching an area for submarines drops sharply, it is a signal to the command that something has gone wrong.

These concepts can also be applied to some business problems, for there are close analogies between military and business operations. In fact, a rough dictionary can be constructed that will translate one into the other. For "weapons" read "materials"; for "command" read "management" or "executive"; for "enemy" read "competitor" or, curiously enough, "customer"; for "destroy" read "out-compete" or "acquire"; for "enemy losses" read "own gains," and so on. The notion of exchange rate becomes, in business, the ratio of gains to expenditures. The notion of sweep rate is directly applicable to the search for customers.

THE use of operations research in business is not entirely new. Under such names as "business analysis" or "business research" sporadic activities of this kind have been conducted for a long time by some firms. What the operations research of World War II introduced was the development of systematic techniques and the enlistment of groups of trained scientists in such work.

To illustrate how operations research may be used in business let us take a study that was actually made of the effectiveness of department-store newspaper advertising. The particular type of advertising analyzed was the kind designed to produce immediate sales—what may be called "quick response" advertising. Since department stores spend millions of dollars each year on this "QR" advertising, the scientific measurement of its results is evidently a worth-while project.

The success of such advertising cannot be measured simply by the amount of extra sales of the particular goods advertised. The advertising is intended to attract customers to the store and increase the total sales. It is not effective if it merely increases the sales of one department at the expense of other departments in the store or of future sales of this department itself. For example, suppose a store advertises a coat that has been selling for $30 at a reduced price of $24. This will naturally attract a lot of quick sales. But how many of these sales are to customers who would have bought the coat anyway at its normal price of $30, either at the time or later on, if the advertisement had not been run? In how many cases did this $24 purchase take the place of purchases that would have been made in other departments of the store? How many customers attracted by the coat bargain also made spur-of-the-moment purchases elsewhere in the store? And finally, how much business did this advertisement bring to the store that would otherwise have gone to competing stores?

It is clear that to assess the net returns from this type of advertising the study must cover the store's total sales and all QR advertising over a considerable period of time. Its goal must be to determine the "true plus volume," that is, the extra volume of sales for the store as a whole which would not have been obtained if the advertising had not been run. Such a study was conducted some years ago by the research director of a certain department store. He made a week-by-week comparison of the QR advertising and total sales of this store with those of the competing department stores in the same city. His analysis of these data was then based on the following reasoning: Of the total sales in a given week a certain percentage is due to QR advertising. This fraction changes from week to week, both for the store and for the competing group, due to fluctuations in their respective QR expenditures. Moreover, the fluctuations in advertising by this store do not parallel those for the competing group: in some weeks it does relatively more advertising, in others relatively less. Consequently there should be corresponding fluctuations in the ratio of total sales by the store to total sales by the competing group, reflecting the variations in advertising ratio. The problem was to isolate these fluctuations.

In order to do so the research director

resorted to mathematics. Let S represent the portion of the store's sales volume that does not include the sales attributable to QR advertising, in other words, the total sales minus the QR sales for a week. Let O represent the corresponding sales of the competing group. It is reasonable to assume that the ratio S/O is a statistical constant over an extended period, since sales due to the variable factor of QR advertising are eliminated and the effects of weather and of economic changes, if not too violent, will be uniform for all the stores. This assumption is the key to the solution, for it leads to a set of equations which, using the known figures on total sales and QR advertising expenditures, can be solved numerically to determine the unknown statistical constant and the pulling power of the advertising.

This study yielded the following conclusions, among others: 1) the QR advertising produced a large true plus volume; 2) the amount of true plus volume depended sensitively on price reductions of the advertised goods; 3) the average pulling power of the advertising remained practically constant over a period of several months, although individual advertisements varied greatly in effectiveness. The analysis also had important by-products not involving advertising: it threw much light on some phases of the store's operations and led to improvements in efficiency.

THE peacetime applications of operations research have included the analysis of such problems as the proper use of equipment and manpower, operating procedures in factories and public utilities, the planning of government projects. One operations research study of the laying of road surface materials in Britain, for example, resulted in an annual saving of a million pounds sterling.

Operations research is already a machine of great power. Like a farm tractor it must be expertly manned. One of the main objectives of the Committee on Operations Research in the U. S. is to create a supply of trained workers in this field. The Committee believes that operations research is particularly important and urgent during the present national emergency. To the extent that nonmilitary operations research is successful in increasing the efficiency of U. S. industry, it will contribute to reducing the critical shortage of manpower. And the more young scientists are trained in operations research, the greater will be the supply available to the armed forces in case of necessity.

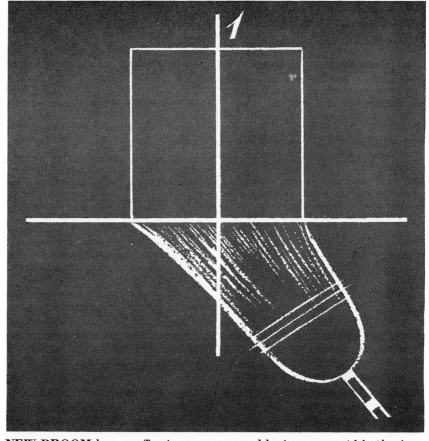

NEW BROOM has an effectiveness measured by its sweep width (*horizontal coordinate*) and its sweep rate (*vertical coordinate*). The probability that the broom will encounter an object in its path is 1, or certainty.

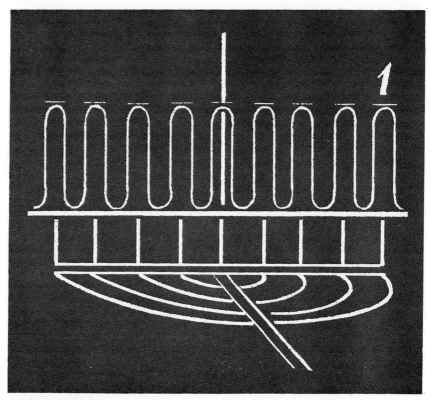

GARDEN RAKE obviously has less effectiveness than a broom. The probability that a tooth will encounter an object in its path is 1, but the probability that an object between the teeth will be encountered is 0.

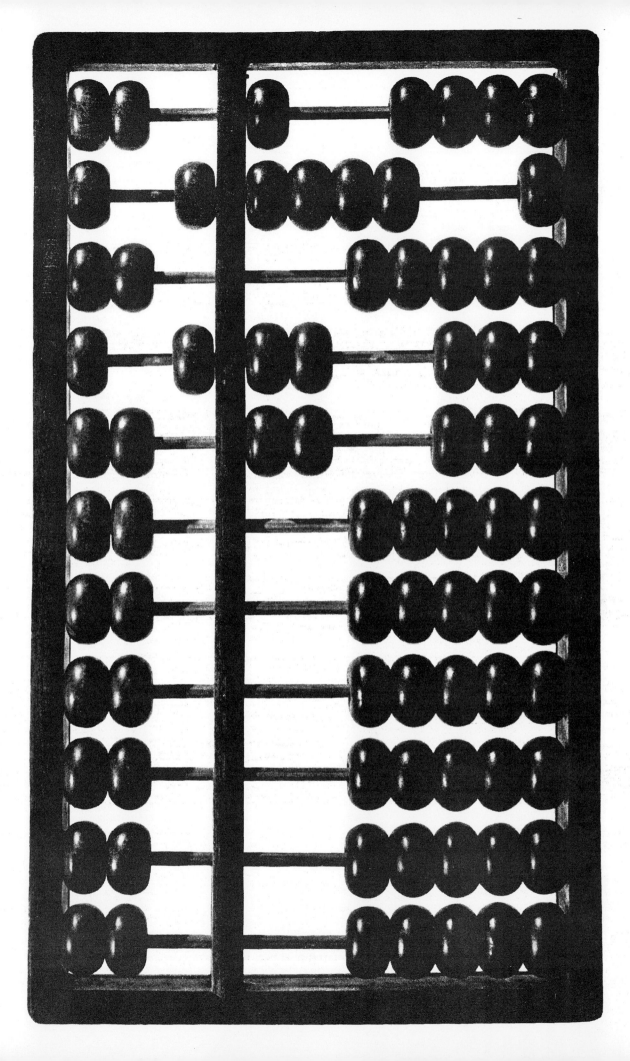

44 MATHEMATICAL MACHINES

HARRY M. DAVIS · April 1949

A NEW revolution is taking place in technology today. It both parallels and completes the Industrial Revolution that started a century ago. The first phase of the Industrial Revolution meant the mechanization, then the electrification, of brawn. The new revolution means the mechanization and electrification of brains.

The 19th-century revolution was based on the transformation and transmission of energy—call it what you will: calories, ergs, horsepower-hours, foot-pounds, joules, British thermal units, kilowatt-hours.

The 20th-century revolution is based on the transformation and transmission of information: a number, a letter of the alphabet; a dark or light spot in a picture; an "on" or "off" signal; a decision between "yes" and "no"; a judgment as to "more" or "less"; a logical discrimination among "and," "or," and "neither." These are the raw materials and the products of "information-processing systems" that are assuming many of the human functions of calculation, communication and control.

How far has this revolution gone? Much of it is already taken for granted in our daily lives—in the shape of radio, television, telephone dial systems. Other phases affect us less obviously—robot pilots for aircraft; electronic navigation systems; automatic controls in factories; the many kinds of radar. All such devices have functions that are comparable, in one way or another, with the processes of human thinking.

But the machines that above all others deserve the title of "brains" are the elec-

THE ABACUS was perhaps the earliest mathematical machine. The number indicated by the Chinese abacus on the opposite page is 27,091.

tronic computers which easily solve problems so intricate and laborious that they stagger the most patient mathematician. They read, they write, they do arithmetic—all at rates ranging from a thousand to a million times faster than the human eye, mind, and hand.

Do They Really Think?

To the question, "Do these machines really think?" one can get various semantic interpretations of the words "really" and "think," including the rejoinder, "How much do people really think?" Calculator designers and psychologists seem to gain more respect for the human brain the more they learn about its mechanical competitors. In strictly electrical and chemical terms, the human brain is the most efficient of computing machines, although it is also the slowest. It does not need kilowatts of power to energize its nerves, nor blowers to ventilate it; the electrical brains definitely emit more hot air. Warren McCulloch, the neuropsychiatrist, has pointed out that if a calculator were built fully to simulate the nerve connections of the human brain, it would require a skyscraper to house it, the power of Niagara Falls to run it, and all the water of Niagara to cool it.

"The more I deal with these machines," said one expert, "the more impressed I am with how dumb they are." They do nothing creative. They can only follow instructions, which must be reduced to the simplest terms. If the instructions are wrong, the machines go wrong.

On the other hand, the machines are not subject to distraction. They concentrate all their faculties on the problem at hand. They can do a complicated calculation in less time than it takes a human

being, for example, to react to a red traffic light by signaling his right foot to move from gas pedal to brake. Thus they can take over an immense burden of mental labor, handling mathematical and logical data in quantity just as the assembly lines have converted hand labor to mass production.

Claude E. Shannon of the Bell Telephone Laboratories aptly answered the "do they think" question when he said that the performance of the newest machines "will force us either to admit the possibility of mechanized thinking or to further restrict our concept of thinking." Shannon made this remark at the March meeting of the Institute of Radio Engineers, where he explained how the computers could be taught to play an adequate, though not brilliant, game of chess. Against the greater inventiveness of the human chess master, the machine, with its built-in procedures for choosing the next move, would have the advantage of high-speed operation, freedom from errors, and freedom from laziness.

A New Industry

Already the building and operating of automatic brains is becoming a big business. The electronic brains cost from $50,000 to $1,000,000 each, and there are eager waiting lists of customers—airplane manufacturers, insurance companies, statistical services and, above all, the various agencies of the Government. The census of 1950, it is hoped, will be the first to be analyzed by all-electronic computers, extracting a wealth of information about the nation's economic life that has never before been refinable from the statistical ore despite the use of punch-card tabulating machines.

The electronic machines are versatile. Nuclear physicists in Chicago send problems to Aberdeen, Md., for processing on the famous Eniac computer. The International Business Machines Selective Sequence Calculator, a streamlined roomful of tubes and relays behind plate glass on New York's 57th Street, is more than an advertising showplace. While shoppers and art-gallery goers on the fashionable street glance in, the machine silently works out problems such as the motions of the moon or the control of guided missiles.

IBM has already incorporated some of the best circuits from this big machine into a little one, the size of two filing cabinets, neatly packaged in crackle-finish gray metal and mounted on casters so that it can be installed near the electric socket of any business office. Ten times faster than the previous IBM commercial calculating punches, the electronic Type 604 is now coming off the production lines in quantity.

But these instruments are only the pioneers of the new age of electronic thinking. At the computer sessions of the American Institute of Electrical Engineers in February and of the Institute of Radio Engineers in March, it became clear that every calculator now in operation will soon be as outdated as an earphone-and-crystal radio compared with the frequency modulation-television models of 1949. The older machines, however, will not become obsolete, because problems exist suitable for every type to handle.

Fantastic new computers, geared not to split-second but to split-microsecond speed, are being rushed to completion. The Moore School of the University of Pennsylvania, birthplace of the Eniac, is building a machine called Edvac which has a far more capacious memory and greater versatility. This it is doing without the further aid of the Eniac's principal designers and the Edvac's original conceivers, John Mauchly and J. Prosper Eckert, Jr., who have gone into business with the Eckert-Mauchly Computer Corporation. Occupying two floors in a Philadelphia building, Eckert-Mauchly is testing a pair of computers known as Binac. Eckert-Mauchly also has contracts for six more elaborate machines known as Univac, to cost about $200,000 each, for government, industrial, and commercial use.

At Princeton, N. J., in a special computer building belonging to the Institute for Advanced Study, John von Neumann and other eminent mathematicians have been at work more than two years on a colossal computing device that is still some distance from completion. This is the machine that has been described by Vladimir Zworykin, research director of the Radio Corporation of America (which is cooperating in the project) as a future "world weather model." It might be set up to simulate every weather-making force and have these forces work upon one another a bit faster than in nature; thus tomorrow's weather could be read off today and not, as would be the case if every factor were taken into account by present methods, a year from now. But Dr. von Neumann is just as much interested in putting the machine to work on questions of atomic physics and economic statistics.

Meanwhile the Raytheon Manufacturing Company of Waltham, Mass., previously best known for manufacturing the magnetron tube of microwave radar, has accepted a big Government contract for a computer comparable with the Univac. Harvard University, having shipped its Mark II computer to the Naval Proving Ground at Dahlgren, Va., is up to a Mark III. The Massachusetts Institute of Technology has its "Project Whirlwind" for the construction of electronic brains needed for military purposes.

British scientists are active in the picture, too. They have a proud tradition in the field, for the Englishman Charles Babbage more than a century ago outlined the essential features of modern computers with his plans for a "difference engine." Advanced computers are now under construction by four British laboratories.

Not all of this activity is on the surface, nor is the picture one of uniform sweetness. There are military secrets and there are commercial secrets. Behind the scenes one senses intense rivalry and competition, with privately voiced charges of unfair publicity claims and pirated inventions, and hints of patent litigation to come. These are the symptoms of a big new industry in the making, with people fighting for their place on the ground floor.

What is at stake in the competition can be understood from a simple comparison. Some of the new machines under development will have the basic ability to carry out the multiplication of two 10-digit numbers in approximately a thousandth of a second. The same task would take five minutes (about 300,000 times as long) for a man with pencil and paper. The machine is equivalent to about 25,000 operators of desk computing machines.

Digital v. Analogue

There are two families of computers—the digital and the analogue. Those discussed above are of the digital type. It is with these that this article is primarily concerned. But the analogue computers came first; the celebrated "mechanical brain" at M.I.T., for which Vannevar Bush gained fame two decades ago, was an analogue machine. Radar and gun directors leaned heavily upon them, and they will continue to be important in many ways. So let us examine these machines before clarifying the distinction between analogue and digital computers and dissecting the latter.

The speedometer in your automobile is a simple example of the analogue computer. In proportion to the speed of the drive shaft, a centrifugal force is set up which moves a needle to the appropriate place on the "miles per hour" dial. This is an operation of differential calculus—a stationary needle position on the dial displays the rate of change in the position of the car.

The gears of your car, or of your watch, also do arithmetic: they multiply and divide, although, of course, the multiplier is fixed by a built-in gear ratio. The differential, between the rear wheels, is what its name implies: a mechanical subtracting machine, any extra speed gained by one wheel being subtracted from the other. All these ideas are actually used in mechanical computing machines of the analogue type; among their components are gears and cams and differentials.

Bush's "differential analyzer" solved problems in calculus. Different elements of the machine were set for various parts of the equation, all being geared together so that the only answers to come out would be the ones that were true to the equation's requirements.

There are electrical counterparts of the mechanical analogue computer. Instead of a mechanical position, we can have an electrical charge; instead of a velocity, we may have an electrical current, or the magnetic force induced by it. Circuits with resistance, inductance and capacitance are set up to behave in accordance with stipulated equations. An electrical transformer can multiply in the same manner as a pair of gears. Vacuum tube circuits can integrate. Such machines are being produced in considerable numbers—the Reac made by the Reeves Instrument Company is a successful example, automatically tracing out the answer to a calculus problem in a series of curves. M. I. T. has an electrical successor to the mechanical analyzer which looks like a telephone central station.

The analogue computers are likely to be less bulky and expensive than the digital type; they provide quick solutions. But like the slide rule (which is also of the analogue class, because it translates logarithms into physical distances) they have a limit to their possible accuracy. For the higher refinements of calculation, the digital or logical computer is now coming to the fore.

The Digital Idea

The digital computer is distinguished by the fact that it does not measure; it counts. It never responds to a greater or lesser degree; at every stage of its action, it is an "all or nothing" device, operating with discrete signals that either exist or do not exist.

The simplest digital computer is the human hand, from which, of course, we have our decimal system. Corresponding to such primitive indicators of a numerical unit as a finger, a pebble or a stylus scratch, the new automatic computers represent digits by such methods as:

A round hole in a strip of tape.

A square hole in a piece of cardboard.

A current in an electromagnet.

An armature attracted to the magnet.

A closed pair of electrical contacts.

A pulse of current in an electrical transmission line.

An electronic tube in which current is permitted to flow from filament to plate.

A magnetized area on a steel or alloyed wire.

A magnetized area on a coated tape.

A darkened area on a strip of photographic film.

A charged area on the face of a cathode-ray tube.

A moving ripple in a tank of mercury.

In each case there is no measurement of gradations in the signal. There is either a hole or no hole, contact or no contact, current or no current, pulse or no pulse. The designers simply have to make sure that there will be no ambiguity. They have to leave enough room on a tape, for example, so that a magnetized area will not get confused with an unmagnetized one. This sort of consideration, however, only limits the compactness and in some respects the speed of the machine; it does not affect the accuracy or the number of decimal places to which a calculation can be carried out.

Any such imprint or setting is called a "memory." The use of "memory" as a technical term of the computer trade has bolstered their anthropomorphic analogy to "brains." But there really is nothing surprising in it. Every photograph, every printed page, every canceled check, is a form of mechanical memory.

The important thing about the computer devices is not that they can record and remember numbers, but the fact that they are peculiarly adapted to yield up the memory content quickly, and in a form suited for immediate transportation and processing in other parts of the same machine. The "on-off" or "yes-no" kind of contrast makes it easy to transfer a record from one form to another: a pattern of punched holes instantly becomes a pattern of closed switches, or a pattern of conducting electronic tubes; it is the pattern that represents the number.

Of course, the number 1,000,000 is not represented by a million spots, holes, or ripples. Even when transmitted at the rate of a microsecond per unit, that would mean a million steps and take the uncon-

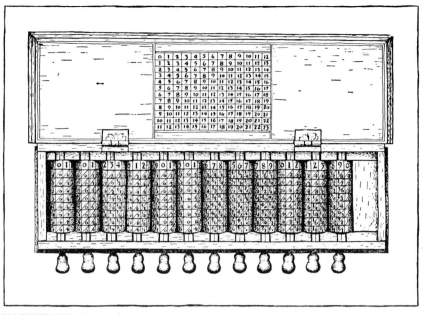

NAPIER'S RODS were a 17th-century attempt to mechanize multiplication. They were never made to work satisfactorily. The inventor, John Napier of Edinburgh, is better remembered because he was the inventor of logarithms.

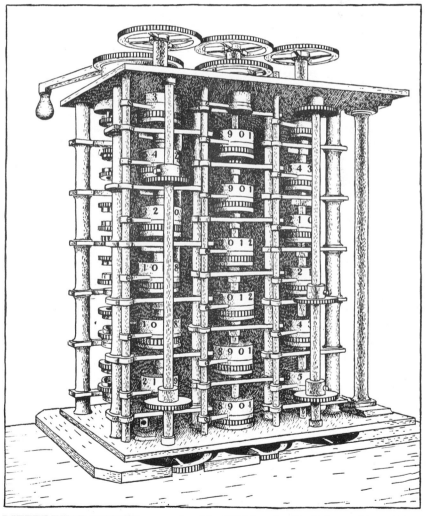

DIFFERENCE ENGINE, conceived in 1820 by the English mathematician Charles Babbage, was the first modern mathematical machine. It did not work because artisans of his time could not make sufficiently accurate parts.

DIFFERENTIAL ANALYZER in the Ballistic Research Laboratories of Aberdeen Proving Ground was built in the 1930s by the Massachusetts Institute of Technology and the Moore School of the University of Pennsylvania.

KEY ELEMENT of the differential analyzer is the integrator. The essential parts of this device are a disk and a small wheel which turns on its surface. These turning parts are regulated to integrate two separate rates of change.

scionable time of a full second. The answer, obviously, is the same one we use in ordinary calculation—position value coding, of which the decimal system is the most familiar example.

Digits Mechanized

The first artificial digital computing device was the abacus, a manually operated mechanical memory of great antiquity, yet far in advance of mere finger counting. It is still efficiently used in many parts of the world, including the Chinese laundries of the U. S. The next advance was the adding wheel. Gottfried Wilhelm Leibnitz, who invented the calculus independently of Isaac Newton, also invented the stepped wheel that became the basis for the first commercial calculator. Adding wheels of one sort or another led to the modern desk calculator. Without the various office machines that add, subtract, and multiply at the touch of fingers on a keyboard, it would be difficult to imagine an economy that includes vast insurance companies, closely audited chain stores, and banks competing for personal accounts at 10 cents a check. Were it not for the mechanization of business mathematics, modern industry would need more bookkeepers than factory hands. The scientists, ranging from social statisticians to nuclear physicists, have made full use of these commercial devices. The adding machine is as much a tool of the laboratory as the test tube and the oscilloscope.

A further development, suitable to an electrified era, began in the U. S. with the census expert Herman Hollerith. He developed the first punched-card machine using the position of holes to remember numerical data. In the 1890 census it proved its worth by reducing the labor in half. The Tabulating Machine Company which he organized in 1896 was later consolidated into the International Business Machines Corporation.

The IBM card, standardized in a size of three and a quarter by seven and three-eighths inches, with its 80 columns of 12 punching positions each, has become a kind of mathematical coinage. It is interchangeable among a variety of punching, sorting, tabulating, calculating, and accounting machines, which deal with the cards mechanically, electrically, and electronically. The same kind of card may hold the data of an astronomical orbit, an accountant's audit, a corporation's income tax, or a subscription to this magazine.

The IBM cards, or variations thereof, not only paved the way to the modern electronic brains, but in many cases they constitute a vital part of them. The cards with punched holes speak just the kind of language that an electrical machine understands. From them the machine reads its assignment, upon them it spells out its answers, and with stacks of them it forms its library or memory.

Quite comparable in importance to the development of modern computers, although somewhat overlooked, is the telegraphic printer or teletype. This is the machine that can be seen typing, no hands, in every newspaper office, every news agency bureau, every telegraph office; it is the machine that reads and writes at a distance. The essential elements in this mechanized communication are the relay and the perforated tape. The relay is the lineal descendant of the telegraph relay, switching on new electrical circuits as an armature responds to the electromagnetic pull induced by an incoming signal. The perforated tape has room for five meaningful holes, plus a sixth little sprocket hole which serves to advance it through the reading apparatus.

Note well the mathematical meaning of five holes, or lack of holes, across the width of a paper tape. How many different meanings can be conveyed by this "five-unit code?" The answer is 32, and the way we arrive at it illustrates the binary system of numeration that appears in the most advanced electronic brains.

The first position on the tape may be either perforated or blank; that accounts for two possibilities. Each of these can be associated with a second position that either has a hole or has not; that makes four possibilities. The third, fourth, and fifth positions each in turn doubles the number of alternatives, giving a total of 2^5 or 32. Of these, 26 are used for ordinary purposes of communication to represent the letters of the alphabet, and five for other commands to the mechanical typist: space (between words), carriage return, line feed, shift to letters, shift to figures. (One of the 32 positions is usually not utilized for any signal.) The ability to put such commands in code and to have them carried out by relays is another major ingredient of the electronic brain.

The width of such a tape, with its 2^5 choices, represents a five-digit number in the binary system. Some tapes employ a six-unit code, providing 64 choices.

The Relay Computers

It is possible to build a fairly fast computer using nothing much besides teleprinters and tape punchers, a switchboard and wiring, and a collection of adroitly interconnected relays. It is not only possible—it has been done by the Bell Telephone Laboratories.

The perforator presents the problem in the form of punched tape. The relays (standard items of any telephone dial center) do the calculating. The trick of adding is to wire their contacts and coils

in such a way that the closing of any two relays energizes the relay that represents the sum. For instance, if relay No. 1 and relay No. 3 are simultaneously closed, the only possible path presented to an incoming current is the one leading through its closed contacts to the coil of relay No. 4. However, if the incoming current arrives from the "carry in 1" wire (meaning that there was a "1 to carry" from the previous column of the addition), the path leads to relay No. 5.

The Bell Telephone Laboratories are not in the computer business except as it serves the telephone business. But the engineers had to do a lot of calculating in that business, and George R. Stibitz, then of Bell Labs (now an independent consultant to the computer industry), conceived the idea of building a robot computer out of the familiar machinery of the telephone system, and the first of a series of five progressively more complicated computers was built by Bell in 1939.

Characteristically, the communication engineers were not satisfied merely with a relay robot that could calculate. What good was all that saving of mental labor if they had to walk around the labyrinthine corridors of the laboratories to get to the machine? So they also substituted wiring for walking, and rigged up three remote stations, on various floors, at which mathematical problems were teletyped in (unless, of course, they got a busy signal), and at which the answers were typed back. This feature seemed fairly commonplace to the telephone men, and they were somewhat surprised at the amazement of members of the American Mathematical Society when, in a 1940 meeting at Dartmouth College, problems put on a long-distance circuit from Hanover to New York received an immediate answer on the teletype printer. Actually it was no more difficult than sending the answers across the room.

Compared with the electronic devices we shall discuss below, the relay computers are slow. On the other hand, they are reliable. One machine ran 1,500 hours without a failure. They check themselves, refusing to let an error go through even when they are unattended. When some element in the apparatus fails, the machine simply drops that portion of the problem and proceeds to the next.

During the war IBM built several relay computers, two of which have been installed at Columbia University, and, under the supervision of W. J. Eckert, are available to scientists engaged in basic research The first of the large-scale calculators was the Mark I, or the Automatic Sequence Controlled Calculator, which IBM presented to Harvard University, where it went to work in April, 1944. Using adding wheels controlled by electrical impulses, with re-

lays for traffic direction, it calculates with numbers of 23 decimal digits and computer products to 46-digit accuracy. It gets its instructions from perforated tape, from IBM cards, and from the manual setting of 1,440 dial switches. It emits its answers either on IBM cards or by typing columns of figures on a roll of paper.

Electronic Computers

What do relays really do? They are nothing but switches operated by electricity, so that one signal opens a valve or gate through which another current can pass. The very same thing can be done by an electronic tube—it is for this reason that the British use the word "valve" where we use "tube." The electronic valve does what the relay does—and does it thousands of times faster. In the relay, a mechanical object must move through space to open and close the gate. In the electronic tube, only electrons move, and their speed can best be indicated by the fact that in a radar set, electronic currents reverse themselves millions and even billions of times per second.

The first mathematical computer to employ the electronic swiftness of radio and radar was built in wartime secrecy for the Army Ordnance Department at the University of Pennsylvania, and later moved, at a cost of about $100,000, to the Ballistic Research Laboratories at the Aberdeen Proving Ground. It is the Electronic Numerical Integrator and Computer, the previously mentioned Eniac. This phenomenal machine is so complicated that no single person, even among its inventors, knows every part of its wiring or the function of each of its 18,000-odd tubes. However, some of its arrangements are quite simple. The system of electronic number storage, or memory, is obvious almost at first glance.

If you were admitted by Army Ordnance officers to the new air-conditioned quarters of the Eniac, you would observe the walls lined with panels of radio tubes. You are shown one panel called an accumulator, and you are told that it is capable of remembering a 10-digit number. It can register any number from zero to 9,999,999,999—but only one such number at a time.

An accumulator consists essentially of 100 vacuum tubes (one might say 200 tubes, since each is a double triode). They are arranged in 10 columns of 10 tubes each. Reading from right to left, you have the units column, the tens column, the hundreds column, and so on. In each column, the bottom tube represents zero, the second tube represents 1, the third tube 2, and so on to 9.

To make things even easier, there is a neon light in front of each tube which goes on when that tube is in the "indicat-

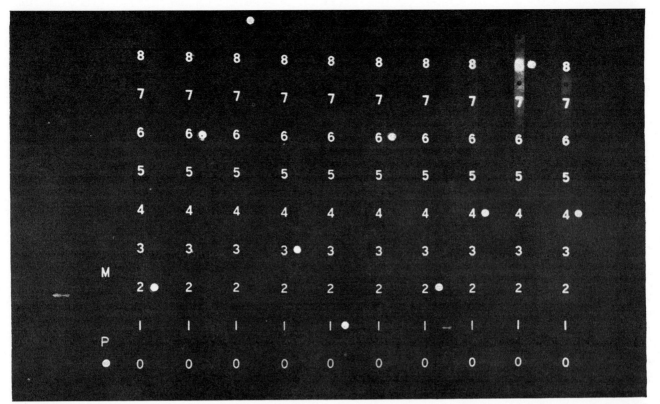

ACCUMULATOR of the Eniac computer operates on the decimal system. It has a "memory" of 10 digits (*hori-* *zontal rows*). Letters M and P at left stand for minus and plus. Number indicated by neon lights is 2,693,162,484.

ing" state. Only one tube in each column can be indicating. If the number is 5,-384,293,768, tube 5 will be excited in the first column, tube 3 in the second column, and so on. If the number stays put for a few seconds (which in practice it does not, except during demonstrations or checkups) it is quite easy even for the untutored to read the number written on the wall.

The Eniac has 20 such accumulators, which occupy about half of the machine's total space. Thus it can store just 20 numbers (of 10 digits each) in its "electronic memory." At least one of the accumulators will be in use at any given moment in a dynamic way—either sending out the number which it has been holding or receiving a new number. The new number may come into a blank accumulator, on which it registers, or it may come into an accumulator which already holds a number. In the latter case, the new one is automatically added.

And here, at a flash, we see the machine's wonderful possibilities. An accumulator can absorb a 10-digit number (adding it, if necessary, to its existing contents) in just one five-thousandth of a second. Or, to use the kind of time unit which is more suitable to this discussion—in 200 microseconds.

One peculiarity of the high-speed calculators is that it takes no more time to do the most elaborate addition than the simplest. The Eniac needs as long to add 1 and 1 as to add two full 10-digit numbers. In fact, an accumulator gets its maximum workout when it is required to subtract 1 from 1. Since it works in one direction only, it cannot simply go back one step from 1 to zero. Instead, the minus 1 is set in as 9,999,999,999, *i.e.*, 10 billion minus 1. It then adds 1 to 9,999,999,999.

In performing this addition, the machine functions as follows: A single pulse of electricity representing the number 1 goes into the units column. At the first tube position it finds that a free path exists for it to go to the second tube. There, also, the gate is open, and so on through successive tubes to the top of the column. The impulse travels to the tube that represents number 9. The "flip-flop" circuit at 9 position has been in the "on" condition. At this point three things happen: First, the impulse turns the top tube to "off," clearing away the 9. Second, it continues to the next tube position, representing zero, and switches that to the indicating condition. The units column now reads zero, as it should. But if you were doing this mentally you would say "zero and one to carry." To correspond to this, as the third step the activation of zero causes a single pulse to be carried to the tens column. Here the pulse runs through precisely the same routine, finding its way up the column to change the excitation from 9 to zero, and sending a carry into the hundreds column. This is repeated until the entire array has been changed from 9,999,999,999 to 0,000,000,000. The machine, doing it the hard way, has car-

ried out the calculation 1 minus 1 equals zero.

Suppose the number to be added is 1,000,000,011. Then single pulses will enter at the same time into the units column, the tens column, and the billions column. After each one runs through its cycle, another timed signal comes along which instructs each column to yield its "carry" signal, if it has one in store, to the column on its left.

What about multiplying and dividing? These could be done, and in some calculators are done, by repeated addition and subtraction. Multiplying 52 by 7 simply means setting up the number 52 and adding 52 six times. Similarly, division is repeated subtraction. There are, however, some short cuts. Eniac uses a built-in multiplication table. This is wired up to give immediately the product of any two digits. The sums of all the products are then fed into an accumulator and added up. By this method the entire multiplicand can be multiplied by one digit in the time corresponding to one addition. The complete multiplication of a pair of 10-digit numbers can be accomplished in 1/350 of a second.

Any numerical computation, whether it deals with an equation or a table of numbers, can be reduced to a succession of the basic arithmetical operations.

Eniac was designed for a specific purpose. The Ordnance Department needed firing tables—a different one for every new kind of gun, and for every different size and shape of shell. The Army had

ELECTRONIC TUBES are the counting units of the Eniac accumulator. Each light of the panel on the opposite page represents a tube. There are 10 columns of 10 tubes. Bright tubes at right and bottom are auxiliaries.

large numbers of skilled mental laborers, sitting at desks with their fingers punching the keys of office-type adding and computing machines, figuring out the necessary tables. It took such a person 20 hours to work out the trajectory of a single shell, making allowance for air resistance and the many other factors. Eniac does the same thing in half a minute. The implications of such speeds for the remote control of guided missiles are evident.

Although Eniac was a tremendous success in its way, opening the path to all-electronic computation, nothing exactly like it will ever be built again. It has serious limitations. Chief among them is a vast discrepancy between the speed with which it can compute and the time it takes for it to become aware of the problem and to spell out its answers.

For a given kind of problem, it must be instructed by plugging in wires and setting switches—both of them manual operations that go at the poor speed of human hands. In addition it has so many components that there are numerous sources of malfunction requiring elaborate maintenance routines. Another limitation, which became evident to its designers even while it was being built, is the limited electronic memory and the large space required for storing numbers in electronic tubes. The tubes require 120 kilowatts of power, and another 20 kilowatts is needed for the blower equipment to take away the heat in the tubes.

This led to the conclusion that the use of 100 tubes to spell out a 10-digit number is wasteful of space and power.

There is a way to make a memory composed of electronic tubes more compact. The IBM Selective Sequence Electronic Calculator in New York is an example. The machine deals with 14-digit numbers. On the Eniac principle each number would require 1,400 double tubes. This machine gets by with 560. (In both the Eniac and the IBM machine there are various auxiliary tubes to control the circuits, but these are ignored here.) This is done by modifying the decimal system, using a hybrid called "binary decimal."

Any number from zero to 9 can be represented by only four tubes, provided each tube has a numerical value associated with its position in the group, and provided that more than one of the group can be "on" at the same time. The values chosen are 1, 2, 4 and 8. Thus:

1 is represented by tube 1.
2 is represented by tube 2.
3 is represented by tubes 1 and 2.
4 is represented by tube 4.
5 is represented by tubes 4 and 1.
6 is represented by tubes 4 and 2.
7 is represented by tubes 4, 2 and 1.
8 is represented by tube 8.
9 is represented by tubes 8 and 1.
0 is represented by all tubes off.

This system of binary-decimal digits is applied not only to electronic tubes but also to banks of relays and rolls of paper tape, which provide a vast storage

of numbers and sequence instructions. At the input and output connections to the external world, the machine has an automatic device for translating between the decimal system and the binary-decimal.

In many cases there are good reasons for sticking to the decimal system, at least as far as the machine's external relations are concerned. One very practical reason is that the IBM calculators and the Eniac were built to receive their problems from the punched holes of standard IBM cards. IBM's newest calculator, the Type 604 mentioned earlier, employs the binary decimal system, four tubes per digit, in connection with standard punched cards that are completely read and processed at the rate of 100 per minute.

The decimal system is also desirable wherever the machine must handle large amounts of "outside" numerical material. Thus it will probably continue to be used in any "business" type machine which handles accounting problems, inventories, tax computations, or in any "scientific" machine which deals with statistical material. One of the most advanced calculator designs—the Univac, being built by the Eckert-Mauchly Computer Corporation for the use of the Census Bureau—also will operate on the decimal system.

On the other hand, when the Eckert-Mauchly group got orders for a computer to do engineering problems where the prime purpose was to solve equa-

CODED PULSES are fed into the Eniac machine by cycling unit. Characteristics of pulses may be observed on the face of the cathode-ray tube at the top. A four-peak signal is shown on the tube. Key to code is in the center.

TABLE OF FUNCTIONS is used as an Eniac auxiliary. Numerical values representing quantities that change in relation to each other may be set up on table. These are fed into machine at appropriate points in a problem.

tions, it was designed for the binary system (hence the name Binac—binary automatic computer). The calculator being built at the Institute for Advanced Study, in Princeton, for theoretical analysis of problems in mathematical physics, weather forecasting, and other problems of that nature, also will work on a pure binary system.

Binary Numbers

The binary system permits the "on-off" kind of memory to be used with 100 per cent efficiency. As long as we have no special reason for compromising with the decimal notation, we can have our tubes signify 1, 2, 4, 8, 16, 32, 64, 128, 256, 512, 1,024, doubling at each stage, as far as we like. Any intermediate number can always be assembled by appropriate combinations of the tubes.

At this point we find that we no longer need the decimal notation at all. There is another notation which serves the purpose better. The binary system of numbers really requires only two symbols, which are usually written as 0 and 1. Let us first compare it with the above list of doubling numbers:

Decimal notation	Binary notation
0	0
1	1
2	10
4	100
8	1,000
16	10,000
32	100,000
64	1,000,000
128	10,000,000
256	100,000,000

One inference is obvious at a glance. To multiply a number by 2, just add a zero. Or, in a machine, shift the columns one step to the left. Thus multiplying becomes as easy as adding.

Now let us see how the other numbers fit in. We will take just the first few:

Decimal	Binary
3	11
5	101
6	110
7	111
9	1,001

Thus it is clear that every number can be represented by some combination of the two symbols 1 and 0. The presence of one or the other constitutes a binary digit. The phrase binary digit has been abbreviated in a new term—"bit," a rather neat usage because it is essentially a bit of information. In the binary system we need 10 bits to represent a decimal thousand, 20 bits to represent a million, 30 bits to represent a billion, and approximately 33 bits to represent the ten-billion figure of an Eniac accumulator. It takes only one electronic tube to represent a bit. Thus 33 tubes do the work that in the Eniac requires 100 and in the binary-decimal system would require 40.

In addition, binary notation thrives on the simple contrast of two alternatives—the ultimate in interchangeability and transportability. The 1 and 0 we have used in the above explanation can be translated physically, and without any further coding, into all sorts of interchangeable effects—spatial, electrical, magnetic. For example, 1 may be represented by an electric pulse and 0 by the absence of a pulse; 1 by magnetic north and 0 by magnetic south, and so on.

Any such representation may be used as long as it is consistent and interchangeable. As a magnetized tape passes under a coil, the presence or absence of a magnetized spot is converted into the presence or absence of an electrical signal, which in turn can be routed to an electronic tube. If there is a signal (meaning 1) the tube can be flipped from a 0 position to a 1, or from a 1 to a 0. The beauty of the binary system is that addition of a digit always means a simple reversal of the condition of the "memory"—adding a pulse where there is none, or wiping it out if there is one (converting 1 to 0).

Logic and Control

The next step is the realization that the binary system does not merely apply to numbers. It applies to logic. For 1 and 0, we can substitute "yes" and "no." Thus, for example, a binary machine may be adjusted to deal with double negatives, making "no" and "no" add up to "yes." The vacuum tube lends itself especially well to acting out such logical concepts as "and," "or" and "neither." To illustrate the idea of "and," a four-element tube has two grids that act as "gates" controlling the current from grid to plate. If both of them are normally held at a strong negative voltage, current can flow only if both are turned positive by an incoming signal. Signals on each are a "necessary" condition for any current to come out of the tube; neither alone provides a "sufficient" condition. On the other hand, external circuits can be so arranged that a signal from either one of two sources will make the tube conduct; such an arrangement carries out the idea of "or," since one source or the other will suffice.

Such electronic gates are at the heart of the traffic and control systems of the high-speed calculators. Each gate may have one, two, or more locks, requiring certain simultaneous conditions to be satisfied before they will permit the machine to proceed to the next step.

The speed of the electronic tube is the key to the speed of the new calculators. We have already seen that the tubes are used in three ways: first, as a memory device which can receive and hold numbers; second, as an arithmetical unit; and third, as a gate for directing the flow of electrical traffic to different parts of the machine in accordance with instruction signals. Vacuum tubes have a fourth important function in making the calculators possible; they are employed, somewhat as in radio and television sets, to amplify worn-out signals that have lost their sharpness and strength, reshaping them as good as new.

Of the four functions, the least efficient is the one described at the beginning of this article—storage. And that is because it takes the length of a wall to store any appreciable quantity of numbers, whether the tubes are used 10 to a decimal digit, or four per decimal digit, or even one per binary digit. For really large-scale computations, machines need a memory that is both more compact and more capacious than any that can be achieved with electronic tubes.

One recourse is to have the machine print out partial answers which can then be fed back into it—or other machines—when needed. The IBM Selective Sequence Calculator makes considerable use of this method. As the machine solves some mathematical function, the resulting table of values is perforated in a coded set of punched holes on a wide roll of heavy paper, not unlike an old-fashioned player-piano roll. This is mounted on an arrangement of cylinders and pulleys. Later, when the machine is ready to refer to the table, it "looks up" the proper constant by letting the paper run through it until it finds the appropriate value. On a similar principle, the machines can have a virtually infinite memory capacity in the form of punched cards, but the speed of this method is limited by the slow rate at which the machine reads the cards—100 cards per minute.

To get to another order of magnitude for compactness and speed of memory, designers have turned to methods other than perforated paper. Among them are: magnetic tape, photographic film, charged cathode-ray-tube surfaces and, most remarkable of all, columns of mercury in which numbers are stored in the dynamic form of waves moving at the speed of sound.

Magnetic tape, the same kind now coming into favor for recording the sound waves of radio programs and dictating machines, is being used widely in machines now under construction: both the Edvac and the Univac will make important use of it. Its advantage is compactness: a one-inch strip of eight-millimeter tape can hold 800 distinguishable "spots" of magnetization—carrying as much information as an entire IBM card. Besides, as users of tape-recording equipment know, the magnetization can be applied at high speed, can be read back just as fast, and can be erased more easily than a blackboard.

Another experimental approach is through electrostatic storage. The principle starts with the cathode-ray tube that forms the viewing screen of both radar and television sets. The memory that such tubes have for a picture can also be used to store patterns of electrical charge. The idea is attractive because the "reading" of stored numbers can be done very quickly by means of a beam of electrons. RCA engineers have built a tube for the purpose called the Selectron, with a mesh of wires built in to control the area on which electric charge is deposited, and this is one of the elements under test for the computer being built at the Institute for Advanced Study. A new British calculator at Manchester University uses a regular television tube, with dots on its face for zero and dashes for 1. The U. S. Bureau of Standards has plans for employing the same device.

But what really seems to symbolize the speed of the modern computer is the new tendency to resort to memory-in-motion through the use of the mercury column.

Pulses in Mercury

Mercury memory came out of wartime radar. One tactical difficulty with radar was the fact that an enemy plane could not well be distinguished against a solid background. It could conceal itself from the radar eye by hiding in front of a mountain as well as behind it. Engineers reasoned they could get around this difficulty if they could find some automatic way of canceling out a fixed echo and showing only those received from a moving object. This was finally accomplished, toward the end of the war, with a device called the delay line. The idea was to make an echo signal travel tardily within the set so that the following echo, arriving perhaps a thousandth of a second later, would overtake it. If the two matched, they would cancel each other out. Thus echoes from fixed terrain would not show. But if the echoes came from different places, as they would from a moving airplane, both of them would appear on the face of the oscilloscope.

One of the best means of delaying such a signal was found to be an "acoustic" line in which the signal would generate a ripple in a tube of liquid mercury. Traveling in the mercury at the speed of sound, the signal would come out at the far end an appreciable interval after its entrance. The exact period of delay could be adjusted by changing the temperature of the mercury or the length of the path through it. For example, at 65 degrees Centigrade ripples travel through mercury at a mile a second. In electronic matters, where most events occur closer to the 186,000-mile-per-second speed of light, this is slow.

In the Binac now being completed by Eckert-Mauchly, an 18-inch column of mercury maintained at 65 degrees provides a delay of 336 microseconds. Since successive pulses in this machine are separated by only one quarter of a microsecond, this delay means that at any given moment the 18-inch length of mercury has in storage four times 336, or 1,344 binary digits. For convenience of executive administration, this is divided into 32 "words," each containing 30 binary digits, a pulse space for plus or minus sign, and 11 more unused spaces (or time intervals) to separate successive words.

The mercury tube is the kind of "brain" in which information is supposed to go in one ear and come out of the other. An electrical signal arriving at the delay line causes a quartz crystal to expand by the well-known piezoelectric effect. The crystal pushes against the mercury, and a ripple runs through faster than the eye could follow. After 1/3,000 of a second it arrives at the far end, presses against another crystal, and generates a new electrical impulse. This is built up in an amplifier and fed back into the front end again. The cycle repeats 3,000 times a second. Thus the digit goes around and around, and would do so just about forever if nothing intervened. At the desired moment, however, an electronic gate opens in the amplifier to switch the signal into some other circuit—the electronic adder, for example. Or the signal can be erased, simply by instructing the amplifier not to amplify at the moment when the signal comes around.

At the present writing the most popular system for calculating machines is based on the mercury ripples, supplemented by electronic computing circuits, magnetic wire or tape for intermediate and erasable memory, punched cards or paper tape for a still more permanent library of memories and accumulated answers, and automatic printers for spelling out the answers.

Future Applications

What does this all mean in practical terms, for today and tomorrow? How will it affect business, government, military affairs, science, and mathematics itself?

It is tempting to make grand generalizations. The writer is indebted to Samuel N. Alexander, chief of the Bureau of Standards' electronic computer section, for a rather hardheaded appraisal of some real prospects—purposes for which various branches of the government are submitting their bids to be among the first to get such machines.

First, there is the matter of enormous numbers of routine substitutions in formulas. An important example, aside from the mission of wringing more results from the figures of the 1950 census, is the adjustment of maps. Many nations may be correctly mapped, but two adjoining countries are likely to have a discrepancy of several feet at their mutual boundaries; the corrections require a tremendous number of separate calculations, and both the Army Map Service and the Coast and Geodetic Survey would like electronic assistance.

Secondly, there are elaborate engineering computations which now require enormous effort—for example, a roomful of people spending more than a year and a half checking stress estimates to transfer a design from a model to a full-size airplane. This kind of thing, along with many problems in hydrodynamics, supersonic airplane characteristics, and so on, can henceforth be relegated to the computing machine. The slowness of ordinary computation was partly responsible for the fact that no U. S. bomber flew in the last war which had not been designed before the war began. This lag should be greatly reduced by the new computers.

Thirdly, there is a group of uses that have to do with "program procedure." What is the best way to distribute available manpower, funds, equipment, and so forth, to maximize a particular effect or to minimize cost? For example, the armed forces can make up various menus which will satisfy the soldier's needs for calories, vitamins and minerals. But each food item also has various such qualities as perishability, compactness and cost. How can you meet the dietary requirements with minimum cost, minimum shipping weight, or minimum time of delivery? Normally the mathematical labor in figuring out the advantages of every possible combination is too great, so only a few combinations are studied thoroughly.

Fourthly, since the digital calculator is essentially a logical machine, it can make all sorts of quick decisions that now require an alert and hard-pressed human being. The Air Navigation Development Board is considering the use of computing machines at airport control towers to relieve the traffic control men of many elementary, stereotyped decisions. And the Research and Development Board of the National Military Establishment has a committee at work considering how electrical computers can be rigged to play out war games.

In the present state of world affairs military applications are still uppermost in the thinking about calculators. The last war undoubtedly stimulated the development of these machines, and the threat of renewed war is a continued stimulant. It seems that electronic computers, associated with radar, will be the main defense against high-speed bombers, tracking the bomber and guiding the anti-aircraft missile to a collision course. And future long-range offensive missiles will most likely radio back what position information they can gather, and have it processed in a home computer, out of which radio-transmitted answers will give the missile its instructions for further navigation.

Should the war clouds dissipate, the cleared air would show the electronic brains contributing mightily to the advance of science and the efficiency of both business and government. They may even offer a technical means of contributing to world peace by helping to make world government practical. The "curse of bigness," which has affected big corporations and big governments alike, is very largely due to the difficulty of any small group of men knowing what is going on in a vast and far-flung enterprise. The trouble with planning is that the planners cannot know all the facts bearing on their plans; much less have they the time and ability to figure out all the consequences that will result from one or another course of action. These considerations have brought about a feeling for an optimum size for any single administration, whether government or business, beyond which the operation gets too unwieldy to compete with smaller, better integrated units. The electronic computers or information processing systems may well move that optimum size upward.

Though they replace other kinds of human mental effort, the mathematical machines will never replace the mathematician. More mathematicians will be needed, but the nature of their work will be changed. As theoretical physicists make ever more general equations expressing the basic forces of the universe with fewer and fewer symbols, their abstractions get ever farther from the numerical values of the laboratory experiment and ordinary life. Even Albert Einstein is not free of this difficulty. His approach toward a unified field theory, a generalization into which relativity fits as a part, may or may not be correct. Einstein does not know. The trouble, he once told the writer, is that "tremendous labors of the most brilliant minds, possibly for several generations, will be needed to translate the general theory into specific cases which can be tested by experiment." Perhaps the new computers, like the one being built by Einstein's colleagues at the Institute for Advanced Study, will help to shorten this labor, and thus allow investigators of the mysteries of the universe to test their own theories to determine whether they are on the right track.

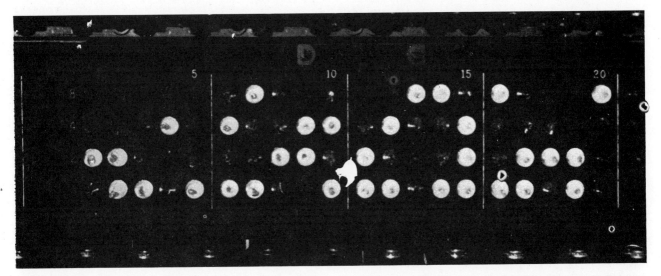

INDICATOR LIGHTS of IBM Selective Sequence Calculator depict binary decimal counting system. Four lights in each column represent 1, 2, 4 and 8. These may be added to indicate any number from zero to 9. Column at left notes plus or minus. Each of 19 other columns is one digit. Number is +3.141592653589793238, or *pi*.

ELECTRONIC-MEMORY SECTION of the Selective Sequence machine is an array of tubes. Each of the panels that contains 24 tubes represents one digit. Four of the 24 tubes indicate the digit by system outlined above. Remainder control route of signals through calculator. Twelve-tube panels are auxiliary control units.

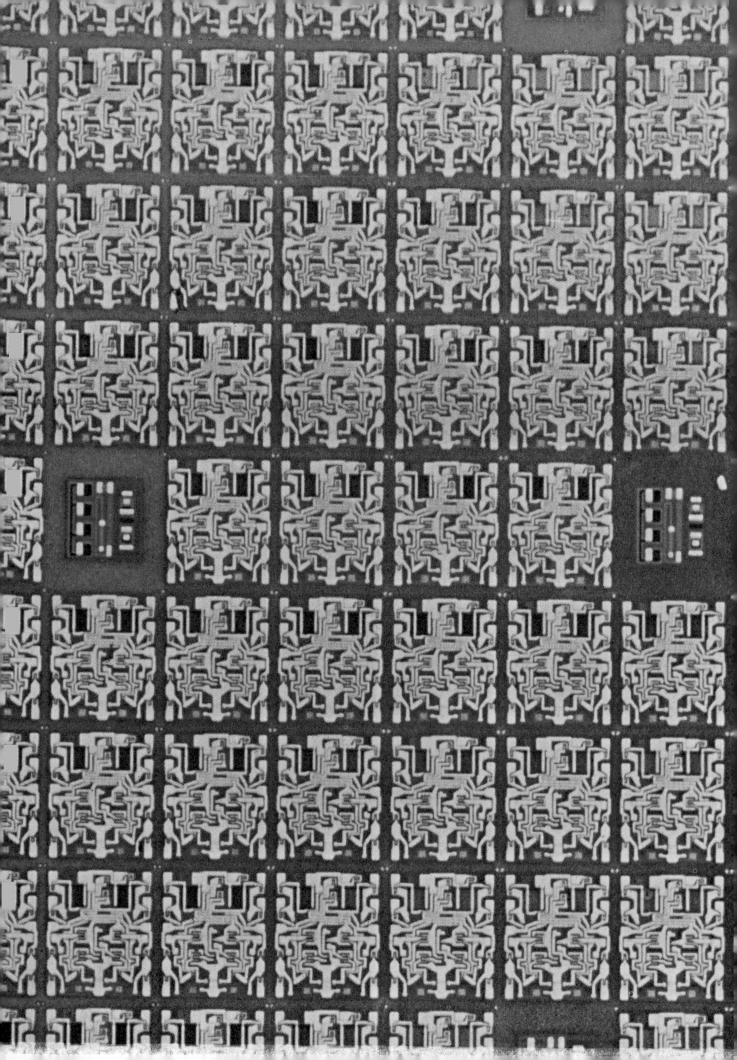

45 COMPUTERS

STANISLAW M. ULAM · September 1964

Although to many people the electronic computer has come to symbolize the importance of mathematics in the modern world, few professional mathematicians are closely acquainted with the machine. Some, in fact, seem even to fear that individual scientific efforts will be pushed into the background or replaced by less imaginative, purely mechanical habits of research. I believe such fears to be quite groundless. It is preferable to regard the computer as a handy device for manipulating and displaying symbols. Even the most abstract thinkers agree that the simple act of writing down a few symbols on a piece of paper facilitates concentration. In this respect alone—and it is not a trivial one—the new electronic machines enlarge our effective memory and provide a marvelous extension of the means for experimenting with symbols in science. In this article I shall try to indicate how the computer can be useful in mathematical research.

The idea of using mechanical or semiautomatic means to perform arithmetical calculations is very old. The origin of the abacus is lost in antiquity, and computers of some kind were evidently built by the ancient Greeks. Blaise Pascal in the 17th century constructed a working mechanism to perform arithmetical operations. Gottfried Wilhelm von Leibniz, one of the creators of mathematical logic as well as the coinventor of the infinitesimal calculus, outlined a program for what would now be called automatized thinking. The man who clearly visualized a general-purpose computer, complete with a flexible programming scheme and memory units, was Charles Babbage of England. He described a machine he called the analytical engine in 1833 and spent the rest of his life and much of his fortune trying to build it.

Among the leading contributors to modern computer technology were an electrical engineer, J. Presper Eckert, Jr., a physicist, John W. Mauchly, and one of the leading mathematicians of this century, John von Neumann. In 1944 Eckert and Mauchly were deep in the development of a machine known as ENIAC, which stands for Electronic Numerical Integrator and Computer. Designed to compute artillery firing tables for the Army Ordnance Department, ENIAC was finally completed late in 1945. It was wired to perform a specific sequence of calculations; if a different sequence was needed, it had to be extensively rewired. On hearing of the ENIAC project during a visit to the Aberdeen Proving Ground in the summer of 1944, von Neumann became fascinated by the idea and began developing the logical design of a computer capable of using a flexible stored program: a program that could be changed at will without revising the computer's circuits.

A major stimulus for von Neumann's enthusiasm was the task he faced as consultant to the theoretical group at Los Alamos, which was charged with solving computational problems connected with the atomic-bomb project. After a discussion in which we reviewed one of these problems von Neumann turned to me and said: "Probably in its solution we shall have to perform more elementary arithmetical steps than the total in all the computations performed by the human race heretofore." I reminded him that there were millions of schoolchildren in the world and that the total number of additions, multiplications and divisions they were obliged to perform every day over a period of a few years would certainly exceed that needed in our problem. Unfortunately we could not harness this great reservoir of talent for our purposes, nor could we in 1944 command the services of an electronic computer. The atomic-bomb calculations had to be simplified to the point where they could be solved with paper and pencil and the help of old-fashioned desk calculators.

Down the hall from my present office at the Los Alamos Scientific Laboratory is an electronic computer known as MANIAC II (Mathematical Analyzer, Numerical Integrator and Computer), an advanced version of MANIAC I, which von Neumann and his associates completed at the Institute for Advanced Study in 1952. MANIAC II, which was put in operation in 1957, can add two numbers consisting of 13 decimal digits (43 binary digits) in about six microseconds (six millionths of a second). In a separate building nearby is a still newer computer called STRETCH, built by the International Business Machines Corporation, which can manipulate numbers containing 48 binary digits with about 10 times the overall speed of MANIAC II.

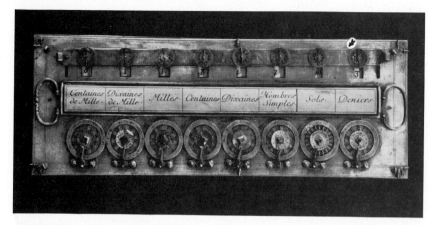

FIRST MECHANICAL COMPUTER was probably this adding machine, designed in 1642 by the French philosopher and mathematician Blaise Pascal. The machine adds when the wheels are turned with a stylus. Gears inside automatically "carry" numbers from one wheel to the next. Similar but somewhat simpler devices, made of plastic, are widely sold.

"DIFFERENCE ENGINE," often called the first modern mathematical machine, was conceived in 1820 by the English mathematician Charles Babbage. He built a small version of it but the larger engine he envisioned was never completed. Parts of it, such as this unit, are now in South Kensington Science Museum. Babbage spent many years trying unsuccessfully to create an "analytical engine" that would do almost everything the modern computer does.

MANIAC II and STRETCH are examples of dozens of custom-designed computers built throughout the world in the past 20 years. The first of the big commercially built computers, UNIVAC I, was delivered to the Bureau of the Census in 1951; three years later the General Electric Company became the first industrial user of a UNIVAC I. In the 13 years since the first UNIVAC more than 16,000 computer systems of various makes and sizes have been put to work by the U.S. Government, industry and universities. Of these about 250 are of the largest type, with speed and power roughly comparable to MANIAC II.

Together with increases in arithmetical speed have come increases in memory capacity and in speed of access to stored numbers and instructions. In the biggest electronic machines the memory capacity is now up to about 100,000 "words," or several million individual binary digits. I am referring here to the "fast" memory, to which the access time can be as short as a microsecond. This time is steadily being reduced; a hundredfold increase in speed seems possible in the near future. A "slow" memory, used as an adjunct to the fast one, normally consists of digits stored on magnetic tape and can be of almost unlimited capacity. The size of memory devices and basic electronic circuits has been steadily reduced, until now even the most elaborate computers can fit into a small room. The next generation of computers, employing microelectronic circuits, will be smaller by a factor of 100 to 1,000.

It is apparent that many problems are so difficult that they would tax the capacity of any machine one can imagine being built in the next decade. For example, the hydrodynamics of compressible fluids can be studied reasonably well on existing machines if the investigation is limited to problems in two dimensions, but it cannot be studied very satisfactorily in three dimensions. In a two-dimensional study one can imagine that the fluid is confined in a "box" that has been divided into, say, 10,000 cells; the cells are expressed in terms of two coordinates, each of which is divided into 100 parts. In each cell are stored several values, such as those for density and velocity, and a new set of values must be computed for each successive chosen unit of time. It is obvious that if this same problem is simply extended to include a third dimension, storage must be provided for a million cells, which exceeds the capacity of present machines. One of the studies that is limited in this way is the effort to forecast the weather, for which it would be desirable to use a many-celled three-dimensional model of the atmosphere.

Sometimes when a problem is too complex to be solved in full detail by computer, it is possible to obtain a representative collection of specific solutions by the "Monte Carlo" method. Many years ago I happened to consider ways of calculating what fraction of all games of solitaire could be completed satisfactorily to the last card. When I could not devise a general solution, it occurred to me that the problem could be examined heuristically, that is, in such a way that the examination would at least give an idea of the solution. This would involve actually playing out a number of games, say 100 or 200, and simply recording the results. It was an ideal task for a computer and was at the origin of the Monte Carlo method.

This method is commonly applied to problems of mathematical physics such as those presented by the design of nuclear reactors. In a reactor neutrons are released; they collide, scatter, multiply and are absorbed or escape with various probabilities, depending on the geometry and the composition of the fuel elements and other components. In a complicated geometry no way is known to compute directly the number of neutrons in any given range of energy, direction and velocity. Instead one resorts to a sampling procedure in which the computer traces out a large number of possible histories of individual particles. The computer does not consider all the possible things that might happen to the particle, which would form a very complicated tree of branching eventualities, but selects at each branching point just one of the eventualities with a suitable probability (which is known to the physicist) and examines a large class of such possible chains of events. By gathering statistics on many such chains one can get an idea of the behavior of the system. The class of chains may have to be quite large but it is small compared with the much larger class of all possible branchings. Such sampling procedures, which would be impracticable without the computer, have been applied to many diverse problems.

The variety of work in mathematical physics that has been made possible in recent years through the use of computers is impressive indeed. Astronomy journals, for instance, contain an increasing number of computer results bearing on such matters as the history of stars, the motions of stars in clusters, the complex behavior of stellar atmospheres and the testing of cosmological theories. It has long been recognized that it is mathematically difficult to obtain particular solutions to problems involving the general theory of relativity so that the predictions of alternative formulations can be tested by observation or experiment. The computer is

FIRST ELECTRONIC DIGITAL COMPUTER, the Electronic Numerical Integrator and Computer (ENIAC), was built at the University of Pennsylvania for the Army Ordnance Department. Completed in the fall of 1945, it had 19,000 vacuum tubes, 1,500 relays and hundreds of thousands of resistors, capacitors and inductors. It consumed almost 200 kilowatts of electric power. Power and tube failures and other difficulties plagued its first few years of operation. To change its program it was necessary to rewire thousands of circuits. With constant improvements ENIAC was kept in service at the Ballistic Research Center, Aberdeen, Md., until late 1955.

now making it possible to obtain such predictions in many cases. A similar situation exists in nuclear physics with regard to alternative field theories.

I should now like to discuss some particular examples of how the computer can perform work that is both interesting and useful to a mathematician. The first examples are problems in number theory. This subject deals with properties of ordinary integers and particularly with those properties that concern the two most fundamental operations on them: addition and multiplication.

As in so much of "pure" mathematics the objective is to discover and then prove a theorem containing some general truth about numbers. It is often easy to see a relation that holds true in special cases; the task is to show that it holds true in general.

Karl Friedrich Gauss, called "the prince of mathematicians" by his contemporaries, greatly favored experiments on special cases and diligent work with examples to obtain his inspirations for finding general truths in number theory. Asked how he divined some of the remarkable regularities of numbers, he replied, *"Durch planmässiges tattonieren"* —through systematic trying. Srinivasa Ramanujan, the phenomenal Indian number theorist, was equally addicted to experimentation with examples. One can imagine that in the hands of such men the computer would have stimu-

lated many more discoveries in number theory.

A fascinating area of number theory is that dealing with primes, the class of integers that are divisible only by themselves and by one. The Greeks proved that the number of primes is infinite, but even after centuries of work some of the most elementary questions about primes remain unanswered.

For example, can every even number be represented as the sum of two primes? This is the famous Goldbach conjecture. Thus $100 = 53 + 47$ and $200 = 103 + 97$. It has been shown that all even numbers smaller than 2,000,000 can be represented as the sum of two primes, but there is no proof that this holds true for *all* even integers.

MANIAC II (Mathematical Analyzer, Numerical Integrator and Computer) was built at the Los Alamos Scientific Laboratory in 1957. STRETCH, built by the International Business Machines Corporation and installed at Los Alamos four years later, is about 10 times faster than MANIAC II. Both have been used extensively by the author and his colleagues for experimentation in mathematics.

It is an interesting fact that there are many pairs of primes differing by two, for instance 11 and 13, 17 and 19, 311 and 313. Although it might seem simple to show that there are infinitely many such pairs of "twin primes," no one has been able to do it. These two unsolved problems demonstrate that the inquiring human mind can almost immediately find mathematical statements of great simplicity whose truth or falsehood are inordinately difficult to decide. Such statements present a continual challenge to mathematicians.

The existence of a proof does not always appease the mathematician. Although it is easily proved that there is an infinite number of primes, one would like to have a formula for writing down an arbitrarily large prime. No such formula has been found. No mathematician can now write on demand a prime with, say, 10 million digits, although one surely exists.

One of the largest known primes was found not long ago with the help of an electronic computer in Sweden. It is $2^{3217} - 1$, a number containing 967 digits. A number of this form, $2^n - 1$, is called a Mersenne number. There may be an infinite number of primes of this form. No one knows.

Other special numbers that may or may not yield many primes are Fermat numbers, which have the form $2^{2^n} + 1$. For n's of 0, 1, 2 and 3 the corresponding Fermat numbers are 3, 5, 17 and 257. Even for moderate values of n Fermat numbers become extremely large. It is not known, for instance, if the Fermat number with an n of 13 is a prime (the number is $2^{2^{13}} + 1$, or $2^{8192} + 1$).

It is convenient for computer experimentation that both Mersenne and Fermat numbers have a particularly simple appearance when they are written in binary notation [*see top illustration on next page*]. Fermat numbers start with a 1, are followed by 0's and end with a 1. Mersenne numbers in binary notation consist exclusively of 1's. With computers it is an easy matter to study empirically the appearance of primes written in binary form.

The following statement is most likely true: There exists a number n such that an infinite number of primes can be written in a binary sequence that contains exactly n 1's. (The number of 0's interspersed among the 1's, of course, would be unlimited.) Although this statement cannot be proved with the present means of number theory, I sus-

SHRINKAGE OF COMPONENTS has meant greater reliability and speed plus substantial savings in construction and operation of computer systems. The vacuum-tube assembly at top was used in first generation of computers built by International Business Machines Corporation, starting in 1946. First transistorized computers, built in 1955, used circuits such as that at lower left. At lower right is a card of six microminiaturized circuits, each containing several transistors and diodes, which is going into the newest IBM computers.

pect that experimental work with a computer might provide some insight into the behavior of binary sequences containing various numbers of 1's. The following experience may help to explain this feeling.

A few years ago my colleague Mark B. Wells and I planned a computer program to study some combinatorial properties of the distribution of 0's and 1's in prime numbers when expressed in binary form. One day Wells remarked: "Of course, one cannot expect the primes to have, asymptotically, the same number of ones and zeros in their development, since the numbers divisible by three have an even number of ones." This statement was based on the following argument: One would expect a priori that in a large sample of integers expressed in binary form the number of 1's and 0's ought to be randomly distributed and that this should also be the case for a large sample of primes. On

the other hand, if it were true that all numbers divisible by three contain an even number of 1's, then the distribution of 1's and 0's in a large sample of primes should not be random.

Returning to my office, I tried to prove Wells's statement about numbers divisible by three but was unsuccessful. After a while I noticed that the statement is not even true. The first number to disprove it is 21, which has three 1's in its binary representation [*see middle illustration on next page*].

Nevertheless, a great majority of the integers divisible by three seem to have an even number of 1's. Beginning with this observation, Wells managed to prove a general theorem: Among all the integers divisible by three from 1 to 2^n, those that have an even number of 1's always predominate, and the difference between their number and the number of those with an odd number of 1's can be computed exactly: it is

MERSENNE NUMBER $(2^n - 1)$			FERMAT NUMBER $(2^{2^n} + 1)$		
n	DECIMAL	BINARY	n	DECIMAL	BINARY
1	1	1	0	3	11
2	3	11	1	5	101
3	7	111	2	17	10001
4	15	1111	3	257	100000001
5	31	11111	4	65,537	10000000000000001

MERSENNE AND FERMAT NUMBERS have a simple appearance when written in binary notation. Although many Mersenne numbers are not primes (for example 15), there may be an infinite number of primes of this form. There may also be an infinite number of Fermat primes, but even the Fermat number for an n as small as 13 has not yet been tested.

3	11	27	11011
6	110	30	11110
9	1001	33	100001
12	1100	36	100100
15	1111	39	100111
18	10010	42	101010
21	10101	45	101101
24	11000	48	110000

INTEGERS DIVISIBLE BY THREE usually contain an even number of 1's when written in binary form. This observation led to the proof of a general theorem, described in the text.

$3^{(n-1)/2}$. Wells developed corresponding proofs for statements on integers divisible by five, seven and certain other numbers, although he found these theorems increasingly harder to prove.

By now quite a few problems in number theory have been studied experimentally on computers. Not all of this work is restricted to tables, special examples and sundry curiosities. D. H. Lehmer of the University of California at Berkeley has made unusually effective use of the computer in number theory. With its help he has recently obtained several general theorems. Essentially what he has done is to reduce general statements to the examination of a large number of special cases. The number of cases was so large that it would have been impracticable, if not impossible, to go through them by hand computation. With the help of the computer, however, Lehmer and his associates were able to determine all exceptions explicitly and thereby discover the theorem that was valid for all other cases. Unfortunately Lehmer's interesting work is at a difficult mathematical level and to describe it would take us far afield.

It must be emphasized that Lehmer's theorems were not proved entirely by machine. The machine was instrumental in enabling him to obtain the proof. This is quite different from having a program that can guide a computer to produce a complete formal proof of a mathematical statement. Such a program, however, is not beyond the realm of possibility. The computer can operate not only with numbers but also with the symbols needed to perform logical operations. Thus it can execute simple orders corresponding to the basic "Boolean" operations. These are essentially the Aristotelian expressions of "and," "or" and "not." Under a set of instructions the computer can follow such orders in a prescribed sequence and explore a labyrinth of possibilities, choosing among the possible alternatives the ones that satisfy, at any moment, the result of previous computations.

With such techniques it has been possible to program a computer to find proofs of elementary theorems in Euclid's geometry. Some of these efforts, particularly those pursued at the International Business Machines Research Center, have been quite successful. Other programs have enabled the computer to find proofs of simple facts of

1,2	1,3	1,4	1,5	1,6	1,7
	2,3	2,4	2,5	2,6	2,7
		3,4	3,5	3,6	3,7
			4,5	4,6	4,7
				5,6	5,7
					6,7

1,2,3	1,3	1,4,5,	1,5	1,6,7	1,7
	2,3	2,4,6	2,5,7	2,6	2,7
		3,4,7	3,5,6	3,6	3,7
			4,5	4,6	4,7
				5,6	5,7
					6,7

STEINER PROBLEM poses this question: Given n objects, can they be arranged in a set of triplets so that every pair of objects appears once and only once in every triplet? The problem can be solved only when $n = 6k + 1$ or $6k + 3$, in which k can be any integer. One solution for $k = 1$, in which case $n = 7$, is shown here. The table at left lists all possible pairs of seven objects. The table at right shows seven triplets that contain all pairs only once. The 21 digits in these triplets can be regrouped into other triplets.

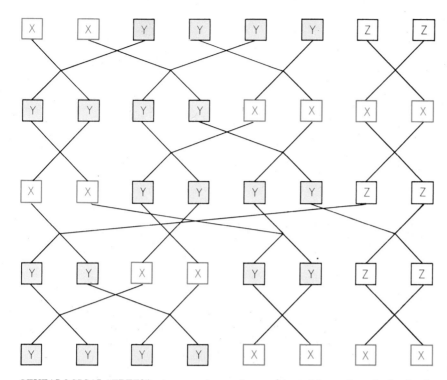

GENEALOGICAL "TREES" raise many interesting combinatorial questions. In the simple case shown here individuals of three different colors mate in pairs. Strictly, x, y and z specify the fraction of each color in each generation, but here they also identify color type. Each mating produces a pair of offspring and the color of the offspring is uniquely determined by the colors of the parents according to a fixed rule. (For example, 2 y's or 2 z's produce 2 x's.) Assuming an initial population containing hundreds of members, one might ask such questions as these: Given an individual in the fifth generation, how many different ancestors does he have in, say, the first generation? What are the proportions of x's, y's and z's among the ancestors of a given individual in the nth generation?

projective geometry. I have no doubt that these efforts mark only the beginnings; the future role of computers in dealing with the "effective" parts of mathematics will be much larger.

I shall now turn from the study of integers to combinatorial analysis and discuss some of the uses of the computer in this field. Very briefly, combinatorial analysis deals with the properties of arrangements and patterns defined by means of a finite class of "points." Familiar examples are the problems on permutations and combinations studied in high school algebra. In a typical case one starts with a finite set of n points and assumes certain given, "or prescribed, relations between any two of them or, more generally, among any k of them. One may then wish to enumerate the number of all possible structures that are related in the prescribed way, or one may want to know the number of equivalent structures. In some cases one may consider the finite set of given objects to be transformations of a set on itself. In the broadest sense one could say that combinatorial analysis deals with relations and patterns, their

classification and morphology. In this field too electronic computers have proved to be extremely useful. Here are some examples.

Consider the well-known problem of placing eight queens on a chessboard in such a way that no one of them attacks another. For an ordinary 8×8 chessboard there are only 12 fundamentally different solutions. The mathematician would like to know in how many different ways the problem can be solved for n queens on an $n \times n$ board. Such enumeration problems are in general difficult but computer studies can assist in their solution.

The following problem was first proposed in the 19th century by the Swiss mathematician Jakob Steiner: Given n objects, can one arrange them in a set of triplets in such a way that every pair of objects appears once and only once in a triplet? If n is five, for example, there are 10 possible pairs of five objects, but a little experimentation will show that there is no way to put them all in triplets without repeating some of the pairs. The problem can be solved only when $n = 6k + 1$ or $6k + 3$, in which k is any integer. The solution for

$k = 1$ (in which case $n = 7$) is shown at the bottom of page 342. The number of triplets in the solution is seven. In how many ways can the problem be solved? Again, the computer is very useful when k is a large number.

The shortest-route problem, often called the traveling-salesman problem, is another familiar one in combinatorics. Given are the positions of n points, either in a plane or in space. The problem is to connect all the points so that the total route between them is as short as possible. Another version of this problem is to find the route through a network of points (without necessarily touching all the points) that would take the minimum time to traverse [see "Control Theory," SCIENTIFIC AMERICAN, September 1964]. These problems differ from the two preceding ones in that they necessitate finding a method, or recipe, for constructing the minimum route. Strictly speaking, they are problems in "metacombinatories." This term signifies that a precise formulation of the problem requires a definition of what one means by a recipe for contruction. Such a definition is possible, and precise formulations can be made. When the n points are distributed in a multidimensional space, the problem can hardly be tackled without a computer.

A final example of combinatorics can be expressed as a problem in genealogy. Assume, for the sake of simplicity, that a population consists of many individuals who combine at random, and that each pair produces, after a certain time, another pair. Let the process continue through many generations and assume that the production of offspring takes place at the same time for all parents in each generation. Many interesting questions of combinatorial character arise immediately.

For instance, given an individual in the 15th generation of this process, how many different ancestors does he have in, say, the ninth generation? Since this is six generations back it is obvious that the maximum number of different ancestors is 2^6, but this assumes no kinship between any of the ancestors. As in human genealogy there is a certain probability that kinship exists and that the actual number is smaller than 2^6. What is the probability of finding various smaller numbers?

Suppose the original population consists of two classes (that is, each individual has one or the other of two characteristics); how are these classes mixed in the course of many generations? In other words, considering any individual in the nth generation, one would like to know the proportion of the two characteristics among all his ancestors.

Let us now make a slightly more realistic assumption. Consider the process as before but with the restriction removed that all offspring appear at the same time from parents of the same age. Assume instead that the production of the new generation is spread over a finite period of time according to a specific probability distribution. After this process has continued for some time the individuals of the most recent generation will be, so to speak, of different generations. A process of this kind actually occurs in human populations because mothers tend to be younger, on the average, than fathers. Therefore going back, say, 10 generations through the chain of mothers yields a smaller number of total years than going back through the chain of 10 fathers. It becomes a complex combinatorial problem to calculate the average number of generations represented in the genealogical history of each individual after many years have elapsed from time zero. This and many similar questions are difficult to treat analytically. By imitating the process on a computer, however, it is easy to obtain data that throw some light on the matter.

The last mathematical area I should like to discuss in connection with computers is the rather broad but little-explored one of nonlinearity. A linear function of one variable has the form $x' = ax + b$, where a and b are constants. Functions and transformations of this form are the simplest ones mathematically, and they occur extensively in the natural sciences and in technology. For example, quantum theory employs linear mathematics, although there are now indications that future understanding of nuclear and subnuclear phenomena will require nonlinear theories. In many physical theories, such as hydrodynamics, the equations are nonlinear from the outset.

The simplest nonlinear functions are quadratic; for one variable such functions have the form $y = ax^2 + bx + c$, where a, b and c are constants. It may surprise nonmathematical readers how little is known about the properties of such nonlinear functions and transformations. Some of the simplest questions concerning their properties remain unanswered.

As an example, mathematicians would like to learn more about the behavior of nonlinear functions when subjected

to the process known as iteration. This simply means repeated application of the function (or transformation) to some starting value. For instance, if the point described by a function is the square root of x, the iteration would be the square root of the square root of x; each succeeding iteration would consist of again taking the square root.

A transformation given by two functions containing two variables each defines a point on a plane; its iteration gives rise to successive points, or "images" [see illustration below]. Finding the properties of the sequence of iterated images of a single point, when described by a nonlinear function, is in general difficult. Present techniques of analysis are inadequate to unravel the behavior of these quite simply defined transformations.

Here again empirical work with the

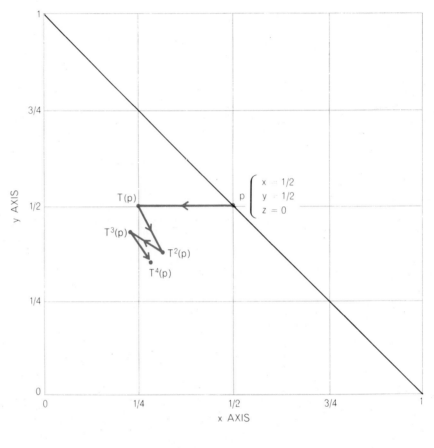

$$x' = y^2 - z^2 \qquad y' = 2xy - 2xz \qquad z = x^2 + 2yz$$

INITIAL POINT p	FIRST ITERATION $T(p)$	SECOND ITERATION $T^2(p)$	THIRD ITERATION $T^3(p)$	FOURTH ITERATION $T^4(p)$
$x = 1/2$	$x' = 1/4$	$x'' = 5/16$	$x''' = 61/256 = .238$	$x'''' = .295$
$y = 1/2$	$y' = 2/4$	$y'' = 6/16$	$y''' = 110/256 = .430$	$y'''' = .363$
$z = 0$	$z' = 1/4$	$z'' = 5/16$	$z''' = 85/256 = .332$	$z'''' = .342$
SUM 1	1	1	1 = 1.000	1.000

PROCESS OF ITERATION involves repeated application of a function (or transformation) to an initial value or a point. Here three equations containing three variables define a point in a plane. Iteration gives rise to successive points, or "images." Because the three variables always add up to 1, only two variables (say x and y) need be plotted. The first iteration, $T(p)$, is obtained by inserting the initial values of x, y and z ($\frac{1}{2}, \frac{1}{2}, 0$) in the three equations. The new values, x', y', z' ($\frac{1}{4}, \frac{1}{2}, \frac{1}{4}$), are then inserted to produce the second iteration, $T^2(p)$, and so on. Computers can quickly compute and display thousands of iterations of a point so that their behavior can be studied (*see examples on next page*).

computer can be of great help, particularly if the computer is equipped to display visually the location of many iterated points on the face of an oscilloscope. MANIAC II at Los Alamos has been equipped in this way and enables us to see at a glance the results of hundreds of iterations.

In examining such displays the mathematician is curious to learn whether or not the succession of iterated images converge to a single location, or "fixed point." Frequently the images do not converge but jump around in what appears to be a haphazard fashion—when they are viewed one by one. But if hundreds of images are examined, it may be seen that they converge to

curves that are often most unexpected and peculiar, as illustrated in the four oscilloscope traces below. Such empirical work has led my associates and me to some general conjectures and to the finding of some new properties of nonlinear transformations.

What are the obvious desiderata that would make the electronic computer an even more valuable tool than it is today? One important need is the ability to handle a broader range of logical operations. As I have noted, the simplest operations of logic, the Boolean operations, have been incorporated in electronic computers from the outset. In order to encompass more of con-

temporary mathematics the computer needs a "universal quantifier" and an "existential quantifier." The universal quantifier is required to express the statement one sees so frequently in mathematical papers: "*For all x* such and such holds." The existential quantifier is needed to express another common statement: "*There exists* an *x* so that such and such is true." If one could add these two quantifiers to the Boolean operations, one could formulate for computer examination most of traditional and much of modern mathematics. Unfortunately there is no good computer program that will manipulate the concepts "for all" and "there exists."

One can take for granted that there will be continued increases in processing speed and in memory capacity. There will be more fundamental developments too. Present computers operate in a linear sequence: they do one thing at a time. It is a challenge to design a machine more on the model of the animal nervous system, which can carry out many operations simultaneously. Indeed, plans exist for machines in which arithmetical operations would proceed simultaneously in different locations.

A multitrack machine would be of great value in the Monte Carlo method. The task of the machine is to compute individual histories of fictitious particles, and in many problems the fates of the particles are independent of one another. This means that they could be computed in parallel rather than in series. Moreover, it is not necessary that the computations be carried out to the many decimal places provided by present high-speed machines; an accuracy of four or five digits would often be enough. Thus it would be valuable to have a machine that could compute hundreds of histories simultaneously with only moderate accuracy. There are many other cases where a machine of such design would be efficient.

Further development is also desirable in facilitating the ease of transaction between the computer and its operator. At present it is difficult to change the course of a calculation as partial results become available. If access to the machine were more flexible and if the problem could be studied visually during the course of its development, many mathematicians would find experimentation on the computer more congenial than they do today.

One can imagine new methods of calculation specifically adapted to the automatic computer. Thanks to the speed of the machine one will be able to explore,

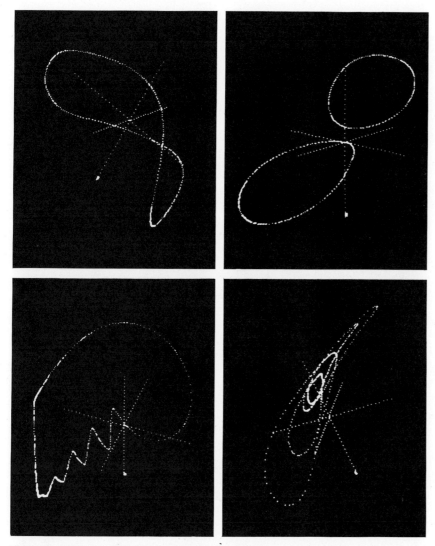

ITERATIONS OF NONLINEAR TRANSFORMATIONS performed by high-speed Los Alamos computers are displayed on the face of an oscilloscope. The objective of this study by P. R. Stein and the author was to examine the asymptotic properties, or "limit sets," of iterates of certain nonlinear transformations of relatively simple form. These iterations are for sets of four functions containing four variables and therefore must be plotted in three dimensions; the straight dotted lines indicate the coordinate axes (*see two-dimensional plotting on preceding page*). The figure at top left is a twisted space curve. That at top right consists of two plane curves. The two bottom figures are more complicated.

almost palpably, so to say, geometrical configurations in spaces of more than three dimensions and one will be able to obtain, through practice, new intuitions. These will stimulate the mathematician working in topology and in the combinatorics of new mathematical objects. These objects may be ordinary integers, but integers far exceeding in size and number any now used for experimentation. One should also be able to develop mathematical expressions with many more existential quantifiers than are now employed in formal mathematical definitions. New games will be played on future machines; new objects and their motions will be considered in spaces now hard to visualize with our present experience, which is essentially limited to three dimensions.

The old philosophical question remains: Is mathematics largely a free creation of the human brain, or has the choice of definitions, axioms and problems been suggested largely by the external physical world? (I would include as part of the physical world the anatomy of the brain itself.) It is likely that work with electronic machines, in the course of the next decade or so, will shed some light on this question. Further insight may come from the study of similarities between the workings of the human nervous system and the organization of computers. There will be novel applications of mathematics in the biological sciences, and new problems in mathematics will be suggested by the study of living matter.

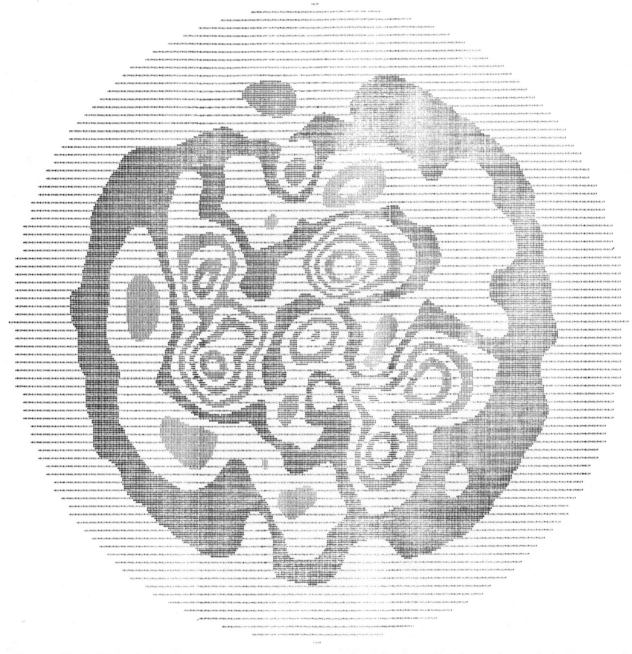

SIMULATED WEATHER PATTERN for the entire Northern Hemisphere was produced by the STRETCH computer at the General Circulation Research Laboratory of the U.S. Weather Bureau. In an effort to develop and test new theories of atmospheric behavior, investigators program the computer with equations that attempt to account for atmospheric phenomena. Data from real observations are then fed in, from which the computer produces changing model weather patterns for days and weeks. These are compared with actual observations over the period. The shaded "contours" on this map show simulated sea-level atmospheric pressure during one of these studies. The pattern is built up entirely of densely packed numbers and letters printed out directly by the computer itself.

46 COMPUTER LOGIC AND MEMORY

DAVID C. EVANS · September 1966

Electronic digital computers are made of two basic kinds of components: logic elements (often called switching elements) and memory elements. In virtually all modern computers these elements are binary, that is, the logic elements have two alternative pathways and the memory elements have two states. Accordingly all the information handled by such computers is coded in binary form. In short, the information is represented by binary symbols, stored in sets of binary memory elements and processed by binary switching elements.

To make a digital computer it is necessary to have memory elements and a set of logic elements that is functionally complete. A set of logic elements is functionally complete if a logic circuit capable of performing any arbitrary logical function can be synthesized from elements of the set. Let us examine one such functionally complete set that contains three distinct types of circuit designated *and, or* and *not*. Such circuits can be depicted with input signals at the left and output signals at the right [*see middle illustration on next page*]. Since the logic elements are binary, each input and output is a binary variable that can have the value 0 or 1. In an electrical circuit the logical value 0 corresponds to a particular voltage or

current and the logical value 1 to another voltage or current. For each symbolic circuit one can construct a "truth table," in which are listed all possible input states and the corresponding output states. Each truth table, in turn, can be represented by a Boolean statement (named for the 19th-century logician George Boole) that expresses the output of the circuit as a function of the input. Truth tables and Boolean statements are shown in the illustrations on the next page. In the case of the *and* circuit the output variable C has the value 1 if, and only if, the input variables A and B both have the value 1. In the Boolean statement the operation *and* is designated by the dot; it reads "C is equal to A and B." In the *or* circuit C has the value 1 if at least one of the input variables has the value 1. The Boolean statement is read "C is equal to A or B." The *not* circuit has for its output the logical complement of the input. Its Boolean statement is read "B is equal to *not* A." The *and* and *or* circuits described have only two input variables. Circuits that have a larger number of input variables are normally used.

There are a number of other functionally complete sets of logic elements. Two sets are particularly interesting because each contains only one element, in one case called *nand* (meaning "not

and") and in the other case called *nor* (meaning "not or"). The bottom illustration at the left on the next page shows a symbolic representation of a two-input *nand* circuit with its truth table. Although a practical *nand* circuit is designed as an entity, it is evident that it can be realized by an *and* and a *not* circuit. The reader can easily devise *and, or* and *not* circuits from *nand* circuits to demonstrate to himself that the *nand* circuit is also functionally complete.

With *and* and *not* circuits it is not difficult to construct a decoding circuit that will translate binary digits into decimal digits. The top illustration on page 352 shows such a circuit and its truth table. The decimal digits are each represented by a four-digit binary code (A_0, A_1, A_2, A_3). In the decoding circuit, which yields the first four decimal digits, the input signals A_0, A_1, A_2, A_3 are applied. The signal at each of the numbered outputs is 0 unless the input code is the code for one of the numbered outputs, in which case the signal at that output is 1.

The circuits that store information in a computer can be divided into two classes: registers and memory circuits. Registers are combined with logic circuits to build up the arithmetic, control and other information-processing parts of the computer. The information stored in registers represents the instantaneous state of the processing part of the computing system. The term "memory" is commonly reserved for those parts of a computer that make possible the general storage of information, such as the instructions of a program, the information fed into the program and the results of computations. Memory devices for such storage purposes will be discussed later in this article.

THIN-FILM MEMORY (*opposite page*) consists of an array of rectangular storage elements, only four millionths of an inch thick, deposited on a thin glass sheet. The rectangles are oriented in one of two magnetic states, corresponding to 0 or 1, when electric currents are passed through conductors (*vertical stripes*) printed on the back of the glass. The films can be switched in a few billionths of a second. The states can be made visible if the thin-film surface is illuminated with plane-polarized light and photographed through a suitably adjusted polarizing filter. The magnetic film causes a slight rotation in the plane of polarization of the reflected light. Here the predominantly dark rectangles are in the 1 state; the light rectangles are in the 0 state. The photograph is a 100-diameter enlargement of a thin-film memory developed by the Burroughs Corporation for use in its newest computers.

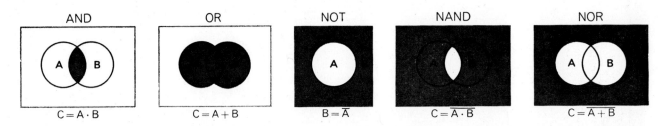

AND	OR	NOT	NAND	NOR
$C = A \cdot B$	$C = A + B$	$B = \overline{A}$	$C = \overline{A \cdot B}$	$C = \overline{A + B}$

VENN DIAGRAMS use circles to symbolize various logic concepts and relations. Circles represent statements that can be either true or false; they are placed in a universe, or field, that represents all other statements. The logical relation *and* is represented by the shaded area where two circles overlap. This area, C, is "true" only if both circles, A and B, are true; it is "false" if either A or B or both are false. The logical relation *or* (the "inclusive or") is represented by shading the entire area within both circles. This area,

C, is true when either A or B or both are true. *Not* is represented by a circle, A, surrounded by a universe, B, which is not A. The equations below the Venn diagrams are Boolean statements. The dot in the *and* statement stands for "and." The plus sign in the *or* statement stands for "or." The $\overline{A}$ in the *not* statement signifies "not A." *Nand* and *nor* stand respectively for "not and" and "not or," as is made clear in the shading of their Venn diagrams. Such diagrams are named for John Venn, a 19th-century English logician.

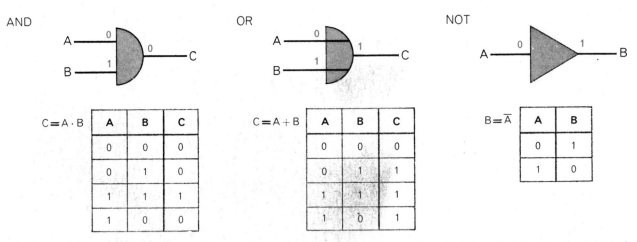

AND

$C = A \cdot B$

A	B	C
0	0	0
0	1	0
1	1	1
1	0	0

OR

$C = A + B$

A	B	C
0	0	0
0	1	1
1	1	1
1	0	1

NOT

$B = \overline{A}$

A	B
0	1
1	0

AND, OR AND NOT constitute a set of binary logic elements that is functionally complete. The three symbols represent circuits that can carry out each of these logic functions. Input signals, either 0

or 1, enter the circuits at the left; outputs leave at the right (*colored digits are examples*). Below each circuit is a "truth table" that lists all possible input states and corresponding output states.

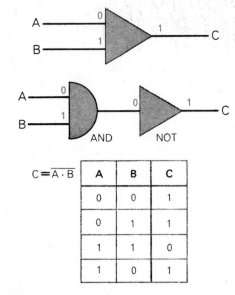

NAND

$C = \overline{A \cdot B}$

A	B	C
0	0	1
0	1	1
1	1	0
1	0	1

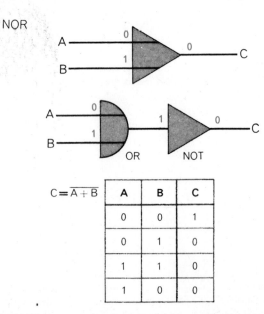

NOR

$C = \overline{A + B}$

A	B	C
0	0	1
0	1	0
1	1	0
1	0	0

NAND CIRCUIT, which contains only one logic element, is functionally complete; it can do everything that *and, or* and *not* circuits can perform collectively. The two-input *nand* circuit symbolized at top is equivalent to the combined *and* and *not* circuit. Outputs of the *nand* truth table are opposite to those of the *and* table.

NOR CIRCUIT is also functionally complete. The two-input *nor* circuit symbolized at top is equivalent to the combined *or* and *not* circuit shown immediately below. The *nor* truth table is the converse of the *or* table. Electronic embodiment of a circuit that can serve as either *nand* or *nor* appears on the opposite page.

Registers are usually made up of one-bit storage circuits called flip-flops. A typical flip-flop circuit, called a set-reset flip-flop, has four terminals [*see bottom illustration on next page*]. It is convenient to refer to such a flip-flop by giving it the name of the variable it happens to store; thus a flip-flop for storing the variable A will be named A. If the inputs to the terminals S and R are 0, the flip-flop will be in one of two states. If A has the value 1, it is in the set state; if it has the value 0, it is in the reset state. It can be switched to the set state by applying a 1 signal to the S terminal and switched to the reset state by applying a 1 to the R terminal. The application of 1's to the S and R terminals at the same time will not yield a predictable result. The flip-flop can therefore be regarded as remembering the most recent input state.

Memories for general storage could be made up of logic circuits and flip-flops, but for practical reasons this is not done. A memory so constructed would be large and expensive and would require much power; moreover, the stored information would be lost if the power were turned off.

We are now ready to consider how logic circuits and registers can be combined to perform elementary arithmetical operations. The upper illustration on page 353 includes a truth table describing one-digit binary addition. The inputs to the adder are the binary digits X and Y, together with the "input carry" C_{i-1}. The outputs are the sum digit S and the "carry out" C_i. Also illustrated is an implementation of the binary adder using *and, or* and *not* logic elements. A logic circuit such as this binary adder, which contains only switching elements and no storage circuits, is called a combinatorial circuit.

In a computer employing binary arithmetic the arithmetic unit may have to process numbers consisting of 60 or more digits in order to produce results with the desired precision. (A computer able to handle 60-digit numbers is said to have 60 bits of precision.) Numbers of such length can be added in two general ways. One way is to use an adder for each digit; the other is to use a single "serial" adder and process the digits sequentially. When an adder is used for each digit, the assembly is called a parallel adder. The lower illustration on page 353 shows a four-digit parallel adder. The inputs for this adder are two four-digit binary numbers: $X_3 X_2 X_1 X_0$ and $Y_3 Y_2 Y_1 Y_0$. The adder

produces the five binary-digit sum $S_4 S_3 S_2 S_1 S_0$. This four-digit adder is also a combinatorial circuit. The X and Y inputs to the parallel adder can be provided by two four-bit registers of four flip-flops each. The inputs are all provided at the same time. The sum can be stored in a five-bit register that has previously had all its stages reset to 0.

For the serial adder we need a means of delivering the digits of the inputs to the adder in sequence and of storing the sum digits in sequence. To implement these requirements special registers that have the ability to shift information from one stage to the next are employed; such a register is called a shift register. Each of the three shift registers of a serial binary adder has an input from the terminal called SHIFT [*see bottom figure on page 354*]. Normal-

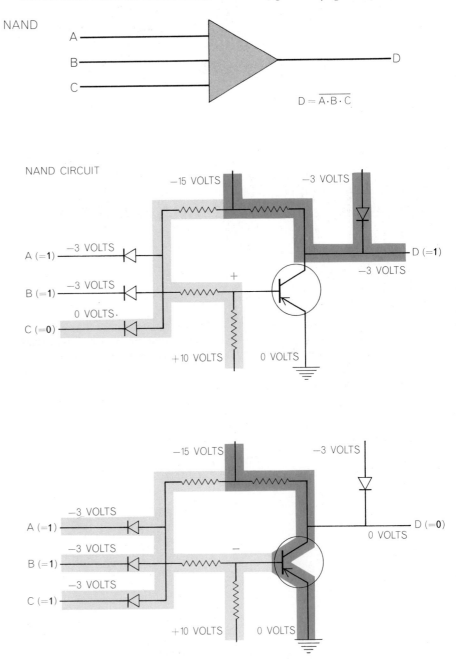

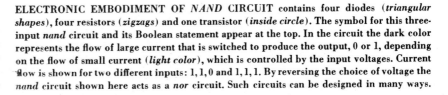

ELECTRONIC EMBODIMENT OF *NAND* CIRCUIT contains four diodes (*triangular shapes*), four resistors (*zigzags*) and one transistor (*inside circle*). The symbol for this three-input *nand* circuit and its Boolean statement appear at the top. In the circuit the dark color represents the flow of large current that is switched to produce the output, 0 or 1, depending on the flow of small current (*light color*), which is controlled by the input voltages. Current flow is shown for two different inputs: 1, 1, 0 and 1, 1, 1. By reversing the choice of voltage the *nand* circuit shown here acts as a *nor* circuit. Such circuits can be designed in many ways.

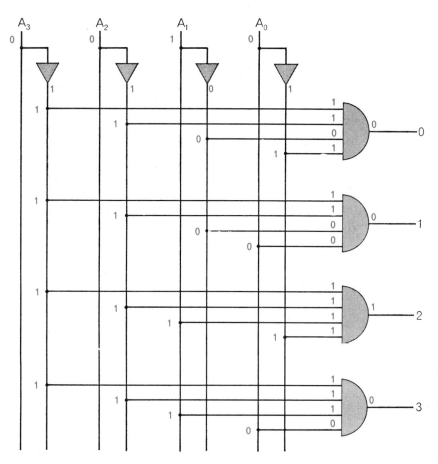

DECIMAL	BINARY			
	A_3	A_2	A_1	A_0
0	0	0	0	0
1	0	0	0	1
○ 2	0	0	1	0
3	0	0	1	1
4	0	1	0	0
5	0	1	0	1
6	0	1	1	0
7	0	1	1	1
8	1	0	0	0
9	1	0	0	1

CONVERSION OF BINARY to decimal digits is accomplished by this circuit, made up of four *not* circuits and four *and* circuits. The truth table at left shows the binary equivalent for the decimal digits from 0 to 9. To show the principle involved in decoding binary digits, the circuit carries the decoding only as far as decimal digit 3. The signal at each of the numbered outputs is 0 unless all the inputs are 1. In the example this is true for the third *and* circuit from the top, labeled 2. Thus the binary digits 0010 are decoded to yield the decimal digit 2.

ly the SHIFT signal has the value 0, but when it is desired to shift the three registers, the SHIFT signal is given the value 1 for a brief period, causing the registers to shift their contents one bit to the right. As in the case of the parallel adder, the serial adder can add one group of binary digits (such as $X_3\,X_2\,X_1\,X_0$) to another group (such as $Y_3\,Y_2\,Y_1\,Y_0$). At the first command to shift, the serial adder stores the sum of the first pair of digits (X_0 and Y_0); at the second command to shift, it stores the sum of the second pair of digits (X_1 and Y_1), and so on. The carry-out (C_i) of each addition is passed along at each command to shift.

Registers are needed for both serial and parallel adders. For the serial adder the registers must be shift registers and only a one-digit binary adder is required. For the parallel adder a binary adder is required for each bit of precision, that is, for each pair of X and Y inputs. The parallel adder is simply a large combinatorial circuit. The serial adder includes the binary adder, a flip-flop (known in this case as the C flip-flop) and associated circuitry. It is not a combinatorial circuit because its output (S) is not merely a function of the immediate inputs (X and Y); it is also a function of the internal state as represented by the value stored in the C flip-flop. Circuits in which the output is not only a function of the immediate inputs but also a function of the circuit's history as represented by its internal state are called sequential circuits. Such circuits are fundamental to the design of computers. Multiplication, for example, is usually implemented by a sequential circuit that repetitively uses an adder circuit.

For most of the period during which computers have evolved, the limiting factor in their design and cost has been memory. The speed of computers has been restricted by the time required to store and retrieve information. The cost of computers has been determined by the information-storage capacity of the memory. As a result much effort has been devoted to the development and improvement of memory devices.

A typical memory, which I have previously described as an array of registers of uniform size, is characterized by word length, storage capacity and access time. Each register in a memory is called a word; its size is expressed in bits and typically is in the range of 12 to 72 bits. The total storage capacity of a memory can be expressed in bits

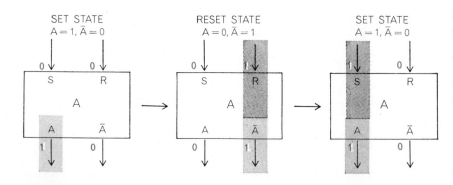

TYPICAL ONE-BIT STORAGE ELEMENT is represented by a "set-reset flip-flop." The one shown here is given the name A because it stores the variable A. A flip-flop "remembers" the most recent input state. If A has the value 1, it is in the set state; if A has the value 0, it is in the reset state. Applying a 1 to the S terminal yields the set state; applying a 1 to the R terminal yields the reset state. Flip-flops provide the transient memory in a computer.

C_{i-1}	X	Y	C_i	S
0	0	0	0	0
0	0	1	0	1
0	1	0	0	1
0	1	1	1	0
1	0	0	0	1
1	0	1	1	0
1	1	0	1	0
1	1	1	1	1

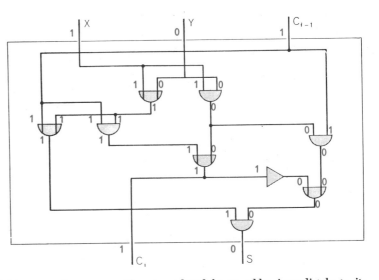

BINARY ADDER CIRCUIT (*right*) can add two one-digit binary numbers. It is made up of *and*, *or* and *not* logic elements. Because the adder will usually be one of several linked in parallel (*see illustration below*) it must also be able to accept a digit known as the input carry (C_{i-1}) produced by an adder immediately to its right. The truth table (*left*) shows the "carry-out" (C_i) and the sum digit (S) for all combinations of three inputs. In the example the inputs are 1, 0 and 1. This is known as a combinatorial circuit.

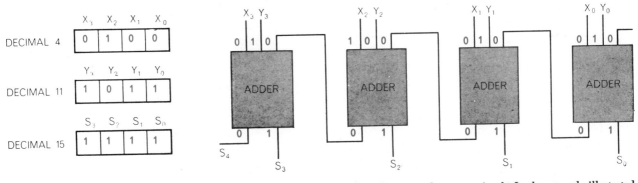

FOUR-DIGIT PARALLEL ADDER consists of four one-digit binary adders like the one shown at the top of the page. In a computer, registers (*not shown*) would be needed to supply the input signals and to store the output signals. In the example illustrated here the binary number 0100 (decimal 4) is being added to 1011 (decimal 11). The sum is the binary number 1111 (decimal 15).

but is more often expressed in words; depending on various factors, which will be examined below, the storage capacity can vary from 100 words to billions of words. The time required to store (write) or retrieve (read) a specified word of information is called the access time; it can range from a fraction of a microsecond to several seconds or minutes.

Access to a particular word in a memory is achieved by means of an addressing scheme. There are two classes of addressing schemes: "structure-addressing" and "content-addressing." In the first, which is the more common, each word is given a number by which it is identified; this number is called its address. Access to a particular word of a memory is achieved by specifying the address as a binary-coded number. In content-addressing, access is determined by the content of the word being sought. For example, each word of a content-addressed memory might contain a person's name and certain information about him (such as his bank balance or his airline reservation); access to that information would be achieved by presenting the person's name to the memory. The internal logic of the memory would locate the word containing the specified name and deliver the name and the associated information as an output. Since most memories are structurally addressed, no further consideration will be given to content-addressing.

Among the various memory designs there is a wide range of compromises among cost, capacity and access time [*see top illustration on page 356*]. Most memories fall into one of three access categories: random, periodic or sequential. In random-access memories the access time is independent of the sequence in which words are entered or extracted. Memories with short random-access times are the most desirable but also the most costly per bit of storage capacity. Magnetic-core devices are the most widely used random-access memories. An example of a memory device that provides periodic access is the magnetic drum, in which information is recorded on the circumference of a cylinder that rotates at a constant rate. Sequentially located words may be read at a high rate as they pass the sensing position. The maximum access time is one revolution of the drum, and the average access time to randomly selected words is half a drum revolution. The most common sequential memories—used when neither random nor periodic access is required—are provided by reels of magnetic tape. To run a typical 2,400-foot reel of tape containing 50 million bits of information past a reading head can take several minutes.

Since magnetic materials, in one form or another, supply the principal

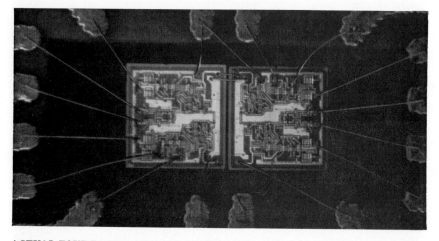

ACTUAL FOUR-DIGIT PARALLEL ADDER can be produced by linking two monolithic integrated circuits; each chip measures only 60 mils (.06 inch) on a side. This adder made by Texas Instruments Incorporated contains the equivalent of 166 discrete components.

storage medium in computers, I shall describe magnetic memories somewhat more fully. The high-speed random-access memory in a typical computer is generally provided by a three-dimensional array of about a million tiny magnetic cores, or rings, each of which can store one bit of information. The cores are threaded on a network of fine wires that provide the means for changing the magnetic polarity of the cores; the polarity determines whether a particular core stores a 1 or a 0. The cores are made of ferrite, a ferromagnetic ce-

ramic. Highly automatic methods have been devised for forming, firing, testing and assembling the cores into memory arrays. In early magnetic-core memories the cores had an outside diameter of about a twelfth of an inch and cost about $1 per bit of storage capacity. The cycle time of these memories (the minimum time from the beginning of one access cycle to the beginning of the next) was in the range of 10 to 20 microseconds.

As the art has developed, the size of the cores has decreased, the cycle time has decreased and the maximum capacity has increased. The cores in most contemporary computers have a diameter of a twentieth of an inch; cycle times are between .75 microsecond and two microseconds. The fastest core memories have cores less than a fiftieth of an inch in diameter and cycle times of less than 500 nanoseconds (half a microsecond).

The essential requirement of a material for a random-access magnetic memory is a particular magnetic characteristic that allows a single element of

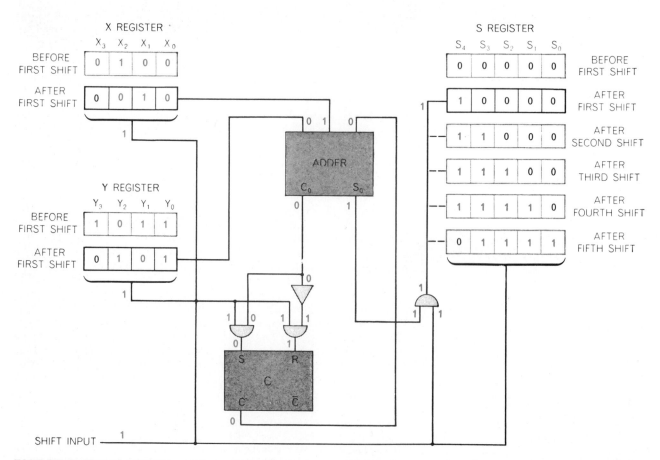

FOUR-DIGIT SERIAL ADDER uses only one adder like the one shown at the top of the preceding page but requires three shift registers and a flip-flop to pass along the carry-out of each addition. Each register has an input from the terminal called SHIFT. At the shift signal each register shifts its contents one bit to the right. Simultaneously the digits shifted out of the X and Y registers enter the adder, together with the input-carry from the C flip-flop. Five shift signals are needed to add two four-digit binary numbers.

a large array of elements of the material to be stably magnetized in either of two directions. Early in the 1950's it was discovered that certain thin metallic films also have this characteristic [*see illustration on page 348*]. The constant dream of computer designers since this discovery was made has been the development of a practical large-capacity memory that can be constructed directly from bulk materials without fabrication, test or assembly of discrete components for individual bits. Many geometries for thin-film memories, including flat films and films deposited on wires or glass rods, have been devised. Some film memories are in service and many more will be used in the future. It is anticipated that there will be dramatic reductions in the cost of random-access memories over the next few years.

In another widely used memory technology a thin film of magnetic material is deposited on some surface such as a plastic tape or card, or a metallic drum or disk. This magnetic surface is moved with respect to a head that can produce or detect patterns of magnetization in the magnetic film; the patterns are of course coded to represent the binary digits 1 and 0. The film for magnetic recording usually consists of finely ground iron oxides bonded together and to the surface by a small amount of organic binder. For magnetic drums and disks the magnetic medium often consists of a metallic film of a nickel-cobalt alloy.

Magnetic tape about a thousandth of an inch thick, half an inch wide and up to 2,400 feet long per reel has provided the main bulk information store for many years. Tape systems have reached a high state of development: they are able to transport the tape past the head at a rate of more than 100 inches per second and to start or stop the tape in a few milliseconds. Six or eight bits are usually written across the width of the tape; it is common for 800 of these six-bit or eight-bit groups to be written per inch along the tape. A current trend in information-processing systems is toward using tape for dead storage or for transporting data from one location to another. Magnetic recording devices with shorter random-access times are taking over the function of active file storage.

Storage devices with a capacity of a few hundred million words and an access time of a few seconds or less are just beginning to be delivered. These devices employ a number of magnetic

EVOLUTION OF CIRCUITS is reflected in these close-ups showing the central processing units in four generations of computers. UNIVAC I (*top*), the first large commercial electronic computer, used vacuum-tube logic circuits. The first model was delivered to the Bureau of the Census in 1951. International Business Machines' Model 704 (*second from top*) was a widely used large-scale vacuum-tube computer with a magnetic-core memory. The first 704 was installed in late 1955. In 1963 IBM delivered the first 7040 (*third from top*), a typical transistorized computer using discrete components. The Spectra 70/45 (*bottom*), recently delivered by the Radio Corporation of America, represents the latest generation. It uses monolithic integrated circuits similar to the one shown at the top of the opposite page.

TYPE OF MEMORY	RANDOM ACCESS TIME (MICROSECONDS)	INFORMATION TRANSFER RATE (BITS PER SECOND)	CAPACITY (BITS)	COST (DOLLARS PER BIT)
INTEGRATED CIRCUIT	$10^{-2} - 10^{-1}$	$10^9 - 10^{10}$	$10^3 - 10^4$	10
TYPICAL CORE OR FILM	1	10^8	10^6	10^{-1}
LARGE SLOW CORE	10	10^7	10^7	10^{-2}
MAGNETIC DRUM	10^4	10^7	10^7	10^{-3}
TAPE LOOP OR CARD	10^6	10^6	10^9	10^{-4}
PHOTOGRAPHIC	10^7	10^6	10^{12}	10^{-6}

COMPARISON OF MEMORY SYSTEMS shows a range of roughly a billion to one in access time and capacity and about 10 million to one in cost per bit. The spread in the rate of information transfer is smaller: about 10,000 to one from the fastest memories to the slowest. Integrated circuit memories (similar to logic circuits) and photographic memories (for digital storage) are just appearing.

cards or tape loops handled by various ingenious mechanisms [*see illustration on page 359*].

In memory systems that use magnetic drums and disks rotating at high speed, the heads for reading and writing information are spaced a fraction of a thousandth of an inch from the surface. The surface velocity is about 1,000 or 2,000 inches per second. In early drum systems severe mechanical and thermal problems were encountered in main-taining the spacing between the heads and the recording surface. In recent years a spectacular improvement in performance and reliability has been achieved by the use of flying heads, which maintain their spacing from the magnetic surface by "flying" on the boundary layer of air that rotates with the surface of the drum or disk. One modern drum memory has a capacity of 262,000 words and rotates at 7,200 revolutions per minute; it has a random-access time of about four milliseconds and an information-transfer rate of 11.2 million bits per second.

Magnetic information storage is meeting competition from other memory technologies in two areas: where fairly small stores of information must be accessible in the shortest possible time and where ultralarge stores must be accessible in a matter of seconds. For the first task, which today is usually performed by magnetic cores and thin

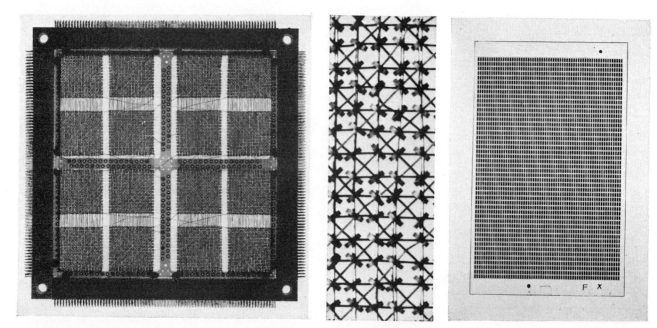

MAGNETIC-CORE MEMORY has been the standard high-speed memory in computers for many years. A typical core memory plane is shown two-thirds actual size at the left; a portion of the plane is enlarged about 10 diameters at the right. This example, made by Fabri-Tek Incorporated, contains 16,384 ferrite cores, each a fiftieth of an inch in diameter.

THIN-FILM MEMORY made by Burroughs, which operates even faster than magnetic-core memories, is shown here actual size. An enlargement in color appears on page 348.

films, one can now obtain memories fabricated by the same techniques used to produce monolithic integrated circuits [see "Microelectronics," by William C. Hittinger and Morgan Sparks; SCIENTIFIC AMERICAN, November, 1965]. Such circuits, resembling flip-flops, can be built up from tiny transistors and resistors; scores of such elements can be packed into an area no more than a tenth of an inch square [see bottom left of illustration on page 359]. A memory of this kind can store about 100 words and have a random-access time of 100 nanoseconds. Although the present cost of such memories is a few dollars per bit, the cost will probably decline to a few cents per bit by 1970. Integrated-circuit memories have the drawback that power is continuously dissipated by each element (unlike magnetic elements) whether it is actively being read (or altered) or not.

For very-high-volume storage and moderately fast access time, magnetic devices are being challenged by high-resolution photography. In these systems bits are recorded as densely packed dots on transparent cards or short strips of photographic film. During the next year or so several such systems will go into service; each will have a capacity of 10^{11} or 10^{12} bits and a maximum access time of a few seconds.

To combine rapid average access time and large storage capacity at a minimum cost to the user, computer designers have recently introduced the concept of the "virtual memory." Such a memory simulates a single large, fast random-access memory by providing a hierarchy of memories with a control mechanism that moves information up and down in the hierarchy, using a strategy designed to minimize average access time.

The logic and main memory of a very large modern computer contains nearly half a million transistors and a somewhat larger number of resistors and other electrical components, in addition to 10 million magnetic cores. In such a machine—or even in a smaller one with a tenth or a hundredth of this number of components—the matters of packaging, interconnection and reliability present very serious design problems.

The active circuit elements in early electronic computers were vacuum tubes. These computers encountered three major problems. First, the rate at which tubes failed was so high that in large computers the ratio of nonproduc-

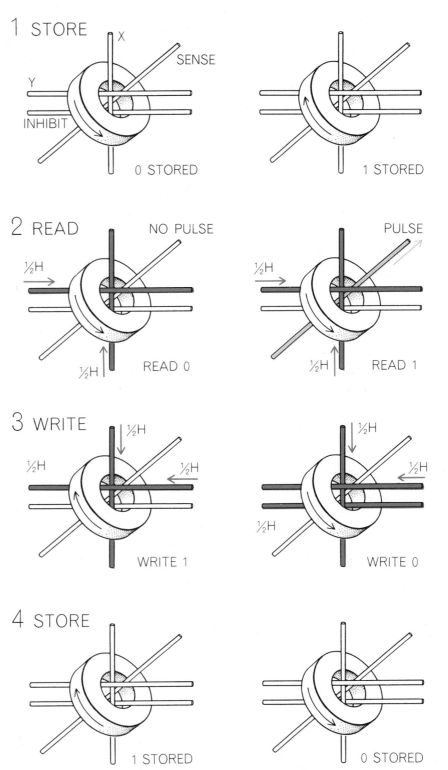

OPERATION OF MAGNETIC-CORE MEMORY involves switching the direction of magnetization, or polarity, of a ferrite core between two positions 180 degrees apart. One position is selected to represent 0, the other to represent 1. "Reading" and "writing" signals are carried on two wires (X and Y), each of which carries only half of the current ($\frac{1}{2}H$) needed to change the core's direction of polarization. During the reading cycle the direction of current flow is selected so that the pulses reverse the polarity of a core that is storing a 1, with the result that a voltage pulse signifying 1 (light color) is created in the "sense" wire. No pulse emanates from a core that is storing a 0. During the writing cycle the flow in the X and Y wires is reversed. This reverses the polarity of the core and writes 1 unless an opposing current is coincidentally passed through an "inhibit" wire, in which case the core polarity remains in the 0 position. A typical memory will contain a million cores.

tive time was nearly prohibitive. Second, power consumed by vacuum tubes was so large that adequate cooling was extremely difficult to achieve. Third, the components were so large that the distances over which signals had to travel would have limited computer speeds to levels that today would be regarded as slow.

In 1948 the point-contact transistor was invented. It was small and used little power, but it was too unstable a device to replace the vacuum tube in large-scale computers. A few years later the junction transistor was developed, but it was too slow. In 1957 the planar silicon transistor was invented. It provided high-speed transistors that were reliable and made possible the design of the present high-speed computers. Further development of the planar technology led to the monolithic integrated circuit, in which scores of components are created and linked together in a single tiny "chip" of silicon. A variation of this technique is used to create the integrated-circuit memories.

The integrated logic circuit, which is just beginning to make its way into large-scale use for computers, contributes substantially to the solution of the three problems that beset the vacuum-tube computer and that were only partially solved by discrete transistors. An integrated circuit on one chip of silicon can have the logic capacity of several of the logic circuits described earlier. It occupies far less space and consumes less power than an equivalent transistor circuit. Its small size makes possible systems with higher speeds because the interconnections of the circuits are shorter. Reliability is increased because the interconnections are themselves reliable. Indeed, the reliability of an entire integrated circuit is expected to approach that of an individual transistor. The latest integrated circuits have a signal delay of only a few nanoseconds, and still faster circuits are being developed. However, the physical size of a computer's components, together with their interconnections, remains a fundamental limitation on the complexity of the computer: an electrical signal can travel along a wire at the rate of only about eight inches per nanosecond (two-thirds the speed of light).

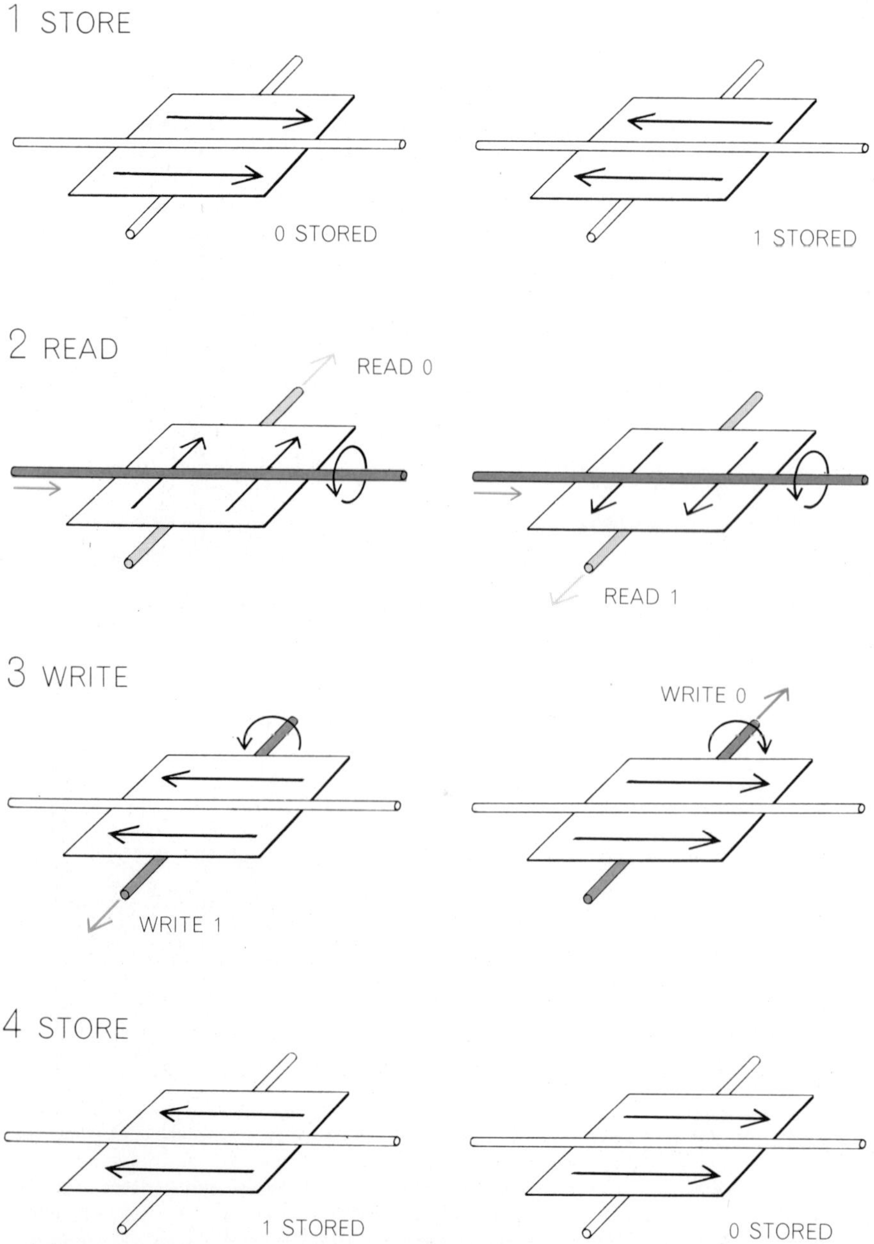

Computer technology has a way of confounding those who would predict its future. The thin-film memory, for example, has been "just around the corner" for more than 10 years, but the ferrite core is still the main element of random-access memories. Nevertheless, one can try to make certain predictions based on the situation at present. It now seems clear that integrated-circuit technology will soon produce circuits of great complexity at very low cost. These circuits will include high-speed memory circuits as well as logic circuits. Already one can get commercial delivery of a 100-bit register on a single chip of silicon that is a tenth of an inch in its largest dimension. It is my personal opinion that computer designers will be hard-pressed to develop concepts adequate to exploit the rapid advances in components.

Because computers built with integrated components promise to be much cheaper than present machines, one can expect significant changes in the comparative costs of information processing and information transmission. This in turn will influence the rate of growth of data-transmission facilities. Low-cost computers will also change the cost factors that help in deciding whether it is cheaper to do a job with human labor or to turn it over to a machine.

1 STORE
0 STORED
1 STORED

2 READ
READ 0
READ 1

3 WRITE
WRITE 1
WRITE 0

4 STORE
1 STORED
0 STORED

OPERATION OF THIN-FILM MEMORY differs from that of a magnetic-core memory, illustrated on the preceding page. One difference is that the read-out for a 0 or 1 is determined by the polarity of the voltage pulse in the sense wire rather than by the presence or absence of a voltage. Also, in the thin-film memory reading and writing are performed by passing current through different wires. Finally, the change in direction of magnetization that induces a read-out pulse involves a rotation of only 90 degrees rather than 180 degrees.

VARIETY OF MEMORY SYSTEMS are based on magnetism, electronic circuitry and photography. Magnetic-drum memory (*top left*), built by Univac Division of Sperry Rand Corporation, provides access in 17 milliseconds to any one of 786,432 36-bit words or some 4.7 million alphanumeric characters. "Random Access Computer Equipment" (*top right*), built by RCA, stores information on 2,048 flexible plastic cards. The basic unit holds 340 million alphanumeric characters; the average access time is 385 milliseconds. Magnetic-disk memory (*middle left*), made by Control Data Corporation, provides access in 34 to 110 milliseconds to any one of 131.9 million six-bit characters. "Data cell" system (*middle right*), offered by IBM, stores data on 2,000 narrow strips of magnetic film. It provides random access in 175 to 600 milliseconds to 800 million bits of information. Integrated-circuit memory (*bottom left*) provides access to 16 bits of information in about .01 microsecond. This example is made by Motorola Semiconductor Products Inc. A new photo-digital memory (*bottom right*) has been devised by IBM to provide rapid access to memory files containing a trillion bits. A single film chip, 1⅜ by 2¾ inches, can store several million bits of information; IBM is not yet ready to disclose the exact number.

47 THE USES OF COMPUTERS IN SCIENCE

ANTHONY G. OETTINGER · September 1966

In its scientific applications the computer has been cast in two quite distinct but complementary roles: as an instrument and as an actor. Part of the success of the computer in both roles can be ascribed to purely economic factors. By lowering the effective cost of calculating compared with experimenting the computer has induced a shift toward calculation in many fields where once only experimentation and comparatively direct measurement were practical.

The computer's role as an instrument is by far the more clear-cut and firmly established of the two. It is in its other role, however, as an active participant in the development of scientific theories, that the computer promises to have its most profound impact on science. A physical theory expressed in the language of mathematics often becomes dynamic when it is rewritten as a computer program; one can explore its inner structure, confront it with experimental data and interpret its implications much more easily than when it is in static form. In disciplines where mathematics is not the prevailing mode of expression the language of computer programs serves increasingly as the language of science. I shall return to the subject of the dynamic expression of theory after considering the more familiar role of the computer as an instrument in experimental investigations.

The advance of science has been marked by a progressive and rapidly accelerating separation of observable phenomena from both common sensory experience and theoretically supported intuition. Anyone can make at least a qualitative comparison of the forces required to break a matchstick and a steel bar. Comparing the force needed to ionize a hydrogen atom with the force that binds the hydrogen nucleus together is much more indirect, because the chain from phenomenon to observation to interpretation is much longer. It is by restoring the immediacy of sensory experience and by sharpening intuition that the computer is reshaping experimental analysis.

The role of the computer as a research instrument can be readily understood by considering the chain from raw observations to intuitively intelligible representations in the field of X-ray crystallography. The determination of the structure of the huge molecules of proteins is one of the most remarkable achievements of contemporary science. The highlights of this work have been reported in a number of articles in *Scientific American*, notably "The Three-dimensional Structure of a Protein Molecule," by John C. Kendrew [Offprint #121], and "The Hemoglobin Molecule," by M. F. Perutz [Offprint #196]. The labor, care and expense lavished on the preparation of visual models of protein molecules tes-

tify to a strong need for intuitive aids in this field. The computational power required to analyze crystallographic data is so immense that the need for high-speed computers is beyond doubt.

The scope and boldness of recent experiments in X-ray crystallography have increased in direct proportion to increases in computer power. Although computers seem to be necessary for progress in this area, however, they are by no means sufficient. The success stories in the determination of protein structures have involved an interplay of theoretical insight, experimental technique and computational power.

In work of this kind a rotating protein crystal is bombarded by a beam of X rays; the rays diffracted by the crystal are recorded on a photographic plate, where they produce characteristic patterns of bright spots on the dark background. Measurements of the relative positions and intensities of the spots in the diffraction pattern are the raw material for calculations that have as their result a table of coordinates of the three-dimensional distribution of electrons in the molecule. The electron-density data are then used to draw density-contour maps, which are interpreted as a three-dimensional model of the particular protein molecule under study.

Many of the links in this chain are now automated. The laborious manual measurement of photographs, for example, is no longer necessary. In the laboratory of William N. Lipscomb, Jr., at Harvard University a mounted crystal is rotated automatically through the required sequence of orientations while a photomultiplier tube measures the intensity of the diffracted X rays [*see top illustration on next page*]. Machines convert information about position and intensity into digital form and record it on punched cards for input to a computer.

X-RAY DIFFRACTION APPARATUS in the laboratory of William N. Lipscomb, Jr., at Harvard University makes unnecessary the laborious manual measurement of X-ray diffraction photographs of crystal structures. A beam of X rays (*from housing at center*) is directed at a mounted crystal (for example a protein), which is rotated automatically through a series of orientations while a photomultiplier tube (*top left*) measures the intensity of the diffracted rays. Information about the position and intensity of the diffracted rays is then converted from analogue to digital form and recorded on punched cards for input to a computer.

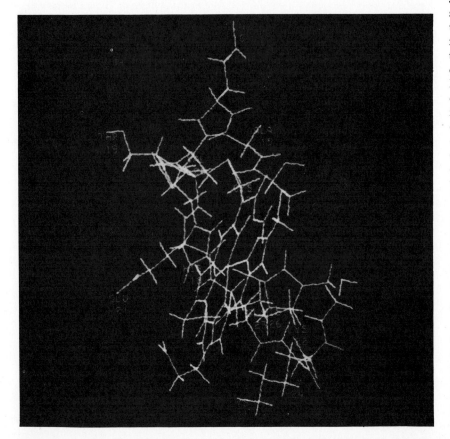

MODEL OF PROTEIN MOLECULE is displayed on an oscilloscope screen in the laboratory of Cyrus Levinthal at the Massachusetts Institute of Technology. The electron density of the molecule was determined by an analysis of X-ray diffraction photographs. A computer program converted the electron-density measurements into an image of a fragment of the molecular structure on the oscilloscope. Once the picture of the molecule has been calculated for a standard orientation the orientation can be changed at will by simple controls.

At the other end of the chain Cyrus Levinthal of the Massachusetts Institute of Technology and Robert Langridge of Harvard have used the time-shared computer and display facilities of M.I.T.'s Project MAC to develop a remarkable set of programs that accept electron densities calculated for a three-dimensional region and turn these into an image of molecular structure on an oscilloscope [*see bottom illustration at left*]. Gone is the time-consuming task of drawing and building the electron-density map. Once the picture of a molecule has been calculated for a standard orientation the orientation can be changed at will by simple controls that actuate special circuits for transforming the coordinates of the picture before displaying it. Slight motions provide excellent depth perception without the expense of stereoscopic image pairs. The molecule can be turned in order to view it from any angle, or it can be sliced by a plane in order to see it in cross section [see "Molecular Model-building by Computer," by Cyrus Levinthal; SCIENTIFIC AMERICAN, Offprint #1043].

Joining these two links is the next step. A new coaxial-cable network will soon carry Lipscomb's raw data directly to a computer at the Harvard Computing Center. No technical obstacle bars the further transmission of calculated electron densities to the system at M.I.T., where the molecular display could be prepared and then sent back for direct viewing on a screen at the experimental site. Once the time-shared computer utility emerges from its present experimental stage to spread throughout institutions and regions, such doings will very likely be commonplace [see "Time-sharing on Computers," by Fano and Corbató; SCIENTIFIC AMERICAN, September, 1966]. It is only tame speculation to visualize a graduate student "looking through" a computer at a protein molecule as directly as he now looks at a cell through a microscope.

The metaphor of the transparent computer describes one of the principal aims of contemporary "software" engineering, the branch of information engineering concerned with developing the complex programs (software) required to turn an inert mound of apparatus (hardware) into a powerful instrument as easy to use as pen and paper. As anyone can testify who has waited a day or more for a conventional computing service to return his work only to find that a misplaced comma had kept the work from being done at all, instant transparency for all is not yet here. Nevertheless, the advances described in the accompanying articles toward making computer languages congenial and expressive, toward making it easy to communicate with the machine and toward putting the machine at one's fingertips attest to the vigor of the pursuit of the transparent computer.

A few critics object to the principle of transparency because they fear that the primary consequence will be atrophy of the intellect. It is more likely that once interest in the *process* of determining molecular structure becomes subordinate to interest in the molecule itself, the instrument will simply be accepted and intellectual challenge sought elsewhere. It is no more debasing, unromantic or unscientific in the 1960's to view a protein crystal through the display screen of a computer than it is to watch a paramecium through the eyepiece of a microscope. Few would wish to repeat the work of Christian Huygens each time they need to look at a microscope slide. In any case, computers are basically so flexible that nothing but opaque design or poor engineering can prevent one from breaking into the chain at any point, whenever one thinks human intuition and judgment should guide brute calculation.

It is essential, of course, for anyone to understand his instrument well enough to use it properly, but the computer is just like other commonplace instruments in this regard. Like any good tool, it should be used with respect. Applying "data reduction" techniques to voluminous data collected without adequate experimental design is a folly of the master not to be blamed on the servant. Computer folk have an acronym for it: GIGO, for "garbage in, garbage out."

X-ray crystallography is the most advanced of many instances in which similar instrumentation is being developed.

Four experimental stations at the Cambridge Electron Accelerator, operated jointly by Harvard and M.I.T., are currently being connected to a time-shared computer at the Harvard Computing Center to provide a first link. A small computer at each experimental station converts instrument readings from analogue to digital form, arranges them in a suitable format and transmits them to the remote computer. There most data are stored for later detailed calculation; a few are examined to instruct each of the small local machines to display information telling the experimenter whether or not his experiment is going well. Heretofore delays in conventional batch-processing procedures occasionally led to scrapping a long experiment that became worthless because poor adjustments could not be detected until all calculations were completed and returned.

This type of experiment is described as an "open loop" experiment, since the computer does not directly affect the setting of experimental controls. Closed-loop systems, where the experiment is directly controlled by computer, are currently being developed. Their prototypes can be seen in industrial control systems, where more routine, better-understood devices, ranging from elevators to oil refineries, are controlled automatically.

The problem of "reading" particle-track photographs efficiently has been a persistent concern of high-energy physicists. Here the raw data are not nearly as neat as they are in X-ray diffraction patterns, nor can photography as readily be bypassed. Automating the process of following tracks in bubble-chamber photographs to detect significant events presents very difficult and as yet unsolved problems of pattern recognition, but computers are now used at least to reduce some of the tedium of scanning

the photographs [*see illustration on next page*]. Similar forms of man-machine interaction occur also in the study of brain tumors by radioactive-isotope techniques. Where the problem of pattern recognition is simpler, as it is in certain types of chromosome analysis, there is already a greater degree of automation [see "Chromosome Analysis by Computer," by Robert S. Ledley and Frank H. Ruddle; SCIENTIFIC AMERICAN, Offprint #1040].

Let us now turn from the computer as instrument to the computer as actor, and to the subject of dynamic expression of theory. To understand clearly words such as "model," "simulation" and others that recur in this context, a digression is essential to distinguish the functional from the structural aspects of a model or a theory.

A robot is a functional model of man. It walks, it talks, but no one should be fooled into thinking that it is a man or that it explains man merely because it acts like him. The statements that "the brain is like a computer" or that "a network of nerve cells is like a network of computer gates, each either on or off," crudely express once popular structural theories, obviously at different levels. Both are now discredited, the first because no one has found structures in the brain that look anything like parts of any man-made computer or even function like them, the second because nerve-cell networks were found to be a good deal more complicated than computer networks.

A functional model is like the electrical engineer's proverbial "black box," where something goes in and something comes out, and what is inside is unknown or relevant only to the extent of somehow relating outputs to inputs. A structural model emphasizes the contents of the box. A curve describing the

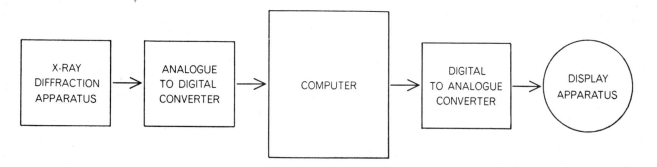

X-RAY DIFFRACTION APPARATUS → ANALOGUE TO DIGITAL CONVERTER → COMPUTER → DIGITAL TO ANALOGUE CONVERTER → DISPLAY APPARATUS

LINKUP of the two facilities represented on the opposite page is the next step toward the goal of a "transparent" computer in the field of X-ray crystallography. A new coaxial-cable network will soon carry Lipscomb's raw data directly to a computer at the Harvard Computing Center. No technical obstacle bars the further transmission of the calculated electron densities to the system at M.I.T., where the molecular display could be prepared and then sent back for direct viewing on a screen at the experimental site. It should then be possible to "look through" a computer at a protein molecule as directly as one now looks at a cell through a microscope.

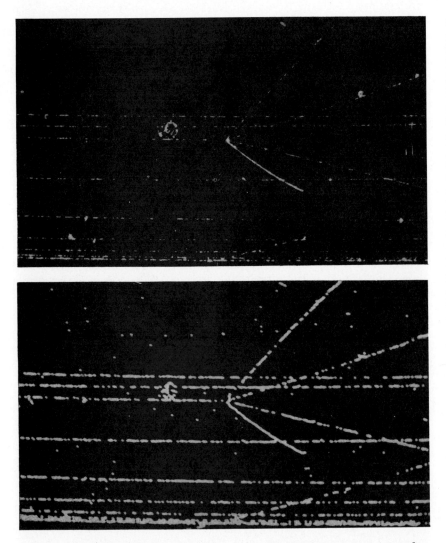

BUBBLE-CHAMBER PHOTOGRAPH (*top*) of a typical particle interaction was made at the Lawrence Radiation Laboratory of the University of California. The negative of the photograph was scanned by a device called the "flying spot digitizer," and the digitized information was sent directly to a computer, which produced a copy of the original photograph (*bottom*). No operator is required in the scanning process. The machine is directed to the location of a significant event by instructions on magnetic tape. Other computer programs further analyze the data to provide a description of the interaction recorded in photograph.

current passing through a semiconductor diode as a function of the voltage applied across its terminals is a functional model of this device that is exceedingly useful to electronic-circuit designers. Most often such curves are obtained by fitting a smooth line to actual currents and voltages measured for a number of devices. A corresponding structural model would account for the characteristic shape of the curve in terms that describe the transport of charge-carriers through semiconductors, the geometry of the contacts and so forth. A good structural model typically has greater predictive power than a functional one. In this case it would predict changes in the voltage-current characteristic when the geometry of the interfaces or the impurities in the semiconductors are varied.

If the black box is opened, inspiration, luck and empirical verification can turn a functional model into a structural one. Physics abounds with instances of this feat. The atom of Lucretius or John Dalton was purely functional. Modern atomic theory is structural, and the atom with its components is observable. The phlogiston theory, although functional enough up to a point, evaporated through lack of correspondence between its components and reality. Although the description of the behavior of matter by thermodynamics is primarily functional and its description by statistical mechanics is primarily structural, the consistency of these two approaches reinforces both.

The modern computer is a very versatile and convenient black box, ready to act out an enormous variety of func-

tional or structural roles. In the physical sciences, where the script usually has been written in mathematics beforehand, the computer merely brings to life, through its program, a role implied by the mathematics. Isaac Newton sketched the script for celestial mechanics in the compact shorthand of differential equations. Urbain Leverrier and John Couch Adams laboriously fleshed out their parts in the script with lengthy and detailed calculations based on a wealth of astronomical observations. Johann Galle and James Challis pointed their telescopes where the calculations said they should and the planet Neptune was discovered. In modern jargon, Leverrier and Adams each ran Neptune simulations based on Newton's model, and belief in the model was strengthened by comparing simulation output with experiment. Computers now routinely play satellite and orbit at Houston, Huntsville and Cape Kennedy. Nevertheless, there is little danger of confusing Leverrier, Adams or a computer with any celestial object or its orbit. As we shall see, such confusion is more common with linguistic and psychological models.

The determination of protein structures provides an excellent example of how computers act out the implications of a theory. Finding a possible structure for a protein molecule covers only part of the road toward understanding. For example, the question arises of why a protein molecule, which is basically just a string of amino acid units, should fold into the tangled three-dimensional pattern observed by Kendrew. The basic physical hypothesis invoked for explanation is that the molecular string will, like water running downhill, fold to reach a lowest energy level. To act out the implications of this hypothesis, given an initial spatial configuration of a protein chain, one might think of calculating the interactions of all pairs of active structures in the chain, minimizing the energy corresponding to these interactions over all possible configurations and then displaying the resultant molecular picture. Unfortunately this cannot be done so easily, since no simple formula describing such interactions is available and, with present techniques, none could be written down and manipulated with any reasonable amount of labor. Sampling more or less cleverly the energies of a finite but very large number of configurations is the only possibility. An unsupervised computer searching through a set of samples for a minimum would, more likely than not, soon find itself blocked at some local minimum—unable, like a man in a hollow at the top of a mountain, to see deeper valleys beyond the ridges that surround him.

The close interaction of man and machine made possible by new "on line" time-sharing systems, graphical display techniques and more convenient programming languages enables Levinthal and his collaborators to use their intuition and theoretical insight to postulate promising trial configurations. It is then easy for the computer to complete the detail work of calculating energy levels for the trial configuration and seeking a minimum in its neighborhood. The human operator, from his intuitive vantage point, thus guides the machine over the hills and into the valley, each partner doing what he is best fitted for.

Even more exciting, once the details of the interactions are known theoretically, the X-ray diffraction pattern of the molecule can be calculated and compared with the original observations

to remove whatever doubts about the structure are left by ambiguities encountered when going in the other direction. This closing of the circle verifies not only the calculation of molecular structure but also the theoretical edifice that provided the details of molecular interactions.

In this example the computer clearly mimics the molecule according to a script supplied by underlying physical and chemical theory. The computer represents the molecule with a sufficient degree of structural detail to make plausible a metaphorical identification of the computer with the molecule. The metaphor loses its force as we approach details of atomic structure, and the submodels that account for atomic behavior are in this case merely functional.

The remarkable immediacy and clarity of the confrontation of acted-out theory and experiment shown in the preceding example is by no means an isolated phenomenon. Similar techniques are emerging in chemistry [see

"Computer Experiments in Chemistry," by Don L. Bunker; SCIENTIFIC AMERICAN, July, 1964], in hydrodynamics [see "Computer Experiments in Fluid Dynamics," by Francis H. Harlow and Jacob E. Fromm; SCIENTIFIC AMERICAN, March, 1965] and in other branches of science. It is noteworthy, as Don L. Bunker has pointed out, that computers used in this way, far from reducing the scientist to a passive bystander, reinforce the need for the creative human element in experimental science, if only because witless calculation is likely to be so voluminous as to be beyond the power of even the fastest computer. Human judgment and intuition must be injected at every stage to guide the computer in its search for a solution. Painstaking routine work will be less and less useful for making a scientific reputation, because such "horse work" can be reduced to a computer program. All that is left for the scientist to contribute is a creative imagination. In this sense scientists are subject to techno-

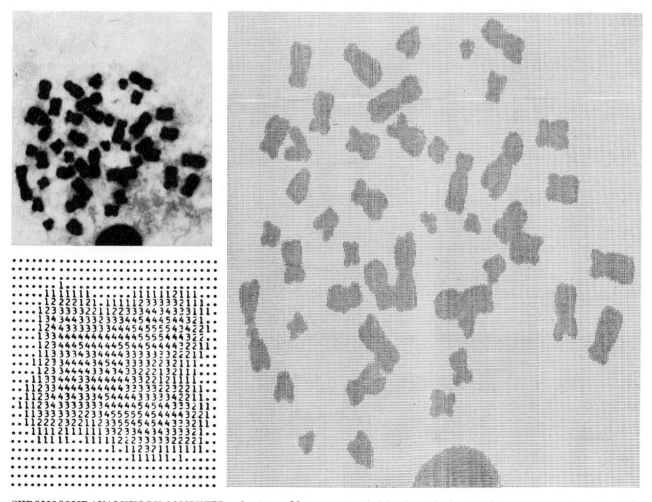

CHROMOSOME ANALYSIS BY COMPUTER makes it possible to examine automatically large numbers of cells for chromosome abnormalities. A photomicrograph of a complement of human chromosomes is shown at top left. An image of the photomicrograph is provided by the grid of numerals in computer print-out at right. Enlargement of a single chromosome appears at bottom left. Print-outs were made with a scanning device called FIDAC and an IBM 7094 computer at the National Biomedical Research Foundation.

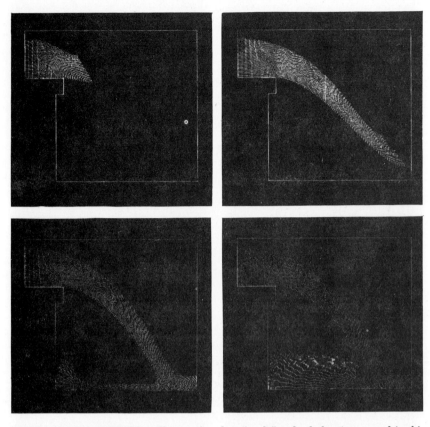

SIMULATED WATERFALL spills over the edge of a cliff and splashes into a pool in this computer experiment performed by John P. Shannon at the Los Alamos Scientific Laboratory as part of a general study of dynamic behavior of fluids with the aid of numerical models.

logical unemployment, just like anyone else.

In the "softer" emerging sciences such as psychology and linguistics the excitement and speculation about the future promise of the computer both as instrument and as actor tend to be even stronger than in the physical sciences, although solid accomplishments still are far fewer.

From the time modern computers were born the myth of the "giant brain" was fed by the obvious fact that they could calculate and also by active speculation about their ability to translate from one language into another, play chess, compose music, prove theorems and so on. That such activities were hitherto seen as peculiar to man and to no other species and certainly to no machine lent particular force to the myth. This myth (as expressed, for example, in *New Yorker* cartoons) is now deeply rooted as the popular image of the computer.

The myth rests in part on gross misinterpretation of the nature of a functional model. In the early 1950's, when speculation about whether or not computers can think was at the height of fashion, the British mathematician A. M. Turing proposed the following experiment as a test. Imagine an experimenter communicating by teletype with each of two rooms (or black boxes), one containing a man, the other a computer. If after exchanging an appropriate series of messages with each room the experimenter is unable to tell which holds the man and which the computer, the computer might be said to be thinking. Since the situation is symmetrical, one could equally well conclude that the man is computing. Whatever the decision, such an experiment demonstrates at most a more or less limited functional similarity between the two black boxes, because it is hardly designed to reveal structural details. With the realization that the analogy is only functional, this approach to the computer as a model, or emulator, of man loses both mystery and appeal; in its most naïve form it is pursued today only by a dwindling lunatic fringe, although it remains in the consciousness of the public.

In a more sophisticated vein attempts continue toward devising computer systems less dependent on detailed prior instructions and better able to approach problem-solving with something akin to human independence and intelligence. Whether or not such systems, if they are achieved, should have anything like the structure of a human brain is as relevant a question as whether or not flying machines should flap their wings like birds. This problem of artificial intelligence is the subject of speculative research described by Marvin Minsky [SCIENTIFIC AMERICAN, Sept., 1966]. Once the cloud of misapplied functional analogy is dispelled the real promise of using the computer as an animated structural model remains.

Mathematics has so far made relatively few inroads in either linguistics or psychology, although there are now some rather beautiful mathematical theories of language. The scope of these theories is generally limited to syntax (the description of the order and formal relations among words in a sentence). Based as they are on logic and algebra, rather than on the now more familiar calculus, these theories do not lend themselves readily to symbolic calculation of the form to which mathematicians and natural scientists have become accustomed. "Calculations" based on such theories must generally be done by computer. Indeed, in their early form some of these theories were expressed only as computer programs; others still are and may remain so. In such cases the language of programs is the language of science; the program is the original and only script, not just a translation from mathematics.

Early claims that computers could translate languages were vastly exaggerated; even today no finished translation can be produced by machine without human intervention, although machine-aided translation is technically possible. Considerable progress has been made, however, in using computers to manipulate languages, both vernaculars and programming languages. Grammars called phrase-structure grammars and transformational grammars supply the theoretical backdrop for this activity. These grammars describe sentences as they are generated from an initial symbol (say S for sentence) by applying rewrite rules followed (if the grammar is transformational) by applying transformation rules. For example, the rewrite rule $S \rightarrow SuPr$, where Su can be thought of as standing for subject and Pr as standing for predicate, yields the string $SuPr$ when it is applied to the initial symbol S. By adding the rules $Su \rightarrow John$ and $Pr \rightarrow sleeps$ one can turn this string into the sentence "John sleeps." Transformations can then be applied in order to turn, for example, the active sentence "John followed the girl" into the passive one "The girl was followed by John."

Under the direction of Susumu Kuno and myself a research group at Harvard has developed, over the past few years, techniques for inverting this generation process in order to go from a sentence as it occurs in a text to a description of its structure or, equivalently, to a description of how it might have been generated by the rules of the grammar. Consider the simple sentence "Time flies like an arrow." To find out which part of this sentence is the subject, which part the predicate and so on, a typical program first looks up each word in a dictionary. The entry for "flies" would show that this word might serve either as a plural noun denoting an annoying domestic insect or as a verb de-

noting locomotion through the air by an agent represented by a subject in the third person singular.

The specific function of a word in a particular context can be found only by checking how the word relates to other words in the sentence, hence the serious problem of determining which of the many combinations of possible functions do in fact fit together as a legitimate sentence structure. This problem has been solved essentially by trying all possibilities and rejecting those that do not fit, although powerful tests suggested by theory and intuition can be applied to eliminate entire classes of possibilities at one fell swoop, thereby bringing the process within the realm of practicality.

A grammar that pretends to describe

English at all accurately must yield a structure for "Time flies like an arrow" in which "time" is the subject of the verb "flies" and "like an arrow" is an adverbial phrase modifying the verb. "Time" can also serve attributively, however, as in "time bomb," and "flies" of course can serve as a noun. Together with "like" interpreted as a verb, this yields a structure that becomes obvious only if one thinks of a kind of flies called "time flies," which happen to like an arrow, perhaps as a meal. Moreover, "time" as an imperative verb with "flies" as a noun also yields a structure that makes sense as an order to someone to take out his stopwatch and time flies with great dispatch, or like an arrow.

A little thought suggests many minor modifications of the grammar sufficient to rule out such fantasies. Unfortunately too much is then lost. A point can be made that the structures are legitimate even if the sentences are meaningless. It is, after all, only an accident of nature, or for that matter merely of nomenclature, that there is no species of flies called "time flies." Worse yet, anything ruling out the nonexisting species of time flies will also rule out the identical but legitimate structure of "Fruit flies like a banana."

Still more confusing, the latter sentence itself is given an anomalous structure, namely that which is quite sensible for "Time flies. . ." but which is nonsensical here since we know quite well that fruit in general does not fly and that when it does, it flies like maple seeds, not like bananas.

A theory of syntax alone can help no further. Semantics, the all too nebulous notion of what a sentence means, must be invoked to choose among the three structures syntax accepts for "Time flies like an arrow." No techniques now known can deal effectively with semantic problems of this kind. Research in the field is continuing in the hope that some form of man-machine interaction can yield both practical results and further insight into the deepening mystery of natural language. We do not yet know how people understand language, and our machine procedures barely do child's work in an extraordinarily cumbersome way.

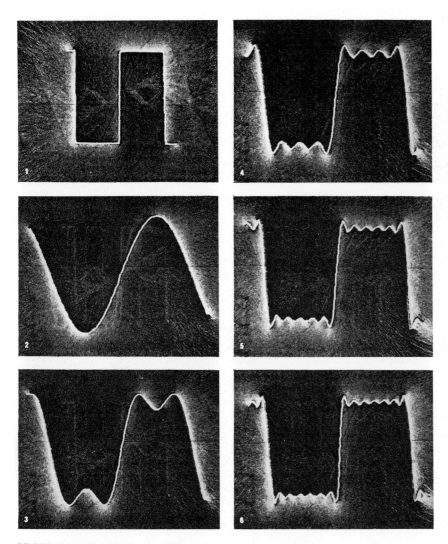

PROBLEM IN MATHEMATICS illustrates the author's experimental use in Harvard classrooms of a keyboard-and-display system developed by Glen Culler of the University of California at Santa Barbara. It is well known that any periodic function (in this example the square wave at top left) can be approximated by the sum of a series of terms that oscillate harmonically, converging on the curve of the function. Culler's apparatus makes possible quick intuitive exploration of the nature of this approximation. The other curves show the effect of increasing the number of terms in the partial sum of the series. The spikes near the corners of the square wave are caused by nonuniform convergence near a discontinuity.

The outlook is brighter for man-made programming languages. Since these can be defined almost at will, it is generally possible to reduce ambiguity and to systematize semantics well enough for practical purposes, although numerous challenging theoretical problems remain. The computer is also growing in

has suffered from exaggerated early claims and recurrent confusion between the functional and the structural aspects of theory. Psychology and the study of artificial intelligence are both concerned with intelligent behavior, but otherwise they are not necessarily related except to the extent that metaphors borrowed power as an instrument of routine language data processing. Concordances, now easily made by machine, supply scholars in the humanities and social sciences with tabular displays of the location and context of key words in both sacred and profane texts.

Psychologists have used programming languages to write scripts for a variety of structural models of human behavior. These are no more mysterious than scripts for the orbit of Neptune or the structure of hemoglobin. The psychological models differ from the physical ones only in their subject and their original language. Convincing empirical corroboration of the validity of these models is still lacking, and the field

from one discipline may be stimulating to the other.

In actuality it is the languages, not the scripts, that are today the really valuable products of the attempts at computer modeling of human behavior. Several languages, notably John McCarthy's LISP, have proved invaluable as tools for general research on symbol manipulation. Research on natural-language data processing, theorem-proving, algebraic manipulation and graphical display draws heavily on such languages. Nevertheless, the computer as instrument is rapidly making a useful place for itself in the psychology laboratory. Bread-and-butter applications include the administration, monitoring and evaluation of tests of human or animal subjects in studies of perception and learning.

The business of science, both in principle and in practice, is inextricably involved in the business of education, particularly on the university level. The

paradigm of the computer as instrument and as actor, although described in terms of research, seems to apply to instruction as well. Because on-line, time-shared systems are still experimental and expensive, especially with graphical display facilities, their use for instruction lags somewhat behind their use for research.

Hopes for computers in education at the elementary or secondary level are described in an article by Patrick Suppes [SCIENTIFIC AMERICAN, September, 1966]. My own current exploration of the potential value of technological aids to creative thought focuses rather on the undergraduate or graduate student and in the transition from learning in the classroom to learning when practicing a profession.

The desire to keep labor within reasonable bounds generally leads to oversimplified and superficial experiments in student laboratories. Where the observation and intelligent interpretation of a variety of significant phenomena

```
*****  ANALYSIS NUMBER   1        SENTENCE NUMBER  000001                CORPUS NUMBER

ENGLISH   SENTENCE STRUCTURE    SWC    SWC MNEMONIC    SYNTACTIC ROLE              RL NUM  PREDICTION POOL
                                                                                          SE
TIME      1S                    NOUS   NOUN 1          SUBJECT OF PREDICATE VERB   SENNNO
                                                                                          PD VSA
FLIES     1V                    VI1S   COMPLETE VI     PREDICATE VERB              VXVI10
                                                                                          PD
LIKE      1VPR                  PRE    PREPOSITION     PREPOSITION                 PDPREO
                                                                                          PD NQG
AN        1VPOA                 ART    PRO-ADJECTIVE   OBJECT OF PREPOSITION       NQAAAO
                                                                                          PD N5G
ARROW     1VPO                  NOUS   NOUN 1          OBJECT OF PREPOSITION       N5MMMO
                                                                                          PD
.         1.                    PRD    PERIOD          END OF SENTENCE             PDPRDO

-----------------------------------------------------------------------------------------------------

*****  ANALYSIS NUMBER   2        SENTENCE NUMBER  000001                CORPUS NUMBER

ENGLISH   SENTENCE STRUCTURE    SWC    SWC MNEMONIC    SYNTACTIC ROLE              RL NUM  PREDICTION POOL
                                                                                          SE
TIME      1SA                   NOUS   NOUN 1          SUBJECT OF PREDICATE VERB   SENOUO
                                                                                          PD VZA7ZA
FLIES     1S                    NOUP   NOUN 1          SUBJECT OF PREDICATE VERB   7XMMMO
                                                                                          PD VPA
LIKE      1V                    VT1P   NOUN-OBJECT VT  PREDICATE VERB              VXVT11
                                                                                          PD N2A
AN        10A                   ART    PRO-ADJECTIVE   OBJECT OF PREDICATE VERB    N2AAAO
                                                                                          PD N5A
ARROW     10                    NOUS   NOUN 1          OBJECT OF PREDICATE VERB    N5MMMO
                                                                                          PD
.         1.                    PRD    PERIOD          END OF SENTENCE             PDPRDO

-----------------------------------------------------------------------------------------------------

*****  ANALYSIS NUMBER   3        SENTENCE NUMBER  000001                CORPUS NUMBER

ENGLISH   SENTENCE STRUCTURE    SWC    SWC MNEMONIC    SYNTACTIC ROLE          RL NUM  PREDICTION POOL
                                                                                      SE
TIME      3V                    IT1    INFINITE VT1    IMPERATIVE VERB         SEIT10
                                                                                      PD N2B
FLIES     30                    NOUP   NOUN 1          OBJECT OF IMPERATIVE VERB  N2NNNO
                                                                                      PD
LIKE      30PR                  PRE    PREPOSITION     PREPOSITION             PDPREO
                                                                                      PD NQG
AN        30POA                 ART    PRO-ADJECTIVE   OBJECT OF PREPOSITION   NQAAAO
                                                                                      PD N5G
ARROW     30PO                  NOUS   NOUN 1          OBJECT OF PREPOSITION   N5MMMO
                                                                                      PD
.         3.                    PRD    PERIOD          END OF SENTENCE         PDPRDO

-----------------------------------------------------------------------------------------------------
```

SYNTACTIC ANALYSIS BY COMPUTER of the sentence "Time flies like an arrow" yields three different structural interpretations, which are represented here by computer print-out (*left*) and by conventional sentence-structure diagrams (*right*). The first structure is one in which "time" is the subject of the verb "flies" and "like an arrow" is an adverbial phrase modifying the verb (*Analysis Number 1*). "Time" can also serve attributively, however, as in "time bomb," and "flies" of course can serve as a noun. Together with "like" interpreted as a verb, this yields a structure that becomes obvious only if one thinks of a kind of domestic insect called "time flies," which happen to like an arrow, perhaps as a meal (*2*). Moreover, "time" as an imperative verb with "flies" as a noun also yields a

are the primary objectives of a laboratory exercise, using a transparent computer should reduce unnecessary drudgery to the point where judgment and interpretation, even of realistic experiments, can prevail.

The transparent computer also promises to be effective as a kind of animated blackboard. This hardly implies the disappearance of chalk, films or books. The computer merely adds another powerful and versatile tool to the teacher's kit. In fact, where repetition or polish is necessary, the computer itself can serve to make films or equivalent visual recordings. We have found that whereas films cannot be interrupted or altered, a recorded computer sequence can easily be stopped in response to a student's question; the lecturer can then explore alternatives by returning either to the informal direct use of the computer or to the conventional blackboard. The prerecorded sequence can then be resumed.

Best of all, there need be no distinc-

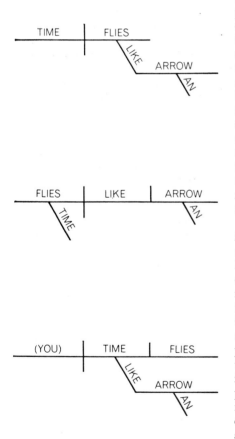

structure that makes sense as an order to someone to take out his stopwatch and time flies with great dispatch, or like an arrow (3). No computer techniques now known can deal effectively with semantic problems of this kind, but research in the field is continuing.

tion between the classroom tool and that available to students for homework assignments, laboratory calculations or individual research projects. The transition from classroom to life therefore promises to be made smoother. Since computers are not yet either as transparent or as cheap as one might wish, many problems of technique and finance remain to be faced. In any case, no panacea has been found for education's ills, only a richer range of choices to be made.

An example based on our experimental use in Harvard classrooms of a keyboard-and-display system developed by Glen Culler at the University of California at Santa Barbara will illustrate both the promise and the problems. Since the static printed page cannot adequately portray the effect of dynamic display, the problems may be more evident than the promise. The topic chosen is mathematical in nature, since such problems are best suited for the equipment currently available. The objective is to develop a natural and perspicuous presentation of topics traditionally reserved for more advanced treatment, to develop others in greater depth than conventional methods allow and to stimulate the student's intuition and his resourcefulness in solving problems. The objective is not to eliminate theory and rigor in favor of witless calculation, but rather to restore the close link between theory and calculation that characterized mathematics before the advent of rigor late in the 19th century led to the aberrant but currently fashionable split between pure and applied mathematics.

It is well known that any periodic function can be approximated by the sum of a series of terms that oscillate harmonically, converging on the curve of the function. Culler's apparatus makes possible quick intuitive exploration of the nature of this approximation. Consider, for example, the square wave shown at top left in the illustration on page 367. The accompanying computer-generated curves show the effect of increasing the number of terms in the partial sum of the series. The spikes near the corners of the square wave are caused by nonuniform convergence near a discontinuity. For the pure mathematician this demonstration can motivate a more formal treatment of nonuniform convergence. For the engineer the phenomenon can be clarified by displaying the components of the approximation in such a way as to make it obvious intuitively why the spikes occur. In prin-

ciple the instructor, or an interested student on his own, could follow up such a demonstration by modeling the effect of a linear circuit element, say a resistor or a simple amplifier, on a square wave, on its individual components and on their sum.

At present any concurrent formal algebraic manipulations require pencil or chalk. Current progress toward machine-aided algebraic manipulation raises the exciting possibility that machines will eventually help with both symbolic and numerical manipulation and with easy transitions between these two modes of expression. Working in both modes simultaneously or in whatever combination rigor and intuition demand would profoundly affect the thought of pure and applied mathematicians alike.

Other types of teaching experiment can be conducted by building an appropriate structural model into the computer. One might assume the structure and examine its behavior, as is frequently done in management games, or one might treat only the behavior as observable, leaving the model to be determined as an exercise in theory-building. As paradigms are developed by research in some area, these paradigms could then be applied as well to teaching in that area. It will be interesting, for example, to experiment with the teaching of a foreign language for which a transformational grammar of the type I described earlier has been implemented on a computer.

It is also interesting to speculate on the use of on-line computers as tools for the investigation of the psychology of learning and problem-solving. Experiments in this area have been difficult, contrived and unrealistic. When the interactive computer serves as a problem-solving tool, it is also easily adapted to record information about problem-solving behavior. Here again the problem will not be the collection of data but rather devising appropriate experimental designs, since an hour's problem-solving session at a computer console can accumulate an enormous amount of data.

In short, computers are capable of profoundly affecting science by stretching human reason and intuition, much as telescopes or microscopes extend human vision. I suspect that the ultimate effects of this stretching will be as far-reaching as the effects of the invention of writing. Whether the product is truth or nonsense, however, will depend more on the user than on the tool.

SYSTEM ANALYSIS AND PROGRAMMING

CHRISTOPHER STRACHEY · September 1966

It is a profoundly erroneous truism, repeated by all copy-books and by eminent people when they are making speeches, that we should cultivate the habit of thinking of what we are doing. The precise opposite is the case. Civilization advances by extending the number of important operations which we can perform without thinking about them. Operations of thought are like cavalry charges in a battle—they are strictly limited in number, they require fresh horses, and must only be made at decisive moments.

—ALFRED NORTH WHITEHEAD

This article is about how to get a computer to do what you want, and why it almost always takes longer than you expect. What follows is not a detailed report on the state of the art of programming but an attempt to show how to set about writing a program. The process of writing a program is primarily intuitive rather than formal; hence we shall be more concerned with the guiding principles that underlie programming than with the particular language in which the program is to be presented to the machine.

We shall start with a specific example of a programming problem that is decidedly nontrivial and yet sufficiently simple to be understood without any previous knowledge of programming. I have chosen an unorthodox approach to the problem, one that will look strange to many professional programmers. This approach enables us to tackle an example that would be much too elaborate to explain otherwise.

Our problem is to program a computer to play checkers. How should we set about it? There are two main aspects to the problem. To equip the computer to deal with the game at all we must find a way to represent the board and positions on it and furnish the computer with a program for identifying legal moves and making them. This is a programming problem. Secondly, we must provide the machine with a method of selecting a suitable move from the ones available. This is mainly a problem in game-playing. Arthur L. Samuel of the International Business Machines Corporation has studied this game-playing aspect extensively and with considerable success [see "Artificial Intelligence," by Minsky; SCIENTIFIC AMERICAN, September, 1966]. Here, however, since we are concerned with programming rather than game-playing, we shall content ourselves with a simple general strategy and leave most of the details unsettled.

The usual approach to writing a program, particularly for a complex problem, divides the process into two stages. The first of these is called system analysis. It involves analyzing the task to decide exactly what needs to be done and adopting an overall plan. Once the general outline of the work to be performed has been decided on, the second stage is to write the required operations in a form suitable for the computer. This involves a large number of more detailed decisions (for example how information is to be represented in the machine and how the representations are to be stored). The detailed form of the program will depend on the particular computer to be used.

Confusion has developed about the naming of these two stages. Some programmers reserve the term "programming" for the second stage; others call the first stage "programming" and the second stage "coding"; still others use the term "programming" for the entire process—stages one and two. My own view is that the distinction between system analysis and programming is not a very useful one. If the system analysis were carried through to a description of the program outline in a slightly more rigorous language than is used at present, it should be possible to relegate the whole of the remaining process of producing a detailed program in machine language to the computer itself.

ORTHODOX APPROACH to the problem of writing a computer program is illustrated on the opposite page. The problem in this example is comparatively simple: to find the function e^x by summing the series $1 + x + x^2/2! + x^3/3! + \ldots$ until the terms become negligible. The process of writing a program to solve such a problem is usually divided into two stages. The first stage, sometimes called system analysis, involves analyzing the task to decide exactly what needs to be done and adopting an overall plan; this stage is represented by the block diagram at left. The second stage, called programming by some programmers and coding by others, involves writing the required operations in a form suitable for the computer. The problem in question is expressed in three different programming languages at right. The diamond-shaped box in the block diagram contains a "decision function"; the straight vertical lines before and after the word "term" signify "absolute value of," and the symbol $\ll$ means that "|term|" is negligible compared with "sum." In CPL (Combined Programming Language) the expression "value of" governs the immediately following statement; "repeat" governs the immediately preceding statement, and the symbols § and $ act as statement brackets. In both CPL and ALGOL the operator ":=" stands for assignment: the quantities on the right of this operator are evaluated and simultaneously assigned to the variables on the left. The symbol * in FORTRAN is a multiplication sign.

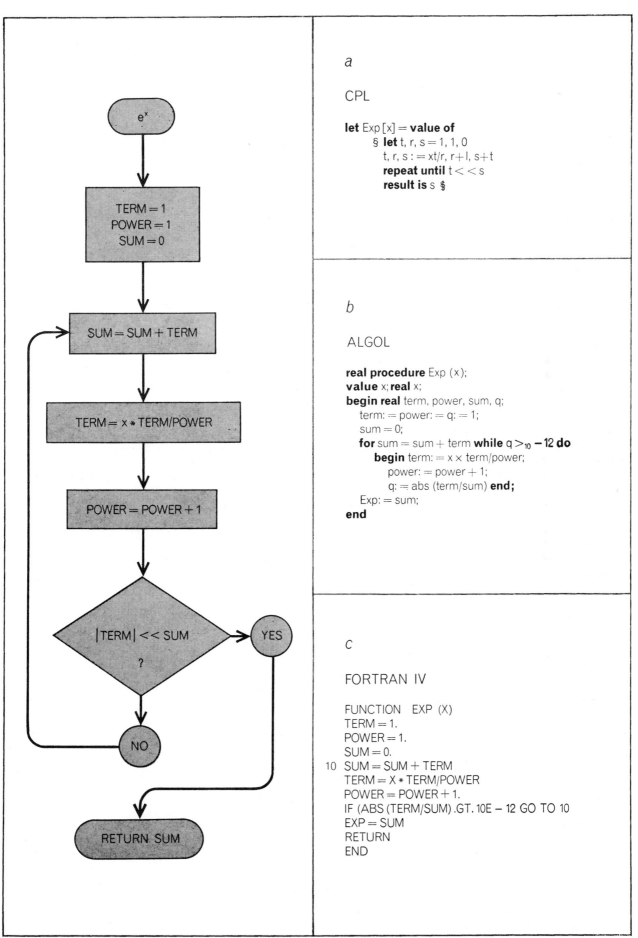

a

CPL

let Exp [x] = **value of**
    § **let** t, r, s = 1, 1, 0
        t, r, s := xt/r, r+l, s+t
        repeat until t << s
        result is s §

b

ALGOL

real procedure Exp (x);
value x; **real** x;
begin real term, power, sum, q;
    term: = power: = q: = 1;
    sum = 0;
    for sum = sum + term **while** q >₁₀ − 12 **do**
        begin term: = x × term/power;
            power: = power + 1;
            q: = abs (term/sum) **end**;
    Exp: = sum;
end

c

FORTRAN IV

```
FUNCTION   EXP (X)
TERM = 1.
POWER = 1.
SUM = 0.
10  SUM = SUM + TERM
TERM = X * TERM/POWER
POWER = POWER + 1.
IF (ABS (TERM/SUM) .GT. 10E − 12 GO TO 10
EXP = SUM
RETURN
END
```

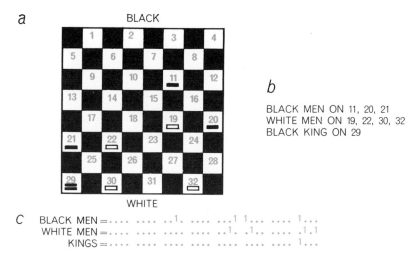

a

BLACK

WHITE

b

BLACK MEN ON 11, 20, 21
WHITE MEN ON 19, 22, 30, 32
BLACK KING ON 29

c   BLACK MEN = ...1. ....1 1... .... 1...
       WHITE MEN = ...1. .1.. .... .1.1
          KINGS = ... 1...

POSITIONS on a checkerboard can be represented in a computer in two different ways. To describe a particular position one has the choice of specifying either what is on each square (*a*) or where the pieces that are still in play are located (*b*). An equivalent alternative to *a* is given in *c*, which uses only binary numbers. Three binary digits, or "bits," are needed to specify each square: one to show the presence of a black man or king, another to show the presence of a white man or king and a third to show the presence of kings of either color.

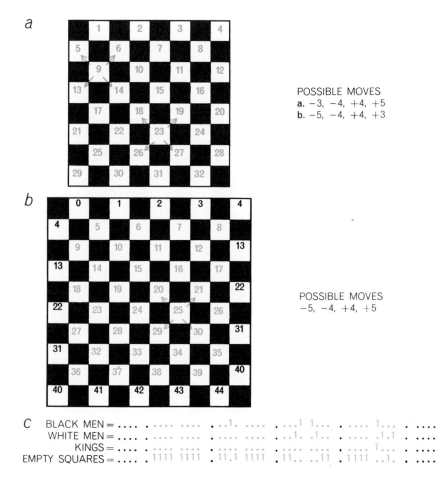

a

POSSIBLE MOVES
a. −3, −4, +4, +5
b. −5, −4, +4, +3

b

POSSIBLE MOVES
−5, −4, +4, +5

c   BLACK MEN = ...1 ...1 1... . 1... . ....
       WHITE MEN = ...1. .1.. . .1.1 . ....
          KINGS = ... 1... . ....
EMPTY SQUARES = ... 1111 1111 . 11.1 1111 . 11.. ..11 . 1111 ..1. . ....

MOVES on a checkerboard can be represented using the numbering scheme of an ordinary checkerboard (*a*), but this is inconvenient, as there are two kinds of squares (on alternate rows), which need different rules. Arthur L. Samuel of the International Business Machines Corporation devised a neat method of avoiding this difficulty. By extending the board with rows and columns that are not used and renumbering the squares, he produced a scheme in which the possible moves are similar for all squares on that part of the board which is actually used (*b*). The position shown at the top of this page is represented in this new scheme of notation in *c*. Empty squares are indicated by 1's for all the squares on the board proper.

Let us get on to the problem of programming a computer to play checkers against an opponent. How shall we represent the relevant features of the game, and what kind of operations do we want to be able to perform on them? A good working rule is to start with the operations and allow them to determine what it is you need to represent in the machine. In this case we clearly require, to begin with, representations of positions and moves and of the values associated with them.

We can approach the kind of precision the computer requires and still avoid getting bogged down in premature detail by using a functional notation. We let *P* stand for a position and agree to include in *P* not only the number and arrangement of the pieces on the board but also various other important facts such as which player is to move. The value of a position can be expressed by a function PositionValue(*P*). The value of any move (say *M*) obviously depends on the position from which it is made; therefore we must specify the position in writing the function MoveValue(*M*,*P*). Next, in order to be able to look ahead and examine the possible consequences of moves, the computer will need a third function: MakeMove(*M*,*P*), with *P* representing the position from which the move is made. The result of this function is the new position produced by the move. Finally, the program needs a fourth function to find all the legal moves that can be made from a given position: LegalMovesFrom(*P*). This function has as its result a list of moves.

These four functions, together with the two types of object (*P* and *M*), are sufficient to specify the kernel of our checkers program. There are two players in a game of checkers (in our case the machine and its opponent), and a position that is good for one will be bad for the other. We must therefore make our idea of the value of a position more precise by saying that PositionValue(*P*) gives the value of the position *P* to the player who has to move from it. We can plausibly assume that the value of the position *P* to the other player is the negative of this; that is, if the value of a position to one player is *v*, its value to the other will be −*v*. (This assumption is expressed in the terms of game theory by saying that checkers is a zero-sum game.)

Next we can define the value of a move to the player who makes it as the value *to him* of the resulting position. Suppose the result of making the move

M from the position P is the position P'. Remembering that it is the opponent who has to make the move from P', we can see that the value of the move M to the player who makes it will be $-\text{PositionValue}(P')$. Thus in our notation we can define the value of a move as follows: $\text{MoveValue}(M,P) = -\text{PositionValue}[\text{MakeMove}(M,P)]$. This formal statement could be paraphrased by saying that to value a move for yourself you make it, find the value of the resulting position to your opponent and change its sign.

How shall we find the value of a position? The basic procedure of the game is to explore all your possible moves and all possible replies by the opponent to some depth and evaluate the resulting positions. Let us call these "terminal" positions and say that their values are produced by the function TerminalValue(P). This function makes an immediate assessment of a position (in terms, perhaps, of such factors as the number of pieces still in play, their mobility, the command of the center of the board and so forth) without any further look-ahead. We can now say that if P is a terminal position, its value is TerminalValue(P), and that if it is not, its value is that of the best legal move that could be made from it. Note that the question of whether a position is terminal or not may depend not only on the position itself but also on what depth (d) the look-ahead has reached. This is necessary in order to put some limit on how far the machine looks ahead.

The definitions we have been writing are in fact circular (for example, the definition of PositionValue involves the use of MoveValue and vice versa), and the functions are called recursive, because each is defined in terms of the others. This circularity is no disadvantage; indeed, it makes it possible to start right in the middle of things, to set up a number of functions whose purpose is only intuitively understood at the beginning and to define each of them in terms of the others. This recursive, or hierarchical, approach to programming is by far the simplest method of handling complicated operations, since it allows them to be broken up into smaller units that can be considered separately.

We have now constructed a general game-playing scheme without having decided on either the details of the strategy or the structure of the game itself. We can complete the outline of our program by deciding on the representation of positions and moves and defining four functions. The functions Legal-

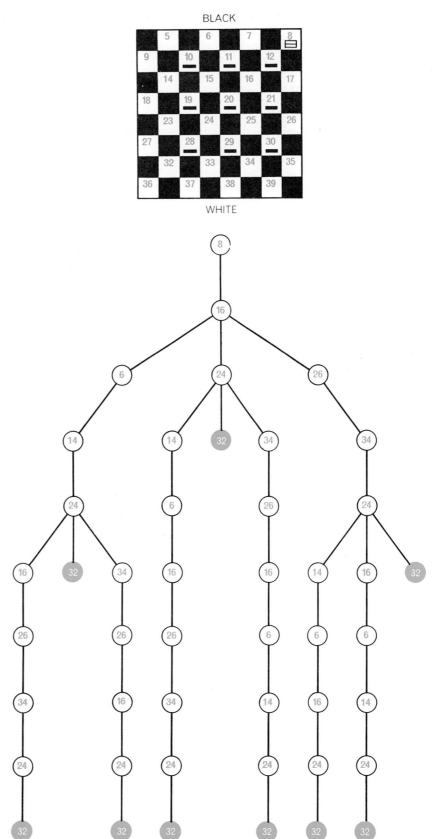

CAPTURE "TREE" depicts all the possible "partial capture moves" for a given piece after the first such move. In checkers a move is not complete until no more captures can be made. A maximum of nine captures in a single move is possible, as shown in this example. Capture-move situation, like that in the main game, can be programmed by using "recursive" functions, that is, functions that are defined in a circular manner in terms of other functions. Program for this situation is incorporated in the complete checkers program on page 375.

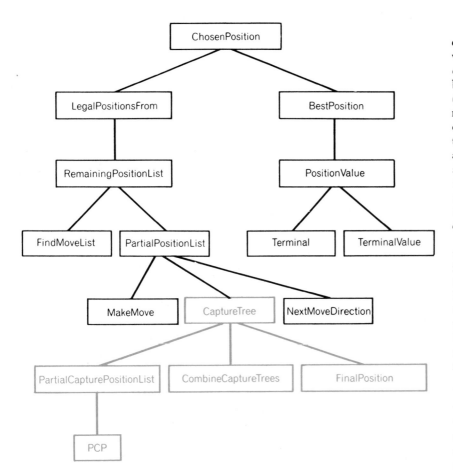

HIERARCHICAL STRUCTURE of the author's checkers program is evident in this diagram. Since there is a limit to the size and complexity of a problem one can keep in mind at one time, it appears that the best way to deal with large and complicated problems is to treat fairly sizable operations as separate units and then combine them hierarchically. The logical function "ChosenPosition" is defined recursively in terms of two other functions: "LegalPositionsFrom" and "BestPosition." The function "LegalPositionsFrom" deals with the problem of finding legal positions on the checkerboard at a given point in the game; all the functions that branch out from "LegalPositionsFrom" treat various aspects of this problem. The part of this major branch that deals with capture moves, for example, is in color. The function "BestPosition" and all the functions that branch out from it deal with the problem of choosing the best position from the list supplied by "LegalPositionsFrom."

When we come to a detailed consideration of the representation of moves, we find that the numbering of squares on the ordinary board is inconvenient because there are two kinds of squares (on alternate rows) that need different rules. Samuel devised a neat method of avoiding this difficulty. By extending the board with rows and columns that are not used and renumbering the squares, he produced a scheme in which the possible moves were similar for all squares on that part of the board which is actually used [*see bottom illustration on page 372*].

All the possible moves (other than those in which pieces are captured) fall into four types, each of which can be represented by a word (consisting of 45 bits, or binary digits) that can specify any move of its type. Within the framework of the scheme of notation we have been using it is also a simple matter to represent capture moves and the promotion of men to kings.

It would go beyond the scope of this article to discuss all the details of a working checkers program. The main outlines of the process of writing such a program should, however, be apparent by now. The first step is to have a vague idea of how to solve the problem. The second step is to specify the operations needed to carry out this initial plan, formalizing it by giving names to the objects on which these operations are to act. The third step is to clarify the definitions of the objects and to settle on a representation for each of them. These representations should be determined primarily by the operations to be performed on the objects. Once the representations have been decided on, the component operations can be defined more precisely in terms of them. One can then go on to refine the program, correcting errors or deficiencies that may show up in the representations and adjusting the operations accordingly.

At this stage the major intellectual

MovesFrom(*P*) and MakeMove(*M,P*), together with the form of *P* and *M*, will determine the nature of the game, and the functions Terminal(*P,d*) and TerminalValue(*P*) between them will determine the strategy.

The selection of ways to represent objects in the computer is an art, and there is little we can do in a systematic fashion to decide the best way. The main requirements are that the representation should be as compact as possible and yet as easy as possible to manipulate.

For representing the various positions on a checkerboard we have two distinct possibilities. To describe a particular position we could either specify whether each of the 32 available squares on the board is or is not occupied, and if it is, by what, or we could merely

give the locations of the pieces still in play. The first of these alternatives is more convenient from the standpoint of finding the legal moves, because it makes it easier to discover which squares are unoccupied [*see top illustration on page 372*].

COMPLETE CHECKERS PROGRAM is given in the left-hand column on the opposite page. The language used in the program is an informal and somewhat extended version of CPL. The names of the logical functions that are specific to this particular program ("ChosenPosition" and so on) were selected to be suggestive of the operations they govern. A list of the primitive, or generalized, functions and the specific data structures used in the program is provided in the right-hand column. The chief omissions from the program are the input and output arrangements and the functions that define the game-playing strategy [Terminal (*P,d*) and Terminal Value (*P*)]. The program has not been debugged on a machine and so, in accordance with the views expressed in the article, probably still contains some errors; interested readers may like to look for them. The general notation "Condition → *A,B*" is a conditional expression whose value is *A* if the condition is satisfied (that is, if it is true) and *B* otherwise. The section that deals with capture moves is in color.

ChosenPosition(P) = **value of**
§ **let** L = LegalPositionsFrom(P)
if Null(L) **then** Resign
let (p,v) = BestPosition(NIL, − ∝,L,0)
result is p §

BestPosition(P,V,L,d) = Null(L) → (P,V), **value of**
§ **let** (p,l) = Next (L)
let v = − PositionValue(p,d + 1)
result is (v > V) → BestPosition(p,v,l,d),
BestPosition(P,V,l,d) §

PositionValue(P,d) = Terminal(P,d) → TerminalValue(P), **value of**
§ **let** L = LegalPositionsFrom(P)
let (p,v) = BestPosition(NIL, − ∝,L,d)
result is v §

LegalPositionsFrom(P) = **value of**
§ **let** L = RemainingPositionList(P,Capture,5)
result is Null(L)→RemainingPosition List(P,NonCapture,5),L §

RemainingPositionList(P,C,s) =
PartialPositionList(P,C,s,FindMoveList(P,C,s))

PartialPositionList(P,C,s,L) =
Null(L)→((s = −5)→NIL,
RemainingPositionList(P,C,NextMoveDirection(s)),
value of
§ **let** φ = SingleDigitFrom(L)
let lp = MakeMove(P,C,s,φ)
let l = (C = Capture)→CaptureTree(lp),
FinalPosition(lp)
result is Join (l,PartialPositionList(P,C,s,L − φ)) §

NextMoveDirection(s) = (s = 5) → 4, ((s = 4) → − 4, − 5)

FindMoveList(P,C,s) = **value of**
§ **let** (X,Y,K,σ) = P
let Empty = ∼ X ∧ ∼ Y ∧ Board
let ψ = (C = Capture) → (Shift(Empty,σs)∧ Y),Empty
let φ = Shift(ψ,σs)∧ X
result is (s > 0) → φ,φ ∧ K §

MakeMove(P,C,s,φ) = **value of**
§ **let** (X,Y,K,σ) = P
let ψ = (C = Capture) → Shift(φ, − σs),NIL
let θ = (C = Capture) → Shift(ψ, − σs),
Shift(φ, − σs)
let Xk = Null(φ ∧ K) → (θ ∧ LastRows),(θ − φ)
result is ((X − φ + θ),(Y −ψ),(K − ψ ∧ K + Xk),σ,θ) §

FinalPosition(lp) = **value of**
§ **let** (X,Y,K,σ,φ) = lp
result is (Y,X,K, − σ) §

CaptureTree(lp) = **value of**
§ **let** L = PartialCapturePositionList(lp)
result is Null(L) → (FinalPosition(lp)),
CombineCaptureTrees(L) §

PartialCapturePositionList(lp) = **value of**
§ **let** (X,Y,K,σ,φ) = lp
let P = (X,Y,K,σ)
result is MinList(PCP(P,φ,5),PCP(P,φ,4),
PCP(P,φ ∧ K, − 4),PCP(P,φ ∧ K, − 5)) §

PCP(P,φ,s) = **value of**
§ **let** (X,Y,K,σ) = P
let ψ = Shift(φ, − σs) ∧Y
let Empty = ∼ X ∧ ∼Y∧ Board
let θ = Shift(ψ, − σs) ∧ Empty
let Xk = Null(φ ∧ K) → (θ ∧ LastRows),(θ − φ)
result is Null(θ) → NIL,
((X − φ + θ),(Y − ψ),(K − ψ ∧ K + Xk),σ,θ) §

CombineCaptureTrees(L) = Null(L) → NIL, **value of**
§ **let** (lp,l) = Next (L)
result is Join(CaptureTree(lp),CombineCaptureTrees(l)) §

PRIMITIVE FUNCTIONS
a LIST FUNCTIONS

L	LIST
Null(L)	TRUE IF L IS THE EMPTY LIST (NIL), FALSE OTHERWISE
Head(L)	FIRST MEMBER OF L
Tail(L)	WHAT REMAINS OF L AFTER Head(L) IS REMOVED
Next(L)	LIST WHOSE MEMBERS ARE Head(L) AND Tail(L)
Join(L$_1$,L$_2$)	A SINGLE LIST FORMED FROM THE MEMBERS OF L$_1$ AND L$_2$
MinList(L$_1$,L$_2$...)	A SINGLE LIST FORMED FROM THE MEMBERS OF SEVERAL LISTS; ALSO LEAVES OUT NULL LISTS AND REPETITIONS

b BIT-STRING FUNCTIONS

∼	NOT
∧	AND
∨	INCLUSIVE OR
x +y	SAME AS x ∨ y
x − y	SAME AS x ∧ (∼ y)
SingleDigitFrom(x)	A BIT STRING OF THE SAME LENGTH AS x WITH A SINGLE 1 IN A POSITION CORRESPONDING TO ONE OF THE 1'S IN BIT-STRING x
Shift(x,n)	THE BIT-STRING x SHIFTED n PLACES TO THE RIGHT. IF n < 0, THE SHIFT WILL BE TO THE LEFT. DIGITS THAT ARE SHIFTED OFF THE END OF THE BOARD ARE LOST. DIGITS SHIFTED ONTO THE BOARD ARE 0'S.

c STRATEGY FUNCTIONS

Terminal(P,d)	TRUE IF P IS TERMINAL, FALSE OTHERWISE
TerminalValue(P)	VALUE OF P (COMPUTED WHEN LOOK-AHEAD BEYOND P IS UNDESIRABLE)

DATA STRUCTURES
a 45-BIT STRINGS

X	PLAYER'S MEN AND KINGS
Y	OPPONENT'S MEN AND KINGS
K	KINGS ON BOTH SIDES
φ	SQUARE MOVED FROM
ψ	CAPTURED PIECE (IF ANY)
θ	SQUARE MOVED TO
Board	1'S ON BOARD SQUARES, 0'S ELSEWHERE
LastRows	1'S ON SQUARES NUMBERED 5, 6, 7, 8, 36, 37, 38, 39

b POSITIONS

σ	NEXT PLAY
	σ = +1: BLACK TO PLAY
	σ = −1: WHITE TO PLAY
P,p	ORDINARY POSITIONS WITH COMPONENTS X, Y, K, σ
lp	INTERMEDIATE POSITIONS WITH COMPONENTS X, Y, K,σ,φ, WHERE φ INDICATES THE PIECE THAT CAN MOVE

c MISCELLANEOUS

C	CAPTURE OR NONCAPTURE
s	DIRECTION OF MOVE
	s = 5: FORWARD, LEFT
	s = 4: FORWARD, RIGHT
	s = − 4: BACKWARD, LEFT
	s = − 5: BACKWARD, RIGHT
V,v	POSITION VALUE
d	DEPTH OF LOOK-AHEAD

work of the program seems to be finished. We have specified precisely what we want the computer to do. The rest—converting the program into instructions for the computer—should be merely routine. Unfortunately it does not quite work out that way, and anyone who has not had the experience of using a computer will be unpleasantly surprised by the amount of time and effort that is still needed.

In the first place, the computer is unable to accept directly the rather sophisticated kind of instructions we should like to give it. It is almost certain that we shall have made use of operations that are too much for any computer. To get around the inability of the machine to do directly what we want, we can write our program in a standard programming language and make the machine translate this into its own much simpler code. This seems an excellent use of a computer to do the donkey work for us, but unfortunately it does not get rid of all the labor. We have to do a good deal of apparently irrelevant and *ad hoc* work to force the program into a form suitable for existing programming languages.

There are now a considerable number of these programming languages: FORTRAN, ALGOL and MAD (used primarily for scientific problems); JOVIAL (for military applications); COBOL; SIMSCRIPT; LISP; PL/I; CPL, and others. To give an indication of the varying styles of the languages, three samples are given: a simple program (to find the mathematical function e^x) is written in CPL, in ALGOL and in FORTRAN [*see illustration on page 371*].

The advent of programming languages of this kind some nine years ago vastly enriched the art of programming. Before then a program containing 5,000 instructions was considered quite large, and only the most experienced or foolhardy programmers would attempt one. Today an individual can tackle programs about 10 times larger; a team by cooperative effort may produce a program still larger by a factor of five to 10.

By far the most important of the new programming languages was FORTRAN; until recently, it has been estimated, more than 90 percent of all scientific and engineering programs were written in it. In the past few years it has gradually become clear that current programming languages are by no means perfect and that the great success of FORTRAN was due to its relative merits rather than its absolute ones. Other programming languages such as ALGOL and LISP have shown that

there are easier ways to do at least some things on computers.

To get back to our checkers program: I have written the complete program (except for certain details, including the input and output arrangements) in an informal and somewhat extended version of CPL (which stands for "Combined Programming Language"). The program in symbolic form, together with a list of the terms used and their definitions, is shown on the preceding page. The program is not by any means in final form; it has not been run on a machine and therefore, in accordance with the views expressed below, probably still contains some errors. Interested readers may like to look for them.

In the early days of computer programming—say 15 years ago—mathematicians used to think that by taking sufficient care they would be able to write programs that were correct. Greatly to their surprise and chagrin, they found that this was not the case and that with rare exceptions the programs as written contained numerous errors. The process of discovering, locating and correcting these errors proved to be one of major difficulty, often taking considerably longer than writing the program in the first place and using a great deal of machine time.

Although programming techniques have improved immensely since the early days, the process of finding and correcting errors in programs—known, graphically if inelegantly, as "debugging"—still remains a most difficult, confused and unsatisfactory operation. The chief impact of this state of affairs is psychological. Although we are all happy to pay lip service to the adage that to err is human, most of us like to make a small private reservation about our own performance on special occasions when we really try. It is somewhat deflating to be shown publicly and incontrovertibly by a machine that even when we do try, we in fact make just as many mistakes as other people. If your pride cannot recover from this blow, you will never make a programmer.

It is not, in fact, in the nature of human beings to be perfectly accurate, and it is unrealistic to believe they ever will be. The only reasonable way to get a program right is to assume that it will at first contain errors and take steps to discover these and correct them. This attitude is quite familiar to anyone who has been in contact with the planning of any large-scale operation, but it is completely strange to most people who have not.

The trouble, I think, is that so many educational processes put a high premium on getting the correct answer the first time. If you give the wrong answer to an examination question, you lose your mark and that is the end of the matter. If you make a mistake in writing your program—or, indeed, in many other situations in life outside a classroom—it is by no means a catastrophe; you do, however, have to find your error and put it right. Maybe it would be better if more academic teaching adopted this attitude also.

It is when we first come to grips with a computer and actually try to run a program, either to test it or to obtain some useful results, that we really begin to get frustrated. In spite of the much vaunted speed of the machine itself, it is normally several hours and sometimes several days before one can actually get back the answer to even the shortest program. When this delay is added to the fact that computers and their programming languages and compilers are often most unhelpful, so that the only information you receive at the end of a day's wait may be that your program is still wrong, it is easy to understand why so many people get the impression that using a computer is more a matter of fighting the machine and the system than it is one of cooperation.

The reason for this curious situation is the desire to keep the computer, which is a very expensive machine, fully occupied for as much of the time as possible. The organization outside the computer, which frequently employs quite a large human operating staff, accounts for almost all the "turn-around time" and a fair proportion of the frustration. The introduction of time-sharing systems should remove this source of frustration, at the cost of greatly increasing the size and complexity of the operating programs [see "Time-sharing on Computers," by Fano and Corbató; SCIENTIFIC AMERICAN, Sept., 1966].

A large part of the work involved in actually getting a program running can be done by the computer itself. Operations such as translating the programming language into detailed machine code, allocating storage space inside the computer, keeping records to assist in the diagnosis of program errors, organizing the scheduling and accounting for a sequence of short jobs from various users and the like are precisely the kind of high-grade routine clerical work a computer can handle, and it is therefore only rational to expect the machine to do it.

The programs to make the machine carry out these operations are of the greatest importance. Most users of the computer will have far more contact with them than they do with the computer itself, and for this reason the operating programs are known as the software of the system (as opposed to the computer itself, which is known as the hardware). In actuality the performance of a system is as much dependent on its software as on its hardware, and the planning and writing of software systems is rapidly becoming a major problem for computer manufacturers. The entire set of these programs, known as the software package, can easily cost the machine manufacturer as much to produce and debug as the machine itself. As a result there is strong pressure not to change either the programming language or the operating system, in spite of the fact that in many respects they are seriously inadequate.

Why is the road from the conception of a program to its execution by the machine so long and tiresome? Why are the operating systems today—the software—so costly and unsatisfactory? Are we perhaps reaching the limit of human ability to write complicated programs, and is the present software crisis really the result of attempting the humanly impossible? Anyone who deals with the large computer systems today knows how close the whole thing is to collapsing under the weight of its own complexity.

There is no doubt that with the current techniques we have nearly reached our limit in programming. Could we not, however, improve the techniques? The checkers example we have considered in this article gives a strong hint that a simplified approach and improvement of the programming language would make things a great deal easier. If a suitable programming language existed, it should clearly be possible to write the entire checkers program in the way outlined above and leave nearly all the remaining stages to be performed by the computer. As a matter of fact, that can almost be done now, and it would probably not be too difficult to construct a language in which it was possible.

The only reasonable way to set up a large and complicated program is to use a hierarchical method. Since there is a limit to the size and complexity of a problem we can hold in our head at one time, it appears that the best way to extend our capability is to treat relatively large and complex operations as single units and combine these units hierarchically. The present programming languages all pay at least lip service to this idea, but many do not allow for a genuine and unlimited hierarchy—only for two or three levels of operation (such as "local" and "global") the programmer has to consider simultaneously. Those languages that do allow a truly hierarchical treatment of a problem have only a limited ability to deal with representations.

The present-day computer is itself a stumbling block to the use of programs that are written hierarchically (or recursively). Because the computers are unsuitable for this kind of organization, the running of such a program is much slower than it is for a program written and coded in the conventional way. I am convinced, however, that the advantages of this kind of programming will far outweigh any increase of machine time that may be required. The advantages are so great that I believe the hierarchical method will eventually be adopted universally. After all, the chief purpose of any machine is to save human beings trouble; therefore we should not be unduly alarmed about giving the computer more of man's work. In addition, there is good reason to expect that it will be possible to design computers that will deal much more naturally and efficiently with deeply hierarchical programs. These machines will probably be slightly more complex than present ones, but the difference in cost will be well worthwhile.

I have left to the end what seems to me to be the most difficult, but also the most interesting and potentially rewarding, problem concerning programming languages. This is to lay a firm mathematical foundation for the construction of hierarchical systems of programs and to develop a calculus for manipulating them.

The difficulty arises basically from the fact that programming presents us with certain new questions that are not present, or at least not important, in any other branch of mathematics. The mathematical problem has two aspects. The first is how to deal explicitly and in a detailed way with complicated structures (involving representations of data) when not only the structure as a whole but also its component parts must be given names and have values assigned to them. The second aspect of the difficulty is that the use of imperatives (or commands) in programming introduces variables, and mathematics in general does not recognize the existence of variables in this sense, that is, values varying over a period of time. In its traditional branches mathematics deals only with static situations. Even the calculus, which is concerned with the approaches of objects to a limit, deals with the subject in terms of a series of fixed values. In general the things mathematicians call variables are either constants whose values are not yet known or nonexistent quantities (such as "nobody") that are introduced for purposes of logical syntax. In programming, on the other hand, we deal with time-varying variables by the very nature of the process; a program is essentially a schedule of changes.

An experienced programmer reading this article will have been struck by the fact that in the formulation of the checkers program I have used no commands, and in particular by the fact that the program contains no assignment statements (statements assigning values to names or objects). The reason for this is that we know how to combine recursively defined functions into hierarchical structures only in the absence of assignment statements. There is still no satisfactory way of doing the same thing if they are included.

Investigation of the mathematical problems I have discussed has now begun. It is clear at the start that the field to be explored is almost entirely new, without established guidelines such as exist in most other areas of mathematical research. It is also evident that the first and most difficult task is to clarify what we mean, in a programming context, by terms such as "name" and "value." The chief trouble is that the introduction of assignments (changes of value with changes in circumstances) makes the meaning of the terms ambiguous from the standpoint of the way they are ordinarily used in mathematics, so that it seems probable we shall need to generate new concepts in order to get a firm grasp of the situation.

Much of the theoretical work now being done in the field of programming languages is concerned with language syntax. In essence this means the research is concerned not with *what* the language says but with *how* it says it. This approach seems to put almost insuperable barriers in the way of forming new concepts—at least as far as language *meaning* is concerned. I believe the way to progress for programmers lies along the path of research on meaning rather than syntax. It is primarily through the study of meaning that we shall develop the concepts required to build up hierarchical structures.

49 CYBERNETICS

NORBERT WIENER · November 1948

Cybernetics is a word invented to define a new field in science. It combines under one heading the study of what in a human context is sometimes loosely described as thinking and in engineering is known as control and communication. In other words, cybernetics attempts to find the common elements in the functioning of automatic machines and of the human nervous system, and to develop a theory which will cover the entire field of control and communication in machines and in living organisms.

It is well known that between the most complex activities of the human brain and the operations of a simple adding machine there is a wide area where brain and machine overlap. In their more elaborate forms, modern computing machines are capable of memory, association, choice and many other brain functions. Indeed, the experts have gone so far in the elaboration of such machines that we can say the human brain behaves very much like the machines. The construction of more and more complex mechanisms actually is bringing us closer to an understanding of how the brain itself operates.

The word cybernetics is taken from the Greek *kybernetes*, meaning steersman. From the same Greek word, through the Latin corruption *gubernator*, came the term governor, which has been used for a long time to designate a certain type of control mechanism, and was the title of a brilliant study written by the Scottish physicist James Clerk Maxwell 80 years ago. The basic concept which both Maxwell and the investigators of cybernetics mean to describe by the choice of this term is that of a feedback mechanism, which is especially well represented by the steering engine of a ship. Its meaning is made clear by the following example.

Suppose that I pick up a pencil. To do this I have to move certain muscles. Only an expert anatomist knows what all these muscles are, and even an anatomist could hardly perform the act by a conscious exertion of the will to contract each muscle concerned in succession. Actually what we will is not to move individual muscles but to pick up the pencil. Once we have determined on this, the motion of the arm and hand proceeds in such a way that we may say that the amount by which the pencil is not yet picked up is decreased at each stage. This part of the action is not in full consciousness.

To perform an action in such a manner, there must be a report to the nervous system, conscious or unconscious, of the amount by which we have failed to pick up the pencil at each instant. The report may be visual, at least in part, but it is more generally kinesthetic, or to use a term now in vogue, proprioceptive. If the proprioceptive sensations are wanting, and we do not replace them by a visual or other substitute, we are unable to perform the act of picking up the pencil, and find ourselves in a state known as ataxia. On the other hand, an excessive feedback is likely to be just as serious a handicap. In the latter case the muscles overshoot the mark and go into an uncontrollable oscillation. This condition, often associated with injury to the cerebellum, is known as purpose tremor.

Here, then, is a significant parallel between the workings of the nervous system and of certain machines. The feedback principle introduces an important new idea in nerve physiology. The central nervous system no longer appears to be a self-contained organ receiving signals from the senses and discharging into the muscles. On the contrary, some of its most characteristic activities are explainable only as circular processes, traveling from the nervous system into the muscles and re-entering the nervous system through the sense organs. This finding seems to mark a step forward in the study of the nervous system as an integrated whole.

The new approach represented by cybernetics—an integration of studies which is not strictly biological or strictly physical, but a combination of the two—has already given evidence that it may help to solve many problems in engineering, in physiology and very likely in psychiatry.

This work represents the outcome of a program undertaken jointly several years ago by the writer and Arturo Rosenblueth, then of the Harvard Medical School and now of the National Institute of Cardiology of Mexico. Dr. Rosenblueth is a physiologist; I am a mathematician. For many years Dr. Rosenblueth and I had shared the conviction that the most fruitful areas for the growth of the sciences were those which had been neglected as no-man's lands between the various established fields. Dr. Rosenblueth always insisted that a proper exploration of these blank spaces on the map of science could be made only by a team of scientists, each a specialist but each possessing a thoroughly sound acquaintance with the fields of his fellows.

Our collaboration began as the result of a wartime project. I had been assigned, with a partner, Julian H. Bigelow, to the problem of working out a fire-control apparatus for anti-aircraft artillery which would be capable of tracking the curving course of a plane and predicting its future position. We soon came to the conclusion that any solution of the problem must depend heavily on the feedback principle, as it operated not only in the apparatus but in the human operators of the gun and of the plane. We approached

Dr. Rosenblueth with a specific question concerning oscillations in the nervous system, and his reply, which cited the phenomenon of purpose tremor, confirmed our hypothesis about the importance of feedback in voluntary activity.

The ideas suggested by this discussion led to several joint experiments, one of which was a study of feedback in the muscles of cats. The scope of our investigations steadily widened, and as it did so scientists from widely diverse fields joined our group. Among them were the mathematicians John von Neumann of the Institute for Advanced Study and Walter Pitts of Massachusetts Institute of Technology; the physiologists Warren McCulloch of the University of Pennsylvania and Lorente de No of the Rockefeller Institute; the late Kurt Lewin, psychologist, of M.I.T.; the anthropologists Gregory Bateson and Margaret Mead; the economist Oskar Morgenstern of the Institute for Advanced Study; and others in psychology, sociology, engineering, anatomy, neurophysiology, physics, and so on.

The study of cybernetics is likely to have fruitful applications in many fields, from the design of control mechanisms for artificial limbs to the almost complete mechanization of industry. But in our view it encompasses much wider horizons. If the 17th and early 18th centuries were the age of clocks, and the latter 18th and 19th centuries the age of steam engines, the present time is the age of communication and control. There is in electrical engineering a division which is known as the split between the technique of strong currents and the technique of weak currents; it is this split which separates the age just passed from that in which we are living. What distinguishes communication engineering from power engineering is that the main interest of the former is not the economy of energy but the accurate reproduction of a signal.

At every stage of technique since Daedalus, the ability of the artificer to produce a working simulacrum of a living organism has always intrigued people. In the days of magic, there was the bizarre and sinister concept of the Golem, that figure of clay into which the rabbi of Prague breathed life. In Isaac Newton's time the automaton became the clockwork music box. In the 19th century, the automaton was a glorified heat engine, burning a combustible fuel instead of the glycogen of human muscles. The automaton of our day opens doors by means of photocells, or points guns to the place at which a radar beam picks up a hostile airplane, or computes the solution of a differential equation.

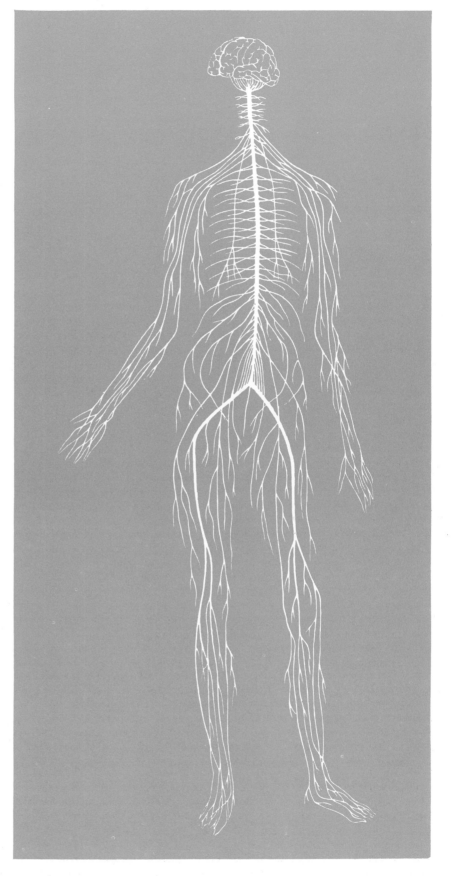

THE NERVOUS SYSTEM, in the cybernetic view, is more than a self-contained apparatus for receiving and transmitting signals. It is a circuit in which a feedback principle operates as certain impulses enter muscles and re-enter the nervous system through the sense organs.

Under the influence of the prevailing view in the science of the 19th century, the engineering of the body was naturally considered to be a branch of power engineering. Even today this is the predominant point of view among classically minded, conservative physiologists. But we are now coming to realize that the body is very far from a conservative system, and that the power available to it is much less limited than was formerly believed. We are beginning to see that such important elements as the neurones—the units of the nervous complex of our bodies—do their work under much the same conditions as vacuum tubes, their relatively

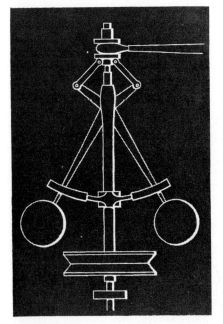

GOVERNOR of a steam engine is an example of feedback, one of the most important fundamental concepts in cybernetics.

small power being supplied from outside by the body's circulation, and that the bookkeeping which is most essential to describe their function is not one of energy.

In short, the newer study of automata, whether in the metal or in the flesh, is a branch of communications engineering, and its cardinal ideas are those of the message, of the amount of disturbance or "noise" (a term taken from the telephone engineer), of the quantity of information to be transmitted, of coding technique, and so on.

This view obviously has implications which affect many branches of science. Let us consider here the application of cybernetics to the problem of mental disorders. The realization that the brain and computing machines have much in common may suggest new and valid approaches to psychopathology, and even to psychiatry.

These begin with perhaps the simplest question of all: how the brain avoids gross blunders or gross miscarriages of activity due to the malfunction of individual parts. Similar questions referring to the computing machine are of great practical importance, for here a chain of operations, each of which covers only a fraction of a millionth of a second, may last a matter of hours or days. It is quite possible for a chain of computational operations to involve a billion separate steps. Under these circumstances, the chance that at least one operation will go amiss is far from negligible, even though the reliability of modern electronic apparatus has exceeded the most sanguine expectations.

In ordinary computational practice by hand or by desk machines, it is the custom to check every step of the computation and, when an error is found, to localize it by a backward process starting from the first point where the error is noted. To do this with a high-speed machine, the check must proceed at the pace of the original machine, or the whole effective order of speed of the machine will conform to that of the slower process of checking.

A much better method of checking, and in fact the one generally used in practice, is to refer every operation simultaneously to two or three separate mechanisms. When two such mechanisms are used, their answers are automatically collated against each other; and if there is a discrepancy, all data are transferred to permanent storage, the machine stops and a signal is sent to the operator that something is wrong. The operator then compares the results, and is guided by them in his search for the malfunctioning part, perhaps a tube which has burned out and needs replacement. If three separate mechanisms are used for each stage, there will practically always be agreement between two of the three mechanisms, and this agreement will give the required result. In this case the collation mechanism accepts the majority report, and the machine need not stop. There is a signal, however, indicating where and how the minority report differs from the majority report. If this occurs at the first moment of discrepancy, the indication of the position of the error may be very precise.

It is conceivable, and not implausible, that at least two of the elements of this process are also represented in the nervous system. It is hardly to be expected that any important message is entrusted for transmission to a single neurone, or that an important operation is entrusted to a single neuronal mechanism. Like the computing machine, the brain probably

works on a variant of the famous principle expounded by Lewis Carroll in *The Hunting of the Snark:* "What I tell you three times is true."

It is also improbable that the various channels available for the transfer of information generally go from one end of their course to the other without connecting with one another. It is much more probable that when a message reaches a certain level of the nervous system, it may leave that point and proceed to the next by one or more alternative routes. There may be parts of the nervous system, especially in the cortex, where this interchangeability is much limited or abolished. Still, the principle holds, and it probably holds most clearly for the relatively unspecialized cortical areas which serve the purpose of association and of what we call the higher mental functions.

So far we have been considering errors in performance that are normal, and pathological only in an extended sense. Let us now turn to those that are much more clearly pathological. Psychopathology has been rather a disappointment to the instinctive materialism of the doctors, who have taken the view that every disorder must be accompanied by actual lesions of some specific tissue involved. It is true that specific brain lesions, such as injuries, tumors, clots and the like, may be accompanied by psychic symptoms, and

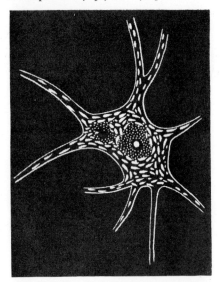

NERVE CELL performs its functions under much the same conditions as a vacuum tube, obtaining its power from outside.

that certain mental diseases, such as paresis, are the sequelae of general bodily disease and show a pathological condition of the brain tissue. But there is no way of identifying the brain of a schizophrenic of one of the strict Kraepelin types, nor of a manic-depressive patient, nor of a paranoiac. These we call functional disorders.

This distinction between functional and organic disorders is illuminated by the consideration of the computing machine. It is not the empty physical structure of the computing machine that corresponds to the brain—to the adult brain, at least— but the combination of this structure with the instructions given it at the beginning of a chain of operations and with all the additional information stored and gained from outside in the course of its operation.

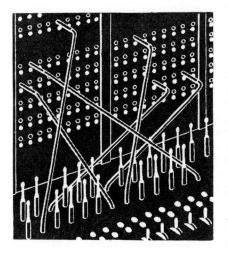

TELEPHONE EXCHANGE, when it is overloaded, has breakdowns rather similar to the kind that occur in human beings.

This information is stored in some physical form — in the form of memory. But part of it is in the form of circulating memories, with a physical basis that vanishes when the machine is shut down or the brain dies, and part is in the form of long-time memories, which are stored in a way at which we can only guess, but probably also in a form with a physical basis that vanishes at death.

There is therefore nothing surprising in considering the functional mental disorders fundamentally as diseases of memory, of the circulating information kept by the brain in active state and of the long-time permeability of synapses. Even the grosser disorders such as paresis may produce a large part of their effects not so much by the destruction of tissue which they involve and the alteration of synaptic thresholds as by the secondary disturbances of traffic, the overload of what remains of the nervous system and the rerouting of messages which must follow such primary injuries.

In a system containing a large number of neurones, circular processes can hardly be stable for long periods of time. Either they run their course, dissipate themselves and die out, as in the case of memories belonging to the specious present, or they

embrace more and more neurones in their system, until they occupy an inordinate part of the neurone pool. This is what we should expect to be the case in the malignant worry that accompanies anxiety neuroses. In such a case, it is possible that the patient simply does not have the room —i.e., a sufficient number of neurones— to carry out his normal processes of thought. Under such conditions, there may be less going on in the brain to occupy the neurones not yet affected, so that they are all the more readily involved in the expanding process. Furthermore, the permanent memory becomes more and more deeply involved, and the pathological process which began at the level of the circulating memories may repeat itself in a more intractable form at the level of the permanent memories. Thus what started as a relatively trivial and accidental disturbance of stability may build itself up into a process totally destructive to the normal mental life.

Pathological processes of a somewhat similar nature are not unknown in the case of mechanical or electrical computing machines. A tooth of a wheel may slip under such conditions that no tooth with which it engages can pull it back into its normal relations, or a high-speed electrical computing machine may go into a circular process that seems impossible to stop.

How do we deal with these accidents in the case of the machine? We first try to clear the machine of all information, in the hope that when it starts again with different data the difficulty will not recur. If this fails and the difficulty is inaccessible to the clearing mechanism, we shake the machine or, if it is electrical, subject it to an abnormally large electrical impulse in the hope that we may jolt the inaccessible part into a position where the false cycle of its activities will be interrupted. If even this fails, we may disconnect an erring part of the apparatus, for it is possible that what remains may be adequate for our purpose.

In the case of the brain, there is no normal process, except death, that can clear it of all past impressions. Of the normal non-fatal processes, sleep comes closest to clearing the brain. How often we find that the best way to handle a complicated worry or an intellectual muddle is to sleep on it! Sleep, however, does not clear away the deeper memories, nor indeed is a malignant state of worry compatible with adequate sleep.

Thus we are often forced to resort to more violent types of intervention in the memory cycle. The most violent of these

involve surgery on the brain, leaving behind permanent damage, mutilation and the abridgement of the powers of the victim, for the mammalian central nervous system seems to possess no power of regeneration. The principal type of surgical intervention that has been practiced is known as prefrontal lobotomy, or leucotomy. It consists in the removal or isolation of a portion of the prefrontal lobe of the cortex. It is currently having a certain vogue, probably not unconnected with the fact that it makes the custodial care of many patients easier. (Let me remark in passing that killing them makes their custodial care still easier.) Prefrontal lobotomy does seem to have a genuine effect on malignant worry, not by bringing the patient nearer to a solution of his problem, but by damaging or destroying the capac-

AUTOMATON of the 15th century was one of a long series of attempts to produce a working simulacrum of a living organism.

ity for maintained worry, known in the terminology of another profession as the conscience. It appears to impair the circulating memory, i.e., the ability to keep in mind a situation not actually presented.

The various forms of shock treatment— electric, insulin, metrazol — are less drastic methods of doing a very similar thing. They do not destroy brain tissue, or at least are not intended to destroy it, but they do have a decidedly damaging effect on the memory. In so far as the shock treatment affects recent disordered memories, which are probably scarcely worth preserving anyhow, it has something to recommend it as against lobotomy, but it is sometimes followed by deleterious effects on the permanent memory and the personality. As it is used at present, it is another violent, imperfectly understood, imperfectly controlled method to interrupt a mental vicious circle.

In long-established cases of mental disorder, the permanent memory is as badly deranged as the circulating memory. We do not seem to possess any purely pharmaceutical or surgical weapon for intervening selectively in the permanent memory. This is where psychoanalysis and the other psychotherapeutic measures come in.

Whether psychoanalysis is taken in the orthodox Freudian sense or in the modified senses of Jung and of Adler, or whether the psychotherapy is not strictly psychoanalytic at all, the treatment is clearly based on the concept that the stored information of the mind lies on many levels of accessibility. The effect and accessibility of this stored information are vitally conditioned by affective experiences that we cannot always uncover by introspection. The technique of the psychoanalyst consists in a series of means to discover and interpret these hidden memories, to make the patient accept them for what they are, and thus to modify, if not their content, at least the affective tone they carry, and make them less harmful.

All this is perfectly consistent with the cybernetic point of view. Our theory perhaps explains, too, why there are circumstances in which a joint use of shock treatment and psychotherapy is indicated, combining a physical or pharmacological therapy for the malignant reverberations in the nervous system and a psychological therapy for the damaging long-time memories which might re-establish the vicious circle broken up by the shock treatments.

We have already mentioned the traffic problem of the nervous system. It has been noted by many writers that each form of organization has an upper limit of size beyond which it will not function. Thus insect organization is limited by the length of tubing over which the spiracle method of bringing air by diffusion directly to the breathing tissues will function; a land animal cannot be so big that the legs or other portions in contact with the ground will be crushed by its weight, and so on. The same sort of thing is observed in engineering structures. Skyscrapers are limited in size by the fact that when they exceed a certain height, the elevator space needed for the upper stories consumes an excessive part of the cross section of the lower floors. Beyond a certain span, the best pos-

sible suspension bridge will collapse under its own weight. Similarly, the size of a single telephone exchange is limited.

In a telephone system, the important limiting factor is the fraction of the time during which a subscriber will find it impossible to put a call through. A 90 per cent chance of completing calls is probably good enough to permit business to be carried on with reasonable facility. A success of 75 per cent is annoying but will permit business to be carried on after a fashion; if half the calls are not completed, subscribers will begin to ask to have their telephones taken out. Now, these represent all-over figures. If the calls go through a number of distinct stages of switching, and the probability of failure is independent and equal for each stage, in order to get a high probability of final success the probability of success at each stage must be higher than the final one. Thus to obtain a 75 per cent chance for the completion of the call after five stages, we must have about 95 per cent chance of success at each stage. The more stages there are, the more rapidly the service becomes extremely bad when a critical level of failure for the individual call is exceeded, and extremely good when this critical level of failure is not quite reached. Thus a switching service involving many stages and designed for a certain level of failure shows no obvious signs of failure until the traffic comes up to the edge of the critical point, when it goes completely to pieces and we have a catastrophic traffic jam.

So man, with the best developed nervous system of all the animals, probably involving the longest chains of effectively operated neurones, is likely to perform a complicated type of behavior efficiently very close to the edge of an overload, when he will give way in a serious and catastrophic manner. This overload may take place in several ways: by an excess in the amount of traffic to be carried; by a physical removal of channels for the carrying of traffic; or by the excessive occupation of such channels by undesirable systems of traffic, such as circulating memories that have accumulated to the extent of becoming pathological worries. In all these cases, a point is reached—quite suddenly — when the normal traffic does not have space enough allotted to it, and we have a form of mental breakdown, very possibly amounting to insanity.

This will first affect the faculties or operations involving the longest chains of neurones. There is appreciable evidence, of various kinds, that these are precisely the processes recognized as the highest in our ordinary scale of valuation.

If we compare the human brain with that of a lower mammal, we find that it is much more convoluted. The relative thickness of the gray matter is much the same, but it is spread over a far more involved system of grooves and ridges. The effect of this is to increase the amount of gray matter at the expense of the amount of white matter. Within a ridge, this decrease of the white matter is largely a decrease in length rather than in number of fibers, as the opposing folds are nearer together than the same areas would be on a smooth-surfaced brain of the same size. On the other hand, when it comes to the connectors between different ridges, the distance they have to run is increased by the convolution of the brain.

Thus the human brain would seem to be fairly efficient in the matter of the short-distance connectors, but defective in the matter of long-distance trunk lines. This means that in the case of a traffic jam, the processes involving parts of the brain quite remote from one another should suffer first. That is, processes involving several centers, a number of different motor processes and a considerable number of association areas should be among the least stable in cases of insanity. These are precisely the processes which we should normally class as higher, thereby confirming our theory, as experience does also, that the higher processes deteriorate first in insanity.

The phenomena of handedness and of hemispheric dominance suggest other interesting speculations. Right-handedness, as is well known, is generally associated with left-brainedness, and left-handedness with right-brainedness. The dominant hemisphere has the lion's share of the higher cerebral functions. In the adult, the effect of an extensive injury in the secondary hemisphere is far less serious than the effect of a similar injury in the dominant hemisphere. At a relatively early stage in his career, Louis Pasteur suffered a cerebral hemorrhage on the right side which left him with a moderate degree of one-sided paralysis. When he died, his brain was examined and the damage to its right side was found to be so extensive that it has been said that after his injury "he had only half a brain." Nevertheless, after his injury he did some of his best work. A similar injury to the left side of the brain in a right-handed adult would almost certainly have been fatal; at the least it would have reduced the patient to an animal condition.

In the first six months of life, an extensive injury to the dominant hemisphere may compel the normally secondary hemi-

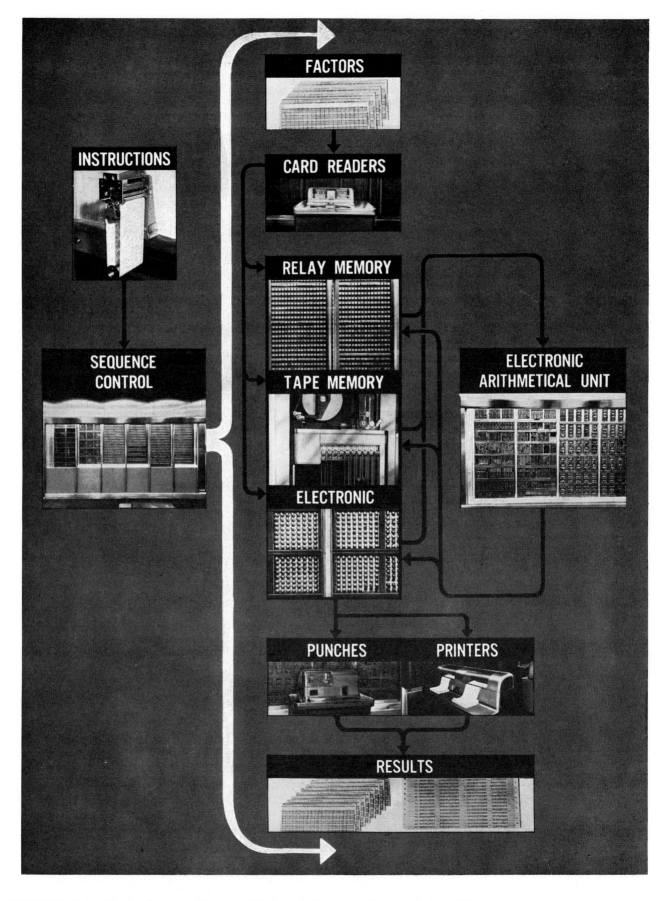

DIAGRAM of the Selective Sequence Electronic Calculator built by the International Business Machines Corporation, provides another cybernetic comparison. Physical structure of the machine is not analogous to the brain. The structure plus instructions and stored memories is analogous. The machine has electronic and relay circuits for temporary memory, punched cards for permanent memory.

sphere to take its place, so that the patient appears far more nearly normal than he would have been had the injury occurred at a later stage. This is quite in accordance with the great flexibility shown by the nervous system in the early weeks of life. It is possible that, short of very serious injuries, handedness is reasonably flexible in the very young child. Long before the child is of school age, however, the natural handedness and cerebral dominance are established for life. Many people have changed the handedness of their children by education, though of course they could not change its physiological basis in hemispheric dominance. These hemispheric changelings often become stutterers and develop other defects of speech, reading and writing.

We now see at least one possible explanation for this phenomenon. With the education of the secondary hand, there has been a partial education of that part of the secondary hemisphere which deals with skilled motions such as writing. Since these motions are carried out in the closest possible association with reading, and with speech and other activities which are inseparably connected with the dominant hemisphere, the neurone chains involved in these processes must cross over from hemisphere to hemisphere, and in any complex activity they must do this again and again. But the direct connectors between the hemispheres in a brain as large as that of man are so few in number that they are of very little help. Consequently the interhemispheric traffic must go by roundabout routes through the brain stem. We know little about these routes, but they are certainly long, scanty and subject to interruption. As a consequence, the processes associated with speech and writing are very likely to be involved in a traffic jam, and stuttering is the most natural thing in the world.

The human brain is probably too large already to use in an efficient manner all the facilities which seem to be present. In a cat, the destruction of the dominant hemisphere seems to produce relatively less damage than in man, while the destruction of the secondary hemisphere probably produces more damage. At any rate, the apportionment of function in the two hemispheres is more nearly equal. In man, the gain achieved by the increase in the size and complexity of the brain is partly nullified by the fact that less of the organ can be used effectively at one time.

It is interesting to reflect that we may be facing one of those limitations of nature in which highly specialized organs reach a level of declining efficiency and ultimately lead to the extinction of the species. The human brain may be as far along on its road to destructive specialization as the great nose horns of the last of the titanotheres.

50 MAN VIEWED AS A MACHINE

JOHN G. KEMENY · April 1955

Is man no more than a machine? The question is often debated these days, usually with more vigor than precision. More than most arguments, this one tends to bog down in definition troubles. What is a machine? And what do we mean by "no more than"? If we define "machine" broadly enough, everything is a machine; and if by "more than" we mean that we are human, then machines are clearly less than we are.

In this article we shall frame the question more modestly. Let us ask: What could a machine do as well or better than a man, now or in the future? We shall not concern ourselves with whether a machine could write sonnets or fall in love. Nor shall we waste time laboring the obvious fact that when it comes to muscle, machines are far superior to men. What concerns us here is man as a brain-machine. John von Neumann, the mathematician and designer of computers, not long ago made a detailed comparison of human and mechanical brains in a series of lectures at Princeton University. Much of what follows is based on that discussion.

We are often presented with Utopias in which all the hard work is done by machines and we merely push buttons. This may sound like a lazy dream of heaven, but actually man is even lazier than that. He is no sooner presented with this Utopia than he asks: "Couldn't I build a machine to push the buttons for me?" And indeed he began to invent such machines as early as the 18th century. The flyball governor on a steam engine and the thermostat are elementary brain-machines. They control muscle machines, while spending only negligible amounts of energy themselves. Norbert Wiener compared them to the human nervous system.

Consider the progress of the door. Its earliest form must have been a rock rolled in front of a cave entrance. This may have provided excellent protection, but it must also have made the operation of going in and out of the cave quite difficult. Slowly, as man found better means of defending himself, he made lighter and more manageable doors, until today it is literally child's play to open a door. But even this does not satisfy us. To the delight of millions of railroad passengers, the Pennsylvania Railroad installed electric eyes in its New York terminal. Man need only break the invisible signal connecting the two photoelectric "eyes," and immediately the little brain-machine commands the door to open. This control device needs only a negligible amount of energy, is highly efficient and is vastly faster than any doorman.

The central switchboard in an office is another brain-machine, especially if the office has installed the dial system. Messages are carried swiftly and efficiently to hundreds of terminals, at the expense of only a small quantity of electricity. This is one of those brain-machines without which modern life is supposed to be not worth living.

And, finally, there is the example most of us are likely to think of when brain-machines are mentioned: namely, the high-speed computer. Electric eyes and telephone exchanges only relieve us of physical labor, but the calculators can take the place of several human brains.

The Slow Brain

In economy of energy the human brain certainly is still far ahead of all its mechanical rivals. The entire brain with its many billions of cells functions on less than 100 watts. Even with the most efficient present substitute for a brain cell—the transistor—a machine containing as many cells as the brain would need about 100 million watts. We are ahead by a factor of at least a million. But von Neumann has calculated that in theory cells could be 10 billion times more efficient in the use of energy than the brain cells actually are. Thus there seems to be no technical reason why mechanical brains should not become more efficient energy-users than their human cousins. After all, just recently by inventing the transistor, which requires only about a hundredth of a watt, we have improved the efficiency of our machines by a factor of 100; in view of this the factor of a million should not frighten us.

While we are still ahead in the use of energy, we are certainly far behind in speed. Whereas a nerve cannot be used more than 100 times a second, a vacuum tube can easily be turned on and off a million times a second. It could be made to work even faster, but this would not contribute much to speeding

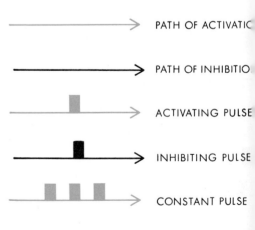

PATH OF ACTIVATIO[N]

PATH OF INHIBITIO[N]

ACTIVATING PULSE

INHIBITING PULSE

CONSTANT PULSE

SIMPLE CIRCUITS for a brain machine are depict ed on the next five pages. The activating and inhib iting pulses are identical but follow different paths

up the mechanical brain at the moment. No machine is faster than its slowest part, so we must evaluate various components of the machine.

In a calculating machine four different problems confront the designer: the actual computations, the "logical control," the memory and the feeding of information to the machine and getting answers out. Speed of computation, a bottleneck in mechanical computers such as the desk calculator, has been taken care of by the vacuum tube. The next bottleneck was the logical control—the system for telling the machine what to do next after each step. The early IBM punch-card machine took this function out of the hands of a human operator by using a wiring setup on a central board which commanded the sequence of operations. This is perfectly all right as long as the machine has to perform only one type of operation. But if the sequence has to be changed frequently, the wiring of the board becomes very clumsy indeed. To improve speed the machine must be given an internal logical control. Perhaps the greatest step forward on this problem has been accomplished by MANIAC, built at the Institute for Advanced Study in Princeton. This machine can change instructions as quickly as it completes calculations, so that it can operate as fast as its vacuum tubes will allow.

That still leaves the problems of speeding up the memory and the input and output of information. The two problems are closely related. The larger the memory, the less often the operator has to feed the machine information. But the very fact that the machine performs large numbers of computations between instructions clogs its memory and slows it down. This is because an accumula-

tion of rounding errors makes it necessary to carry out all figures in a calculation to a great number of digits. In each computation the machine necessarily rounds off the last digit; in succeeding operations the digit becomes less and less precise. If the computations are continued, the next-to-last digit begins to be affected, and so on. It can be shown that after 100 computations the last digit is worthless; after 10,000 the last two digits; after 1,000,000, the last three. In the large new computers an answer might easily contain four worthless figures. Hence to insure accuracy the machine must carry more digits than are actually significant; it is not uncommon to carry from eight to 12 digits for each number throughout the calculation. When the machine operates on the binary system of numbers, instead of the decimal system, the situation is even worse, for it takes about three times as many digits to express a number in the binary scale.

MANIAC uses up to 40 binary digits to express a number. Due to the necessity for carrying this large number of digits, even MANIAC's celebrated memory can hold no more than about 1,000 numbers. It has an "external memory," in the form of a magnetic tape and magnetic drums, in which it can store more information, but reading from the tape or drums is a much slower operation than doing electrical computations.

In spite of the present limitations, the machines already are ahead of the human brain in speed by a factor of at least 10,000—usually a great deal more than 10,000. They are most impressive on tasks such as arise in astronomy or ballistics. It would be child's play for MANIAC to figure out the position of the planets for the next million years.

Still we are left with the feeling that there are many things we can do that a machine cannot do. The brain has more than 10 billion cells, while a computer has only a few tens of thousands of parts. Even with transistors, which overcome the cost and space problems, the difficulty of construction will hardly allow more than a million parts to a machine. So we can safely say that the human brain for a long time to come will be about 10,000 times more complex than the most complicated machine. And it is well known that an increase of parts by a factor of 10 can bring about differences in kind. For example, if we have a unit that can do addition and multiplication, by combining a few such units with a logical control mechanism we can do subtraction, division, raising to powers, interpolation and many other operations qualitatively different from the original.

The Complex Memory

Part of man's superior complexity is his remarkable memory. How does MANIAC's memory compare with it? For simplicity's sake let us measure the information a memory may hold in "bits" (for binary digits). A vacuum tube can hold one digit of a binary number (the digit is 1 if the tube is on, 0 if it is off). In vacuum-tube language it takes 1,500 bits to express the multiplication table. Now MANIAC's memory holds about 40,000 bits, not in 40,000 separate tubes but as spots on 40 special picture tubes, each of which can hold about 1,000 spots (light or dark). Estimates as to how much the human memory holds vary widely, but we certainly can say conservatively that the brain can remember at least 1,000 items as complex

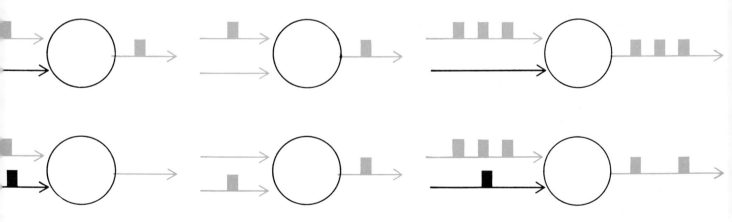

IC CELL (*circle*) will fire when it is *vated* (*top*). It will not fire, however, if inhibited (*bottom*).

"OR" CIRCUIT requires two paths of activation. The cell fires if a pulse arrives on one path (*top*) "or" the other (*bottom*).

"NOT" CIRCUIT incorporates constant activating pulses. The cell can thus fire constantly (*top*). It signals "not" when it is briefly inhibited (*bottom*).

as the multiplication table (1.5 million bits), and a reasonable guess is that its capacity is closer to 100 million bits—which amounts to acquiring one bit per 20 seconds throughout life. So our memory exceeds that of MANIAC by a factor of 1,000 at least.

Is the difference just a matter of complexity? No, the fact is that machines have not yet imitated the human brain's method of storing and recovering information. For instance, if we tried to increase MANIAC's memory by any considerable amount, we would soon find it almost impossible to extract information. We would have to use a complex system of coding to enable the machine to hunt up a given item of information, and this coding would load down the memory further and make the logical control more complex. Only when we acquire a better understanding of the brain's amazing ability to call forth information will we be able to give a machine anything more than a limited memory.

The Logical Machine

Let us now consider the inevitable question: Can a machine "think"? We start with a simple model of the nervous system such as has been constructed by Walter Pitts and Warren S. McCulloch of the Massachusetts Institute of Technology. Its basic unit is the neuron—a cell that can be made to emit pulses of energy. The firing of one neuron may activate the next or it may inhibit it. The neurons are assumed to work in cycles. This corresponds to our knowledge that after firing a neuron must be inactive for a period. To simplify the model it

is assumed that the various neurons' cycles are synchronized, i.e., all the neurons active during a given period fire at the same time. For a given neuron to fire in a given cycle two conditions must be satisfied: in the previous cycle it must have been (1) activated and (2) not inhibited. If, for example, a neuron has two others terminating in it of which one activates and one inhibits, and if the former fires in a given cycle and the latter does not, then the neuron will fire in the following cycle. Otherwise it will be inactive for a cycle.

Out of this basic pattern we can build the most complex logical machine. We can have a combination that will fire if a connected neuron did not fire (representing "not") or one that will fire if at least one of two incoming neurons fired (representing "or") or one that will fire only if both incoming neurons fired (representing "and"). Combining these, we can imitate many logical operations of the brain. The simple arrangement diagrammed on pages 390 and 391 will count up to four, and it is easy to see how to generalize this technique.

We can also construct a very primitive memory: e.g., a system that will "remember" that it has been activated until it is instructed to "forget" it. But if it is to remember anything at all complex, it must have an unthinkably large number of neurons—another illustration of the fact that human memory acts on different principles from a machine.

The Turing Machine

If we were to stop here, we might conclude that practical limitations of memory and complexity must forever re-

strict the cleverness or versatility of any machine. But we have not yet plumbed the full possibilities. The late A. M. Turing of England showed, by a brilliant analysis, that by combining a certain few simple operations in sufficient number a machine could perform feats of amazing complexity. Turing's machines may be clumsy and slow, but they present the clearest picture of what a machine can do.

A Turing machine can be thought of as a mechanical calculator which literally works with pencil and paper. The paper it uses is a long tape divided into successive squares, and it operates on one square at a time. As it confronts a particular square it can do one of six things: (1) write down the letter X; (2) write down the digit 1; (3) erase either of these marks if it is already in the square; (4) move the tape one square to the left; (5) move the tape one square to the right; (6) stop.

Essentially this machine is a number writer. It writes its numbers in the simplest possible form, as a string of units. This is even simpler than the binary system. In the binary system the number 35, for example, is written 100011. In a Turing machine it is a string of 1's in 35 successive squares. The X's are merely punctuation marks to show where each number starts and ends.

The machine has the following parts: a device that writes or erases, a scanner, a motor to move the tape, a numbered dial with a pointer, and a logical control consisting of neuron-like elements, say vacuum tubes. The logical control operates from a prepared table of commands which specifies what the machine is to do in each given state. The

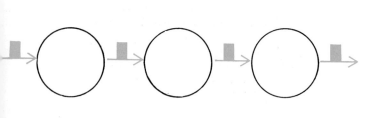

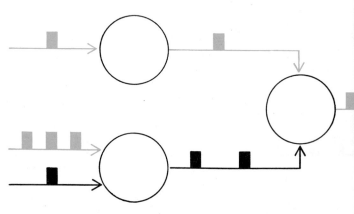

DELAY CIRCUIT is based on the fact that the basic cell receives a pulse in one "cycle" and fires it in the next. In this arrangement of three basic cells the pulse would be delayed three cycles.

"AND" CIRCUIT utilizes three cells. The first (*upper left*) has only an a[...] vating input. The second (*lower left*) has a constant activating input and [...] inhibiting input. The third (*right*) is the conventional basic cell. In the fi[...]

state consists of two elements: what the scanner "sees" in the square before it, and where the pointer is on the dial. For example, the table of instructions may say that whenever the square has an X and the pointer is at the number 1 on the dial, the machine is to erase the X, and move the pointer to the number 2 on the dial. As the machine proceeds from step to step, the logical control gives it such commands, the command in each case depending both on the position of the dial and on what the scanner sees in the square confronting it. Observe that the dial functions as a primitive "memory," in the sense that its position at any stage is a consequence of what the scanner saw and where the pointer stood at the step immediately preceding. It carries over the machine's experience from step to step.

Turing's machine thus consists of a tape with X's and 1's in some of its squares, a dial-memory with a certain number of positions, and a logical control which instructs the machine what to do, according to what it sees and what its memory says. The diagram on pages 392 and 393 shows a very simple version of the machine, with a dial having only six positions. Since the scanner may see one of three things in a square—blank, 1 or X—the machine has 18 possible states, and the logical control has a command for each case [see table at right of illustration]. This machine is designed to perform a single task: it can add two numbers—any two numbers. Suppose it is to add 2 and 3. The numbers are written as strings of 1's with X's at the ends. Say we start with the dial at position 1 and the scanner looking at the second digit of the number 3

[see diagram]. The instructions in the table say that when it is in this state the machine is to move the tape one square to the right and keep the dial at position 1. This operation brings the square to the left, containing another digit 1, under the scanner. Again the instructions are the same: "Move the tape one square to the right and keep the dial at position 1." Now the scanner sees an X. The instructions, with the dial at position 1, are: "Erase (the X) and move the dial to position 2." The machine now confronts a blank square. The command becomes: "Move the tape one square to the right and keep the dial at position 2." In this manner the machine will eventually write two digit 1's next to the three at the right and end with the answer 5—a row of five digits enclosed by X's. When it finishes, an exclamation point signifies that it is to stop. The reader is advised to try adding two other numbers in the same fashion.

This surely is a cumbersome method of adding. However, the machine becomes more impressive when it is expanded so that it can solve a problem such as the following: "Multiply the number you are looking at by two and take the cube root of the answer if the fifth number to the left is less than 150." By adding positions to the dial and enlarging the table of instructions we can endow such a machine with the ability to carry out the most complex tasks, though each operational step is very simple. The Turing machine in fact resembles a model of the human nervous system, which can be thought of as having a dial with very many positions and combining many simple acts to accomplish the enormous number

of tasks a human being is capable of.

Turing gave his machines an infinite memory. Of course the dial can have only a finite number of positions, but he allowed the machine a tape infinite in length, endless in both directions. Actually the tape does not have to be infinite—just long enough for the task. We may provide for all emergencies by allowing the machine to ask for more tape if it needs it. The human memory is infinite in the same sense: we can always make more paper to make notes on.

The Universal Machine

If we allow the unlimited tape, the Turing idea astounds us further with a universal machine. Not only can we build a machine for each task, but we can design a single machine that is versatile enough to accomplish all these tasks! We must try to understand how this is done, because it will give us the key to our whole problem.

The secret of the universal machine is that it can imitate. Suppose we build a highly complex machine for a difficult task. If we then supply the universal machine with a description of the task and of our special machine, it will figure out how to perform the task. It proceeds very simply, deducing from what it knows about our machine just what it would do at each step. Of course this slows the universal machine down considerably. Between any two steps it must carry out a long argument to analyze what our machine would do. But we care only about its ability to succeed, not its speed. There is no doubt about it: anything any logical machine can do can be done by this single mechanism.

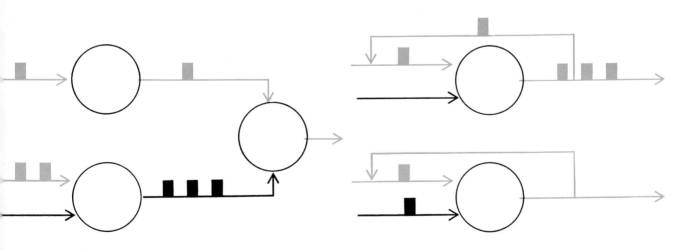

gram the pulse received by the first cell is not fired by the third. The third will fire the pulse only if the activating pulse of the first cell "and" the inhibiting pulse of the second are fired on the same cycle (second diagram).

MEMORY CIRCUIT feeds the output of a cell back into its input. Thus if the cell is activated, it "remembers" by firing constantly (top). If it is inhibited at any time later, it stops firing (bottom).

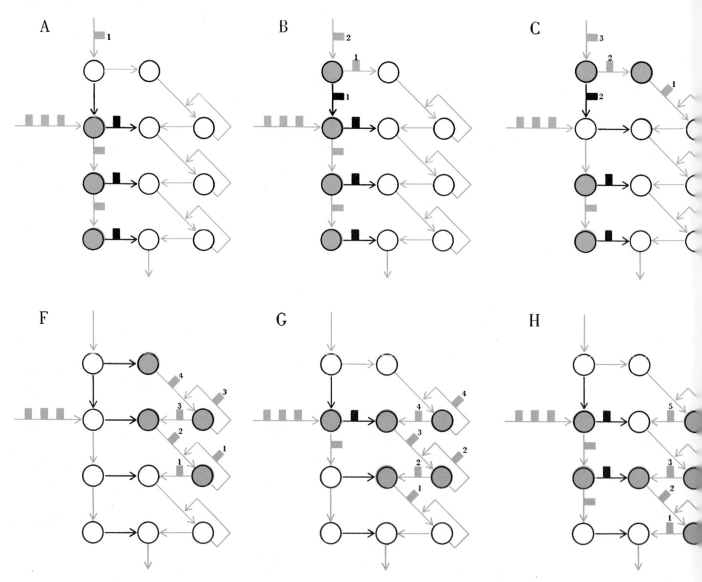

COUNTING CIRCUIT "counts" to four and then fires. The conventions in this series of diagrams are the same as those in the illustrations on the four preceding pages, with two important exceptions. The first is that, where the diagrams on the preceding pages show each circuit during two or more cycles, each of these diagrams shows the circuit during a single cycle. The second exception is that, when a cell fires, it lights up *(green tone)*. The input of this circuit is the activating pathway at the top. The output of the circuit is the activating pathway at the bottom. In addition one of the cells has a constant activating input *(left)*. The three cells at the right are memory cells *(see diagram at the right on preceding page)*. These cells can activate the three cells to the left of them.

The key question is: How do you describe a complex machine in terms that a relatively simple machine can understand? The answer is that you devise a simple code which can describe any machine (or at least any Turing machine), and that you design the universal machine so that it will be able to understand this code. To understand a Turing machine we need only know its table of commands, so it suffices to have a simple code for tables of commands. We will sketch one possible way of representing each conceivable table of commands by an integer. Of course there are infinitely many such tables, but there are also infinitely many integers—that is

why they are so useful in mathematics.

A table of commands consists of P rows. Each row has three commands in it, corresponding to seeing a blank, an X or a 1. The first step is to get rid of the letters in the table [*refer again to page 393*]. This can be done by replacing E, X, D, L, R and S by 1 through 6 respectively. Thus the commands on the first line of the table of our sample machine become 3–6, 1–2, 5–1. Step two: Get rid of the question mark and the exclamation point, say by putting 1 and 2 for them respectively. (Since these occur only in conjunction with an S, there is no danger of confusing them with memory positions 1 and 2.) Thus

the second row of our table becomes 5–2, 1–3, 6–1. Step three: Represent each row by a single integer. There is a famous simple way of doing this; namely by treating the numbers as exponents to primes and obtaining a product which completely specifies the series of numbers. As the final step, we epresent the entire table with a single number obtained by the same trick. Our code number for this table will be $2^{2991509440920}$ times 3 raised to the number of the second row. It is an enormous number, but it does identify our table of commands uniquely. And it is a straightforward mechanical task to design the universal machine so that it can

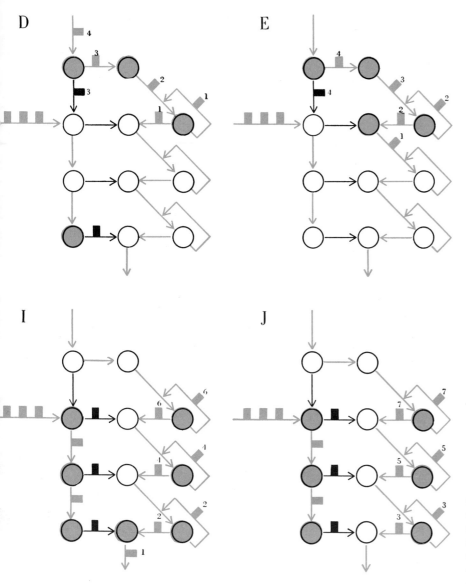

These three cells can in turn be inhibited by the three cells to the left of them. Now in the first four cycles (A, B, C and D) four pulses are put into the circuit. The position of each pulse in succeeding cycles is indicated by small numbers. In the ninth cycle (I) the circuit, having "counted" the four pulses, fires once. In the 10th cycle (J) the circuit returns to its original state with the exception that pulses are still circulating through the memory cells. A practical counting circuit would be fitted with a device to wipe out these memories.

sand entries, it seems to be able to do essentially all the problem-solving tasks that we can. Of course it might take a billion years to do something we can do in an hour. The "outside world" from which it can learn is much more restricted than ours, being limited to Turing machines. But may not all this be just a difference of degree? Are we, as rational beings, basically different from universal Turing machines?

The usual answer is that whatever else machines can do, it still takes a man to build the machine. Who would dare to say that a machine can reproduce itself and make other machines?

Von Neumann would. As a matter of fact, he has blue-printed just such a machine.

The Reproducing Machine

What do we mean by reproduction? If we mean the creation of an object like the original out of nothing, then no machine can reproduce, but neither can a human being. If reproduction is not to violate the conservation of energy principle, building materials must be available. The characteristic feature of the reproduction of life is that the living organism can create a new organism like itself out of inert matter surrounding it.

If we agree that machines are not alive, and if we insist that the creation of life is an essential feature of reproduction, then we have begged the question: A machine cannot reproduce. So we must reformulate the problem in a way that won't make machine reproduction logically impossible. We must omit the word "living." We shall ask that the machine create a new organism like itself out of simple parts contained in the environment.

Human beings find the raw material in the form of food; that is, quite highly organized chemicals. Thus we cannot even say that we produce order out of complete disorder, but rather we transform more simply organized matter into complex matter. We must accordingly assume that the machine is surrounded with pieces of matter, simpler than any part of the machine. The hypothetical parts list would be rolls of tape, pencils, erasers, vacuum tubes, dials, photoelectric cells, motors, shafts, wire, batteries and so on. We must endow the machine with the ability to transform pieces of matter into these parts and to organize them into a new machine.

Von Neumann simplified the problem by making a number of reasonable assumptions. First of all he realized that it is inessential for the machine to be

decode the large number and reproduce the table of commands. With the table of commands written down, the machine then knows what the machine it is copying would do in any given situation.

The universal machine is remarkably human. It starts with very limited abilities, and it learns more and more by imitation and by absorbing information from the outside. We feel that the potentialities of the human brain are inexhaustible. But would this be the case if we were unable to communicate with the world around us? A man robbed of his five senses is comparable to a Turing machine with a fixed tape, but a normal

human being is like the universal machine. Given enough time, he can learn to do anything.

But some readers will feel we have given in too soon to Turing's persuasive argument. After all a human being must step in and give the universal machine the code number. If we allow that, why not give the machine the answer in the first place? Turing's reply would have been that the universal machine does not need a man to encode the table; it can be designed to do its own coding, just as it can be designed to decode.

So we grant this amazing machine its universal status. And although its table of logical control has only a few thou-

able to move around. Rather, he has the mechanism sending out impulses which organize the surroundings by remote control. Secondly, he asssumed that space is divided into cubical cells, and that each part of the machine and each piece of raw material occupies just one cell. Thirdly, he assumed that the processes are quantized not only in space but in time; that is, we have cycles during which all action takes place. It is not even necessary to have three dimensions: a two-dimensional lattice will serve as well as the network of cubes.

Our space will be a very large (in principle infinite) sheet, divided into squares. A machine occupies a connected area consisting of a large number of squares. Since each square represents a part of the machine, the number of squares occupied is a measure of the complexity of the machine. The machine is surrounded by inert cells, which it has to organize. To make this possible the machine must be a combination of a brain and a brawn machine, since it not only organizes but also transforms matter. Accordingly the von Neumann machine has three kinds of parts. It has neurons similar to those discussed in the model of the nervous system. These provide the logical control. Then it has transmission cells, which carry messages

from the control centers. They have an opening through which they can receive impulses, and an output through which the impulse is passed on a cycle later. A string of transmission cells, properly adjoined, forms a channel through which messages can be sent. In addition the machine has muscles. These cells can change the surrounding cells, building them up from less highly organized to more complex cells or breaking them down. They bring about changes analogous to those produced by a combination of muscular and chemical action in the human body. Their primary use is, of course, the changing of an inert cell into a machine part.

As in the nervous system, the operation proceeds by steps: the state of every cell is determined by its state and the state of its neighbors a cycle earlier. The neurons and transmission cells are either quiescent or they can send out an impulse if properly stimulated. The muscle cells receive commands from the neurons through the transmission cells, and react either by "killing" some undesired part (*i.e.*, making it inert) or by transforming some inert cell in the environment to a machine part of a specified kind. So far the machine is similar in structure to a higher animal. Its neurons form the central nervous system;

the transmission cells establish contact with various organs; the organs perform their designated tasks upon receiving a command.

The instructions may be very long. Hence they must in a sense be external. Von Neumann's machine has a tail containing the blueprint of what it is to build. This tail is a very long strip containing coded instructions. The basic box performs two types of functions: it follows instructions from its tail, and it is able to copy the tail. Suppose the tail contains a coded description of the basic box. Then the box will, following instructions, build another box like itself. When it is finished, it proceeds to copy its own tail, attaching it to the new box. And so it reproduces itself.

The secret of the machine is that it does not try to copy itself. Von Neumann designed a machine that can build any machine from a description of it, and hence can build one like itself. Then it is an easy matter to copy the large but simple tail containing the instructions and attach it to the offspring. Thereafter the new machine can go on producing more and more machines until all the raw material is used up or until the machines get into conflict with each other—imitating even in this their human designers.

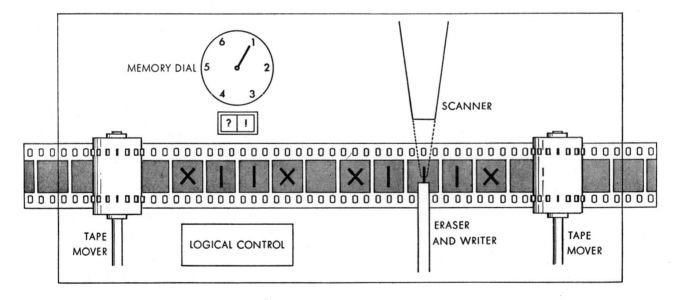

TURING MACHINE designed for simple addition is confronted with the numbers 2 and 3. The numbers are indicated on the tape; each digit is represented by a 1. X is a signal that a number is about to begin or has just ended. The logical control of the machine is depicted in the table on the opposite page. The horizontal rows of the table represent the position of the memory dial (*1, 2, 3, 4, 5 or 6*). The vertical columns represent the symbol on the tape (*blank, X or 1*). The symbols at the intersection of the rows and columns are commands to the machine. E means erase the symbol on the tape; X, write an X on the tape; D, write the digit

1 on the tape; R, move the tape one frame to the right; L, move the tape one frame to the left; S, stop; ?, something is wrong; !, the operation is completed; 1, 2, 3, 4, 5 or 6, turn the memory dial to that position. Thus at the upper left in the table the memory dial is in position 1 and the tape is blank; the command is D6, or write the digit 1 on the tape and turn the memory dial to position 6. Then in the beginning position shown above the machine begins to operate as follows. In the first step the memory dial is in position 1 and the tape shows a 1. The command is R1: move the tape one frame to the right and leave the memory dial in position 1. In the second

It is amazing to see how few parts such a machine needs to have. Von Neumann's blueprints call for a basic box of 80 by 400 squares, plus a tail 150,000 squares long. The basic box has the three kinds of parts described—neurons, transmission cells and muscle cells. The three types of cells differ only as to their state of excitation and the way in which they are connected. The tail is even simpler: it has cells, which are either "on" or "off," holding a code. So we have about 200,000 cells, most of which are of the simplest possible kind, and of which only a negligible fraction is even as complex as the logical control neuron. No matter how we measure complexity, this is vastly simpler than a human being, and yet the machine is self-reproducing.

The Genetic Tail

Pressing the analogy between the machine and the human organism, we might compare the tail to the set of chromosomes. Our machine always copies its tail for the new machine, just as each daughter cell in the body copies the chromosomes of its parent. It is most significant that while the chromosomes take up a minute part of the body, the tail is larger than the entire basic box

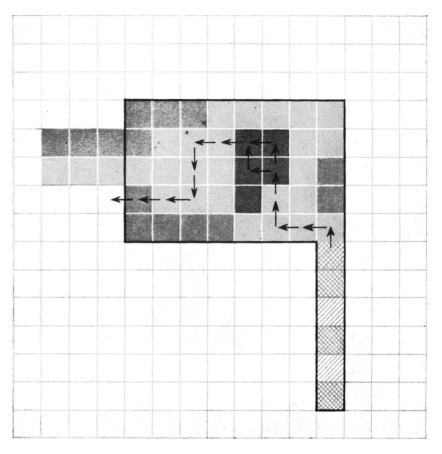

VON NEUMANN MACHINE is theoretically capable of reproducing itself. This is a highly simplified diagram of its conceptual units. The darkest squares are the "nerve cells" of the "brain." The next lightest squares are "muscle cells." The next lightest are transmission cells. The crosshatched squares are the "tail" which bears the instructions of the machine. The double hatching represents an "on" signal; the single hatching, an "off" signal. The empty squares are units of the environment which the machine manipulates. The arrows indicate that instructions are coming from the tail, on the basis of which the brain instructs a muscle cell to act on its surroundings. The machine has sent out a "feeler" to the left.

		X	I
1	D6	E2	R1
2	R2	E3	?2
3	R3	E4	E5
4	L4	?4	R6
5	L5	?5	R1
6	X6	!6	R3

step the situation and the response are the same. In the third step the memory dial is in position 1 and the tape shows an X. The command is E2: erase the X and turn the memory dial to position 2. In this way the machine comes up with the answer 5 on its memory dial in 36 steps. On the 37th step the machine stops and signals with a ! that it is finished. If the reader is skeptical and hardy, he is invited to trace the whole process!

in the machine. This indicates that the coding of traits by chromosomes is amazingly efficient and compact. But in all fairness we must point out that the chromosomes serve a lesser role than the tail. The tail contains a complete description of the basic box, while the chromosome description is incomplete: the offspring only resembles the parent; it is not an exact duplicate. It would be most interesting to try to continue von Neumann's pioneer work by designing a machine that could take an incomplete description and build a reasonable likeness of itself.

Could such machines go through an evolutionary process? One might design the tails in such a way that in every cycle a small number of random changes occurred (e.g., changing an "on" to an "off" in the code or vice versa). These would be like mutations; if the machine could still produce offspring, it would pass the changes on. One could further arrange to limit the supply of raw ma-

terial, so that the machines would have to compete for Lebensraum, even to the extent of killing one another.

Of course none of the machines described in this article has actually been built, so far as I know, but they are all buildable. We have considered systematically what man can do, and how much of this a machine can duplicate. We have found that the brain's superiority rests on the greater complexity of the human nervous system and on the greater efficiency of the human memory. But is this an essential difference, or is it only a matter of degree that can be overcome with the progress of technology? This article attempted to show that there is no conclusive evidence for an essential gap between man and a machine. For every human activity we can conceive of a mechanical counterpart.

Naturally we still have not answered the question whether man is more than a machine. The reader will have to answer that question for himself.

BIOGRAPHICAL NOTES
AND BIBLIOGRAPHIES

SECTION I: THE NATURE OF MATHEMATICS

1. Innovation in Mathematics

The Author

PAUL R. HALMOS, a professor of mathematics at the University of Michigan, was born in Budapest, emigrated to Chicago as a boy, and, in 1934, graduated from the University of Illinois at the age of 18. The next year he became a mathematician, when, having failed the examinations for an M.A. degree in philosophy, he was given an M.S. in mathematics instead. Halmos went on to acquire a Ph.D. in mathematics at Illinois; then he worked for two years as assistant to John von Neumann at the Institute for Advanced Study in Princeton, N.J. After a year at the Radiation Laboratory of the Massachusetts Institute of Technology, he joined the University of Chicago staff in 1946, where he remained until 1961, when he transferred to the University of Michigan. Halmos's honors include a Guggenheim Fellowship and the Chauvenet prize for mathematical exposition.

Bibliography

AN ESSAY ON THE PSYCHOLOGY OF INVENTION IN THE MATHE-MATICAL FIELD. Jacques Hadamard. Princeton University Press, 1945.

WHAT IS MATHEMATICS? AN ELEMENTARY APPROACH TO IDEAS AND METHODS. Richard Courant and Herbert Robbins. Oxford University Press, 1941.

2. Mathematical Creation

The Author

JAMES R. NEWMAN, who edited and wrote the introduction for Henri Poincaré's essay "Mathematical Creation," was a member of the Board of Editors of *Scientific American* and editor of its book department until his death in 1966. He graduated from Columbia Law School in 1929 and later developed a love for mathematics and science. He practiced law, served the Government in many capacities during World War II, and after the war was counsel to the Senate Committee on Atomic Energy and helped draft the Atomic Energy Act. He held a Guggenheim Fellowship in 1946 and 1947. His books include *Science and Sensibility, What is Science?*, and *World of Mathematics*.

3. Mathematics in the Modern World

The Author

RICHARD COURANT is professor emeritus of mathematics at New York University. Courant was born in Lublinitz, Poland, in 1888 and was educated at the universities of Breslau, Zurich and Göttingen, receiving a Ph.D. from the last-named institution in 1910. He taught at Göttingen and at the University of Münster until 1920, when he was appointed professor of mathematics and director of the Mathematics Institute at Göttingen. In 1932 he left Göttingen to serve short terms as visiting professor of mathematics at the University of California, Princeton University and the University of Cambridge. He joined the N.Y.U. faculty in 1934 and in 1936 became head of the mathematics department and director of the Institute of Mathematical Sciences at N.Y.U. He served in these capacities for 22 years until his retirement in 1958. Courant has written six books, including *Methods of Mathematical Physics* (with David Hilbert) and *What Is Mathematics?* (with Herbert Robbins).

Bibliography

ELEMENTARY MATHEMATICS FROM AN ADVANCED STANDPOINT. Felix Klein. The Macmillan Company, 1939.

THE ENJOYMENT OF MATHEMATICS: SELECTIONS FROM MATHEMATICS FOR THE AMATEUR. Hans Rademacher and Otto Toeplitz. Princeton University Press, 1957.

MATHEMATICS AND THE IMAGINATION. Edward Kasner and James R. Newman. Simon and Schuster, 1963.

MATHEMATICS IN WESTERN CULTURE. Morris Kline. Oxford University Press, 1953.

SCIENCE AND HYPOTHESIS. Henri Poincaré. Dover Publications, Inc., 1952.

SYMMETRY. Hermann Weyl. Princeton University Press, 1952.

Additional References

Hardy, G. H. *A Mathematician's Apology*. Cambridge University Press, 1967.

Kline, Morris. *Mathematics in Western Culture*. Oxford University Press, 1953.

Poincaré, Henri. *The Value of Science*. Dover Publications, 1958. [Reprint.]

Poincaré, Henri. *Science and Method.* Dover Publications, 1952. [Reprint.]

Poincaré, Henri. *Last Thoughts.* Dover Publications, 1963. [Reprint.]

Polya, George. *Mathematical Discovery.* 2 vols., John Wiley and Sons, 1962–1965.

Polya, George. *Mathematics and Plausible Reasoning.* 2 vols., Princeton University Press, 1954.

SECTION II: BIOGRAPHY

4. Descartes

The Author

A. C. CROMBIE lectures on the history and philosophy of science at the University of Oxford. His books include *Medieval and Early Modern Science* and *Robert Grosseteste and the Origins of Experimental Science: 1100-1700.* The author of numerous articles, he was also the original editor of the *British Journal for the Philosophy of Science.* He was visiting professor of philosophy at the University of Washington, and Shreve Fellow at Princeton University. Crombie is working on a study of Descartes as a scientific thinker, especially his influence on the development of physiological and biological theory.

Bibliography

CORRESPONDANCE: RENÉ DESCARTES. Edited by C. Adam and G. Milhaud. Presses Universitaire de France, 1936-56.

DESCARTES' DISCOURSE ON METHOD. Leon Roth. The Clarendon Press, 1937.

EXPERIENCE AND THE NON-MATHEMATICAL IN THE CARTESIAN METHOD. Alan Gewirtz in *Journal of the History of Ideas,* Vol. II, No. 2, pages 183-210; April, 1941.

NEW STUDIES IN THE PHILOSOPHY OF DESCARTES. Norman Kemp Smith. The Macmillan Co., 1952.

THE PHILOSOPHIC WORKS OF DESCARTES. Elizabeth S. Haldane and G. R. T. Ross. Cambridge University Press, 1934.

THE SCIENTIFIC WORK OF RENÉ DESCARTES (1596-1650). Joseph Frederick Scott. Taylor & Francis, 1952.

5. Isaac Newton

The Author

I. BERNARD COHEN is a professor of the history of science and of general education at Harvard University. He held a Guggenheim fellowship in 1956 and a National Science Foundation fellowship in 1960–61. Cohen is a past editor of *Isis,* the history of science journal, and is the author of several books, including *Birth of a New Physics* and *Franklin and Newton.*

Bibliography

ISAAC NEWTON. E. N. da C. Andrade. The Macmillan Company, 1954.

OPTICKS, OR A TREATISE ON THE REFLECTIONS, REFRACTIONS, INFLECTIONS & COLOURS OF LIGHT. Isaac Newton. Dover Publications, Inc., 1952.

THE ROYAL SOCIETY OF LONDON NEWTON TERCENTENARY CELEBRATIONS. Cambridge University Press, 1947.

SIR ISAAC NEWTON'S MATHEMATICAL PRINCIPLES OF NATURAL PHILOSOPHY AND HIS SYSTEM OF THE WORLD. Translated by Andrew Motte and edited by Florian Cajori. University of California Press, 1947.

6. Laplace

The Author

JAMES R. NEWMAN was a member of the Board of Editors of *Scientific American.* For additional information about him, see the biographical note under the second article, "Mathematical Creation."

Bibliography

MEN OF MATHEMATICS. Eric Temple Bell. Simon and Schuster, 1936.

L'OEUVRE SCIENTIFIQUE DE LAPLACE. H. Andoyer. Payot & Cie., 1922.

PIONEERS OF SCIENCE. Sir Oliver Lodge. The Macmillan Company, 1930.

7. William Rowan Hamilton

The Author

SIR EDMUND WHITTAKER spanned several generations of British science until his death in 1956. An eminent mathematician, he was associated with a remarkable galaxy of great modern scientists. He knew FitzGerald; he studied mathematics at Cambridge under Arthur Cayley and Sir George Stokes; as a Fellow of Trinity College he worked with A. N. Whitehead, Bertrand Russell, Sir J. J. Thomson, and Lord Rutherford; among his students were G. H. Hardy, Sir James Jeans, Sir Arthur Eddington, H. W. Turnbull, and Sir Geoffrey Taylor. In 1906 Whittaker was appointed Royal Astronomer of Ireland, occupying the same chair of astronomy at Dublin that had been held by William Rowan Hamilton. In 1912 Whittaker left Ireland for the chair of mathematics at the University of Edinburgh. Outside of mathematics and physics his activities were chiefly in the fields of religion and philosophy.

Bibliography

LIFE OF SIR WILLIAM ROWAN HAMILTON. R. P. Graves. Hodges, Figgis and Company, Ltd., 1882-89.

8. The Strange Life of Charles Babbage

The Authors

PHILIP MORRISON is a member of the Board of Editors of *Scientific American* and the editor of its book review department. He was previously professor of physics at the Massachusetts Institute of Technology and at Cornell. EMILY MORRISON is his wife.

Bibliography

BABBAGE'S CALCULATING ENGINES. Edited by Henry P. Babbage. E. and F. N. Spon, London, 1889.

9. William Kingdon Clifford

The Author

For information about JAMES R. NEWMAN, see the biographical note under the second article, "Mathematical Creation."

Bibliography

THE COMMON SENSE OF THE EXACT SCIENCES. William Kingdon Clifford. Alfred A. Knopf, 1946.
LECTURES AND ESSAYS. Edited by L. Stephen and F. Pollock. The Macmillan Company, 2 vols., 1879.

10. James Clerk Maxwell

The Author

See the biographical note under the second article, "Mathematical Creation."

Bibliography

THE LIFE OF JAMES CLERK MAXWELL. Lewis Campbell and William Garnett. Macmillan and Co., 1882.
THE SCIENTIFIC PAPERS OF JAMES CLERK MAXWELL. Edited by W. D. Niven. Dover Publications, Inc., 1953.
A TREATISE ON ELECTRICITY AND MAGNETISM. James Clerk Maxwell. Dover Publications, Inc., 1954.

11. Srinivasa Ramanujan

The Author

See the biographical note under the second article, "Mathematical Creation."

Bibliography

RAMANUJAN. G. H. Hardy. Cambridge University Press, 1940.
COLLECTED PAPERS OF SRINIVASA RAMANUJAN. Edited by G. H. Hardy, P. V. Seshu Aiyar and B. M. Wilson. Cambridge University Press, 1947.

12. "Nicolas Bourbaki"

The Author

PAUL R. HALMOS is professor of mathematics at the University of Michigan. For additional information about him, see the biographical note under the first article, "Innovation in Mathematics."

Bibliography

A CONTRIBUTION TO THE MATHEMATICAL THEORY OF BIG GAME HUNTING. H. Pétard in *The American Mathematical Monthly,* Vol. 45, No. 7, pages 446–447; 1938.
ELÉMENTS DE MATHÉMATIQUE. N. Bourbaki. Hermann & Cie., 1939. FOUNDATIONS OF MATHEMATICS FOR THE WORKING MATHEMATICIAN. N. Bourbaki in *The Journal of Symbolic Logic,* Vol. 14, No. 1, pages 1–8; March, 1949.

Additional References

Ball, W. W. Rouse. *A Short Account of the History of Mathematics.* Dover Publications, 1960. [Reprint.]
Bell, Eric T. *The Development of Mathematics.* 2nd ed., McGraw-Hill, 1945.
Eves, Howard. *An Introduction to the History of Mathematics.* Rev. ed., Holt, Rinehart and Winston, 1964.
Scott, J. F. *A History of Mathematics.* Taylor and Francis, Ltd., 1958.

SECTION III: SOME CHAPTERS OF MATHEMATICS

13. Number

The Author

PHILIP J. DAVIS is professor of applied mathematics at Brown University. He obtained a B.S. and a Ph.D. in mathematics from Harvard University in 1943 and 1950 respectively. From 1952 to 1963 he worked in the Applied Mathematics Division of the National Bureau of Standards. Davis was awarded the Chauvenet Prize of the Mathematical Association of America in 1963 for his paper "Historical Profile of the Gamma Function." He is the author of three books: *The Lore of Large Numbers,* published in 1961, *Interpolation and Approximation,* published in 1963, and *Mathematics of Matrices,* published in 1966. At present he is working in the field of numerical analysis, which is concerned with the development of techniques for the solution of equations on high-speed computers.

Bibliography

THE DEVELOPMENT OF MATHEMATICS. Eric T. Bell. McGraw-Hill Book Company, Inc., 1945.
EPISODES FROM THE EARLY HISTORY OF MATHEMATICS. Asger Aaboe. Random House, 1964.
HISTORY OF MATHEMATICS, VOL. II: SPECIAL TOPICS OF ELEMENTARY MATHEMATICS. David Eugene Smith. Dover Publications, Inc., 1958.
THE LORE OF LARGE NUMBERS. Philip J. Davis. Random House, 1961.
MATHEMATICS AND THE PHYSICAL WORLD. Morris Kline. Thomas Y. Crowell Company, 1959.
NUMBER: THE LANGUAGE OF SCIENCE. Tobias Dantzig. The Macmillan Company, 1954.
PHILOSOPHY OF MATHEMATICS. Stephen F. Barker. Prentice-Hall, Inc., 1964.

14. The Theory of Numbers

The Author

PAUL S. HERWITZ received his Ph.D. in mathematics from the University of North Carolina. He joined I.B.M. in Armonk, New York as a mathematician and has since served in various advisorial and managerial positions in programming and computer systems planning. Since 1965, he has been Director of Programming Resources.

Bibliography

NUMBER THEORY AND ITS HISTORY. Oystein Ore. McGraw-Hill Book Company, Inc., 1948.

FIRST COURSE IN THEORY OF NUMBERS. Harry N. Wright. John Wiley & Sons, Inc., 1939.

15. Algebra

The Author

W. W. SAWYER is professor of mathematics at the University of Toronto. Sawyer was born in England in 1911 and was graduated from the University of Cambridge, where he specialized in the mathematics of quantum theory and relativity. He taught mathematics at University College in Dundee, Scotland, and at the University of Manchester from 1935 to 1945, when he was appointed head of the mathematics department at the Leicester College of Technology. In 1948 he became head of the mathematics department at the University of Ghana (then University College, Gold Coast). From 1951 to 1956 he was a member of the faculty of the University of Canterbury in Christchurch, New Zealand. He taught in this country at the University of Illinois and at Wesleyan University before joining the staff at the University of Toronto. Sawyer is the author of several popular books on mathematics, including *A Concrete Approach to Abstract Algebra*, *Prelude to Mathematics* and *Mathematician's Delight*.

Bibliography

THE FUNDAMENTAL PROPOSITIONS OF ALGEBRA. Edward V. Huntington in *Monographs on Topics of Modern Mathematics*, edited by J. W. A. Young. Dover Publications, Inc., 1955.

INSIGHTS INTO MODERN MATHEMATICS: TWENTY-THIRD YEARBOOK. The National Council of Teachers of Mathematics, 1957.

MATHEMATICS: THE MAN-MADE UNIVERSE. Sherman K. Stein. W. H. Freeman and Company, 1963.

SOME LESSONS IN MATHEMATICS. Edited by T. J. Fletcher. Cambridge University Press, 1964.

16. Geometry

The Author

MORRIS KLINE, the editor of this volume, is professor of mathematics and chairman of the undergraduate mathematics department at the Washington Square Center of New York University. He is also director of the Division of Electromagnetic Research at N.Y.U.'s Courant Institute of Mathematical Sciences. After receiving a Ph.D. from N.Y.U. in 1936 Kline spent two years doing research at the Institute for Advanced Study in Princeton, N.J. He taught mathematics at N.Y.U. from 1938 to 1942, when he joined the U.S. Army as a physicist at the Signal Corps Engineering Laboratories. He returned to N.Y.U. in 1945 and has been a member of the faculty there ever since. He was a visiting professor at Stanford in 1958, 1961, and 1966. During the academic year 1958–1959 Kline was a Fulbright lecturer at the Technische Hochschule in Aachen, Germany, and held a Guggenheim Fellowship in the same year. In addition to his numerous technical publications Kline has written several popular books on mathematics, including *Mathematics in Western Culture*,

published in 1953, *Mathematics and the Physical World*, published in 1959, and *Mathematics: A Cultural Approach*, published in 1962.

Bibliography

GREAT IDEAS OF MODERN MATHEMATICS: THEIR NATURE AND USE. Jagjit Singh. Dover Publications, Inc., 1959.

A LONG WAY FROM EUCLID. Constance Reid. Thomas Y. Crowell Company, 1963.

PRELUDE TO MATHEMATICS. W. W. Sawyer. Penguin Books Inc., 1955.

WHAT IS MATHEMATICS? AN ELEMENTARY APPROACH TO IDEAS AND METHODS. Richard Courant and Herbert Robbins. Oxford University Press, 1941.

17. Projective Geometry

The Author

For information on MORRIS KLINE, see the preceding biographical note.

Bibliography

ART AND GEOMETRY. William M. Ivins, Jr. Dover Publications, 1964. [Reprint.]

MATHEMATICS IN WESTERN CULTURE. Morris Kline. Oxford University Press, 1953.

PROJECTIVE GEOMETRY. John Wesley Young. The Open Court Publishing Company, 1930.

PROJECTIVE GEOMETRY. Oswald Veblen and John Wesley Young. Ginn and Company, 1910–1918.

18. The Curvature of Space

The Author

P. LE CORBEILLER is emeritus professor of general education and applied physics at Harvard University. Born in Paris, he is a product of France's École Polytechnique, a military school which has turned out some of France's leading mathematicians. He took his doctorate in mathematics at the Sorbonne in 1926 and spent the 1920s and 1930s as a communications engineer in the service of the French Government. Under this rather conventional civil service career he harbored hopes of a quite different order. In 1938 he took a leave of absence from his job to obtain a *licence* (the French M.A.) in philosophy. Three years later he came to the U.S., to which he had long been attracted and where he had met his Chicago-born wife during a French Government mission. He joined the faculty at Harvard in 1941.

Bibliography

THE FOURTH DIMENSION SIMPLY EXPLAINED: A COLLECTION OF ESSAYS SELECTED FROM THOSE SUBMITTED IN THE SCIENTIFIC AMERICAN PRIZE COMPETITION. Peter Smith, 1941.

GENERAL INVESTIGATION OF CURVED SURFACES OF 1827 AND 1825. Karl Friedrich Gauss. Princeton University Library, 1902.

ON THE HYPOTHESES WHICH LIE AT THE FOUNDATIONS OF GEOMETRY. Bernhard Riemann in *A Source Book in Mathematics*, edited by David Eugene Smith. Dover Publications, 1959. [Reprint.]

SPACE—TIME—MATTER. Hermann Weyl. Dover Publications, Inc., 1951.

19. Topology

The Authors

ALBERT W. TUCKER received his B.A. from the University of Toronto in 1928 and his Ph.D. in topology from Princeton in 1932. In 1933 he joined the staff at Princeton, where he is professor of mathematics and former chairman of the department. Tucker has made significant contributions to both mathematics and education.

At the time he collaborated with Tucker on this article, HERBERT S. BAILEY, JR. was science editor of the Princeton University Press. He is now its director.

Bibliography

MATHEMATICS AND THE IMAGINATION. E. Kasner and J. Newman. Simon and Schuster, Inc., 1940.

WHAT IS MATHEMATICS? R. Courant and H. Robbins. Oxford University Press, 1941.

20. The Koenigsberg Bridges

The Author

For information on JAMES R. NEWMAN, who edited this article by Leonhard Euler and wrote the introduction to it, see the biographical note under the second article "Mathematical Creation."

Bibliography

MEN OF MATHEMATICS. Eric Temple Bell. Simon and Schuster, 1937.

21. Fixed-point Theorems

The Author

MARVIN SHINBROT is associate professor of mathematics and engineering science at Northwestern University. He worked as a research scientist with the National Advisory Committee for Aeronautics and with the Lockheed Aircraft Corporation for several years after receiving a master's degree in 1949 at Syracuse University, where he also did his undergraduate work. Obtaining a Ph.D. at Stanford University in 1960, he began a teaching career that took him to the University of Chicago and the University of California at Berkeley before he went to Northwestern in 1965.

Bibliography

GEOMETRY AND THE IMAGINATION. D. Hilbert and S. Cohn-Vossen. Chelsea Publishing Company, 1952.

WHAT IS MATHEMATICS? AN ELEMENTARY APPROACH TO IDEAS AND METHODS. Richard Courant and Herbert Robbins. Oxford University Press, 1941.

22. Chance

The Author

A. J. AYER is Wykeham Professor of Logic at the University of Oxford. He has held that position since 1959; for 13 years before going to Oxford he was Grote Professor of the Philosophy of Mind and Logic at the University of London. A graduate of Eton and Oxford, Ayer began his teaching career in 1932 as a lecturer in philosophy at Christ Church College of the University of Oxford. During World War II he enlisted in the Welsh Guards, receiving an officer's commission the same year. Among the books that Ayer has written are *Language, Truth and Logic, The Foundations of Empirical Knowledge, The Problem of Knowledge* and *The Concept of a Person.*

Bibliography

LOGICAL FOUNDATIONS OF PROBABILITY. Rudolf Carnap. The University of Chicago Press, 1962.

PRINCIPLES OF THE THEORY OF PROBABILITY. Ernest Nagel. The University of Chicago Press, 1939.

A TREATISE ON PROBABILITY. John Maynard Keynes. Harper & Row Publishers, 1962.

23. Probability

The Author

WARREN WEAVER was vice president of the Alfred P. Sloan Foundation until 1964. He is still associated with the Foundation as a trustee and consultant on scientific affairs. Weaver was professor of mathematics at the University of Wisconsin and for four years was chairman of the department. After he left the University of Wisconsin in 1932, he was director of natural sciences at the Rockefeller Foundation and vice president of natural and medical sciences at the Sloan-Kettering Institute. He joined the Sloan Foundation as its director of natural sciences in 1959.

Bibliography

THE SCIENCE OF CHANCE. Horace C. Levinson. Rinehart and Company, Inc., 1950.

PROBABILITY AND ITS ENGINEERING USES. Thornton C. Fry. D. Van Nostrand Company, Inc., 1928.

AN INTRODUCTION TO PROBABILITY THEORY AND ITS APPLICATIONS. William Feller. John Wiley and Sons., Inc., 1950.

24. Probability

The Author

MARK KAC is professor of mathematics at the Rockefeller University. Kac was born in Krzemieniec, Poland, in 1914 and educated at John Casimir University in Lwow, where he received a Ph.D. in 1937. He came to the U.S. in 1938 as a Parnas Foundation Fellow at Johns Hopkins University and a year later joined the faculty at Cornell University. During the academic year 1951–1952 he was a member of the Institute for Advanced Study in Princeton, N.J. He left Cornell in 1961 to take up his present post. Kac was awarded the Chauvenet Prize of the Mathematics Association of America in 1950 for his paper "Random Walk and the Theory of Brownian Motion." His main scientific activity for the past few years has been in statistical mechanics; he is particularly interested in mathematical models of changes of phase.

Bibliography

CHOICE AND CHANCE: WITH ONE THOUSAND EXERCISES. William Allen Whitworth. Hafner Publishing Co., 1951.

A HISTORY OF THE MATHEMATICAL THEORY OF PROBABILITY FROM THE TIME OF PASCAL TO THAT OF LAPLACE. I. Todhunter. Chelsea Publishing Company, 1949.

AN INTRODUCTION TO PROBABILITY THEORY AND ITS APPLICA-
TIONS. William Feller. John Wiley & Sons, Inc., 1957.

LADY LUCK. Warren Weaver. Doubleday & Company, Inc.,
1963.

PROBABILITY, STATISTICS AND TRUTH. Richard von Mises. The
Macmillan Company, 1957.

25. Statistics

The Author

WARREN WEAVER is trustee and consultant on scientific affairs
for the Alfred P. Sloan Foundation. For additional information about him, see the biographical note under article 23,
"Probability."

Bibliography

ELEMENTARY STATISTICAL ANALYSIS. Samuel S. Wilks. Princeton
University Press, 1948.

Additional References

Aleksandrov, A. D., et al., eds. *Mathematics: Its Content, Methods and Meaning.* 3 vols., The M.I.T. Press, 1964.

Blackett, Donald W. *Elementary Topology.* Academic Press,
1967.

Courant, R., and H. E. Robbins. *What is Mathematics?* Oxford University Press, 1941.

Eves, Howard. *A Survey of Geometry.* 2 vols., Allyn and
Bacon, 1963–1965.

Kline, Morris. *Calculus, an Intuitive and Physical Approach.*
2 vols., John Wiley and Sons, 1967.

Moroney, M. J. *Facts from Figures.* Penguin Books, 1951.

Reichmann, W. J. *Use and Abuse of Statistics.* Oxford University Press, 1962.

von Mises, Richard. *Probability, Statistics and Truth.* 2nd ed.,
George Allen and Unwin, 1957.

Weaver, Warren. *Lady Luck.* Doubleday, 1963.

Wolfe, H. E. *Non-Euclidean Geometry.* Holt, Rinehart and
Winston, 1945.

SECTION IV: THE FOUNDATIONS OF MATHEMATICS

26. Geometry and Intuition

The Author

HANS HAHN, who died of cancer in 1934 at the age of 55, was
a talented Viennese mathematician, teacher and researcher.
He had a strong bent toward the philosophical relationship
between logic and mathematics, as this excerpt from one of
his best works shows. After receiving his degree from the
University of Vienna in 1902, he published papers and worked
in seminars with many mathematical giants of the day. In
1905 he took over Otto Stolz's post at the University of Inns-
bruck. During the First World War, in which he served in
the Austrian Army, he was severely wounded and decorated
for bravery. Shortly thereafter he returned as professor to the
University of Vienna.

Bibliography

INTRODUCTION TO MATHEMATICAL THINKING. Friedrich Wais-
mann. Frederick Ungar Publishing Co., 1951.

PARADOXES OF THE INFINITE. Bernard Bolzano. Yale University
Press, 1950.

27. The Foundations of Mathematics

The Author

W. V. QUINE is Edgar Pierce Professor of Philosophy at Harvard
University. He was graduated in 1930 from Oberlin College,
where he majored in mathematics. Two years later he obtained
a Ph.D. from Harvard, having written his dissertation in logic
under Alfred North Whitehead. After a year of informal study
at the universities of Vienna, Prague and Warsaw, Quine was
elected to Harvard's Society of Fellows in 1933. He began
teaching at Harvard in 1936 and in 1948 became professor
of philosophy and Senior Fellow in the Society of Fellows.
Since then he has also lectured and studied at the University
of Oxford, the Institute for Advanced Study in Princeton,
N.J., and the Center for Advanced Study in the Behavioral
Sciences in Palo Alto, Calif. In the summer of 1959 he lectured in Japan and Australia. His books include *Set Theory
and Its Logic,* published in 1963, and *Ways of Paradox and
Other Essays,* published in 1966.

Bibliography

AXIOMATIC SET THEORY. Paul Bernays and A. A. Fraenkel.
North-Holland Publishing Company, 1958.

THE FOUNDATIONS OF ARITHMETIC: A LOGICO-MATHEMATICAL
ENQUIRY INTO THE CONCEPT OF NUMBER. Dr. G. Frege.
Basil Blackwell, 1953.

INTRODUCTION TO MATHEMATICAL PHILOSOPHY. Bertrand Russell. George Allen & Unwin, Ltd., 1919.

SET THEORY AND ITS LOGIC. Willard Van Orman Quine. Harvard University Press, 1963.

28. Paradox

The Author

For information on W. V. QUINE, see the preceding biographical note.

Bibliography

FROM A LOGICAL POINT OF VIEW. Willard Van Orman Quine.
Harvard University Press, 1953. See pages 80–139.

THE FOUNDATIONS OF MATHEMATICS. Evert W. Beth. North-
Holland Publishing Company, 1959. See pages 481–518.

METHODS OF LOGIC. Willard Van Orman Quine. Holt, Rinehart & Winston, Inc., 1959. See pages 225–252.

RIDDLES IN MATHEMATICS: A BOOK OF PARADOXES. E. P. North-
rop. D. Van Nostrand Co., Inc., 1944.

29. Symbolic Logic

The Author

JOHN E. PFEIFFER is a writer. He was formerly on the Board
of Editors of *Scientific American.* His books include *Changing
Universe* and *Cell.*

Bibliography

SYMBOLIC LOGIC. C. I. Lewis and C. H. Langford. The Century Company, 1932.

ELEMENTS OF SYMBOLIC LOGIC. Hans Reichenbach. The Macmillan Company, 1947.

30. Non-Cantorian Set Theory

The Authors

PAUL J. COHEN and REUBEN HERSH are professors of mathematics at Stanford University and the University of New Mexico respectively. Cohen attended Brooklyn College, acquired a Ph.D. from the University of Chicago in 1958 and has taught at the University of Rochester, the Massachusetts Institute of Technology and Harvard University. He is currently visiting at the Institute for Advanced Study in Princeton. Largely for the work described in this article, he was awarded the Fields Medal at the 1966 International Mathematical Congress. He was also a co-winner of the Research Corporation of America's annual $10,000 award for research by an American scientist. In 1963 he won the Bôcher prize, awarded annually by the American Mathematical Society for outstanding research in analysis. Hersh has taught at New York University, Fairleigh Dickinson University and Stanford. He reports that before taking his Ph.D. in mathematics from N.Y.U. in 1962 he had earned a B.A., magna cum laude, in English literature at Harvard, served in the U.S. Army of Occupation in Korea, spent four years as an office boy and editorial assistant with *Scientific American* and four years in the machine-building trade as engine-lathe hand and experimental machinist.

Bibliography

AN INTRODUCTION TO THE FOUNDATIONS AND FUNDAMENTAL CONCEPTS OF MATHEMATICS. Howard Eves and Carroll V. Newsom. Holt, Rinehart and Winston, 1965.

A PROOF OF THE INDEPENDENCE OF THE CONTINUUM HYPOTHESIS. Dana Scott in *Mathematical Systems Theory*, Vol. 1, No. 2, pages 89–111; May, 1967.

SET THEORY AND THE CONTINUUM HYPOTHESIS. Paul J. Cohen. W. A. Benjamin, Inc., 1966.

WHAT IS CANTOR'S CONTINUUM PROBLEM? Kurt Gödel in *Philosophy of Mathematics: Selected Readings,* edited by Paul Benacerraf and Hilary Putnam. Prentice-Hall, Inc., 1964.

31. Gödel's Proof

The Authors

ERNEST NAGEL and JAMES R. NEWMAN are both students of logic and of the philosophy of science, Newman being, in addition, a former student of Nagel. Nagel is John Dewey Professor of Philosophy at Columbia University. His books include *Logic Without Metaphysics* and *Structure of Science: Problems in the Logic of Scientific Explanation.* Newman was a member of the Board of Editors of *Scientific American.* Their book *Gödel's Proof* was published in 1958.

Bibliography

INTRODUCTION TO THE FOUNDATIONS OF MATHEMATICS. Raymond L. Wilder. John Wiley & Sons, Inc., 1952.

THE NATURE OF MATHEMATICS. Max Black. Harcourt, Brace and Company, Inc., 1934.

PRINCIPIA MATHEMATICA. Alfred North Whitehead and Bertrand Russell. Cambridge University Press, 1925.

SYMBOLIC LOGIC. C. I. Lewis and C. H. Langford. D. Appleton-Century Company, Inc., 1932.

Additional References

Benacerraf, Paul, and Hilary Putnam. *Philosophy of Mathematics: Selected Readings.* Prentice-Hall, 1964.

Beth, E. W. *The Foundations of Mathematics.* 2 vols., 2nd ed., Harper and Row, 1966.

Black, Max. *The Nature of Mathematics.* Routledge and Kegan Paul, 1953.

Fraenkel, A. A., and Y. Bar-Hillel. *Foundations of Set Theory.* North-Holland Publishing Company, 1958.

Goodstein, R. L. *Essays in the Philosophy of Mathematics.* Leicester University Press, 1965.

Körner, Stephan. *The Philosophy of Mathematics.* Hutchinson University Library, 1960.

Wilder, R. L. *Introduction to the Foundations of Mathematics.* 2nd ed., John Wiley and Sons, 1965.

SECTION V: THE IMPORT OF MATHEMATICS

32. The Evolution of the Physicist's Picture of Nature

The Author

P. A. M. DIRAC is Lucasian Professor of Mathematics at the University of Cambridge. In 1928 Dirac proposed his theory of the electron, which led him to predict, three years later, the existence of an antiparticle of the electron. The antiparticle, or positron, was discovered in 1932 by C. D. Anderson of the California Institute of Technology. For this work Dirac shared (with the Austrian theoretical physicist Erwin Schrödinger) the 1933 Nobel prize for physics. He was elected Fellow of the Royal Society in 1930.

Bibliography

CAN QUANTUM-MECHANICAL DESCRIPTION OF PHYSICAL REALITY BE CONSIDERED COMPLETE? A. Einstein, B. Podolsky and N. Rosen in *The Physical Review,* Vol. 47, No. 10, pages 777–780; May 15, 1935.

ENTWURF EINER VERALLGEMEINERTEN RELATIVITÄTSTHEORIE UND EINER THEORIE DER GRAVITATION. Albert Einstein in *Zeitschrift für Mathematik und Physik,* Vol. 62; 1914.

ON THE CONSTITUTION OF ATOMS AND MOLECULES. N. Bohr in *The London, Edinburgh and Dublin Philosophical Magazine and Journal of Science.* Part 1: *Binding of Electrons by Positive Nuclei,* Series 6, Vol. 26, No. 151, pages 1–25; July, 1913. Part 2: *Systems Containing only a Single*

Nucleus, Series 6, Vol. 26, No. 153, pages 476–507; September, 1913.

QUANTISIERUNG ALS EIGENWERTPROBLEM. E. Schrödinger in *Annalen der Physik*. Part 1, Vol. 79, No. 4, pages 361–376; 1926. Part 2, Vol. 79, No. 6, pages 489–527; 1926.

SIR ISAAC NEWTON'S MATHEMATICAL PRINCIPLES OF NATURAL PHILOSOPHY AND HIS SYSTEM OF THE WORLD. Edited by Florian Cajori. University of California Press, 1947.

A TENTATIVE THEORY OF LIGHT QUANTA. Louis de Broglie in *The London, Edinburgh and Dublin Philosophical Magazine and Journal of Science*, Series 6, Vol. 47, No. 278, pages 446–457; February, 1924.

ÜBER QUANTEN THEORETISCHE UMDEUTUNG KINEMATISCHER UND MECHANISCHER BEZIEHUNGEN. W. Heisenberg in *Zeitschrift für Physik*, Vol. 33, pages 879–893; 1925.

ZUR ELEKTRODYNAMIK BEWEGTER KÖRPER. A. Einstein in *Annalen der Physik*, Vol. 17, No. 10, pages 891–921; 1905.

ZUR THEORIE DES GESETZES DER ENERGIEVERTEILUNG IN NORMALSPECTRUM. M. Planck in *Verhandlungen der Deutschen Physikalischen Gesellschaft*, Vol. 2, No. 17, pages 237–245; December, 1900.

33. Mathematics in the Physical Sciences

The Author

FREEMAN J. DYSON is professor in the School of Mathematics of the Institute for Advanced Study in Princeton, N.J. A native of England, Dyson was educated at Winchester College and the University of Cambridge. His undergraduate career at Cambridge was interrupted by a wartime stint in the Royal Air Force, where his mathematical talents were employed in investigating the cause of the heavy loss of bombers on night missions. After reading the Smyth report on atomic energy in 1945 he decided to return to Cambridge to study physics. He was a fellow at Trinity College, Cambridge, for a year and then came to the U.S. on a Commonwealth Fund Fellowship to study at Cornell University with Hans A. Bethe and Richard P. Feynman. After two years as professor of physics at Cornell he joined the Institute for Advanced Study in 1953. He has worked on various problems lying on the border line between physics and mathematics, particularly in quantum field theory and in the statistical mechanics of complex systems.

Bibliography

THE SLEEPWALKERS. Arthur Koestler. Grosset & Dunlap, Inc., 1963.

STRONGLY INTERACTING PARTICLES. Geoffrey F. Chew, Murray Gell-Mann and Arthur H. Rosenfeld in *Scientific American*, Vol. 210, No. 2, pages 74–93; February, 1964.

THE UNREASONABLE EFFECTIVENESS OF MATHEMATICS IN THE NATURAL SCIENCES. Eugene P. Wigner in *Communications on Pure and Applied Mathematics*, Vol. 13, No. 1, pages 1–14; February, 1960.

34. On the Generalized Theory of Gravitation

The Author

Wherever we look, the physics of the 20th century bears the indelible imprint of the genius of ALBERT EINSTEIN. His "photoelectric effect," propounded in 1905, set the cornerstone of

quantum theory. At several decisive times in the development of that theory it was Albert Einstein who supplied the ideas that ensured the dominant role it plays in physics today.

In the same *annus mirabilis* of 1905 Einstein also published two papers that launched a parallel revolution in physical thought—the theory of relativity with which his name is primarily identified. The second of these two papers set forth his celebrated deduction of the equivalence of mass and energy: $E = mc^2$. By 1917 he had built upon his "special theory" of relativity the great edifice of his "general theory" that subsumes the large-scale mechanics of the universe into a comprehensive space-time geometry. From that time on he set himself the lofty aim of bringing into this grand generalization the electromagnetic laws that govern the small-scale realm of atomic particles. In his quest he found himself increasingly alone over the last four decades of his life, out of sympathy with the philosophic views that had come from the quantum theory to hold sway among his contemporaries in physics.

In the present article Einstein undertakes to explain to the layman his last and still unsuccessful effort to formulate a "Generalized Theory of Gravitation." He was himself the most engaging and successful popularizer of his work, but he described this article as "not quite easy to grasp." Nonetheless, it offers the reader a warm and intimate insight into the motives and aims of this great natural philosopher.

Bibliography

THE MEANING OF RELATIVITY. Albert Einstein. Princeton University Press, 1950.

RELATIVITY. Albert Einstein. Peter Smith, 1931.

35. Gravity

The Author

GEORGE GAMOW is professor of physics at the University of Colorado. After receiving his doctoral degree in nuclear physics from the Leningrad State University in 1928, Gamow continued his studies under Niels Bohr at the University of Copenhagen and later under Ernest Rutherford at the University of Cambridge. He came to the U.S. in 1934 and taught physics at George Washington University until 1956, when he went to the University of Colorado. A prolific popularizer of science, Gamow was awarded the Kalinga Prize in 1956 for his interpretation of science for the layman. He has published more than a dozen books in 23 languages.

Bibliography

SIR ISAAC NEWTON'S MATHEMATICAL PRINCIPLES OF NATURAL PHILOSOPHY AND HIS SYSTEM OF THE WORLD. Edited by Florian Cajori. University of California Press, 1947.

DIALOGUES CONCERNING TWO NEW SYSTEMS. Galileo Galilei. Dover Publications, Inc., 1953.

MEANING OF RELATIVITY. Albert Einstein. Princeton University Press, 1956.

36. Mathematics in the Biological Sciences

The Author

EDWARD F. MOORE is professor of computer science and mathematics at the University of Wisconsin. A graduate of the

Virginia Polytechnic Institute, Moore acquired a Ph.D. in mathematics from Brown University in 1950. After working on digital-computer programming at the National Bureau of Standards and the University of Illinois, he joined the staff of the Bell Telephone Laboratories, as a mathematician in the switching research department, in 1951. During the academic year 1961–1962 he was simultaneously Gordon McKay Visiting Lecturer on Applied Mathematics at Harvard University and visiting professor of electrical engineering at the Massachusetts Institute of Technology. He has been on the University of Wisconsin faculty since 1966. Moore has done research on a wide variety of computers, ranging from game-playing machines to machines for designing switching circuits. His chief current interest is in the theoretical capabilities and limitations of automata.

Bibliography

THE CONVERSE OF MOORE'S GARDEN-OF-EDEN THEOREM. John Myhill in *Proceedings of the American Mathematical Society*, Vol. 14, No. 4, pages 685–686; August, 1963.

THE GENERAL AND LOGICAL THEORY OF AUTOMATA. John von Neumann in *Cerebral Mechanisms in Behavior*, edited by Lloyd A. Jeffress. John Wiley & Sons, Inc., 1951.

MATHEMATICAL PROBLEMS IN THE BIOLOGICAL SCIENCES: PROCEEDINGS OF SYMPOSIA IN APPLIED MATHEMATICS, Vol. XIV, edited by R. E. Bellman. American Mathematical Society, 1962.

SIMULATION OF BIOLOGICAL CELLS BY SYSTEMS COMPOSED OF STRING-PROCESSING FINITE AUTOMATA. Walter R. Stahl, Robert W. Coffin and Harry E. Goheen in *AFIPS 1964 Spring Joint Computer Conference*. Spartan Books, Inc., 1964.

37. Mathematics in the Social Sciences

The Author

RICHARD STONE is P. D. Leake Professor of Finance and Accounting at the University of Cambridge. Born in London in 1913, Stone studied law and economics at Gonville and Caius College, Cambridge. During World War II he did statistical work for the War Cabinet and also served as assistant to John Maynard Keynes at the Treasury. In 1945 he was appointed the first director of the Department of Applied Economics at Cambridge. He acquired an Sc.D. from Cambridge in 1955. Stone's past work has been mainly in the fields of social accounting and econometrics. At present he is engaged in constructing a computer model of the British economy designed to study the possibilities of stimulating economic growth. He is also working on an international survey of economic planning models.

Bibliography

AN ANATOMY OF KINSHIP: MATHEMATICAL MODELS FOR STRUCTURES OF CUMULATED ROLES. Harrison C. White. Prentice-Hall, Inc., 1963.

FINITE MATHEMATICS WITH BUSINESS APPLICATIONS. John G. Kemeny, Arthur Schleifer, Jr., J. Laurie Snell and Gerald L. Thompson. Prentice-Hall, Inc., 1962.

GAME THEORY AND RELATED APPROACHES TO SOCIAL BEHAVIOR. Edited by Martin Shubik. John Wiley & Sons, Inc., 1964.

INTRODUCTION TO DIFFERENCE EQUATIONS. Samuel Goldberg. John Wiley & Sons, Inc., 1958.

THE MODEL IN ITS ENVIRONMENT: A PROGRESS REPORT. Paper No. 5 in *A Programme for Growth*, general editor Richard Stone. Published for the Department of Applied Economics, University of Cambridge, by Chapman & Hall; July, 1964.

PROBABILITY AND STATISTICS FOR BUSINESS DECISIONS: AN INTRODUCTION TO MANAGERIAL ECONOMICS UNDER UNCERTAINTY. Robert Schlaifer. McGraw-Hill Book Company, Inc., 1959.

38. The Practice of Quality Control

The Author

A. G. DALTON is close to the fountainhead of statistical product control methods in industry. As superintendent of quality control in the Western Electric Company, where many of the original techniques were worked out, he is responsible for maintaining a continuous quality audit of that company's myriad of products. A Britisher by birth, he came to the U.S. in 1919, after a hitch as lieutenant in the Royal Engineers Signal Service, and took his first job in a Mississippi lumber company. There he pressed so hard for the electrification of sawmill operations that his employer suggested he might have a brighter future in the electrical equipment field. Going to work for Western Electric, he became interested in quality control while hunting down defective elements in dial systems. In 1928 this interest transferred him to the Bell Telephone Laboratories, where a group was working on basic statistical methods. In 1943 he transferred back to Western Electric.

Bibliography

ECONOMIC CONTROL OF QUALITY OF MANUFACTURED PRODUCT. W. A. Shewhart. D. Van Nostrand Co., Inc., 1931.

STATISTICAL QUALITY CONTROL. Eugene L. Grant, McGraw-Hill Book Company, 1952.

39. The Theory of Games

The Author

OSKAR MORGENSTERN, a native of Gorlitz, Germany, is professor of political economy and director of the econometric research program at Princeton University. From 1925 to 1928 he was a Rockefeller Foundation fellow at Harvard and the Universities of London, Paris, and Rome. After teaching at the University of Vienna for ten years he returned to the United States in 1938 as a Carnegie visiting professor and joined the staff at Princeton the same year. Morgenstern has also served as a consultant for the Rand Corporation and as a member of the Atomic Energy Commission.

Bibliography

THE THEORY OF GAMES AND ECONOMIC BEHAVIOR. John von Neumann and Oskar Morgenstern. Princeton University Press, 1955.

40. The Use and Misuse of Game Theory

The Author

ANATOL RAPOPORT is professor and senior research mathematician at the Mental Health Research Institute of the University of Michigan. Rapoport was born in Russia, educated in Chicago's public schools and trained in music at the Vienna State Academy of Music, which gave him degrees in composition, piano and conducting. For the next four years he gave concerts in Europe, the U.S. and Mexico. In 1937 (at the age of 26) he enrolled as a freshman at the University of Chicago, and in 1941 he received his Ph.D. in mathematics. Following service in the Air Force as a liaison officer with the Soviet Air Force in Alaska during World War II, Rapoport taught mathematics for a year at the Illinois Institute of Technology, was research associate and later assistant professor of mathematical biophysics at the University of Chicago from 1947 to 1954, and spent a year at the Center for Advanced Study in the Behavioral Sciences. He went to Michigan in 1955.

Bibliography

THE COMPLEAT STRATEGYST: BEING A PRIMER ON THE THEORY OF GAMES OF STRATEGY. J. D. Williams. McGraw-Hill Book Co., Inc., 1954.

INTRODUCTION TO THE THEORY OF GAMES. J. C. C. McKinsey. The Rand Corporation. McGraw-Hill Book Co., Inc. 1952.

STRATEGY AND MARKET STRUCTURE: COMPETITION, OLIGOPOLY AND THE THEORY OF GAMES. Martin Shubik. John Wiley & Sons, Inc., 1959.

THE STRATEGY OF CONFLICT. Thomas C. Schelling. Harvard University Press, 1960.

THEORY OF GAMES AND STATISTICAL DECISIONS. David Blackwell and M. A. Girshick. John Wiley & Sons, Inc., 1954.

THEORY OF GAMES AS A TOOL FOR THE MORAL PHILOSOPHER. R. B. Braithwaite. Cambridge University Press, 1955.

41. The Mathematics of Communication

The Author

WARREN WEAVER is trustee and consultant on scientific affairs for the Alfred P. Sloan Foundation. For additional information about him, see the biographical note under article 23, "Probability."

Bibliography

A MATHEMATICAL THEORY OF COMMUNICATION. C. E. Shannon in *Bell System Technical Journal*, Vol. 27, pages 379–423; July, 1948. Pages 623–656; October, 1948.

42. Linear Programming

The Authors

WILLIAM W. COOPER and ABRAHAM CHARNES were, at the time they collaborated on this article, both at the graduate school of Industrial Administration of the Carnegie Institute of Technology, where they combined both economics and mathematics in their teaching and research. Cooper is currently professor of economics at Carnegie. In 1954, he was president of the Institute of Management Sciences, which is concerned with applying scientific analysis in business. Charnes is professor of applied mathematics and economics at Northwestern University. After he left Carnegie Institute of Technology he was professor of mathematics and director of the research department at Purdue for two years before he joined the staff at Northwestern in 1957. Like Cooper, he has been active in the Institute of Management Sciences and was its president in 1960.

Bibliography

AN INTRODUCTION TO LINEAR PROGRAMMING. A. Charnes, W. W. Cooper and A. Henderson. John Wiley & Sons, Inc., 1953.

ACTIVITY ANALYSIS OF PRODUCTION AND ALLOCATION. Edited by T. C. Koopmans. John Wiley & Sons, Inc., 1951.

BLENDING AVIATION GASOLINES: A STUDY IN PROGRAMMING INTERDEPENDENT ACTIVITIES IN AN INTEGRATED OIL COMPANY. A. Charnes, W. W. Cooper and B. Mellon in *Econometrica*, Vol. 20, No. 2; April, 1952.

43. Operations Research

The Authors

HORACE C. LEVINSON is a scientific writer and consultant. He was chairman of the National Research Council's Operations Research Committee from 1949 to 1955. ARTHUR A. BROWN is on the staff of Arthur D. Little, Inc. He was previously deputy director of the Navy's Operations Evaluation Group.

Bibliography

METHODS OF OPERATIONS RESEARCH. Philip M. Morse and George E. Kimball. The Technology Press of Massachusetts Institute of Technology and John Wiley & Sons, Inc., 1950.

44. Mathematical Machines

The Author

HARRY M. DAVIS was the author of several articles in *Scientific American*. In 1949 he was drowned in a swimming accident at Biloxi, Mississippi. He was one of those rare professional journalists whose reporting of science was admired by scientists.

Bibliography

PUNCHED CARD METHODS IN SCIENTIFIC COMPUTATION. W. J. Eckert. The Thomas J. Watson Astronomical Computing Bureau, Columbia University, 1940.

PROCEEDINGS OF A SYMPOSIUM ON LARGE-SCALE DIGITAL CALCULATING MACHINERY. Harvard University Press, 1948.

45. Computers

The Author

STANISLAW ULAM is a research adviser at the Los Alamos Scientific Laboratory of the University of California. A native of Lwow, Poland, Ulam received an M.A. and a D.Sc. in mathematics from the Polytechnic Institute at Lwow in 1932 and 1933 respectively. He lectured at various institutions in Poland, England and France before coming to the U.S. in 1936 as a visiting member of the Institute for Advanced Study in Princeton, N.J. Shortly thereafter he became a fellow of the Harvard University Society of Fellows. He left Harvard in 1940 to join the faculty of the University of Wisconsin. Since going to Los Alamos in 1943 to work on the atomic bomb as a member of the Manhattan Engineer

District, Ulam has taught for short terms at the University of Southern California, Harvard, the Massachusetts Institute of Technology, the University of Colorado and the University of California at San Diego. At Los Alamos, Ulam collaborated with Edward Teller on the development of the hydrogen bomb. He also invented the so-called Monte Carlo method, a procedure for finding solutions to mathematical and physical problems by random sampling. This technique, made practical by the development of high-speed computers, permits the solution of problems not amenable to more orthodox methods of analysis. Ulam is the author of *Problems in Modern Mathematics,* published in 1964.

Bibliography

AUTOMATIC DIGITAL COMPUTERS. M. V. Wilkes. John Wiley & Sons, Inc., 1956.

A COLLECTION OF MATHEMATICAL PROBLEMS. Stanislaw Ulam. John Wiley & Sons, Inc., 1960.

THE COMPUTER AND THE BRAIN. John von Neumann. Yale University Press, 1958.

SELF-ORGANIZING SYSTEMS: PROCEEDINGS OF AN INTERDISCIPLINARY CONFERENCE. Edited by Marshall C. Yovits and Scott Cameron. Pergamon Press, 1960.

TEACHING COMBINATORIAL TRICKS TO A COMPUTER. D. H. Lehmer in *Combinatorial Analysis: Proceedings of Symposia in Applied Mathematics,* Vol. 10, American Mathematical Society, 1960.

46. Computer Logic and Memory

The Author

DAVID C. EVANS is professor of electrical engineering and director of computer science at the University of Utah. He was graduated from that university in 1949 and obtained a Ph.D. in physics there four years later. From 1953 to 1962 he was director of engineering of the Bendix Corporation's computer division. He then spent three years as professor and associate director of the computing system at the University of California at Berkeley before going to the University of Utah. Evans describes his principal interest as "man-machine systems: the development of interactive computing systems for computer-aided problem-solving."

Bibliography

DESIGN OF TRANSISTORIZED CIRCUITS FOR DIGITAL COMPUTERS. Abraham I. Pressman. John F. Rider Publisher, Inc., 1959.

LOGICAL DESIGN OF DIGITAL COMPUTERS. Montgomery Phister. John Wiley & Sons, Inc., 1958.

SQUARE-LOOP FERRITE CIRCUITRY: STORAGE AND LOGIC TECHNIQUES. C. J. Quartly. Prentice-Hall, Inc., 1962.

SWITCHING CIRCUITS AND LOGICAL DESIGN. S. H. Caldwell. John Wiley & Sons, Inc., 1958.

THEORY AND DESIGN OF DIGITAL MACHINES. Thomas C. Bartee, Irwin L. Lebow and Irving S. Reed. McGraw-Hill Book Company, Inc., 1962.

47. The Uses of Computers in Science

The Author

ANTHONY G. OETTINGER is professor of linguistics and of applied mathematics at Harvard University. Except for the academic year 1951–1952, when he was a Henry fellow at the University of Cambridge, he has been at Harvard since 1947; he obtained a bachelor's degree there in 1951 and a doctorate in 1954. His current interest is the problems of the educational use of computers.

Bibliography

AUTOMATIC PROCESSING OF NATURAL AND FORMAL LANGUAGES. A. G. Oettinger in *Proceedings of IFIPS Congress, 65: Vol. I,* edited by Wayne A. Kalenich. Spartan Books, 1965.

COMPUTER ANALYSIS OF NATURAL LANGUAGES. Susumo Kuno in *Mathematical Aspects of Computer Science,* edited by Jack Schwartz. American Mathematical Society, in press.

COMPUTER AUGMENTATION OF HUMAN REASONING. Edited by Margo A. Sass and William D. Wilkinson. Spartan Books, 1965.

COMPUTING PROBLEMS AND METHODS IN X-RAY CRYSTALLOGRAPHY. C. L. Coulter in *Advances in Computers: Vol. V,* edited by Franz L. Alt and M. Rubinoff. Academic Press Inc., 1964.

DATA COLLECTION AND REDUCTION FOR NUCLEAR PARTICLE TRACE DETECTORS. H. Gelernter in *Advances in Computers: Vol. VI,* edited by Franz L. Alt and M. Rubinoff. Academic Press Inc., 1965.

PLANS AND THE STRUCTURE OF BEHAVIOR. G. A. Miller, E. Galanter and K. H. Pribram. Holt, Rinehart & Winston, 1960.

A VISION OF TECHNOLOGY AND EDUCATION. A. G. Oettinger in *Communications of the ACM,* Vol. 9, No, 7, pages 487–490; July, 1966.

48. System Analysis and Programming

The Author

CHRISTOPHER STRACHEY is leader of the Programming Research Group at the Computing Laboratory of the University of Oxford. He was graduated from the University of Cambridge in 1939 and spent the war years as a physicist working on the design of radar tubes. From 1944 to 1951 he taught in preparatory schools; since then he has been working with computers. "My chief interest," he writes, "is to develop the mathematical foundations of programming and, if possible, to simplify programming (particularly that of large "software" systems) and to make the design of machines more rational."

Bibliography

ADVANCES IN PROGRAMMING AND NON-NUMERICAL COMPUTATION. Edited by L. Fox. Pergamon Press, 1966.

A GUIDE TO FORTRAN PROGRAMMING. Daniel D. McCracken. John Wiley & Sons, Inc., 1961.

INTRODUCTION TO ALGOL. R. Baumann, M. Feliciano, F. L. Bauer and K. Samelson. Prentice-Hall, Inc., 1964.

PROGRAMMING COMPUTERS TO PLAY GAMES. Arthur L. Samuel in *Advances in Computers:* Vol. I, edited by Franz L. Alt. Academic Press, Inc., 1960.

49. Cybernetics

The Author

NORBERT WIENER was emeritus professor of mathematics at the Massachusetts Institute of Technology before his death in 1964. After he received his Ph.D. from Harvard, he held a Sheldon traveling fellowship, taught at Harvard and the University of Maine, and wrote for *Encyclopedia Americana*. Wiener joined the staff at M.I.T. in 1919, interrupting his teaching there in 1926–27, when he was awarded a Guggenheim fellowship, and again in 1935–36, when he went to Tsing Hua University in China as a visiting professor.

Bibliography

A MATHEMATICAL THEORY OF COMMUNICATION. C. E. Shannon in *The Bell System Technical Journal*, Vol. 27, No. 3, pages 379–423; July, 1948.
CYBERNETICS. Norbert Wiener. John Wiley, 1948.

50. Man Viewed as a Machine

The Author

JOHN G. KEMENY is professor of mathematics and chairman of the department at Dartmouth College. Born in Budapest, Hungary, he came to the U.S. at the age of 13 and attended George Washington High School in New York City, graduating first in his class. He then entered Princeton University, but was interrupted by the U.S. Army, which put him to work on calculating machines at Los Alamos. He returned to Princeton, graduated first in his class and went on to take a Ph.D. in mathematics. He spent his last year of graduate study as Albert Einstein's assistant at the Institute for Advanced Study. Most of his own research has been in symbolic logic.

Bibliography

SOLVABLE AND UNSOLVABLE PROBLEMS. A. M. Turing in *Science News*, No. 31, pages 7–23. Penguin Books, 1954.

Additional References

Ahrendt, Myrl H. *The Mathematics of Space Exploration.* Holt, Rinehart and Winston, 1965.
Bailey, Norman T. J. *The Mathematical Approach to Biology and Medicine.* John Wiley and Sons, 1967.
Boas, Mary L. *Mathematical Methods in the Physical Sciences.* John Wiley and Sons, 1966.
Born, Max. *Einstein's Theory of Relativity.* Rev. ed., Dover Publications, 1962.
Dorn, William S., and Herbert Greenberg. *Mathematics and Computing.* John Wiley and Sons, 1967.
Fink, Donald G. *Computers and the Human Mind.* Doubleday, 1966.
Friedman, Bernard. *Principles and Techniques of Applied Mathematics.* John Wiley and Sons, 1956.
Friedrichs, Kurt O. *From Pythagoras to Einstein.* Random House, 1965.
Ryabov, Y. *An Elementary Survey of Celestial Mechanics.* Dover Publications, 1961.
Singh, Jagit. *Great Ideas in Information Theory, Language and Cybernetics.* Dover Publications, 1966.
Stibitz, G. R. *Mathematics in Medicine and the Life Sciences.* Year Book Medical Publishers, 1966.
Sutton, O. G. *Mathematics in Action.* G. Bell, 1957.
Wilf, Herbert S. *Mathematics for the Physical Sciences.* John Wiley and Sons, 1962.

INDEX